Linear Transformations and Matrices

Linear Transformations and Matrices

F. A. Ficken

Department of Mathematics
New York University, University Heights

PRENTICE-HALL, INC., ENGLEWOOD CLIFFS, N.J.

Library of Congress
Catalog Card Number 67-11110

Current printing (last digit) 10 9 8 7 6 5 4 3 2 1

PRINTED IN THE UNITED STATES OF AMERICA

C-53691

PREFACE

This text presents the basic theory of finite-dimensional real and complex linear spaces. The scope and arrangement of the material are clear from the table of contents.

Prerequisites include the algebra and geometry (including rectangular Cartesian and polar coordinates) commonly taught in high school, knowledge of the sine and cosine functions and, speaking strictly, nothing more. One aim is to help the "sand-lotter" to become a "semi-pro."

Addressed to students taking a first "conceptual" course, the first four chapters are rather elementary.

In Chapter 1 we establish basic terminology and introduce some indispensable general ideas.

Chapter 2 is a descriptive account of the system of real numbers. The minimal goal is to make it clear that we can calculate with real numbers according to the familiar rules, and can make, in principle, exact measurements of physical quantities. Essentially the same goal can be reached more quickly, of course, by an axiomatic apparatus. Here we take passing notice also of the integers and the rationals, in order to emphasize tacitly the structural features of these systems and to introduce the recursive method of definition and proof by mathematical induction.

The classical algebra and geometry of vectors in naive physical space is discussed in Chap. 3. Here again structural features receive tacit emphasis, and definitions and results are stated so as to be applicable almost verbatim later on in more general situations. In 3I–K there is a fairly complete vectorial treatment of points, lines, and planes in Euclidean 3-space.

Having available now a large variety of concrete results, we introduce in Chap. 4 those particular abstract ideas which will be useful in our study. Each can be exemplified in several ways from earlier material. Permutations supply further examples, and will have important uses later on. The complex field is contructed from the real, and its essential property of algebraic closure is recorded. The idea of an equivalence relation on a set (and the uniquely associated partition of the set) underlies the extensive discussion of canonical forms in later chapters.

For some students linear algebra is a last course in which genuinely mathematical considerations are emphasized. For this reason some "cultural" material has been included, notably in 1I, 2B, 2C2, 2D3–4, and 3L2–3. It is entirely reasonable, in many situations, to omit these sections and certain other material from the first four chapters.

An incidental purpose of these chapters, on which reviewers have offered a variety of opinions, is to instill certain attitudes and habits of thought that will expedite later progress. My colleagues and I found, in using the pre-publication edition, that this discussion supplies a firm and homogeneous basis for the sequel. Each teacher will have his own ideas, of course, on how this material should be used with his particular class, and a student with a certain maturity may be left to read it for himself. I have felt it better, on the whole, to include these chapters, it being easier to omit something that is available than to produce something that isn't.

Linear spaces are introduced formally in Chap. 5. Most new ideas can be illustrated in the context of Euclidean 3-space (Chap. 3), but metric methods are not needed until much later. From here on the treatment is rather conventional, except for an occasional special emphasis.

For one thing, the notion of a pseudo-inverse of a linear transformation is introduced in 6E. If L maps X linearly into Y and is singular, and W is a complement in X of the nullspace of L, then there is a 1-1 linear correspondence M, defined on the range of L onto W, such that $LML = L$. Such a transformation M is called a pseudo-inverse of L; it may be used to solve the nonhomogeneous equation $Lx = y$ when y is in the range of L. In 9G we show how to obtain a pseudo-inverse of a matrix.

It seems to me that the ideas of the dual space and of the dual of a linear transformation richly deserve inclusion even in an introductory course. They illuminate and deepen the theory. They underlie the distinction between covariance and contravariance in tensor analysis. In certain important problems in analysis the spaces used are self-dual and the dual of a transformation is replaced in a natural way by its adjoint. Duality has therefore received (especially in Chap. 7) more emphasis here than in many presentations. Classroom experience suggests, at the same time, that much of Chap. 7 can be omitted without loss of continuity.

I believe in the primacy of geometric entities such as vectors, spaces and subspaces, functionals, and transformations. Only after a basis has been specified do components, linear and bilinear forms, and matrices have fully defined significance. "Basis-free" methods have therefore been used at every opportunity.

Believing that such questions should be left to more experienced persons, I have made no attempt to offer suggestions on numerical calculation beyond those in 9E; see heading [F] in the bibliography. (References to the bibliography are bracketed.)

Various parts of this material were first presented in an in-service training course at the Union Carbide Nuclear Company (K-25), Oak Ridge. The present version took form during courses at an intermediate level at the University of Tennessee and at New York University.

I have always had the advantage of a full year, with three 50-minute periods or one 125-minute period weekly. The students have always had one or another text in hand. For a class able to cover this book in less time, attractive supplementary material may be found, for example, in multilinear algebra (see [A16], [A27], [C4], [C5], [D4]), linear programming (see [G]), functions of operators (see [A15], [A17]), the theory of groups (see [A44], [B]), and infinite-dimensional linear spaces (see [A24], [A43], and [E]).

There would be no difficulty, I am confident, in adapting this text to a two-quarter course.

My own feeling is that one semester is not enough, but my colleagues who used the pre-publication edition found themselves able to cover most of the material in one semester. I would suggest a rapid survey of Chaps. 1–4, with all feasible omissions, Chaps. 5, 6 (with the pseudo-inverse omitted), 8, 9 (with E and G omitted), 10, 11 (with J, K, L omitted), 12 (A only, and perhaps B), 13 (omitting G), and 14 (omitting H and perhaps C).

Internal references are of the form CSN, where C ($= 1, \ldots, 14$) designates the chapter, S ($= A, B, \ldots$) is a capital Latin letter designating a section of C, and N ($= 1, 2, 3, \ldots$) designates the item in CS. The symbol 12G7 means item 7 in Section G of Chap. 12. The symbol actually used is almost always minimal. Thus "4" means item 4 of the present *section*, and "J6", means the item 6 in section J of the present *chapter*. Occasionally an item is further subdivided; then a decimal point is used: N.1, N.2, ...

There are 760 exercises. Many of those intended for drill have several parts. If an exercise has substantial theoretical importance, its statement is followed by "(T)".

There is a strikingly broad area of agreement between results presented here and those found in other discussions of the same topics. Many sources have been helpful, and I acknowledge with special gratitude the beneficient influence of the excellent texts of Halmos [A17] and of Birkhoff and MacLane [A6].

My obligations to colleagues, students, and the publisher's reviewers are uncountable. A. A. Blank gave me highly perceptive readings of most chapters of the pre-publication edition. J. Nazarian supplied extensive lists of misprints. Useful suggestions have been offered by C. B. Allendoerfer, A. Babakhanian, C. Berger, J. Berkowitz, W. L. Duren, Jr., H. Whitney, M. Machover, D. D. Miller, and R. L. Wilson. One of the publisher's reviewers pointed out an incredible blunder, mercifully sparing me the embarrassment of seeing it in print. For all this generous help I offer warm thanks. I shall welcome further suggestions.

F. A. Ficken

CONTENTS

FOUR
Systems and Structures   92

FIVE
Linear Spaces   119

SIX
Linear Transformations   141

Linear
Transformations
and Matrices

ONE
Basic Ideas

This chapter is devoted to a brief discussion of certain concepts that are widely used in mathematics. These ideas have been present implicitly in much of the student's earlier study, and our work here will be greatly facilitated by an explicit acquaintance with them.

Some concepts must remain undefined; they are to be understood in the sense common in our language, as qualified by accompanying descriptive remarks. Once these concepts have been accepted, it is possible to use them, along with further common-sense ideas, to propose formal definitions of new objects or relations. For example, in plane geometry, if "line" and "intersect" have already been accepted (in the sense customary in geometry), then we can define "parallel" by agreeing that two lines shall be parallel if they do not intersect.

A. Sets

In mathematics as well as in everyday life it is often desirable to think of several objects together as a single unit. Many words in our language reflect this need; one speaks of a flock of sheep, a pile of bricks, the graduating class, the totality of all even integers, a string ensemble, a set of games of tennis, the audience at a play, and so on.

With characteristic preference for brevity, mathematicians have agreed to use the word "set" to denote a single object of thought constituted by several distinct individual objects. The individual objects are said to be *members*, or *elements*, of the set, and are said to *belong* to the set. Synonyms for "set" are *class*, *collection*, and *aggregate*.

We shall have frequent occasion, for example, to refer to the set of *natural numbers*, which will be denoted by N; the elements of N are the numbers denoted by these symbols:

$$0, 1, 2, 3, 4, 5, \ldots.$$

The set of *integers*, denoted by I, has as elements the numbers denoted by these symbols:

$$\ldots, -3, -2, -1, 0, 1, 2, 3, \ldots.$$

One may consider, similarly, the set of all lines in a given plane, the set of all points inside a given sphere, or the set of all integers x such that $x^2 = 9$.

We say that sets S and T are *equal*, and write $S = T$, when and only when they have precisely the same elements. Otherwise, S and T are *unequal*, written $S \neq T$.

To indicate that the object a is an element of the set S, we write $a \in S$; if a is not an element of S, we write $a \in' S$. For example, $5 \in N$, $-3 \in I$, but $-3 \in' N$.

We shall have frequent occasion to say, for example, "$a \in S$, $b \in S$, and $c \in S$". Let us agree, once and for all, to abbreviate this statement as follows: "$a, b, c \in S$".

If the elements of a set S are $a, b, c, \ldots$, then we write $S = \{a, b, c, \ldots\}$. For example, $N = \{0, 1, 2, 3, \ldots\}$.

If every element of a set S is also an element of the set T, then (and only then) we write $S \subset T$ or $T \supset S$ and say that S is a *subset* of T and that T is a *superset* of S. We also say that T *contains* or *includes* S and that S is *contained in* or *included in* T. For example, $N \subset I$. If $S \subset T$ and T has an element not belonging to S, then we say that S is a *proper* subset of T; N is a proper subset of I.

In any situation contemplated in this book all sets actually mentioned will be subsets of some large "universal" set in which, so to speak, the entire discussion takes place. At the level at which we are working, it is practical and customary not to insist always on an explicit specification of the "universe of discourse". This usage is safe because the context always implies a most appropriate "universe"; a larger "universe" may be equally comfortable, but would contain, usually, superfluous elements which might be troublesome.

Having agreed upon "set" as the primary term, for the sake of clarity we may use the word *class* for a set each of whose elements is a set. Therefore we refer, for example, to the class (rather than the set) of subsets of a given set.

It is essential that a set be contemplated in an entirely neutral way, as a mere heap, devoid of all structure, or order, or system, or relationship between its elements. For this reason such words as "system", "group", "structure", and "space" should not be applied to a set not known to have some organization beyond a specification of its members; some of these terms will be given technical meanings later.

The idea of a set is extraordinarily fruitful. It was recognized about a century ago that valuable results could be obtained by studying sets for their own sake, frequently without reference to the specific nature of their elements, and vast areas of mathematics now depend on basic theorems of the theory of sets. Although we shall find sets very helpful, indeed, in our work, we shall use only elementary results, and the student may find elsewhere (e.g., [H5]) the truly profound developments to which the theory of sets owes its dominant position at the present time. (See [H1, Chap. 1] for details of material we treat in this chapter.)

EXERCISES

1. Here are four sets:

$$Q = \{2, 4\}, \qquad R = \{2, 4, 5\},$$
$$S = \{2, 4, 6\}, \qquad T = \{2, 4, 5, 6\}.$$

Which of the following statements are true, and which false? (a) $3 \in Q$; (b) $5 \in R$; (c) $4 \in' T$; (d) $6 \in' Q$; (e) $Q \subset S$; (f) $S \subset R$; (g) $T \supset S$; (h) Q is a proper subset of R; (i) T is a proper subset of S.

2. Let U, V, and W denote sets. Use the definition of "$\subset$" and "$=$" to show that: (a) $V \subset V$; (b) if $V \subset W$ and $W \subset V$ then $V = W$; (c) if $U \subset V$ and $V \subset W$ then $U \subset W$.

B. Properties

A set is often specified to consist of all those elements of a given set T having a certain property. We use the word "property" in one of its common meanings, that of quality or attribute or feature. We do not ascribe a property P to the elements of a set T unless for each $t \in T$ it is in principle either true or false that t has P. The set of all $t \in T$ having P will be denoted by

$$\{t : t \in T \text{ and } t \text{ has } P\};$$

the symbol "$:$" may be read "such that". If it is entirely clear from the context what the set T is, then we may omit the reference to T, writing merely $\{t : t \text{ has } P\}$. As the basis for an example, let us recall that an integer n is *even* if it is a multiple of 2, that is, $n = 2m$ for some $m \in I$; otherwise, n is *odd*. The set E of all even natural numbers is

$$E = \{x : x \in N \text{ and } x \text{ is even}\} = \{0, 2, 4, 6, \ldots\};$$

if it is clear beforehand that we are defining a subset of N, then we may write simply $E = \{x : x \text{ is even}\}$.

Each property P of elements of a set T determines a well-defined subset of T, namely,

$$\{t : t \in T \text{ and } t \text{ has } P\}.$$

In the example just given, $E \subset N$. Conversely, for any two sets S and T, if $S \subset T$ then $S = \{t : t \in T \text{ and } t \in S\} = \{t : t \in T \text{ and } t \text{ has } P\}$, where the property P is membership in S.

There are excellent technical reasons for not insisting that a set have at least two elements. If e is any object, then we recognize a set whose only element is e and denote it by $\{e\}$; this set is called *singleton-e*.

3

It is essential to distinguish with extreme care between the relations $a \in S$ (the object a is an element of the set S) and the relation $\{a\} \subset S$ (the set singleton-a is a subset of the set S). It would be false to say that $a \subset S$ unless a is a subset of the set S. When could it be meaningful to say that $\{a\} \in S$?

It is necessary to go even farther in order to maintain the correspondence just established between sets and properties. Which set, for example, is this:

$$\{x : x \in N \text{ and } x^2 = 2\}?$$

We are forced to recognize a subset of N corresponding to a property possessed by no element of N. Such a set cannot have any members whatever. The set is *empty*, or *void*. We recognize only one empty set, call it the *null set*, and denote it by $\square$. For example,

$$\square = \{a : a \in I \text{ and } a^2 \text{ is negative}\}.$$

If S is any set, then $\square$ is a subset of S; the only subset of $\square$ is $\square$ itself.

EXERCISES

1. Let $S = \{a, b, c, d, e, f, g\}$, where the symbols are letters of the English alphabet. Which elements of S belong to the set $T = \{x : x \in S \text{ and } x \text{ is a consonant}\}$? Is it true that $S \subset T$? That $T \subset S$?

2. With S as in 1, and $R = \{a, e\}$, state a property P such that $R = \{x : x \in S \text{ and } x \text{ has } P\}$.

3. List all the (eight) subsets of the set $S = \{p, q, r\}$.

4. List the elements of the following sets:
$$\{x : x \in I \text{ and } x^2 = 16\}, \qquad \{x : x \in N \text{ and } x^2 = 16\},$$
$$\{x : x \in I \text{ and } x^2 = 17\}, \qquad \{x : x \in I \text{ and } x^2 = 0\}.$$

5. Show that if $a \in E$ then $a^2 \in E$; here $E = \{n : n \text{ is even}\}$.

6. It is evident that if n is odd then $n - 1$ is even. Show that if n is odd then there exists $m \in I$ such that $n = 2m + 1$. Is it true that if $n = 2m + 1$ with $m \in I$ then n is odd?

C. Propositions

A *proposition* is a statement which affirms or denies, conditionally or unconditionally, that certain objects have certain properties or are related to each other in a specified way. Examples: $9 \in N$; $-4 \in N$; $E \subset N$; $a \in \{a\}$; $N \subset \square$. On the other hand, "ho-ho-ho" is not a proposition in the English language.

We agreed above not to recognize a subset S of a set T or a property P of elements of a set T, unless it was for each $x \in T$ in principle either true or false that "$x \in S$" or "x has P". We assume, more generally, that a meaningful proposition must in principle be either true or false, whether or not a procedure has yet been devised for determining its truth or falsehood. Since it excludes any third possibility, this assumption is known in classical logic as the *Law of excluded middle.* We assume further that a meaningful proposition cannot be both true and false. Since the effect of this assumption is to exclude contradiction or inconsistency, we may call it the *Law of consistency.*

Now suppose that it follows from the truth of a proposition p that some proposition q is both true and false. Since the Law of consistency would then be violated, we conclude that p cannot be true; by the Law of excluded middle, p must be false. This method of proving that p is false is called the *indirect method* of proof. In order to prove indirectly that p is true, one assumes that p is false, and on that assumption arrives by further reasoning at a contradiction; then the falsity of p must be rejected, leading to the conclusion that p is true.

For example, we know from B5 that (p) if $n \in N$ and n is even then n^2 is even. Let us now give an indirect proof of this proposition (q): "If $k \in N$ and k^2 is odd then k is odd." First, assume that (q) is false; i.e., assume that we have a specific $m \in N$ such that m^2 is odd while m is even. But then, since m is even, it follows from (p) that m^2 is even, contradicting the hypothesis that m^2 is odd. From the supposition that (q) is false we have obtained a contradiction; we conclude that (q) is true.

EXERCISES

1. Prove directly that if a and b are odd integers then so is ab. (Use B6.)

2. Taking it for granted that if ab is even then either a is even or b is even, give an indirect proof of the same result.

3. Use the result of 1 to show indirectly that if $a \in N$ and $a^2 \in E$ then $a \in E$.

4. Can one find $a, b \in N$, not both even, such that $a^2 = 2b^2$? (Optional (cf. 2C2). What is the significance of this result?)

D. Variables and Constants; Quantifiers

A variable is an ambiguous symbol for an unspecified element of a specified set. When we say "Let x be (or denote) a positive even integer less than 10", then we know that either $x = 2$ or $x = 4$ or $x = 6$ or $x = 8$, in other words, we know that x is an element of the set $T = \{2, 4, 6, 8\}$. Thus the meaning of x is determined to the extent that x is known to denote *some* element of T, but its meaning is indeterminate in that we do not specify *which* element. The advantage of using variables is familiar from earlier studies. In proving, for example, that if $a \in I$ and $b \in I$ then $a + b = b + a$, we have proved infinitely many statements; it is not possible, indeed, even to write down each one separately.

Let the set S be not empty. If the symbol x denotes an unspecified element of S, then x is said to be a *variable* with *domain* S. When a variable x with domain S is replaced by a specific element a of S, then one says that a has been *substituted* for x, or that x *has* (or *takes on*, or *assumes*) *the value a*; the elements of S are therefore referred to as *values of x*.

The notion of a variable is most natural when S has at least two elements. If S has only one element, denoted by a, so that $S = \{a\}$, then a variable x with domain S has the unique fixed value a, and the symbol a is called a *constant*. In the present context, for example, each of the symbols . . . , -2, -1, 0, 1, 2, . . . for an integer is a constant. We have also agreed, for the time being, that the symbols N and I shall be constants.

If the constants a and b denote the same object, we say that a and b are *equal*, writing $a = b$; otherwise they are *unequal*, written $a \neq b$. If b is a given constant and we say "Let $a = b$", then we are saying that a shall be a constant denoting the same object that b denotes. Thus the equality $S = \{0, 1\}$ says that the symbol S is to be (for the time being) a constant denoting the set whose only elements are 0 and 1. It is also convenient to write "Let $x = a$" to mean that the variable x has the value a.

Let us consider a proposition A containing a variable y whose domain is a given set S, assuming that A is meaningful for each $y \in S$. In general, A will be true for some values of y and false for others.

If A is true for *each* $y \in S$, then one says that A is true *identically for* $y \in S$ or, more briefly, is true *identically in* y, or *is an identity in* y, and one uses also the following phraseology: A is true for *every* or *all* $y \in S$.

If A is true for *some* $y \in S$ (at least one and perhaps, but not necessarily, all), then one also says that *there exists* a (value of) $y \in S$ for which A is true.

If A is true for *no* $y \in S$, in other words, A is false for every $y \in S$, one may say that A is *identically false*, or is *never* true.

The words "each", "every", and "all" are called *universal quantifiers*, while "for some" and "there exists" are *existential quantifiers;* these words indicate, roughly, for "how many" values of the variable y proposition A is true.

A complicated proposition may contain more than one quantifier. It is then essential to pay strict attention to the order in which they occur. Consider, for example, the following propositions, in which the variables have the domain I.

(a) For each $x \in I$ there exists a $y \in I$ such that $y + 5 = x$;

(b) There exists a $y \in I$ such that, for each $x \in I$, $y + 5 = x$.

The first is clearly true ($y = x - 5$), while the second is evidently an absurdity.

E. Denial of a Proposition; Complement of a Set

When reference is made to a proposition A, the corresponding assertion is tacitly understood to be "It is true that A" or "A is true". The negative assertion "It is false that A" or "A is false" is denoted by $\sim A$, and this proposition is called the *denial* or *negation* of A, and is often read "not A". By the Law of excluded middle, $\sim A$ is true or false according as A is false or true. It follows that the propositions $\sim(\sim A)$ and A are *equivalent* in the sense that each is true when the other is true and false when the other is false.

For example, let p be the proposition $-1 \in N$, that is, "-1 is a natural number". Then $\sim p$ is $\sim(-1 \in N)$, that is, "-1 is not a natural number", or $-1 \in' N$. The proposition $\sim(\sim p)$ is $\sim(-1 \in' N)$, or $-1 \in N$, that is, p. In this instance, of course, p is false and $\sim p$ is true.

Some care is needed in denying propositions containing quantifiers. A typical error, occurring frequently even in quite literate contexts, can be illustrated by the propositions

"Every integer is even"

and

"Every integer is not even".

Neither proposition is true, of course, and this is direct evidence that neither is the denial of the other, for we are assuming that either A or $\sim A$ must be true.

What does it mean to deny the proposition

"For each $x \in I$, x is even"?

If it is false that each x is even, then there must exist an x that is not even, and conversely. The denial is this: "Not every integer is even"; or this: "There exists an integer which is odd (not even)".

Particular care is needed with expressions in which the quantifier is delayed. The assertion " 'x is even' is not true for every x" can mean either that " 'x is even' is not (true for every x)" or that " 'x is even' is (false (not true) for every x)". The former interpretation yields a true proposition and the latter a false one; the ambiguity can be avoided by earlier correct use of the quantifier, as in the denials in the preceding paragraph.

In general, if S is any set, then "$\sim$(For every $x \in S$, . . .)" has the same meaning as "For some $x \in S$, $\sim$(. . .)", or "There exists an $x \in S$ such that $\sim$(. . .)". Similarly, "$\sim$(There exists an $x \in S$ such that . . .)" is equivalent to "For each $x \in S$, $\sim$(. . .)".

An important tactical principle follows as a corollary. In order to *disprove* that each element of a set S has a certain property, we need merely produce *one* element of S *not* having the property. Any single element not having the property in question is called a *counter-example*, this hybrid word being a literal translation of the equally hybrid but linguistically more appropriate German word "Gegenbeispiel". To disprove, for example, the absurd claim that "For each $x \in I$, x is even", we need merely produce a specific $y \in I$ such that y is not even; $+1$ is such a y, and -1, 3, and 13 are equally convincing counter-examples.

Now let a set S be given. If the proposition "$x \in S$" is meaningful, then either $x \in S$ or $\sim(x \in S)$, that is, $x \in' S$. Evidently $S = \{x : x \in S\}$, and we define the *complement of S* to be the set $S' = \{x : x \in' S\}$. We shall use, actually, a more precise notion. If $S \subset T$, we define the *complement* of S *relative to T* to be the set $S'_T = \{x : x \in T$ and $x \in' S\}$. If P is a property of elements of T and $S = \{x : x \in T$ and x has $P\}$, then $S'_T = \{x : x \in T$ and $\sim(x$ has $P)\}$. If it is perfectly evident what T is, we may safely abbreviate, thus: $S' = \{x : \sim(x$ has $P)\}$.

EXERCISES

1. Form the denial of each of the following propositions:

   (a) $2 + 3 = 5$;

   (b) $1 \neq -1$;

   (c) Every integer is the square of an integer;

   (d) Some integers are odd;

   (e) For some integers x there exists an integer y such that $y^2 = x$;

   (f) There exists an integer z such that for every integer x, $x + z = x$.

2. For the sets Q, R, S, and T of A1, form the sets Q'_R, Q'_S, R'_T, and S'_T.

3. Let P denote a given plane. Describe the set S'_P for each of the following subsets of P:

   (a) $S = \{$Interior and circumference of a given circle$\}$;

   (b) $S = \{$Points distant more than two units from a given line$\}$;

   (c) $S = \{$Points at which a given rectangle subtends an acute angle$\}$.

4. Let S denote the student body at a college. Find the complement in S of the following sets T:

   (a) $T = \{s : s$ is a male$\}$;

   (b) $T = \{s : s$ is at least 19 years old$\}$;

   (c) $T = \{s : s$ has no brothers$\}$;

   (d) $T = \{s : s$ is a freshman or a sophomore$\}$;

   (e) $T = \{s : s$ is a female senior$\}$;

   (f) $T = \{s : s$ is not taking a course in English$\}$;

   (g) $T = \{s : s$ is a junior and is taking a course in history$\}$;

   (h) $T = \{s :$ either s is a freshman or s is on the Dean's list$\}$.

F. Conjunction of Propositions; Intersection of Sets

The conjunction of propositions A and B is the proposition "Both A and B", denoted by $A \wedge B$. The proposition $A \wedge B$ asserts A and B jointly, so to speak, and is true if and only if both A is true and B is true. If A denotes "$0 \neq 1$" and B denotes "$2^2 = 4$" then $A \wedge B$ denotes

"Both $0 \neq 1$ and $2^2 = 4$";

since both A and B are true, $A \wedge B$ is true. The Law of Consistency, for example, is $\sim(\sim A \wedge A)$.

If S and T are sets, their *intersection*, denoted by $S \cap T$, is the set

$$\{x : (x \in S) \wedge (x \in T)\}.$$

Thus $S \cap T$ is that subset of both consisting precisely of those elements common to the two sets; some authors call $S \cap T$ the *meet* of S and T. If $S = \{2, 4, 6\}$ and $T = \{3, 4, 5\}$ then $S \cap T = \{4\}$. Sets S and T are said to be *disjoint* if $S \cap T = \square$; there is then no element common to S and T. For example, $S \cap S' = \square$; S and S' are disjoint.

If $R \subset S$ and $R \subset T$ then $R \subset S \cap T$.

G. Disjunction of Propositions; Union of Sets

The *disjunction* of propositions A and B is the proposition "Either A or B", denoted by $A \vee B$. If A denotes "$0 = 1$" and B denotes "$2 = 3$" then $A \vee B$ denotes "Either $0 = 1$ or $2 = 3$"; since both A and B are false, so is $A \vee B$. It is important to recognize that $A \vee B$ does *not* exclude the possibility that both A *and* B may be true. The explicit understanding, in other words, is *not* "Either A or B (but not both)", but rather "Either A or B (and perhaps both)". The Law of excluded middle, for example, is $A \vee \sim A$; the qualified "perhaps both" is denied in this instance by the Law of consistency: $\sim(A \wedge \sim A)$.

If S and T are sets, their *union*, denoted by $S \cup T$, is the set

$$\{x : (x \in S) \vee (x \in T)\}.$$

Thus $S \cup T$ is that set consisting precisely of those elements belonging either to S or to T (and perhaps to both.) If $S = \{2, 4, 6\}$ and $T = \{3, 4, 5\}$ then $S \cup T = \{2, 3, 4, 5, 6\}$. If $V \subset W$ then $V \cup V'_W = W$.

The terms (logical) *sum* and (logical) *product* were formerly used, respectively, for $S \cup T$ and $S \cap T$, because of a weak analogy with numerical sums and products, but few modern authors use these terms.

If $R \subset T$ and $S \subset T$ then $R \cup S \subset T$.

Each of the two operations, union and intersection, is said to be *distributive* with respect to the other, in the sense that the following laws hold:

9

1.
$$R \cap (S \cup T) = (R \cap S) \cup (R \cap T);$$

2.
$$R \cup (S \cap T) = (R \cup S) \cap (R \cup T).$$

Denial of compound propositions follows de Morgan's laws:

3. $\sim(A \wedge B)$ and $(\sim A) \vee (\sim B)$ have the same meaning;

4. $\sim(A \vee B)$ and $(\sim A) \wedge (\sim B)$ have the same meaning.

Similarly, for complementation of sets,

5.
$$(S \cap T)' = S' \cup T';$$

6.
$$(S \cup T)' = S' \cap T'.$$

Union and intersection of sets can be interpreted visually in terms of plane diagrams (often called *Venn diagrams*).

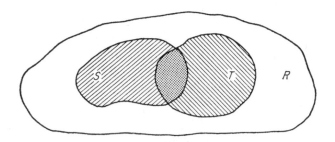

In the illustration, S and T are both subsets of R, the cross-hatched area represents $S \cup T$, and the dotted area represents $S \cap T$, while the clear area represents $(S \cup T)'_R$.

EXERCISES

7. Prove that $S \cap T \subset S \subset S \cup T$.

8. Prove that if *any one* of the following propositions is true, then so is each of the others:
$$S \subset T, \qquad T' \subset S', \qquad S \cap T = S, \qquad S \cup T = T.$$

9. Complete these equations, assuming that $S \subset U$:
$$S \cap U = \qquad, \qquad S \cup U = \qquad, \qquad S \cap \square = \qquad,$$
$$S \cup \square = \qquad, \qquad S \cap S = \qquad, \qquad S \cup S = \qquad.$$

10–15. Prove 1–6.

16. Suppose that $S \cup T = U$ and $S \cap T = \square$. Prove that $T = S'_U$. Is the converse true?

17. Prove that if $R \subset S$ then $R \cap T \subset S \cap T$ and $R \cup T \subset S \cup T$.

18. For which x, precisely, is $x \in S \cap T'$? When is it true that $S \cap T' = T'_S$? (Sometimes authors call the set $S \wedge T'$ the *difference* between S and T, and denote it by $S - T$ or $S \setminus T$.)

19. Let S and T be given sets. Show that $W = S \cap T$ has these properties: $W \subset S$, $W \subset T$, and, if both $V \subset S$ and $V \subset T$ then $V \subset W$. Prove conversely that if W has these properties then $W = S \cap T$. (T)

20. Let S and T be given sets. Suppose that a set W has these properties: $S \subset W$, $T \subset W$, and, if both $S \subset V$ and $T \subset V$ then $W \subset V$. Prove that $W = S \cup T$ and, conversely, that $S \cup T$ has these properties. (T)

H. Implication

In order to describe the relation of implication between propositions, which is of special importance in all branches of mathematics, let us begin by supposing that A and B are propositions and then consider the disjunction $(\sim A) \vee B$. The disjunction is clearly true if A is false, and true if B is true. Suppose, however, that A is true *and* that, at the same time, the disjunction is true; we conclude that B is necessarily true (for otherwise *both* alternatives of the disjunction, and, therefore, the disjunction itself, would be false). If the disjunction is true, accordingly, then the truth of A enables us to infer the truth of B; we say then that A *implies* or *entails* B and write $A \rightarrow B$. Thus our definition of implication is this:

1. $\qquad\qquad A \rightarrow B$ has the same meaning as $(\sim A) \vee B$.

In the relation $A \rightarrow B$, A is the *hypothesis* or *antecedent* and B is the *conclusion* or *consequent*. To prove a proposition is to demonstrate that it is implied by propositions already accepted.

The relation "$A \rightarrow B$" occurs so frequently, in such varied contexts, that it is expressed in several ways, some of which seem more expressive than the others in some situations. In the following schematic formulations, the phrase "the truth of" or "is true" may be supplied, if desired, before or after each symbol for a proposition.

If A then B;
B if A;
A only if B;
B is necessary (or a necessary condition) for A;
A is sufficient (or a sufficient condition) for B.

The implication $B \rightarrow A$ is the *converse* of the implication $A \rightarrow B$. The converse of the true implication "If $x = 2$ then $x^2 = 4$" is the false implication "If $x^2 = 4$ then $x = 2$". That an implication and its converse have generally no connection with each other is clear also from their definitions:

$\qquad A \rightarrow B$ means $(\sim A) \vee B$, while $B \rightarrow A$ means $A \vee (\sim B)$.

When it does happen that both $A \rightarrow B$ and $B \rightarrow A$, we say that "A implies B *and conversely*", writing $A \leftrightarrow B$. Alternative expressions are these:

$$A \text{ if and only if } B;$$
$$B \text{ is necessary and sufficient for } A.$$

If $A \leftrightarrow B$ then A is true when and only when B is true, and they are said to be *equivalent*; the relation $A \leftrightarrow B$ may therefore be called *equivalence* between propositions.

The *contrapositive* of $A \rightarrow B$ is $\sim B \rightarrow \sim A$. It is left as an exercise to prove that an implication and its contrapositive are equivalent:

2.
$$(A \rightarrow B) \leftrightarrow (\sim B \rightarrow \sim A).$$

Thus we may choose to prove the more convenient one, the implication itself or its contrapositive.

It is often possible to prove that $A \rightarrow B$ without knowing whether or not either A or B is true. If this has been done, and we learn later that A is true, then the implication allows us to infer the truth of B.

We observe that quantifiers can be replaced by implications or denials of implications. Thus

$$(\text{For each } x \in S, \ldots) \leftrightarrow (x \in S \rightarrow \ldots)$$
and
$$(\text{For some } x \in S, \ldots) \leftrightarrow \sim(x \in S \rightarrow \sim(\ldots)).$$

EXERCISES

3. Let the variable x have domain I, and consider propositions $A : \text{``} x = 2\text{''}$, $B : \text{``} x^2 = 4\text{''}$, and $C : \text{``} x^3 = 8\text{''}$. Which imply which? Which are necessary for which? Which are sufficient for which? State in explicit mathematical terms the converse and the contrapositive of the implications $A \rightarrow B$ and $C \rightarrow A$.

4. A triangle has vertices α, β, γ with respective opposite sides of lengths a, b, c. What is the relation between these two propositions: "The angle at γ is a right angle" and "$c^2 = a^2 + b^2$"?

5. Let S and T denote sets. Prove that $S \subset T$ if and only if $(x \in S) \rightarrow (x \in T)$.

6. Express the following propositions without using the arrow: $A \rightarrow A \lor B$, $A \land B \rightarrow B$. Are they true? Why?

7. Prove by intuitive arguments:

(a) $(A \rightarrow B) \rightarrow (A \lor C \rightarrow B \lor C)$,

(b) $((A \rightarrow B) \land (B \rightarrow C)) \rightarrow (A \rightarrow C)$.

8. Prove that if A is false and B is any proposition then $A \rightarrow B$. Prove also that if B is true and A is any proposition then $A \rightarrow B$. (There is an anecdote, which the author cannot authenticate, concerning Lord Bertrand Russell, who was one of the first to draw attention to many of the ideas we are studying here. He was challenged at a professional gathering to start with the hypothesis "4 = 5" and arrive at the conclusion "I am the Pope". His argument was this: "If 4 = 5 then I can prove that 2 = 1. You will agree that the Pope and I are two; hence the Pope and I are one.)

9. Propositions A and B are said to be incompatible if $\sim(A \cap B)$. Prove that if A and B are incompatible then one of them must be false.

10. Prove H2.

I. Functions

Let x be a variable with domain X and let Y be a given nonvoid set. A *function f on X into Y* is a correspondence, rule, or principle of association such that to each member x of X there corresponds a unique element of Y. The sets X and Y are called, respectively, the *domain* and a *codomain* of f; any superset of Y is clearly also a codomain of f. If a is a value of x, then the unique element of Y associated by f with a is denoted by $f(a)$ and is called the *value* of f when $x = a$. The function f is said to be *a function of the variable x*.

A function f, as defined in the preceding paragraph, has just one value $f(b)$ for each element b of the domain of f. Such a function is accordingly said to be *single-valued*. It is sometimes desirable to recognize multiple-valued functions; in trigonometry, for example, arcsec $2 = (\pi/3) + 2k\pi$ ($k \in I$). Unless it is stated otherwise, or clearly implied by the context, each function used in our work will be understood to be single-valued.

The correspondence f may be specified in some cases by giving $f(x)$ quite explicitly for each $x \in X$. For example, if $X = \{a, b, c\}$, one might be given a table such as this:

$$
\begin{array}{c|ccc}
x & a & b & c \\
\hline
f(x) & f(a) & f(b) & f(c)
\end{array} ;
$$

or this:

$$
\begin{array}{ccc}
a & b & c \\
\downarrow & \downarrow & \downarrow \\
f(a) & f(b) & f(c).
\end{array}
$$

Even if f is specified by other means, a tabular display may be illuminating.

A function will sometimes be called a *transformation* or a *mapping on* its domain *into* its codomain. If $b = f(a)$, then b is said to be the *image* or *map of a under f*, and a is said to be an *original* or an *antecedent* of *b under f*.

The complete notation for a function will be "f *on X into Y : x → f(x)*", it being implied by the notation that $x \in X$ and $f(x) \in Y$. Some parts of this notation may be omitted if no confusion can result, and after becoming familiar with the idea we shall relax the language and symbolism in ways permitted by the context. The notation "$f : X \to Y$" will mean that f is a function with domain X and codomain Y.

Although the codomain, as we have seen, is in principle not unique, in any practical context there is usually a "natural" codomain; for this reason

13

we allow ourselves in most instances to speak loosely of "the codomain" without meaning to imply that no other codomain would be allowable.

Given $f : X \rightarrow Y$ and $g : X \rightarrow Y$, we say that $f = g$ if and only if $f(x) = g(x)$ for each $x \in X$.

Examples of functions:

(a) $X = Y =$ set of all human beings, f on X into $Y : x \rightarrow f(x) =$ father of x;

(b) $U =$ set of kings of France, g on U into $N : u \rightarrow g(u) =$ age of u (in days, to nearest day) at time of coronation;

(c) $B =$ set of books in English, h on B into $N : b \rightarrow h(b) =$ number of words in B;

(d) g on I into $N : y \rightarrow g(y) = y^2$;

(e) $V =$ any set $\neq \square$, $W =$ class of subsets of V, f on V into $W : v \rightarrow f(v) = \{v\}$;

(f) Given a plane p and a line L in p, let $L' = \{P : P \in p \wedge P \in' L\}$, g on L' into $L : P \rightarrow g(P) =$ point of L nearest P.

The notation "$f :$ domain $\rightarrow$ codomain" would read, for example, in case (b) $g : U \rightarrow N$, and in case (e) $f : V \rightarrow W$.

Given $f : X \rightarrow Y$ and a subset S of X, we define

$$f(S) = \{y : y \in Y \text{ and } y = f(x) \text{ for some } x \in S\}.$$

Thus $f(S)$ is the subset of Y consisting of images of elements of S, and may be called the *image* of S; clearly $f(\square) = \square$. The image $f(X)$ of the domain X is called the *range* of f, and f is said to *map* X onto $f(X)$. Hence f maps X onto Y when and only when $f(X) = Y$; then each $y \in Y$ is the image of some $x \in X$. Each codomain for f must contain the range of f.

In example (a) the range $f(X)$ is the set of all fathers; if $F \subset X$ is the set of all females then $f(F)$ is the set of all fathers of daughters. In example (d) the range $g(I)$ is the set of all perfect squares, $\{0, 1, 4, 9, 16, 25, \ldots\}$; if $E \subset N$ is the set of all even natural numbers then $g(E) = \{0, 4, 16, 36, \ldots\}$. In example (f) the range $g(L')$ is all of L, so that g maps L' onto L; if H is a line in p perpendicular to L, then $g(H \cap L') = H \cap L$.

Given $f : X \rightarrow Y$ and a subset T of Y, we define

$$f^{-1}(T) = \{x : x \in X \text{ and } y = f(x) \text{ for some } y \in T\}.$$

Thus $f^{-1}(T)$ is that subset of X consisting of antecedents of elements of T, and may be called the *antecedent* of T. Obviously, $f^{-1}(\square) = \square$, $f^{-1}(T) = f^{-1}(T \cap f(X))$, and $f^{-1}(f(X)) = X$. If $T = \{b\}$, we abbreviate $f^{-1}(\{b\})$ to $f^{-1}(b)$. The function f^{-1} on $f(X)$ into the class of subsets of X, carrying $y \in T$ onto the subset $f^{-1}(y)$ of X, is called the function *inverse* to f.

In example (a) if $T \subset Y$ is the set of all Dutch fathers, then $f^{-1}(T)$ is the set of all children of Dutchmen; for each $y \in Y$, $f^{-1}(y)$ consists of all children sired by y. In example (d), if $T \subset N$ and S consists of precisely those elements of T which are perfect squares, and S is not empty, then $g^{-1}(T)$ consists of all numbers $\pm s \in I$ for which $s^2 \in S$. In example (f), if $K \subset L$ then $f^{-1}(K)$ consists of all points lying on lines in p perpendicular to L at points of K, with each point of intersection with L removed.

A function $f: X \to Y$ is also said to set up a *correspondence* between its domain X and its range $f(X)$. Each $x \in X$ has a unique image $f(x) \in Y$. Suppose further that each $y \in f(X)$ has a unique antecedent x, whence $f^{-1}(y) = \{x\}$. We may drop the braces and regard X itself as the codomain of f^{-1}, and we see that f^{-1} on $f(X)$ onto X is single-valued. We say in this case that f sets up a *biunique* or *one-to-one* (or 1-1) correspondence between its domain and range, writing $x \leftrightarrow f(x)$ and $X \leftrightarrow f(X)$. Each element of X is *mated* or *paired* with a unique element $f(x)$ of $f(X)$. If, for example, $X = \{1, 2, 3, 4\}$ and $Y = \{a, b, c, d\}$, and f and g on X into Y are given by the following table:

x	1	2	3	4
$f(x)$	c	a	c	b
$g(x)$	c	d	b	a

,

then the correspondence g is biunique but f is not, for $f^{-1}(c) = \{1, 3\}$.

Sets S and T are said to be *equipotent* (or *equipollent*, or *equivalent*) if and only if there exists a biunique mapping of S onto T. Then one says also that S has *just as many* elements as T. If $n \in N$ and $n \neq 0$ and S is equipotent with the set $\{1, 2, \ldots, n\}$, then we say that S is *finite* and *has n elements*; $\square$ is finite and *has 0 elements*. Otherwise, S is said to be *infinite* and to have *infinitely* many elements.

We state without proof the fundamental fact that a set is finite or infinite according as it is not or is equipotent to at least one of its proper subsets (cf. 3 below). For further details see [A6, Chap. 12].

The particular function $f: X \to X$ such that $f(x) = x$ for each $x \in X$ is called the *identity* function.

A function $f: X \to Y$ such that there is a constant $b \in Y$ such that $f(x) = b$ for each $x \in S$, in other words, such that $f(X) = \{b\}$, is said to be a *constant function*; one may say loosely that "f is a constant" as an abbreviation for "f is a constant function", and this usage has the sanction that $f(x)$ is indeed a "constant", in the earlier sense of that word, in spite of the appearance of the variable x.

Now suppose that we are given $f: X \to Y$ and a fixed element b of Y. The indicated equality $f(x) = b$ is called an *equation*. It may be true, generally speaking, for some values of x and false for others. A value a of x is said to *satisfy* or to be a *solution* of the equation if it is true that $f(a) = b$. The *solution-set* of the equation is the set $f^{-1}(b) = \{x : x \in S \text{ and } f(x) = b\}$. The equation is said to be *inconsistent* or *consistent* according as its solution-set is empty or not empty. The equation is clearly consistent if, and only if,

15

b is an element of the range $f(X)$ of f. The problem of *solving* an equation is ordinarily understood to mean finding all solutions. For example, consider f on I into $N : f(x) = x^2$. Here $f(X)$ consists of those integers that are perfect squares. The equation $x^2 = b$ will be inconsistent unless b is a perfect square. If, say, $b = c^2$ ($c \in I$), then the equation $x^2 = c^2$ is consistent, and its solution-set is $f^{-1}(c^2) = \{c, -c\}$.

EXAMPLES

1. f on I into $\{0, 1\}$: $x \rightarrow 0$ or 1 according as x is even or odd. This function f may be called the *parity function*. Here $f^{-1}(0) = \{x : x \text{ is even}\}$.

2. Let S be a fixed subset of a given nonvoid set T and define f on T into $\{0, 1\}$ as follows: if $t \in T$ then $f(t) = 1$ or 0 according as $t \in S$ or $t \in' S$. This function is called the *characteristic function of S* (with respect to T). The parity function of 1 is the characteristic function of the set of odd integers. Vice versa, any function on a set T into $\{0, 1\}$ determines a subset $f^{-1}(1)$ of T. This correspondence between subsets of T and functions $f : T \rightarrow \{0, 1\}$ is biunique (cf. 8).

3. f on I into $I : x \rightarrow 2x$. Since $f^{-1}(1) = \square$, the range $f(I)$ is a proper subset of I, consisting in fact of the set of even integers. If b is a fixed element of I, then the equation $f(x) = b$ is consistent or inconsistent according as b is even or odd. That f is biunique is evident from the following table:

x	$\ldots, -3, -2, -1, 0, 1, 2, 3, \ldots$
$f(x)$	$\ldots, -6, -4, -2, 0, 2, 4, 6, \ldots$

There are in the technical sense, therefore, just as many even integers as there are integers!

4. Let X denote a fixed plane, L a fixed line in X, and P a variable point with domain X. Define $f : X \rightarrow X$ as follows: if $P \in L$ then $f(P) = P$; if $P \in' L$ then drop a perpendicular from P onto L and continue it past its intersection Q with L to a point P' such that $P'Q = PQ$, and define $f(P) = P'$. This mapping is a *reflection of X in L*. Clearly $f(X) = X$ and f is 1-1. For each $P \in X$, $f(f(P)) = P$; a mapping with this property is said to be *involutory*. In general, for $g : X \rightarrow X$, if $g(x) = x$ then x is said to be *fixed under g*; here each $P \in L$ is fixed under f.

5. Consider a map of a portion of the earth's surface. To each point w of a definite area A there corresponds (in principle) just one point $W = f(w)$ on the piece of paper P. Thus f is defined on A into P. On account of margins, space allocated to explanation of symbols, and so on, $f(A)$ is usually a proper subset of P. By cutting down the paper P, one can arrive at a smaller piece of paper Q such that $f(A) = Q$, and the correspondence between A and Q is then (in principle) biunique. (We are ignoring the presence of place-names, compass indication, contour lines on a topographical map, and other special symbols. Part of the cartographer's problem is how to distinguish subsets of Q to indicate corresponding subsets of A, such as rivers, highways, railroads, inhabited areas, and so on.)

16

EXERCISES

6. Prove that New England has six states and that the English alphabet has 26 letters.

7. Prove that $f : X \to Y$ is 1-1 on X onto $f(X)$ if and only if $x \neq x'$ implies $f(x) \neq f(x')$. (T)

8. Prove that the correspondence between subsets of a nonvoid set T and functions $f : T \to \{0, 1\}$ is biunique. Prove that if T has n elements ($n \in N$, $n \neq 0$) then the class of subsets of T has 2^n elements. (T)

9. Let A, B, and C be distinct points in a plane. Let points D on AB and E on AC correspond to each other if DE is parallel to BC. Show that the correspondence between D and E is 1-1. (There are, therefore, just as many points on AB as on AC.)

10. Let S denote the set of circles of radius one lying in a plane p. Define f on S into p so that for $c \in S$, $f(c)$ is the center of c. Does f map S onto p? Is f biunique on S onto $f(S)$?

11. Let S denote the set of squares of side one lying in a plane p. Define f on S into p so that for $s \in S$, $f(s)$ is the center of s. Does f map S onto p? Specify $f^{-1}(P)$ for $P \in p$.

12. Consider f on I into $I : x \to x^3$. What is the range of f? With c a fixed element of I, comment on the consistency of the equation $f(x) = c$. Is f biunique on I onto $f(I)$?

13. Let T be a given nonvoid set, b an element of T, and R and S subsets of T with respective characteristic functions f and g. Specify the characteristic functions of $\square$, $\{b\}$, T, R', $R \cap S$, and $R \cup S$.

14. Prove that the mapping $S \to S' (= S'_X)$ on 2^X onto 2^X (cf. 28) is 1-1 and involutory.

15. Given $f : X \to Y$ and $T \subset Y$. Prove that $(T \cap f(X) = \square) \leftrightarrow (f^{-1}(T) = \square)$.

16. Given $f : X \to Y$ and $S \subset X$ and $T \subset X$. Prove that

(a) $(S \subset T) \to (f(S) \subset f(T))$,

(b) $f(S \cup T) = f(S) \cup f(T)$,

(c) $f(S \cap T) \subset f(S) \cap f(T)$,

(d) $f(S'_X) \supset (f(S))'_{f(X)}$.

17. Given $f : X \to Y$ and $S \subset Y$ and $T \subset Y$. Prove that

(a) $(S \subset T) \to (f^{-1}(S) \subset f^{-1}(T))$,

(b) $f^{-1}(S \cup T) = f^{-1}(S) \cup f^{-1}(T)$,

(c) $f^{-1}(S \cap T) = f^{-1}(S) \cap f^{-1}(T)$,

(d) $f^{-1}(S'_Y) = (f^{-1}(S))'_X$.

18. Given $f : X \to Y$. Given $S \subset X$ and $T \subset Y$, study the relation between S and $f^{-1}(f(S))$, and that between T and $f(f^{-1}(T))$.

We present finally, without proof, some remarkable relationships between certain operations on sets and arithmetic operations on cardinal numbers. Although these relationships themselves will not be used explicitly later on, several of the accompanying ideas will turn up repeatedly.

Until further notice, let us deal exclusively with *finite* sets. We agreed earlier in this section that a set S has n elements if and only if $n \in N$, $n \neq 0$, and S is equipotent with the set $\{1, 2, \ldots, n\}$. We also say that the number of elements in S is n, or that n is the *cardinal number* of S, writing

19.
$$\text{card } S = n.$$

It is consistent and convenient to define card $\square$ to be 0.

Thus "card" is the designation of a function whose domain is the class of all finite sets and whose codomain is N.

If S and T are both empty or both equipotent with $\{1, \ldots, n\}$ then they are easily seen to be equipotent with each other. Conversely, if they are equipotent with each other and one is equipotent with $\square$ or $\{1, \ldots, n\}$ for some $n \in N$, then the other is easily seen to be equipotent, respectively, with $\square$ or with $\{1, \ldots, n\}$ for the same n. Hence, card $S = $ card T if and only if S and T are equipotent.

If $S \cap T = \square$ then:

20.
$$\text{card } S \cap T = 0.$$

21.
$$\text{card } S \cup T = \text{card } S + \text{card } T.$$

Example:

22.
$$S = \{a, b\}, \qquad T = \{p, q, r\},$$
$$\text{card } S = 2, \qquad \text{card } T = 3,$$
$$\text{card } S \cup T = \text{card } \{a, b, p, q, r\} = 5 = 2 + 3.$$

If S and T are not disjoint, then

23.
$$\text{card } S \cup T + \text{card } S \cap T = \text{card } S + \text{card } T;$$

a Venn diagram makes this relaship plausible.

Turning to multiplication, let us first agree that a pair of objects is an *ordered pair* whenever one of the objects is recognized as first and the other as second. To the pair y, z there correspond two ordered pairs, denoted by (y, z) or (z, y) according as y or z comes first; contrast (Mr., Mrs.) with (Mrs., Mr.). If $y = z$ then $(y, z) = (z, y)$. We agree that $(a, b) = (y, z)$ if and only if both $a = y$ and $b = z$.

Now let (finite) sets S and T be given. Their *product*, in the order (S, T), is defined and denoted as follows:

24.
$$S \times T = \{(s, t) : s \in S \text{ and } t \in T\}.$$

Example: With S and T as in 22, their products may be displayed thus:

$$
\begin{array}{llllll}
(a, r) & (b, r) & & & & \\
(a, q) & (b, q) & (p, b) & (q, b) & (r, b) \\
(a, p) & (b, p) & (p, a) & (q, a) & (r, a) \\
& S \times T & & T \times S. &
\end{array}
$$

It will now come as no surprise that

25.
$$\text{card } S \times T = (\text{card } S) \cdot (\text{card } T) = \text{card } T \times S.$$

If either S or T is empty, then so is $S \times T$, and card $S \times T = 0$.

A relationship involving exponentiation arises from a generalization of 8. It turned out there that 2^n is equal to the number of functions on a domain with n elements into a codomain with two elements. If neither S nor T is void, let us write

26. $$S^T = \{f : f \text{ is a function with domain } T \text{ and codomain } S\} \; ;$$

that is, S^T is the set of all functions $f : T \to S$. The desired relationship is this:

27. $$(\text{card } S)^{\text{card } T} = \text{card } (S^T) \qquad (S \neq \square, T \neq \square).$$

The reader may find it entertaining to compare 27 with the more familiar fact that $(\text{card } S)^{\text{card } T}$ is the product of card T factors each equal to card S.

If T is a nonvoid set, then the otherwise meaningless symbol 2^T is often accepted as an abbreviation for $\{0, 1\}^T$; that is,

28. $$2^T \text{ is the class of subsets of } T.$$

The foregoing relationships were first developed about a century ago. Still more remarkable was the discovery at that time that cardinal numbers can be defined for *infinite* sets in such a way that card $S = $ card T if and only if S and T are equipotent. The cardinal number of an infinite set is called a transfinite cardinal number.

Now our definitions of $S \cap T$, of $S \cup T$, of $S \times T$, and, if $S \neq \square$ and $T \neq \square$, of S^T are meaningful whether S and T are both finite or both infinite, or either is finite and the other infinite. How shall we define sum, product, and powers for transfinite cardinal numbers? One way would be to *use* the relation 21 (when $S \cap T = \square$) to *define* sum, relation 25 to *define* product, and relation 27 to *define* powers. Other equally valid procedures are feasible, leading to theories differing only in highly technical respects that lie outside the cognizance of most practicing mathematicians. The relations just mentioned, as well as 23, are valid in all theories. (For further reading see [A6, Chap. 12].)

EXERCISES

29. Suppose that S and T are equipotent and that T is finite. Prove that S is finite.

30. Suppose that S and T are finite and that $S \subset T$. Find a formula for card S'_T (cf. E).

31. In 27 we insisted that both $S \neq \square$ and $T \neq \square$. At the same time, if $n \in I$ and $n \neq 0$ then we know that $0^n = 0$ while $n^0 = 1$. Can you extend 27 to cover these cases?

32. Give a direct proof (not using 25) that card $(S \times T) = $ card $(T \times S)$.

33. Suppose that $a, b \in N$. Assuming 21, prove that $a + b = b + a$. Assuming 25 and 32, prove that $ab = ba$.

34. Show that the mapping $f : V \to W$ in example (e) is 1-1 on V into W (cf. 7). Hence show that if card $V = n \neq 0$ $(n \in N)$, then the set W of subsets of V has at least $n + 1$ elements.

35. Let $S = \{1, 2, \ldots, n\}$ with $n \in N$, $n \neq 0$. Suppose that $T_1, T_2, \ldots, T_n$ are n different subsets of S. Show that the mapping $f : S \to 2^S$ (cf. 28), where $f(n) = T_n$, is biunique on S onto its range. Now define $g : S \to \{0, 1\}$ by this prescription for

$k = 1, 2, \ldots, n$, $g(k) = 0$ if $k \in T_k$, while $g(k) = 1$ if $k \in' T_k$. Let U be that subset of S whose characteristic function is g (cf. 2). Prove that $U \neq T_k$ $(k = 1, \ldots, n)$ and, therefore (by an indirect argument), that S and 2^S cannot be equipotent. It follows, though we omit the argument, that card $S < 2^{\text{card } S}$. A very similar method gives the same result if S is infinite.

36. Let S and T be two infinite sets. Are they necessarily equipotent? (This question is not easy, and even a very good student making no headway with it should not feel at all discouraged; we return to the question in 2D4.)

TWO
The System of Real Numbers

The system of real numbers, denoted by $\Re$ (or R), is indispensable to extensive areas of mathematics and its applications. Arithmetical calculations and the limiting processes of calculus can be carried out within the system R, and it is well-suited to use in physical measurement. We assume familiarity with the properties of R, and shall list them in an orderly manner later on in this chapter. In Chap. 4 we shall use R to construct the system of complex numbers.

It is possible to start with the set N of natural numbers, define addition and multiplication, and establish the properties of these operations; to use the system thus obtained to define the integers (set I of 1A) and the operations of addition and multiplication with integers; to use the system thus obtained to construct the system of rational numbers, and then, finally, to construct real numbers in terms of rationals. It is quite impractical to attempt such a detailed program here. (See [A6, Chaps. 1, 2, 4]; [H2, Chaps. 1, 2]; [H3, Chaps. 1–11]; [H9, Chap. 7].) We shall approach R, nevertheless, by way of these subsystems in order to establish concepts and results that are interesting in their own right and may be useful later. Some familiar ideas will also be reviewed in a more or less organized way.

A. The Natural Numbers

The set N occurs in a succession or a sequence: 0, 1, 2, 3, ... Let X be any nonvoid set, and let f be a function on N into X. It is customary to denote $f(n)$ by x_n, to arrange the values of f in the order of the subscript $n : x_0, x_1, x_2, \ldots$, and to speak of this succession of functional values as an (infinite) *sequence* of elements of X. If f is the identity function, the resulting sequence is simply the set N listed in its natural order, and we may therefore refer to the sequence N. It is sometimes convenient to omit 0 from the domain of f; then the sequence will be $x_1, x_2, x_3, \ldots$. We may also write a sequence as, for example, x_n $(n = 0, 1, 2, \ldots)$ or x_n $(n = 1, 2, 3, \ldots)$.

1. Recursive Definitions. One sometimes defines a sequence by starting with a given x_0, using x_0 in a prescribed way to find x_1, x_1 to find x_2, and proceeding in this stepwise manner to find x_n for each value of n. This process is said to define the sequence *recursively* or *by recursion*.

Or, we may prescribe x_0 and x_1 and give a rule for calculating x_{n+1} from x_{n-1} and x_n. For example, let $x_0 = 1$, $x_1 = 2$, and, for $n = 1, 2, 3, \ldots,$ $x_{n+1} = x_{n-1} + x_n$. The result is the famous Fibonacci sequence: 1, 2, 3, 5, 8, 13, 21, $\ldots$.

An essential feature of a sequence is that each element has a unique immediate successor (whether or not the successor is in any other way related to any of its predecessors is beside the point). In the sequence N, let us for the moment write n^+ to denote the successor of n; for example, $0^+ = 1$ and $4^+ = 5$.

Now let b denote a fixed element of N, and define f on N into N recursively as follows: $f(0) = b$ and, if $n \in N$ and $f(n)$ has been defined, then $f(n^+) = (f(n))^+$. Thus $f(1) = f(0^+) = (f(0))^+ = b^+$, $f(2) = f(1^+) = (f(1))^+ = (b^+)^+$, and so on. This definition is a critical step in one rigorous treatment of addition of natural numbers. We omit details, noting only that in familiar notation the result is $f(n) = b + n$ for each $n \in N$. It is an agreeable consequence that $n^+ = n + 1$.

Once addition has been defined, multiplication can also be defined recursively. A principal step is this: $b \cdot 0 = 0$ and, if $n \in N$ and $b \cdot n$ has been defined, then $b \cdot n^+ = b \cdot n + b$. The familiar properties of addition and multiplication can be established from these definitions.

Another important function is the *factorial* function, whose value is denoted by the special symbol "$n!$". One starts with $0! = 1$ and, if $n!$ has been defined, then $(n + 1)! = (n!)(n + 1)$.

One cannot, of course, obtain $f(n)$ by stepwise calculations for *all* values of n, for an infinite number of steps would be required. In fortunate cases, however, the successive terms of the sequence may show sufficient regularity to suggest a formula by which $f(n)$ may be calculated from n and $f(n - 1)$. For example, we shall see that if $n \neq 0$ then $n! = 1 \cdot 2 \cdot 3 \ldots \cdot n$ (cf. A2.5).

EXERCISES

1.1. Calculate $n!$ for $n = 2, 3, \ldots, 10$.

.2. With $a \in N$ fixed, define $a^0 = 0$ if $a = 0$ and $a^0 = 1$ if $a \neq 0$. If $k \in N$ and a^k has been defined, how shall we define a^{k+1} in order to have a recursive definition of a^n for $n \in N$?

.3. Let $b \in N$ be given. Define $a_0 = b$ and, for $n \in N$, $a_{n+1} = 3a_n$. Calculate a_n for $n = 1, 2, 3, 4$. Try to find for a_n a formula valid for $n \in N$. Can you *prove* that your formula is valid?

1.4. Same as Exercise 3 with $a_0 = b$ and $a_{n+1} = 2a_n + 1$.

.5. Define the symbols $\binom{1}{0} = 1$ and $\binom{1}{1} = 1$. Suppose now that $\binom{n}{k}$ has already been defined for $k = 0, 1, \ldots, n$. Define $\binom{n+1}{0} = 1$, $\binom{n+1}{n+1} = 1$, and, for $k = 1$, $\ldots, n$, define $\binom{n+1}{k} = \binom{n}{k} + \binom{n}{k-1}$. Calculate $\binom{n}{k}$ for $n = 2, 3, 4, 5$ and, for each value of n, $k = 0, \ldots, n$. (T)

.6. From an urn containing n distinct balls, we draw k balls. Let C_k^n denote the number of distinct drawings possible. Since there is clearly only one way of drawing none at all ($k = 0$) or all at once ($k = n$), we have $C_0^n = 1 = C_n^n$; in particular ($n = 1$), $C_0^1 = 1 = C_1^1$. Now suppose that we have learned, in one way or another, the value of C_k^n for $k = 0, 1, \ldots, n$. Let us put into the urn one more ball, say ball b, distinct from those already there, and try to calculate C_k^{n+1} for $k = 1, \ldots, n$. In a new drawing of k balls, either ball b will not be drawn, or it will be drawn. If ball b is *not* drawn, in how many ways can k balls be drawn? If ball b *is* drawn, in how many ways can the remaining $k - 1$ balls be drawn? In how many ways altogether, then, can k balls be drawn from the $n + 1$ balls? (cf. 1.5). (T)

2. Mathematical Induction.

Suppose that we wish to prove that each one of an infinite sequence of propositions P_1, P_2, P_3, $\ldots$ (or, if more convenient, P_0, P_1, P_2, $\ldots$) is true. It may be possible to prove or verify each one separately but, since there are infinitely many of them, no process treating each one separately can possibly succeed in establishing *all* of them. There is a process of proof called mathematical induction which fortunately gets around this difficulty. In recursive definition we started with a_1, and then, with a_n defined, were able to calculate a_{n+1}; in mathematical induction we start by proving P_1, and then, with P_n assumed true, show that P_{n+1} follows as a consequence. (See [H1, Sec. 3.2] for a discussion similar to ours.)

Some mathematicians believe that there is no principle in mathematics more fundamental than mathematical induction. In any event, the principle has nothing to do with "inductive" arguments in the empirical sciences, in which examination of several instances suggests a "general law" which is then tested by further experiments. On the contrary, mathematical induction is a process for firmly establishing an infinite sequence of propositions ("general law") which may originally be suggested by empirical considerations; though the principle may afford heuristic guidance in seeking what to prove, it is primarily a method of proof rather than of investigation. We start with an example.

The celebrated mathematician Gauss was a rather precocious student. According to a persistent anecdote, his mathematics teacher, desiring a few quiet moments, assigned the class the calculation of $s_{100} = 1 + 2 + 3 + \ldots + 99 + 100$. Gauss at once answered 5050, giving to the frustrated teacher the explanation implied by the following display:

$$s_{100} = \quad 1 + \quad 2 + \ldots + \quad 49 + \quad 50 + \ldots + 100$$
$$s_{100} = 100 + 99 + \ldots + \quad 52 + \quad 51 + \ldots + \quad 1$$

$$2s_{100} = 101 + 101 + \ldots + 101 + 101 + \ldots + 101$$

$$s_{100} = \frac{100 \cdot 101}{2} = 50 \cdot 101 = 5050.$$

On replacing 100 by n, we see that the row under the line on the right will be the sum of n terms, each equal to $n + 1$.

We therefore conjecture that

P_n
$$s_n = 1 + 2 + \ldots + n = \frac{n(n + 1)}{2}.$$

But is not P_n already proved for any value of n? The evidence is most convincing, to be sure, and no further proof would be required on the intuitive level at which much mathematical discourse is conducted. More careful examination discloses, however, that the argument depends on the meaning of the notation "$+ \ldots +$", for which a recursive definition, based on the associative law, will be given in C1. Taking that definition for granted, we proceed with a proof by mathematical induction.

Proposition P_1 is evident:

P_1
$$1 = \frac{1(1 + 1)}{2}.$$

It is easy to verify P_2, P_3, and so on, and in a doubtful case such steps may yield either a counter-example or strengthened conviction, but such steps can add nothing to a proof. Instead, we seek a truly general argument. From the set $1, 2, 3, \ldots$, we choose any one, say k. Next, we assume as hypothesis that P_k is true:

P_k
$$s_k = 1 + \ldots + k = \frac{k(k + 1)}{2}.$$

Now add $(k + 1)$ to each side of this equation. The left member is s_{k+1} and the right member can be manipulated to read $(k + 1)[(k + 1) + 1]/2$. Hence

$$s_{k+1} = 1 + \ldots + k + (k + 1) = \frac{(k + 1)[(k + 1) + 1]}{2}.$$

Since this equation is precisely P_{k+1}, we have shown, for $k = 1, 2, 3, \ldots$, that *if* P_k is true *then* P_{k+1} is true.

Since P_1 has already been verified, P_2 must therefore be true (without direct verification), then P_3 must therefore be true, and so on.

Does the "and so on" mean that P_n is true for $n = 1, 2, 3, \ldots$? If, for example, a particular proposition P_{k+1} were false, then P_k would also be false (for if P_k were to be true then P_{k+1} would necessarily be true). By repeating this argument k times, we would arrive at the contradictory conclusion that

P_1 would be false. By this indirect argument we may conclude, at least on intuitive grounds, that P_n is indeed true for $n = 1, 2, 3, \ldots$.

The foregoing argument, however appealing, does not meet the most exacting standards of rigor. The principle involved is perfectly sound, however, and will be used frequently. It is based on the following fundamental postulate, one of the five postulates used by Peano in his original axiomatic treatment of the natural numbers (see [H9, Chap. 1] and [A6, Sec. 2.6]).

2.1. Inductive Postulate. Let S be a set having these two properties: (a) $0 \in S$; (b) if $k \in N \cap S$ then $k + 1 \in S$. Then $N \subset S$.

As a consequence, we have the following method of proof:

2.2. Proof by Mathematical Induction. For each $n \in N$ let P_n be a proposition and suppose that: (a) P_0 is true; (b) if $k \in N$ then P_k implies P_{k+1}. Then P_n is true for each $n \in N$.

In fact, let S denote the set of those values of n for which P_n is true. By (a), $0 \in S$. By (b), if $k \in N \cap S$, then $k + 1 \in S$. By the inductive postulate, therefore, $N \subset S$, that is, $n \in N$ implies $n \in S$ and P_n is indeed true for each $n \in N$.

Postulate A2.1 can be proved on the basis of other postulates, to certain of which, as they apply to N, it is in fact equivalent; see [A6, pp. 47–52] and [H9, Chap. 2].

The postulate and the ensuing principle of proof can be generalized immediately in two directions. In our example, we started with P_1 instead of P_0. This was purely a matter of notational convenience, and our argument can be brought formally under the exact pattern of A2.2 in either of two ways. First, we could have defined s_n to be $0 + 1 + \ldots + n$. Then P_0 would have been $0 = 0(0 + 1)/2$, which is clearly true, and the proof could have proceeded from there. Second, we could simply have renumbered the propositions, putting $Q_n = P_{n+1}$ ($n = 0, 1, 2, \ldots$) and then dealt with Q_n. More generally, the process of proof can start with any first proposition P_m, proceeding stepwise from there; one can write $Q_n = P_{m+n}$ and apply the method to Q_n.

The second generalization is suggested by a feature of recursive definition. When $a_0, \ldots, a_k$ are known, the rule for calculating a_{k+1} may involve $a_0, \ldots, a_{k-1}$ as well as a_k. In proof by induction, it may be necessary to use $P_0, \ldots, P_{k-1}$ as well as P_k in order to prove P_{k+1}. It still follows from the Inductive Postulate that P_n is true for each $n \in N$. We omit an explicit formulation of this method of proof, called by some authors the second (or weak) principle of mathematical induction. In arriving at P_{k+1}, the proposition P_k (or, in the weak form, the proposition $P_0 \wedge P_1 \wedge \ldots \wedge P_k$) is often called the *inductive hypothesis*, sometimes abbreviated to *hyp. ind.*

As a second example of a proof by induction (mathematical, always), let us fix $a, b \in N$ and (using A1.2) prove that for each $n \in N$ it is true that

$(P_n) : (ab)^n = a^n b^n$. If either $a = 0$ or $b = 0$, then each member of the equation is 0 and P_n is true. If neither $a = 0$ nor $b = 0$, then $ab \neq 0$. The left member of P_0 is $(ab)^0 = 1$ and the right member is $a^0 b^0 = 1 \cdot 1 = 1$; hence P_0 is true. We now choose $k \in N$, assume that P_k is true, and seek to prove

P_{k+1} $$(ab)^{k+1} = a^{k+1} b^{k+1}.$$

Now, by definition, $c^{k+1} = c^k \cdot c$, whence $(ab)^{k+1} = (ab)^k (ab)$. By P_k, $(ab)^k = a^k b^k$. Hence

$$(ab)^{k+1} = a^k b^k ab = (a^k a)(b^k b) = a^{k+1} b^{k+1}.$$

Since P_{k+1} is indeed a consequence of P_k, we conclude by A2.2 that P_n is true for each $n \in N$. (Observe that the proof uses the commutative and associative laws of multiplication [see C1.1].)

It must be emphasized that both steps in an inductive proof are absolutely essential in order for the conclusion to be valid. In the first place, consider $P_n : 2^n = (n + 1)!$. P_0 is true, and even P_1, but P_k does not imply P_{k+1} unless $k = 0$, and P_n is patently absurd for $n = 2, 3, 4, \ldots$. On the other hand, consider $Q_n : n$ is among the successors of 10. Now if k is among the successors of 10, then $k + 1$ is also, so that Q_k does imply Q_{k+1}. Since Q_0 is false, however, we cannot conclude by induction that Q_n is true for each $n \in N$.

In the latter instance, of course, we can define R_n to be Q_{11+n} and prove by induction that R_n is true for each $n \in N$.

One final point. The proof that P_k implies P_{k+1} must be valid for each $k \in N$. As an illustration, we propose an amusing fallacy taken from [H2, p. 19]. First define max (a, b) for $a \in N$ and $b \in N$ as follows: if $a = b$ then max $(a, b) = a = b$, and if $a \neq b$ then max (a, b) is the greater of a and b. We shall now "prove" that if $p \in N$ and $q \in N$ then $p = q$. To begin with, let R_n denote this proposition: If $p \in N$ and $q \in N$ and max $(p, q) = n$ then $p = q$. We shall prove R_n for $n \in N$ by induction. For $n = 0$, observe that max $(p, q) = 0$ implies $p = 0$ and $q = 0$, whence $p = q$ and R_0 is true. Now fix $k \in N$ and assume, as the inductive hypothesis, that R_k is true, in other words, that if max $(p, q) = k$ then $p = q$. Now R_{k+1} starts with the hypothesis that max $(p, q) = k + 1$. Define

$$a = p - 1, \qquad b = q - 1.$$

Then max $(a, b) = k$ and it follows, by R_k, that $a = b$. Therefore, and this is the desired conclusion of R_{k+1}, $p = q$. Since R_k is thus seen to imply R_{k+1}, we conclude by induction that R_n is true for each nN. But max $(p, q) = n$ for *some* value of n (namely, $n = p$ or $n = q$, or both), so we conclude that $p = q$. Where is the error?

EXERCISES

2.3. Prove by induction:

(a) $1 + 3 + 5 + \ldots + (2n + 1) = (n + 1)^2$,

(b) $1 + 2 + 2^2 + \ldots + 2^n = 2^{n+1} - 1$,

(c) $1^2 + 2^2 + 3^2 + \ldots + n^2 = \dfrac{n(n + 1)(2n + 1)}{6}$,

(d) $1^3 + 2^3 + 3^3 + \ldots + n^3 = \left[\dfrac{n(n + 1)}{2} \right]^2$,

(e) $1^2 + 3^2 + 5^2 + \ldots + (2n - 1)^2 = \dfrac{n}{3} (2n - 1)(2n + 1)$,

(f) $1 + 2 \cdot 2 + 3 \cdot 2^2 + \ldots + n \cdot 2^{n-1} = 1 + (n - 1)2^n$,

(g) $\left(1 + \dfrac{3}{1} \right) \left(1 + \dfrac{5}{4} \right) \ldots \left(1 + \dfrac{2n + 1}{n^2} \right) = (n + 1)^2$,

(h) $2n \leq 2^n$.

.4. (Cf. A1.4.) Define a_n for $n \in N$ recursively as follows: $a_0 = b$ and if a_n has been defined, then $a_{n+1} = 2a_n + 1$. Prove by induction that, for $n \in N, a_n = 2^n(b + 1) - 1$.

.5. Prove by induction that $n! = 1 \cdot 2 \cdot \ldots \cdot n$ for $n = 1, 2, 3, \ldots$ (T)

.6. The symbols $\dbinom{n}{k}$ defined in A1.5 are called *binomial coefficients*. Use the definition there to prove that

$$\binom{n}{k} = \frac{n!}{(n - k)! \, k!} \qquad (n \in N; k = 0, 1, \ldots, n).$$

Does it follow from A1.5 and A1.6 that $C_k^n = \dbinom{n}{k}$? By induction, or otherwise, prove that each binomial coefficient is a natural number. (T)

.7. In plane geometry, with the distance between points P and Q denoted by $d(P, Q)$, the "triangle" inequality states that for any points P, Q, and R, $d(P, R) \leq d(P, Q) + d(Q, R)$. Use it to prove that if $n \geq 3$ and $P_1, P_2, \ldots, P_n$ are any n points in the plane then

$$d(P_1, P_n) \leq d(P_1, P_2) + d(P_2, P_3) + \ldots + d(P_{n-1}, P_n).$$

B. The Integers; Divisibility Properties

The symbol I designates (in this chapter) the set of the integers:

$$\ldots, -4, -3, -2, -1, 0, 1, 2, 3, 4, \ldots;$$

in this section small Latin letters will denote integers. The integers $1, 2, 3, \ldots$ are said to be *positive* (written > 0); the others are *non-positive* (≤ 0). The integers -1, -2, -3, ... are said to be *negative* (< 0); the others are *non-negative* (≥ 0). The fundamental properties of inequalities are listed later (see D1.1).

The set I (or N) together with the familiar operations of addition and multiplication, and relationships of order, may be called the *system I* (or N). The system I has at least one significant advantage over the system N. If $a \in N$, $b \in N$, and $a \neq b$, then *one* of a, b may be subtracted from the *other*, but *not* vice versa; there is no $x \in N$ such that $5 + x = 3$. In I, on the contrary, *any* $a \in I$ can be subtracted from *any* $b \in I$; there is always one (and only one) $x \in I$ such that $a + x = b$. Our present interest lies, however, in certain divisibility properties of integers.

Suppose that $ab = c$. Then c is the *product* of a and b and is a *multiple* of a and of b, each of which *divides* the *dividend* c, yielding the other as the *quotient;* we write $b = c|a$, $a = c|b$. We also say that each of a and b is a *divisor* or *factor* of c, writing $a|c$ and $b|c$ to express these facts. If it is false that $a|c$ then we write $a \nmid c$. For example, $3|12$, $-7|21$, and $4 \nmid 7$.

From the definition follow these special properties of 0 and ± 1:

For any a, $a|0$ and the quotient is 0; $0 \nmid a$ unless $a = 0$, and then the quotient is indeterminate; for any a, $\pm 1|a$ and $\pm a|a$; if $a|+1$ or $a|-1$, then either $a = 1$ or $a = -1$. Since a quotient whose divisor is zero cannot in any case be given a definite meaning, we must refrain scrupulously from dividing by zero. If a divisor contains a variable we must devote special consideration to each situation arising when the variable has a value making the divisor vanish.

Even if $a \nmid b$, a quite precise statement can be made. The equation $\frac{13}{4} = 3\frac{1}{4}$ is equivalent to the equation $13 = 4 \cdot 3 + 1$. Similarly, $-\frac{31}{7} = -(4 + \frac{3}{7}) = -5 + \frac{4}{7}$ is equivalent to $-31 = 7(-5) + 4$. These relationships illustrate the following result (see [A6, pp. 16–22]):

1. **The Euclidean Algorithm.** For each integer b and positive integer a there exist unique integers q and r such that

$$b = aq + r \qquad \text{and} \qquad 0 \leq r < a.$$

Further examples: $-176 = 17(-11) + 11$; $27 = 2 \cdot 13 + 1$.

Terminology: b is the *dividend*, a the *divisor*, q the *quotient*, and r the *remainder*. We insist that $a > 0$ and $0 \leq r < a$ in order to have q and r uniquely determined by a and b. Evidently $a|b$ if and only if the integer r of 1 is zero.

Now suppose that $a \neq 0$ and $b \neq 0$. They have a common positive divisor d, denoted by (a, b) and called the *greatest common divisor* (or *factor*) of a and b, such that if c is any common divisor of a and b then $c|d$. The Euclidean Algorithm can be used to find (a, b) and to show, moreover, that there exist (non-unique) p, $q \in I$ such that $(a, b) = pa + qb$. For example:

$$(12, 16) = 4 = 1 \cdot 16 + (-1) \cdot 12$$
$$(-75, 150) = 75 = (-3)(-75) + (-1) \cdot 150$$
$$(-176, -208) = 16 = (-6) \cdot (-176) + 5(-208).$$

If $(a, b) = 1$, then a and b are said to be *relatively prime* or *coprime;* $(6, 35) = 1$.

The *least common multiple* of a and b, neither zero, is denoted by $[a, b]$ and is defined to be a positive common multiple which divides every common multiple. Examples: $[6, 10] = 30$ and $[45, -63] = 315$.

Each integer n has, of course, the factors ± 1 and $\pm n$; let us call these the *trivial factors* of n. If $n \neq 0$ and $n \neq \pm 1$, then n is said to be *composite* (or *a composite*) or *prime* (or *a prime*) according as it does or does not have a nontrivial factor. Thus 6 $(= 2 \cdot 3)$ and 24 $(= 4 \cdot 6)$ are composite. The first few positive primes are 2, 3, 5, 7, 11, 13, 17, 19, and 23. It is evident that if q is a positive nontrivial factor of n, then $1 < q < n$.

We now prove that if $n \neq 0$ and $n \neq \pm 1$, then n can be factored into primes; a prime, of course, is already "factored into primes". Since a factorization of $-n$ follows at once from a factorization of n, we assume that $n \geq 2$ and argue by induction. Clearly 2 and 3 can be (are) factored into primes. Suppose now that 2, 3, . . . , k can be factored into primes and consider $k + 1$. If $k + 1$ is prime, there is nothing to prove. If $k + 1$ has the positive nontrivial factors a and b, then these numbers occur among the numbers 2, 3, . . . , k and can therefore be factored into primes; hence $ab = k + 1$ can be factored into primes and the proof is complete.

The order of the factors does not affect the product, but a unique result is obtained by arranging the positive prime factors in non-decreasing order and then grouping equal factors together, thus obtaining a product of powers of primes. We state the essential result.

2. **The Fundamental Theorem of Arithmetic.** If a is an integer, $a \neq 0$, and $a \neq \pm 1$, then there exists a unique natural number k, unique primes $p_1, \ldots,$ p_k such that $1 < p_1 < \ldots < p_k$, and unique positive integers $q_1, \ldots, q_k$ such that

$$a = \pm p_1^{q_1} \cdot p_2^{q_2} \cdot \ldots \cdot p_k^{q_k}$$

where the upper or lower sign is used on the right according as $a > 0$ or $a < 0$.

Much study has been devoted to the distribution of the positive primes, and many very simply-stated problems have turned out to be surprisingly difficult. (See [A6, pp. 14–15] and [H2, pp. 21–31].) We may mention in passing one striking result, known as the "Prime Number Theorem".

For $n = 1, 2, 3, \ldots$, define P_n to be equal to the number of primes in the set $\{1, \ldots, n\}$ and L_n to be the logarithm of n to the base e $(L_n = \int_1^n x^{-1} \, dx)$.

The theorem then states that as n increases indefinitely the product $n^{-1}L_nP_n$ approaches 1 as a limit (in the same sense as the idea of a limit used in calculus). The occurrence of individual primes is highly capricious, but the theorem shows that their distribution is sufficiently regular "on the average" for the stated limiting relation to hold.

EXERCISES

3. Prove that if $a|b$ and $a|c$ then $a|(b+c)$.

4. Find quotient and remainder for the following divisions: (a) 38 by 7, (b) -44 by 5, (c) 278 by 13, (d) -921 by 14.

5. Prove that the quotient q in the Euclidean Algorithm (1) has the same sign as the dividend b.

6. Prove that if $a \neq 0$, $b \neq 0$, and $p > 0$ then $(pa, pb) = p(a, b)$.

7. Obtain the prime factorizations of 84, 96, 75, 30, -81, and -36.

8. Find $(84, 96)$, $[84, 96]$, $(75, 30)$, $[75, 30]$, $(-81, -36)$, and $[-81, -36]$.

9. Guided by the experience of the last two exercises, use 2 to show that $ab = (a, b)[a, b]$. (Cf. D1.14.)

10. Use 2 to prove that if p is prime and $p|ab$ then either $p|a$ or $p|b$. (A more elementary proof can be given.)

11. Prove that $6|n(n^2 + 5)$ for $n = 1, 2, 3, \ldots$.

12. Euclid proved that there can be no largest prime. Suppose that p were the largest positive prime and consider the number $q = p! + 1$. Clearly $q > p$, so that if q were prime we would have a contradiction. How can we still arrive at a prime $> p$ if q is composite?

13. Suppose that $(a, b) = pa + qb$. Try to find all pairs r, s such that $(a, b) = ra + sb$.

14. The proposition

$$P_n : 0 + 1 + \ldots + n = \frac{n(n+1)}{2} + n(n-1)(n-2) \ldots (n-5)$$

is true for $n = 0$. Why does an inductive proof fail? For which values of n is P_n true?

15. Here are three equations:

(a) $2x = -6$,   (b) $3x = 15$,   (c) $5x = 20$.

Discuss the consistency of each equation when the variable x has, in turn, each of the following domains:

(α) all even integers,   (β) all odd integers,
(γ) all positive integers,   (δ) all negative integers,
(ϵ) all integers.

16. Discuss the consistency of the following equations:

(a) $x^2 = 9$,   (b) $x^2 = 10$,   (c) $x^2 = 0$,   (d) $x^2 = -3$, when x has, in turn, each of the domains of $\alpha-\epsilon$ in 15. In the consistent cases, examine also the question of the uniqueness of the solution.

C. The Rational Numbers

It is evident that if $a, b \in I$ then there is an $x \in I$ such that $bx = a$ if and only if $b|a$ (cf. B15ϵ). Now a number system such as I, in which the equation $bx = 2$ is sometimes consistent and sometimes not, is quite inadequate for the purposes of geometry. Given a segment, for example, of length $a \in I$, we know a simple geometric construction for finding its midpoint, but we have no way, using only numbers of I, to say explicitly how far the midpoint is from the ends unless a is even. Similarly, if one is given a rectangle of area a square units with one side of length b units, then one should be able to determine the length of the other side uniquely, though it will be an integer when b and a are, only if $b|a$.

Unlimited division (except by zero) is possible within the system of fractions, or ratios-of-integers, or rational (ratio-nal) numbers; examples, in familiar notation, are $\frac{2}{3}$, $\frac{6}{9}$, $-\frac{7}{15}$, $4/(-7)$, and $\frac{21}{7}$. We shall state the necessary definitions, omitting all proofs. (See [H7].)

The idea of an ordered pair was introduced in order to arrive at 1I24. The set R^* of *rational numbers* consists of all ordered pairs $r = (a, b)$ with $a, b \in I$, and $b \neq 0$, it being agreed that $(a, b) = (c, d)$ if and only if $ad = bc$.

The *sum* $r + s$ of the rational numbers $r = (a, b)$ and $s = (c, d)$ is the rational number $(ad + bc, bd)$, and their *product* $r \cdot s$ is the rational number (ac, bd). By the system $\mathcal{R}^*$ of rational numbers we shall mean the set R^* with these definitions of sum and product, and with the relations of order to be mentioned explicitly later.

In actual calculation it is customary to use the more familiar $r = a/b$ instead of $r = (a, b)$; thus $\frac{2}{3}$, $-\frac{7}{13}$, and $6/(-21)$ are used respectively instead of $(2, 3)$, $(-7, 13)$, and $(6, -21)$.

The rational numbers $(a, 1) = a/1$, when considered by themselves, form a system that cannot be distinguished algebraically from the system I of integers. We accordingly write simply a instead of $a/1$. It is a consequence that if $r = (a, b)$ then $br = b \cdot (a, b) = a$.

In this section (C) small Latin letters will usually denote rational numbers.

1. **Algebraic Properties.** From the foregoing definitions it is possible to prove the validity of the familiar operations of elementary algebra. Instead of trying to list all of these operations, we shall list only a few, selected in such a way that all the others can be shown (though we shall not attempt it) to follow from these.

1.1. PROPERTIES OF NUMERICAL ADDITION AND MULTIPLICATION. Each ordered pair (p, q) with $p, q \in R^*$ determines a unique sum, denoted by $p + q$, and a unique product, denoted by $p \cdot q$, in such a way that if $p, q, r \in R^*$, then the following statements are true.

Closure

A1. $p + q \in R^*$. 　　　　　　　　M1. $p \cdot q \in R^*$.

Associativity

A2. $(p + q) + r = p + (q + r)$. 　　M2. $(p \cdot q) \cdot r = p \cdot (q \cdot r)$.

Identity Element

A3. R^* has an element, denoted by 0, such that $p + 0 = p$.
M3. R^* has an element, denoted by 1, such that $p \cdot 1 = p$.

Inverse Element

A4. R^* has an element $-p$ such that $p + (-p) = 0$.

M4. If $p \neq 0$ then R^* has an element p^{-1} such that $p \cdot p^{-1} = 1$.

Commutativity

A5. $p + q = q + p$. 　　　　　　　　M5. $p \cdot q = q \cdot p$.

Distributivity

MDA. $p \cdot (q + r) = p \cdot q + p \cdot r$.

A few remarks may explain the terminology and certain other features of these statements. We often write, as usual, pq instead of $p \cdot q$.

The set R^* is *closed* under addition and multiplication in the sense that each of these operations, when performed upon elements of R^*, always has a well-defined result which is itself an element of R^*. The subsets N and I of R^* are both also closed under addition and multiplication, but N is not closed under subtraction or division, while I is closed under subtraction, but not under division.

The significance of the *associative* laws A2 and M2 stems from the fact that addition and multiplication are defined in the first instance only for *pairs* of summands or factors. The originally meaningless symbol $p + q + r$ could be given meaning in either of two ways; if p and q are "associated" (added first) the result is $(p + q) + r$, while if q and r are associated the result is $p + (q + r)$. The law A2 says that the two results are equal. The parentheses may therefore be omitted and $p + q + r$ is uniquely determined. Similarly, $(p \cdot q) \cdot r = p \cdot (q \cdot r) = p \cdot q \cdot r$.

Now suppose that for $n = 1, 2, 3, \ldots$ we are given n rational numbers $r_1, \ldots, r_n$. The associative law opens the way for a recursive definition of their sum $s_n = r_1 + \ldots + r_n$ and product $p_n = r_1 r_2 \ldots r_n$. For $n = 1$ we have $s_1 = r_1 = p_1$. We now choose $k \in N$, assume that s_k and p_k have been defined, and use them to define

$$s_{k+1} = s_k + r_{k+1} \quad \text{and} \quad p_{k+1} = p_k r_{k+1}.$$

For $k = 1$, s_2 and p_2 can be calculated from the basic definitions given above. For $k = 2, 3, \ldots$ the associative law shows that s_{k+1} and p_{k+1} are unambiguously determined; it can be shown, in fact, that parentheses may be introduced in any conventionally legitimate manner into either s_n or p_n without altering its value.

Convenient notations for s_n and p_n are these:

$$s_n = \sum_{j=1}^{n} r_j, \quad \text{and} \quad p_n = \prod_{j=1}^{n} r_j;$$

or

$$s_n = {}_j\textstyle\sum_1^n r_j, \quad \text{and} \quad p_n = {}_j\textstyle\prod_1^n r_j;$$

or

$$s_n = \textstyle\sum_1^n r_j, \quad \text{and} \quad p_n = \textstyle\prod_1^n r_j.$$

In the third pair it is assumed to be evident that the index of addition or multiplication is j. If it is also evident, further, that j runs from 1 to n, one may write simply $s_n = \sum r_j$ and $p_n = \prod r_j$.

It is to be emphasized that an index of summation (addition) is a "bound" variable, like the variable of integration in a definite integral. It may therefore be renamed at will, subject to the requirement, of course, that no letter be used with more than one meaning in the same expression. Thus

$${}_j\textstyle\sum_1^4 a_j b_j = {}_\alpha\textstyle\sum_1^4 a_\alpha b_\alpha = {}_B\textstyle\sum_1^4 a_B b_B = {}_n\textstyle\sum_1^4 a_n b_n.$$

A similar observation applies, of course, to an index of multiplication.

We conclude our remarks on the associative law by a reconsideration of the proof in A2, based on an idea of Gauss' that for $n = 1, 2, 3, \ldots$, $s_n = 1 + 2 + \ldots + n = n(n + 1)/2$. The argument will illustrate the handling of indices in the sigma-notation. We now know that the "$+ \ldots +$" is merely a picturesque way of denoting the sum more compactly indicated by the sigma-notation, and that the common meaning of $1 + 2 + \ldots + n = {}_k\textstyle\sum_1^n k = s_n$ is established by the notation and recursive definition of preceding paragraphs. Gauss proposed (in the case $n = 100$) simply listing the integers $1, 2, \ldots, n - 1, n$ in reverse order: $n, n - 1, \ldots, 2, 1$. Now in the expression $s_n = {}_k\textstyle\sum_1^n k$, the index k takes on successively the values $1, 2, \ldots$, $n - 1, n$. If we write $k = n - h$, then, as h takes on the values $0, \ldots, n - 1, k$ will take on the corresponding values $n, n - 1, \ldots, 2, 1$. Hence

$$s_n = {}_k\textstyle\sum_1^n k = {}_h\textstyle\sum_0^{n-1} (n - h).$$

There is now a small inconvenience if we try to add the two sums term-by-term, for the domains of the indices are not precisely the same. The domains can be made the same, however, by a simple step which is often useful. Merely observe that

$$_h\Sigma_0^{n-1} (n - h) = {_k}\Sigma_1^n (n + 1 - k).$$

It is now evident that

$$2s_n = {_k}\Sigma_1^n k + {_k}\Sigma_1^n (n + 1 - k) = {_k}\Sigma_1^n (k + n + 1 - k)$$
$$= {_k}\Sigma_1^n (n + 1) = (n + 1)\cdot{_k}\Sigma_1^n 1 = n(n + 1),$$

completing, essentially, the proof of the desired formula by Gauss' method.

Zero, that is, $(0, 1)$, is an *identity element for addition*, or an *additive identity*, in the sense that if $p = (a, b)$ with $a, b \in I$ and $b \neq 0$ then $p + 0 = (a, b) = p$. Unity, that is, $(1, 1)$, is similarly an *identity element for multiplication*, or a *multiplicative identity*. These elements are "identity" elements, for the respective operations with them upon an element p merely reproduce the element. The respective identity elements can be shown to be unique.

The operations of addition and subtraction are said to be *inverse* to each other, as are the operations of multiplication and division. The elements $-p$ and p^{-1}, which can be shown to be uniquely determined by p, are called respectively the *additive* and *multiplicative inverse* of p, because performing the respective operation with each upon p yields the respective identity element. The number $q + (-p)$ is abbreviated to $q - p$, and one is said to be subtracting p from q. Similarly, $q \cdot p^{-1}$ is often written q/p; one calls q the *numerator* and p the *denominator*, and one is said to be *dividing q by p*, although this term does not have the sense of dividing "exactly", or even "with a remainder", that it has in the system I. We recognize that if $p = (a, b)$ with $a, b \in I$ and $b \neq 0$, then $-p = (-a, b)$ and, if $p \neq 0$, so that $a \neq 0$, then $p^{-1} = (b, a)$; in fact, moreover, $p^{-1} = 1/p$, the *reciprocal* of p, so that the superscript -1 may be understood, if desired, as an exponent.

The *commutative* laws, A5 and M5, say that the order of the summands or factors is immaterial; they may be interchanged, or *commuted*.

The *distributive* law MDA says that multiplication is distributive with respect to addition in the sense that the multiplier p of $q + r$ may be distributed, so to speak, separately to the terms q and r of the sum.

The operations of addition, subtraction, multiplication, and division are called the *rational operations*. The algebraic structure of the system $\Re^*$ can be summarized by saying that addition and multiplication are so defined in the set R as to have the foregoing properties; we shall see later that the rationals exemplify a certain algebraic structure known as a "field". (Cf. 4F.)

It follows from the definition of equality adopted early in 1D that if $r = s$ then either may be substituted for the other at any time in any context. It is evident that if $r = s$ then $s = r$ and that if $r = s$ and $s = t$ then $r = t$. These facts will be used repeatedly in algebraic calculation without explicit mention.

Proofs of even very simple relations may require application of the rules in 1.1. Let us prove another version of the distributive law: $(b + c)a = ba + ca$.

M5 $$(b + c)a = a(b + c).$$

MDA

M5

$$a(b + c) = ab + ac.$$
$$ab = ba, \qquad ac = ca.$$
$$ab + ac = ba + ca.$$
$$(b + c)a = ba + ca.$$

All the familiar rules of calculation in elementary algebra follow from the laws of 1.1. We list a few of these rules, leaving it as an exercise to prove them from the above laws or directly from the definitions. Mention of p^{-1} or of q/p is understood to imply that $p \neq 0$.

$$(-p)^{-1} = -(p^{-1}), \qquad (pq)^{-1} = p^{-1}q^{-1},$$

$$-\left(\frac{q}{p}\right) = \frac{(-q)}{p} = \frac{q}{(-p)},$$

$$\frac{(p/q)}{r} = \frac{p}{(qr)}, \qquad \frac{(p/q)}{(r/s)} = \frac{ps}{qr},$$

$$\frac{p}{q} + r = \frac{p + qr}{q}, \qquad \frac{p}{q} \pm \frac{r}{s} = \frac{ps \pm qr}{qs}.$$

Let us observe that if $r = (a, b)$ with $a, b \in I$ and $b \neq 0$, then the definition of equality of rational numbers allows the removal of common factors of a and b until the numerator and denominator are coprime; then r is said to be in its *lowest terms*. Finally, since $(a, b) = (-a, -b)$, we can adjust the representation of r, whenever convenient, so that the denominator is positive.

EXERCISES

1.2. Assume it known that if $a, b \in I$ and $ab = 0$, then either $a = 0$ or $b = 0$. Show that if $p, q \in R^*$ and $pq = 0$ then either $p = 0$ or $q = 0$.

.3. Suppose that $p, q, r, s \in R^*$, and that $p \neq 0$ and $r \neq 0$. Prove that $q/p = s/r$ if and only if $ps = qr$.

.4. Study the equation $bx = a$ when $a, b \in R^*$ and x has domain R^*. (Consider separately the cases $b = 0$ and $b \neq 0$. To prove uniqueness of the solution when $b \neq 0$, assume that also $by = a$, subtract, and use 1.2 to show that $x = y$.)

.5. Use the rules of 1.1 to give detailed proof that $(\alpha)\ (a + b)^2 = a^2 + 2ab + b^2$ and $(\beta)\ (a + b)(a - b) = a^2 - b^2$.

.6. Prove by induction that if $r \neq 1$ then for $n \in N$

$$1 + r + r^2 + \ldots + r^n = \frac{1 - r^{n+1}}{1 - r}.$$

Multiply up by $1 - r$ and show that the result is valid for any $r \in R^*$. Put $r = q/p\ (p \neq 0)$ and simplify, arriving at a familiar factoring formula, now *proved* for $n \in N$.

1.7. Prove by induction that for $n = 1, 2, 3, \ldots$,

$$\frac{1}{1 \cdot 2} + \frac{1}{2 \cdot 3} + \cdots + \frac{1}{n(n+1)} = 1 - \frac{1}{n+1}.$$

.8. Define $p^{-n}(n \in N)$ to mean $(p^{-1})^n$. Prove that $p^n \cdot p^{-n} = 1$.

.9. Let $r = (a, b)$ with $a, b \in I$ and $b \neq 0, \pm 1$. Use B2 and .8 to obtain an expression for r similar to that of B2 but involving negative as well as positive exponents.

.10. What equation would express distributivity of addition with respect to multiplication? Is the equation identically true in N, or I, or R?

2. Measurement; Density and Gaps.

At the beginning of C we noted the problem of finding a number to measure the length of half of a segment of length $a \in I$. We now know that $a \in R^*$ and that the desired number is therefore $a/2$.

Suppose, more generally, that we are given a straight line; for convenience we assume it to be horizontal. We are also given a unit of measurement of distance; this unit is to consist of a segment whose length is agreed, quite arbitrarily, to be one. The problem of measurement is now this: given *any* two points on the line, to find a number equal to the ratio of the distance between them to the unit distance. We assume that by means of a compass, or otherwise, we can construct a segment with a given endpoint and length equal to that of a given segment. It will then be sufficient to fix one point and find the distance between it and each other point on the line.

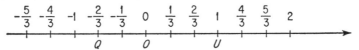

2.1. Rational points on a line.

Let us choose point O on the line (see 1) and assign to it the number 0. There are two points on the line at unit distance from O, one in each direction. Choose one of them (to the right of O in the diagram), call it U and assign to U the number 1.

Now let $a, b \in I$ with $b > 0$ and let $q = a/b$. Divide the segment OU into b equal parts. If $a > 0$ we count off a of these parts from O to the right; if $a < 0$ then $-a > 0$ and we count off $-a$ of these parts from O to the left. We arrive in this way at a unique point Q on the line, to which we assign the number q. In the diagram, $q = -2/3$.

Each $q \in R^*$ is thus associated with a unique point Q on the line; we write $q \to Q$. Any point Q associated in this way with some $q \in R^*$ will be called a *rational point*. It follows readily from a consideration of distances that a rational point Q is associated with a unique rational number q, in such a way that q is the *directed distance from O to Q*, from O to the right if

$q > 0$ and from O to the left if $q < 0$. The line itself is said to be *directed* by the agreement that distances from O shall be measured positively to the right and negatively to the left; that is the significance of the arrow at the right "end".

More generally, if $s \rightarrow S$ and $t \rightarrow T$, then $t - s$ is readily seen to be equal to the directed distance from S to T. We may and will refer to $t - s$ also as the *directed distance from s to t*.

We have set up a 1-1 correspondence $q \leftrightarrow Q$ between R^* and the set of rational points on the line. The critical question now is, is every point on the line a rational point? Does the correspondence map R^* onto (instead of into) the line? Can the distance between *any* two points be measured by a rational number?

The Greeks answered this important question in the negative, but the situation was not fully clarified until the nineteenth century. In order to appreciate the difficulty, let us pick a point Q at random on the line. If for every $q \in I$ it is false that $q \rightarrow Q$ then Q lies between the images N and N' of two consecutive integers, n and $n + 1$. Choose *any* integer $m \geq 2$. Then, for $k = 0, 1, \ldots, m$, the images of the rational numbers $n + (k/m)$ are $m + 1$ rational points dividing the segment between N and N' into m parts, each of length $1/m$. In the diagram, for example, we might have $N = O$, $N' = U$, $m = 3$, and $k = 0, 1, 2, 3$; it is instructive to imagine such cases as $m = 100$, 10^6, or 10^{100}. Now it *may* happen for some particular m and k that $n + (k/m) \rightarrow Q$; in that event Q is a rational point. But the question is, rather, *must* it happen?

One thing is clear. If Q is a point that is not a rational point, then the preceding process produces rational points as close to Q as we please. To say that Q is not rational is to say that for each m (however large) Q lies *between* two rational points whose distance from each other is $1/m$; Q must therefore be at a distance *less* than $1/m$ from one or the other. By taking m sufficiently large we may therefore find a rational point as close to Q as we please. This fact is expressed technically by saying that the rational points are *dense* in the line. But there are gaps!

The Greeks knew the theorem of Pythagoras, which says that if a and b are the sides of a right triangle and h its hypotenuse, then $a^2 + b^2 = h^2$. If d is the diagonal of a square of side one, it follows that $d^2 = 2$. We give Euclid's proof that d cannot be rational.

Suppose that $d = b/a$, $a, b \in I$. Remove common factors of a and b until they have no nontrivial common divisor. We shall obtain a contradiction by showing that if $d^2 = 2$, then a and b do have a nontrivial common divisor.

If $d^2 = 2$ then $b^2 = 2a^2$. Since the right member is even, b^2 is even. Now if b were odd then b^2 would be odd; hence b is even and $b = 2c$ for some integer c. Substituting, we obtain $4c^2 = 2a^2$, whence $2c^2 = a^2$. The same reasoning now shows that a must be even and $a = 2f$ for some integer f.

37

We have produced the required nontrivial common factor of a and b, namely 2, and have thereby reached a contradiction.

A simple geometrical construction has led us to recognize a gap in the rational numbers, a point on the line that is not a rational point. The rational points are those whose distances from O are rational multiples of the unit of distance. It is true that the distance from O to any point P whatever can be measured by a rational number with as small an error as one pleases (exactly, in fact, if P is a rational point) for one can always find a rational point Q as close to P as one pleases. If this is not enough, if one wishes to be able, in principle, to specify *exactly* the distance from O to *any* point on the line, then the system $\mathcal{R}^*$ is too sparse, so to speak, to be adequate for this purpose.

Simple calculations of mechanics also disclose gaps in the system $\mathcal{R}^*$. A physicist knows that a particle of mass m moving with speed v has energy $E = mv^2/2$. He has a particle of known mass, observes its energy, and wishes to calculate its speed. For his purposes the symbol $\sqrt{2E/m}$ must, without essential qualification, denote a specific number; it will do so within the system $\mathcal{R}^*$ if and only if $2E/m$ is the square of a rational number.

Let us say that a point P that is not rational is *irrational*; this technical adjective merely denies the equally technical adjective "rational", and carries no hint of perversity or unreasonableness present in the popular meaning of the word.

In order to measure exactly the distance from O to an irrational point we shall need numbers that are not rational and are therefore called irrational. For any circle, the ratio of the circumference to the diameter is the irrational number π. The natural base of logarithms, used in calculus, is the irrational number e. The number $d > 0$ such that $d^2 = 2$ is an irrational number commonly denoted by $\sqrt{2}$. We shall even see that in a perfectly precise sense there are many *more* irrational than rational numbers!

EXERCISES

2.2. Prove that if a, $b \in R^*$ and $a + b\sqrt{2} = 0$, then $a = b = 0$.

.3. Suppose that $r \in R^*$, $n \in I$, and $r^2 = n$. Prove that $r \in I$.

.4. Suppose that $r \in R^*$ and that s is irrational. Prove that $r + s$ and (if $r \neq 0$) rs are irrational. Can the sum of two irrational numbers be rational? The product?

.5. Suppose that a decimal fraction terminates; show that the decimal represents a rational number. Give an example of a rational number whose expression as a decimal fraction does not terminate. Try to show that if $a \in R^*$ then the expression of a as a decimal fraction will repeat itself from some stage on. It is also true, conversely, that a nonterminating decimal fraction that repeats itself from some stage on is rational; try to prove it.

D. The Real Numbers

A real number may be defined in terms of rational numbers in any one of several ways, and the various definitions lead ultimately, by appropriate considerations, to results that are in complete agreement with each other. Although we shall indicate one definition briefly in 3, we do not have space here to develop any definition fully. (See [H4, H6, H7, H8, and H9, Chap. 7].)

One quite tangible way to think of real numbers follows from the fact that each decimal expansion denotes a real number. Thus $\pi = 3 + .1415\ldots$, and $e = 2 + .7183\ldots$, and $-4 + .703\ldots$ denote real numbers; it should be observed that we have some other knowledge of π and e, and in principle can compute the successive digits of their expansions as far as may be desired, while the last example can be said, as far as we can tell without some way of determining further digits, only to lie between the rational numbers $-4 + .703$ and $-4 + .704$. In general, if $m \in I$ and, for $n = 1, 2, 3, \ldots, d_n$ is a digit (i.e., $d_n \in \{0, 1, \ldots, 8, 9\}$), then

0.1
$$m + \frac{d_1}{10} + \frac{d_2}{10^2} + \ldots + \frac{d_n}{10^n} + \ldots$$

denotes a real number. There may be another decimal expansion for the same real number.

Since we have not given a definition of real numbers, we are in no position to define addition or multiplication. From the appropriate definitions it follows that *addition and multiplication of real numbers have precisely the properties listed in C1.1.* What is more, under a convention that is suitable and usual, the set R of real numbers has as a subset the set R^* of rational numbers, and therefore subsets I and N as well, and the arithmetical operations have the same results and properties in each of these subsets as they do in R.

1. Order; Inequalities. We spoke in B of positive and negative integers. This terminology reflects the fact that the elements of I do occur in a certain natural order. One can develop, moreover, a comprehensive theory of order in I by defining $a > b$ to hold when and only when $a - b$ is positive. The sets N and R^* are also ordered in a rather natural way. We have preferred, however, to postpone a discussion of order until it could be applied to the set R of real numbers, the properties of order in the subsets R^*, I, and N being then implied by those in R.

Although we are in no position to give a formal definition of order between real numbers, we can describe the effect of the definition in terms of the decimal expansion 0.1. The real number r given by 0.1. turns out to be ≥ 0 or ≤ 0 according as m is a non-negative or negative integer; r can equal zero in two situations, when $m = 0$ and $d_n = 0$ ($n = 1, 2, 3, \ldots$), and when $m = -1$ and $d_n = 9$ ($n = 1, 2, 3, \ldots$).

In a systematic development of the theory of real numbers, definitions are adopted which afford a basis for proving the following properties of the *order* relation, from which all other properties of order follow, and by virtue of which the set R is said to be *ordered*.

1.1. PROPERTIES OF ORDER. Relations of order, "$<$" (read "less than") and "$>$" (read "greater than"), are defined for ordered pairs (a, b) of real numbers, in such a way that $a < b$ if and only if $b > a$ and, if a, b, and c are any real numbers, then the following statements are true.

A. (Trichotomy.) One and only one of the following three relations holds: $a < b$, $a = b$, $b < a$.

B. (Transitivity.) If $a < b$ and $b < c$ then $a < c$.

C. (Preservation under addition.) If $a < b$ then $a + c < b + c$.

D. (Preservation under multiplication by a positive number.) If $a < b$ and $c > 0$ then $ac < bc$.

We write "$a \leq b$" to mean "either $a < b$ or $a = b$", so that $a \leq b$ when and only when it is false that $b < a$; similarly for "$a \geq b$". A continued inequality such as $a \leq b \leq c$ shall mean that both $a \leq b$ and $b \leq c$. It follows, for example, from the definitions as they apply to the set N that $0 < 1 < 2 < \ldots$.

The set R of real numbers, with the algebraic structure introduced by the definitions of addition and multiplication, and with the definitions of order from which properties 1.1 follow, will be called the *system* $\mathcal{R}$.

To indicate that r is a variable with domain R we occasionally write $-\infty < r < \infty$. If $a \in R$ is fixed and we wish to keep $r \geq a$ but otherwise unrestricted, we write $a \leq r < \infty$. The inequalities $a < r < \infty$, $-\infty < r < b$, and $-\infty < r \leq b$ have similar interpretations. We shall make no other use of the symbols "∞" and "$-\infty$"; they do *not* denote real numbers.

EXERCISES

Unless the contrary is stated or implied, small Latin letters denote real numbers. Properties C1.1 and D1.1 are assumed to be valid.

1.2. Prove that if both $a \leq b$ and $b \leq a$ then $a = b$.

.3. Prove that if $a > 0$ and $b > 0$ then $ab > 0$.

.4. Prove that if $a < b$ and $c < 0$ then $ac > bc$.

.5. Prove that if $1 < a$ then $0 < a^{-1} < 1$ and conversely.

.6. For which values of x is it true that

(i) $5x > 9$,   (ii) $-3x \leq 7$,   (iii) $3x - 5 > 4$,   (iv) $2x + 3 \geq 4 - 6x$?

1.7. Prove that $2^n < n!$ for $n = 4, 5, 6, \ldots$.

.8. Prove that if $-1 < p$ and $p \neq 0$ then $(1 + p)^n > 1 + np$ for $n = 2, 3, 4, \ldots$. How must the statement be modified if the value $p = 0$ is not excluded?

.9. Prove that if $1 < p$ then $p < p^2$.

.10. Suppose that $a < b$. Show that if $0 \leq t \leq 1$ then $a \leq (1 - t)a + tb \leq b$ and conversely.

.11. Let $a_1, \ldots, a_n \in \Re$, and let $x_1, \ldots, x_n$ be variables with domain $\Re$. Prove that
$$_k\Sigma_1^n \, (x_k - a_k)^2 \geq 0.$$
Do the variables have any values for which the equality holds?

.12. Suppose that $r = a/b$ and $s = c/d \in R^*$ with $a, b, c, d \in I$. If $r > s$ what can be said about a, b, c, d? Is the converse true?

.13. Find all values of x for which (i) $6 + 5x - 6x^2 < 0$, (ii) $6 + 5x - 6x^2 \geq 0$, (iii) $x + \dfrac{1}{x} > 1 \, (x \neq 0)$, (iv) $\sin x > 0$, (v) $\cos x > -1$, (vi) $(x - a)(x - b)(x - c) > 0$ where $a < b < c$.

.14. Let a_1 and a_2 be so ordered, as is possible by trichotomy, that $a_1 \leq a_2$. Define
$$\min(a_1, a_2) = a_1, \qquad \max(a_1, a_2) = a_2.$$
Augment these definitions to arrive at recursive definitions of the *minimum* and *maximum* of $a_1, \ldots, a_n$, denoted respectively by
$$\min(a_1, \ldots, a_n), \qquad \max(a_1, \ldots, a_n).$$
Prove by induction that these numbers are always found among the numbers $a_1, \ldots, a_n$ and that for $k = 1, \ldots, n$
$$\min(a_1, \ldots, a_n) \leq a_k \leq \max(a_1, \ldots, a_n).$$
Prove that $\min(a, b) + \max(a, b) = a + b$. (T)

.15. Prove that
$$n \cdot \min(a_1, \ldots, a_n) \leq {}_k\Sigma_1^n \, a_k \leq n \cdot \max(a_1, \ldots, a_n).$$

.16. Show that a and b can be chosen so as to violate simultaneously both of the inequalities $[\min(a, b)]^2 \leq ab \leq [\max(a, b)]^2$. Seek a further assumption about $a_1, \ldots, a_n$ under which you can show that
$$[\min(a_1, \ldots, a_n)]^n \leq {}_k\Pi_1^n \, a_k \leq [\max(a_1, \ldots, a_n)]^n.$$

.17. Suppose that $a < b$. Does it follow that $a^2 < b^2$? That $a^3 < b^3$? Prove your results. Study the relation between a^{2n} and b^{2n} for $n = 2, 3, 4, \ldots$. Similarly for a^{2n+1} and b^{2n+1}.

.18. Use induction to prove the *Binomial Theorem*,
$$(a + b)^n = {}_k\Sigma_0^n \binom{n}{k} a^{n-k}b^k \quad \text{for} \quad n = 0, 1, 2, \ldots .$$

(Cf. A1.5–6.) (T)

2. **Absolute Value.** Define f on R into R: $x \to \sqrt{x^2}$; thus $x \to x$ if $x \geq 0$ and $x \to -x$ if $x < 0$. This function is so ubiquitous that there is a special notation for its value, namely $|x|$, and a special name; it is called the *absolute* (or *numerical*) *value* of x or the *modulus* or *norm* of x. For example, $|5| = 5$, $|-7| = 7$, and $|-\pi| = \pi$.

It is evident that $-|a| \leq a \leq |a|$; in fact, a is equal either to $|a|$ or to $-|a|$, indeed to both if $a = 0$. It is sometimes helpful to write $a = \pm|a|$ and then study separately the effects of the magnitude $|a|$ and the relevant one of the signs $\pm$.

We observed for $a, b \in R^*$, and it is still true for $a, b \in R$, that $b - a$ measures the directed distance from a to b. It follows that $|b - a|$ measures the (undirected) distance between a and b. If we seek, for example, those x for which $|x - 7| \leq 3$, then we are seeking those x distant at most 3 units from 7, and such x are clearly those for which $4 \leq x \leq 10$. Proceeding "analytically", we start with $-3 \leq x - 7 \leq 3$, add 7, and obtain the same result.

2.1. PROPERTIES OF ABSOLUTE VALUE. For each $a, b \in \Re$ the following statements are true.

A. $|0| = 0$; if $a \neq 0$ then $|a| > 0$.

B. $|ab| = |a||b|$.

C. $||a| - |b|| \leq |a \pm b| \leq |a| + |b|$ for either choice of the ambiguous sign.

On account of an analogy to be brought out later, C is called the "*triangle inequality*".

EXERCISES

Small Latin letters denote real numbers.

2.2. Prove 1A and B. (T)

.3. By adding the inequality $-|a| \leq a \leq |a|$ to the similar one for b, prove that $|a + b| \leq |a| + |b|$. What is the effect of substituting $-c$ for b? Observing that $a = b + (a - b)$ and applying results just obtained, prove the left inequality of 1C. (T)

.4. If $a \neq 0$, prove that $|a^{-1}| = |a|^{-1}$.

.5. For which values of x is it true that (i) $|x + 3| < 5$, (ii) $|x - 2| \geq 1$, (iii) $|x - 1| < |x + 1|$, (iv) $|x + 1| - |2x + 3| = 1$, (v) $|4x + 7| \leq 12$, (vi) $|3x + 8| \geq |2x - 5|$?

.6. Show that $|x - a| < b$ if and only if $a - b < x < a + b$.

.7. Interpreting x and y as rectangular cartesian coordinates in plane analytic geometry, sketch the loci of the following equations: (i) $y = |x|$, (ii) $y = 1 - |x|$, (iii) $y = (x + |x|)/2$, (iv) $y = (x - |x|)/2$, (v) $y = |x + 1| - |2x - 3|$, (vi) $|y| = |x| - 2$, (vii) $y = x|x|^{-1}$.

2.8. Let $p_1 = q_1 = 1$ and for $n = 2, 3, \ldots$, define

$$p_n = p_{n-1} + 2q_{n-1}, \qquad q_n = p_{n-1} + q_{n-1}.$$

Prove that p_n and q_n have no common divisors. Form now the sequence of fractions p_n/q_n; the first few terms are $\frac{1}{1}, \frac{3}{2}, \frac{7}{5}, \frac{17}{12}$. Define $e_n = \sqrt{2} - (p_n/q_n)$. Prove that e_n alternates in sign; that $|e_{n+1}| < |e_n|$, and that $|e_n|$ can be made as small as desired by choosing n sufficiently large. (*Hint:* Study e_{n+1}/e_n.)

3. Completeness. We saw in C2 that the system $\Re^*$ was unsuitable for exact measurement of distances because of gaps in it. These same gaps, in fact, make impossible certain limiting operations of the kind used in calculus. While we shall rarely be concerned with limiting operations, the practical applications of certain of our results (for example, those of Chap. 3) depend on the usefulness of $\Re$ for measurements. Our immediate aim, therefore, is to describe the sense in which the gaps present in $\Re^*$ are absent in $\Re$, thus making $\Re$ appropriate for use in exact measurement and, what amounts essentially to the same thing, for use in properly controlled limiting operations.

Let S be a subset of R. From 1E we recall that A and A'_S are complementary subsets of S if $A \cap A'_S = \square$ and $A \cup A'_S = S$. Now assume that S has at least two elements; our real interest is in the two special cases $S = R^*$ and $S = R$. A (Dedekind) *cut* in S consists of a partition of S into two complementary subsets, A and $B (= A'_S)$, neither empty, such that if $a \in A$ and $b \in B$ then $a < b$. The sets A and B may be called, respectively, the *lower* and *upper* sets of the cut.

We are interested in the presence or absence of a greatest *element* max A of A or a least *element* min B of B. We shall show that max A and min B cannot both exist if S has the following property (D): if $p, r \in S$ and $p < r$ then there exists $q \in S$ such that $p < q < r$. Since max $A \in A$ and min $B \in B$, we see that max $A <$ min B if they were both to exist. By property (D) we could then find $q \in S$ such that max $A < q <$ min B. Now either $q \in A$ or $q \in B$ would violate respectively the definitions of max A or min B, whence $q \in' A$ and $q \in' B$, contradicting the fact that $A \cup B = S$. Since both $\Re^*$ and $\Re$ have property (D), as we see by taking $q = (p + r)/2$, we conclude that if A, B is a cut either in $\Re^*$ or in $\Re$, then either A has no greatest element or B has no least element.

Here is a specific cut in R:

$A = \{x : x \in R$ and either $x \leq 0$ or, both $x > 0$ and $x^2 < 2\}$,

$B = \{x : x \in R$ and $x > 0$ and $x^2 \geq 2\}$.

It is easy to verify that A and B do constitute a cut in $\Re^*$. Suppose now that $b = $ min B and consider

$$c = b - \frac{b^2 - 2}{2b}.$$

Since $0 < b$ and $2 < b^2$ (since $b \in R^*$, $b^2 = 2$ is excluded), we see that $0 < c < b$. At the same time,

$$c^2 = 2 + \left(\frac{b^2 - 2}{2b}\right)^2 > 2,$$

so that $c \in B$, contradicting our assumption that $b = \min B$. Similarly, A has no greatest element. In the cut A, B in $\Re^*$, therefore, neither $\max A$ nor $\min B$ exists. This fact corresponds in an entirely explicit way to the presence of a gap in R where $\sqrt{2}$ "ought to be".

That there are no gaps in $\Re$ is the content of the following fundamental theorem, which is a culminating point in a systematic development of the theory.

3.1. *If A, B is a cut in $\Re$ then either A has a greatest element or B has a least element.*

We may express this fact by saying that $\Re$ is *complete*, but the technical notion of completeness has ramifications into which we cannot enter here.

The completeness of $\Re$ makes it suitable for measurement of distances on a line, for the distance between any two points is in principle a real multiple of the unit of distance. That this is so is essentially an assumption about the nature of a line which underlies the application of geometry to physics. It is assumed, to be more explicit, that the real numbers and the points of a line can be put into a 1-1 correspondence, $p \leftrightarrow P$ in such a way that if $p \leftrightarrow P$ and $q \leftrightarrow Q$ then $q - p$ is equal to the directed distance from P to Q. If the line is horizontal and the correspondence set up in C2 between rational numbers and points is extended to the whole line, then $p < q$ when and only when P is to the left of Q on the line. Thus the correspondence $p \leftrightarrow P$ preserves both distance and order.

It is time to reveal a "secret", making good on our earlier promise to indicate one of the several definitions of a real number on which a comprehensive theory can be based; for details see the references in the first paragraph of D. *A real number is a cut in the set of rational numbers.* In this sense the specific cut in $\Re^*$ defined above *is* $\sqrt{2}$.

4. Countably and Uncountably Infinite Sets. (Digression.) We close our descriptive account of the system $\Re$ by mentioning a very few quite remarkable results that will not be used in our later work. They are so near at hand, however, and of such great intellectual significance, that we owe the reader at least an opportunity to hear of them.

It is the great merit of the German mathematician G. Cantor to have developed useful consequences of the notion of equipotent sets introduced above toward the end of 1I. Regarded at first with considerable suspicion, his ideas have turned out to be indispensable in dealing with infinite sets and have thrown much light on the properties of finite sets as well.

A set S is finite, we recall from 1I, if it is empty or is equipotent to the set $\{1, 2, \ldots, n\}$ for some positive integer n. It was also stated there that a set is finite or infinite according as it is not or is equipotent to at least one of its proper subsets. We saw, indeed, in 1I3 that the set of even integers, although only "half", so to speak, of the set I, is still equipotent to I. As another example, we display a biunique correspondence between I and the set N of natural numbers:

$$
\begin{array}{ccccccccc}
0 & 1 & 2 & 3 & \ldots & 2n-1 & 2n & \ldots \\
\updownarrow & \updownarrow & \updownarrow & \updownarrow & & \updownarrow & \updownarrow & \\
0 & 1 & -1 & 2 & \ldots & n & -n & \ldots .
\end{array}
$$

Let us say that a set is *countably infinite* if it is equipotent with the set N. Such a set can be arranged in an infinite sequence (cf. A). This sequence is called an *enumeration* of the set, which is accordingly said also to be *enumerable* or *denumerable*. A set that is finite or countably infinite is said to be *countable*. It is not surprising, and is easy to prove, that any subset of a countable set is countable; it follows by an indirect argument that if a set S is not countable, then no superset of S is countable. Being concerned at the moment only with the infinite case, we use "countable" for the remainder of this section to mean "countably infinite".

It is interesting to try to see how "large", so to speak, a countable set can be.

4.1. *The union of a countable class of countable sets is countable.*

In fact, for $m \in N$ let S_m be countable, and consider $U = S_0 \cup S_1 \cup \ldots \cup S_m \cup \ldots$. It is helpful to display S_m thus:

$$
\begin{aligned}
S_0 &= \{e_{00},\ e_{01},\ e_{02},\ \ldots,\ e_{0n},\ \ldots\} \\
S_1 &= \{e_{10},\ e_{11},\ e_{12},\ \ldots,\ e_{1n},\ \ldots\} \\
&\cdots\cdots\cdots\cdots\cdots\cdots\cdots\cdots\cdots \\
S_m &= \{e_{m0},\ e_{m1},\ e_{m2},\ \ldots,\ e_{mn},\ \ldots\} \\
&\cdots\cdots\cdots\cdots\cdots\cdots\cdots\cdots\cdots
\end{aligned}
$$

In order to enumerate U we put down, in turn, for $k = 0, 1, 2, \ldots$, the $k+1$ elements e_{mn} for which $m + n = k$; in the following enumeration we put in semicolons to indicate a change in the value of k.

$$
U = \{e_{00};\ e_{01},\ e_{10};\ e_{02},\ e_{11},\ e_{20};\ e_{03},\ e_{12},\ e_{21},\ e_{30};\ \ldots;
$$
$$
e_{0\,k},\ e_{1\,k-1},\ e_{2\,k-2},\ \ldots,\ e_{k-2\,2},\ e_{k-1\,1},\ e_{k\,0};\ \ldots\}.
$$

Having produced an enumeration of U, we conclude that U is indeed countable.

As an application, let us demonstrate that R^* is countable. For $m \in N$ we put into S_m those rationals having denominator m:

45

$$S_1 = \{0, 1, -1, 2, -2, \ldots\}$$
$$S_2 = \{\tfrac{0}{2}, \tfrac{1}{2}, -\tfrac{1}{2}, \tfrac{2}{2}, -\tfrac{2}{2}, \ldots\}$$
$$\cdots\cdots\cdots\cdots\cdots\cdots\cdots\cdots\cdots\cdots\cdots$$
$$S_m = \{0/m, 1/m, -1/m, 2/m, -2/m, \ldots\}$$
$$\cdots\cdots\cdots\cdots\cdots\cdots\cdots\cdots\cdots\cdots\cdots$$

It is clear that every rational number occurs in at least one S_m; that it appears in several is unimportant, for it is enough to show that R^* is a subset of a countable set. We conclude from 4.1. that R^* is countable.

4.2. *The set R^* of rational numbers is countable.*

We recall that the set R^* is equipotent with the set of rational points on the line, and that that set is dense on the line (cf. C2). Having seen that a set as "large" as R is countable, and that the union of a countable class of such sets is countable, one might easily suppose that every infinite set is countable. As Cantor showed, the situation is far more complicated. Here is a most significant specific result (see also D4.4 below).

4.3. *The set $\mathcal{R}$ of real numbers is not countable.*

It will be enough to prove that the set S of real numbers and r such that $0 \le r \le 1$ is uncountable. We shall give an indirect proof, assuming that we have a sequence in which each $r \in S$ occurs and then producing a specific $s \in S$ which is easily seen not to occur in the sequence.

Let each $r \in S$ be represented by its decimal expansion,

$$r = 0.d_1d_2 \ldots d_n \ldots,$$

where the d_n are digits. To assure uniqueness we replace each terminating expansion with the nonterminating one; for example, instead of $.24000\ldots$ ($= \tfrac{6}{25}$) we use $.23999\ldots$ Now an alleged enumeration of S could be written out in full, as follows:

$$r_1 = .d_{11}d_{12}d_{13} \ldots d_{1n} \ldots$$
$$r_2 = .d_{21}d_{22}d_{23} \ldots d_{2n} \ldots$$
$$\cdots\cdots\cdots\cdots\cdots\cdots\cdots\cdots$$
$$r_n = .d_{n1}d_{n2}d_{n3} \ldots d_{nn} \ldots$$
$$\cdots\cdots\cdots\cdots\cdots\cdots\cdots$$

Using "Cantor's diagonal process", we define c_n for $n = 1, 2, 3, \ldots$ to be different from d_{nn} (avoiding 9 and 0 as values for c_n); to be specific, if $d_{nn} = 4$ then $c_n = 5$, while if $d_{nn} \ne 4$ then $c_n = 4$. Since the decimal expansion $s = 0.c_1c_2 \ldots c_n \ldots$ represents a real number between 0 and 1, $s \in S$. But $s \ne r_n$ for $n = 1, 2, \ldots$, since $c_n \ne d_{nn}$. Hence s does not occur in the alleged enumeration, and we conclude that any countable subset of S is a proper subset; S cannot be enumerated and is therefore not countable.

It is quite plausible, and in fact true, that if $S \subset T$, S is countable, and T is uncountable, then the complement S'_T of S in T is uncountable. With $S = R^*$ and $T = R$ we conclude that the set $R^{*'}_R$ of irrational numbers is uncountable. It is in this sense that (cf. C2, end) there are many more irrational than rational numbers. For very many subsets S of R, furthermore, it is possible to give precise meaning to "the probability $p(S)$ that if $r \in R$ is chosen 'at random' then $r \in S$". It turns out that $p(R^*)$ does have meaning and that $p(R^*) = 0$; in other words, the "probability" that a real number chosen "at random" will be rational is flatly equal to zero! A further remarkable result is that *the class 2^{R^*} of all subsets of R^* is equipotent to R.*

It is a celebrated unsolved problem, on which many eminent mathematicians have worked with incomplete success, to settle the following question (the "continuum problem"): Does there exist a set S such that $R^* \subset S \subset R$, and such that S is equipotent neither to R^* nor to R? Many other unsolved problems have been shown to be equivalent to this one. A negative answer to the question was regarded by Cantor as obvious, and is known in the literature as the "continuum hypothesis". It has been proved by Gödel that the continuum hypothesis is consistent with a certain specific comprehensive body of accepted principles in the theory of sets.

EXERCISE

4.4. Let S be any nonvoid set, 2^S the class of its subsets, and suppose that $x \leftrightarrow S(x)$ were a biunique mapping of S onto 2^S. Use the idea underlying Cantor's diagonal process to construct the characteristic function of a subset T of S such that $x \leftrightarrow T$ is false (that is, $T \neq S(x)$ for each $x \in S$. (Cf. 1I2 and 1I13.) It is a corollary that *S and 2^S are not equipotent*, 2^S having in fact "more" elements than S.

THREE
Vectors in Three-Dimensional Euclidean Space

We propose now to develop on an intuitive basis the theory of vectors in three-dimensional Euclidean space, which we denote by $\mathcal{E}_3$, and to use vectors to study the geometry of points, lines, and planes. We shall use freely the system R of real numbers (see Chap. 2), assuming in particular that distances and angles can be measured. Some familiar definitions and results of plane and solid Euclidean geometry will be taken for granted. Although a few ideas from calculus and mechanics will be used in illustrations, they are not essential to the primarily geometric study which is our main goal, and may be ignored with only slight loss.

The ideas in this chapter will illustrate and motivate much of our later work.

A. Vectors

A *vector* is an ordered pair (P, Q) of points P and Q. The vector (P, Q) is said to have *initial* point P and *terminal* point Q, and to be *localized* at P.

We agree that $(P, Q) = (R, S)$ if and only if $P = Q$ and $R = S$. Distinct points P and Q determine a straight line and, on the line, a segment having endpoints P and Q. The vector (P, Q) determines a direction on the segment, that from P to Q. In a diagram (cf. D1) one would draw an arrow with tail at P and tip at Q; the vector is usually denoted, for this reason, by the expressive notation $\overrightarrow{PQ}$, and is often called a *directed segment*. The number measuring the length of the segment, which is the distance between P and Q, is denoted by $\|\overrightarrow{PQ}\|$ and is called the *norm* (or length, or magnitude, or modulus) of $\overrightarrow{PQ}$.

If $Q = P$ then the direction of $\overrightarrow{PP}$ is undefined and $\|\overrightarrow{PP}\| = 0$. This vector is called the *zero vector at P*.

If the initial point P of a nonzero vector $\overrightarrow{PQ}$ is given, then the terminal point Q, and therefore the vector, is uniquely determined by the direction and length of the vector. The vector $\overrightarrow{PQ}$ is said to be the *position vector of Q relative to P.*

EXERCISE

1. For which points X is it true that $||\overrightarrow{PX}|| = 5, \leq3, \geq2, =0, <4, >6$?

Suppose that, at a certain instant, a particle is at the point P and is moving with speed s (units of distance per unit time) in a certain direction. It is natural to draw from P a ray (half-line) in the direction of motion, and then to measure off from P a distance equal to the speed s thus arriving at a point Q such that $||\overrightarrow{PQ}|| = s$. The vector $\overrightarrow{PQ}$ is the *velocity vector.* It represents the velocity of the particle at the instant when the particle is at the point P. The initial point of $\overrightarrow{PQ}$ is the instantaneous position of the particle, the direction of $\overrightarrow{PQ}$ is the instantaneous direction of motion, and $||\overrightarrow{PQ}||$ is the instantaneous speed. The velocity of a particle is referred to in mechanics as a "directed magnitude", and we have just seen that the velocity may quite naturally be represented by a vector. Other directed magnitudes associated with a moving particle are, for example, its acceleration, its momentum, and the resultant force acting on it; all these entities can be represented by vectors.

Other physical quantities, such as temperature, density, and energy, are adequately measured by the designation of a real number on an assigned scale with no specification of direction. Such quantities are called scalars in physics, and it has come to seem natural, for this reason, to refer to the real numbers here also as *scalars.* In this chapter a lower case Latin letter will usually denote a scalar.

B. The Origin

Let O be a fixed point in $\mathcal{E}_3$. For the present we shall be concerned primarily with the set E_O of all vectors $\overrightarrow{OP}$ localized at O, and we shall call O the *origin.* Each point P of $\mathcal{E}_3$ is uniquely determined by the element $\overrightarrow{OP}$ of E_O which is the position vector of P with respect to O, and if $P = Q$ then $\overrightarrow{OP} = \overrightarrow{OQ}$. The correspondence between points P and their position vectors $\overrightarrow{OP} \in E_O$ is therefore biunique.

In the notation $\overrightarrow{OP}$ both the "O" and the "$\rightarrow$" are redundant; we are

49

tempted to omit them and speak briefly of "the vector P". Would the symbol "P" by itself then mean "the point P" or "the vector P ($= \overrightarrow{OP}$)"? In most instances the distinction, when it matters, is implied by the context. For the sake of brevity we accept the ambiguity. According to context, therefore, a capital Latin letter P may denote either the point P or the position vector $\overrightarrow{OP} \in E_0$ of P relative to O.

When the difference is important, the appropriate noun "point" or "vector" will be included. It is important, for example, to know whether "the plane p contains P" means that "p contains the point P" or "p contains the vector P (meaning $\overrightarrow{OP}$)".

The zero vector at O is merely $\overrightarrow{OO}$; it will often be denoted by the numeral 0. Whenever a vector has initial point $A \neq O$ and terminal point B we shall revert to the original notation $\overrightarrow{AB}$; then, of course, $\overrightarrow{AB} \in' E_0$, but $\overrightarrow{AB} \in E_A$.

C. Multiplication of a Vector by a Scalar

If $V \in E_0$ and r is a scalar, then *the product of V by r* is a vector, denoted by $r \cdot V$ or briefly by rV, which is defined as follows:

(a) if either V or r is zero, then $rV = 0$;

(b) if $r \neq 0$ and $V \neq 0$, then $\|rV\| = |r| \cdot \|V\|$ and the direction of rV is the same as that of V, or opposite to that of V, according as $r > 0$ or $r < 0$.

$$(-3)V \qquad \left(-\tfrac{3}{2}\right)V \qquad 0 \qquad V \qquad 2V \qquad 4V$$

1. Diagram of rV for $r = -3, -\tfrac{3}{2}, 0, 1, 2, 4$.

In more general situations it is sometimes possible to define Vr in such a way that it does not necessarily coincide with rV, and in that event it is essential to observe the position of the scalar. We shall have no need, however, for a second kind of multiplication by a scalar, so we simply *define Vr* to be the same as rV.

If $V \neq 0$ then $\hat{V} = V/\|V\|$ is a *unit vector* (that is, $\|\hat{V}\| = 1$) in the direction of V, and is therefore used to characterize the direction of V. The process of dividing V by $\|V\|$ is called *normalization*, and $\hat{V}$ is said to be *normalized*. The terminal points of all unit vectors lie on the surface of the *unit sphere*, which has the vectorial equation $\|X\| = 1$. The representation

50

$V = ||V||\hat{V}$ may be helpful when one wishes to deal by separate methods with the length $||V||$ of V and its direction as determined by $\hat{V}$.

Suppose that $V \neq 0$. It is then clear from the definition that $rV = 0$ if $r = 0$ and that $rV = V$ if $r = 1$; therefore, as in numerical work, a coefficient 1 is usually omitted. If $r = -1$ then $rV = (-1)V = V'$ where the points V', O, and V are collinear, with O between V' and V, and $||V'|| = ||V||$; we say that the point V' is obtained from V by a *reflection* in the origin, and that the vector $(-1)V$ arises from the vector V by *reversal* of direction.

It is left as an exercise (3) to show that if r and s are any scalars and V is any vector then

2.
$$r(sV) = (rs)V.$$

EXERCISES

3. Prove 2. (T)

4. Show that, if $rV \neq 0$, then $\hat{V} = |r|V/||rV||$. What is the relationship between rV, $r\hat{V}$, and $|r|\hat{V}$?

5. Suppose that $V \neq 0$. Illustrating each case with a diagram, describe the locus of the vector $X = rV$ under the following restrictions on r:

(a) $-\infty < r < \infty$ (line);

(b) $-\infty < a \leq r < \infty$ (closed ray);

(c) $-3 \leq r \leq 5$ (closed segment);

(d) $r < 0$ (open ray);

(e) $1 < r < 4$ (open segment).

6. Suppose that $V \neq 0$ and that $0 < r < s$, and let S denote the segment $xV(r \leq x \leq s)$. How may t be restricted so that tV will: (a) be the midpoint of S; (b) divide S in the ratio p/q; (c) lie outside S; (d) be twice as long as sV?

7. Let U and V be given, with neither zero. Show that they will have either the same direction, or opposite directions, if and only if one is a non-zero scalar multiple of the other. (The vectors $\hat{U}$ and $\hat{V}$ may be used.) (T)

8. Suppose that $tV = 0$. Can one conclude that $t = 0$? That $V = 0$? That either $t = 0$ or $V = 0$? That both $t = 0$ and $V = 0$?

D. Addition of Vectors

If $U, V \in E_0$, then their *sum* or *resultant*, denoted by $U + V$, is defined as follows:

(a) $U + 0 = 0 + U = U$;

(b) if both $U \neq 0$ and $V \neq 0$ then the terminal point of $U + V$ is the vertex opposite O of the (possibly degenerate) parallelogram with the segments OU and OV as coinitial edges.

As indicated in 1(c) and (d) the parallelogram is degenerate if the points O, U, and V are collinear. If these points are not collinear then they determine a plane and it is evident from the definition (cf. 1(b)) that this plane contains $U + V$.

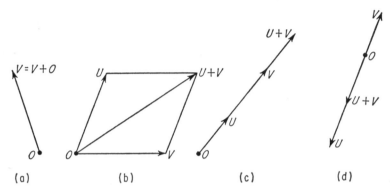

(a)   (b)   (c)   (d)

1. Addition of vectors.

  The parallelogram law of addition of vectors underlies most applications of vectors in physics, where this law and certain of its generalizations are referred to as the "principle of superposition". Near the end of the sixteenth century it was shown by S. Stevin of Bruges that two forces acting on a particle at O and represented by U and V may for every mechanical purpose be replaced by the single force represented by $U + V$. The name "resultant" is used for the sum especially in physical applications. When the resultant of all the forces acting on a particle is zero, the particle is in equilibrium, that is, it experiences no acceleration.

  It is easy to show that if U, V, $W \in E_0$ then

(a) $U + V \in E_0$,   (Closure)

(b) $(U + V) + W = U + (V + W)$,   (Associativity)

2. (c) $U + 0 = U$,   (Additive Identity)

(d) $U + ((-1)U) = 0$,   (Additive Inverse)

(e) $U + V = V + U$.   (Commutativity)

  Each proposition except (b), in fact, is evident from the definition (cf. 1), and (b) follows from an examination of the parallelepiped (possibly degenerate) with coinitial edges U, V, and W. (Some remarks on terminology follow 2C1.1.) It follows from (b) and (a) that if $V_k \in E_0$ ($k = 1, \ldots, n$) then the sum $\sum_k V_k$ can be unambiguously defined (by recursion, cf. 2A1) and belongs to E_O.

It is customary to abbreviate $(-1)V$ to $-V$. When $-V$ is added to U we abbreviate $U + (-V)$ to $U - V$ and say that V itself has been *subtracted* from U. By subtracting V from each side of the vectorial equation $V + X = W$ we see that X will satisfy the equation only if $X = W - V$. We readily verify, conversely, that if $X = W - V$ then indeed $V + X = W$.

It is important to observe (see 3) that the vector $U - V$, which has its initial point at O, agrees in direction and length with the vector $\overrightarrow{VU}$, in other words with the directed segment from the terminal point of V to the terminal point of U. The vector $\overrightarrow{VU}$ may be used to represent a displacement carrying the point V onto the point U; this vector again agrees in length and direction with $U - V$, that is, with the position vector of the *final* location of the point *minus* the position vector of the *initial* location, both taken, of course, with respect to the same origin.

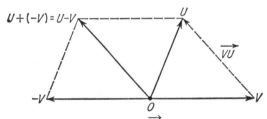

3. Diagram illustrating $U - V$ and its relation to $\overrightarrow{VU}$.

The operations of adding vectors and of multiplying a vector by a scalar are related by two distributive laws: If $r, s \in R$ and $U, V \in E_O$, then

4.   (a) $(r + s)U = rU + sU$;

   (b) $r(U + V) = rU + rV$.

Each is obvious if any scalar or vector appearing in it vanishes. The first becomes evident when $U \neq 0$ if we use $\|U\|$ as unit of distance on the line determined by the points O and U. The second follows from the similarity of the triangle (possibly degenerate) determined by the points O, U, and V to the triangle determined by the points O, rU, and rV.

EXERCISES

5. Let U and V be thus:

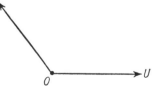

Construct the vector $aU + bV$ for each of the following pairs (a, b): $(2, 1)$ (giving rise to the vector $2U + V$), $(1, -1)$, $(-1, -2)$, and $(1, -2)$.

6. With U and V as in 5, construct the vector $V + tU$ for each of the following values of t: $-3, -2, -1, 0, 1, 2, 3$.

7. With U and V as in 5 construct the vector $W = U + t(V - U) = (1 - t)U + tV$ for each of the following values of t: $-3, -2, -1, 0, 1, 2, 3$. Where will the point W lie for $0 \leq t \leq 1$? For $t = \frac{1}{2}$, or $\frac{1}{3}$, or $\frac{3}{4}$?

8. Prove the *triangle inequality*:

$$|\,||U|| - ||V||\,| \leq ||U + V|| \leq ||U|| + ||V||.$$

What situation prevails if one or the other inequality is an equality? Can both be equalities? What is the result if $-W$ is substituted for V? (T)

9. Given $a \neq 0$, U, and V, solve the equation $aX + U = V$.

10. Suppose that it is desired to introduce a new origin Q. Show how to use the old position vectors Q and P to construct at O a vector agreeing in direction and length with the new position vector $\overrightarrow{QP}$ of the point P.

11. At a certain instant an airplane is headed directly north at a speed (with respect to the air) of 300 knots and the air surrounding the plane is moving east at a speed of 50 knots. In what direction and at what speed as observed from the ground will the plane actually be moving?

12. An oarsman who can row at a speed of five knots in still water wishes to proceed directly across a straight river having a current of two knots. In what direction should he head?

E. Linear Combinations

For $k = 1, \ldots, n$ let $V_k \in E_O$ and a_k be scalars. The vector

1.
$$R = \sum_1^n a_k V_k$$

is said to be a *linear combination* of the vectors V_k. The coefficients a_k are sometimes called the *constants of combination*; when allowed to vary they are sometimes called *parameters*. Each vector constructed in D5–7, for example, is a linear combination of U and V.

Let us consider the set of *all* linear combinations of a given vector V; that is, all $R = xV$ $(-\infty < x < \infty)$. If $V = 0$ then clearly $R = 0$ for all values of x. If $V \neq 0$ then C1, C5(a), and a moment's reflection will convince the student that the points R all lie on the line through the origin in the direction of V and are in a one-to-one correspondence with the numbers x. Thus the variable x may be regarded as the coordinate of a variable point on the line, and the equation $R = xV$ may be regarded as the *vectorial* equation of the line. The vector V is said to be *generate* or *span* the line, and the line will be denoted by $\langle V \rangle$. It may be seen easily that the vectors $V, \hat{V}, -\hat{V}$, and bV ($b \neq 0$) all generate the same line. It follows from the fundamental result of C7 that non-zero vectors U and V generate the same line if and only if one is a non-zero scalar multiple of the other; an equivalent condition is that $\hat{U} = \pm\hat{V}$.

Now suppose that $W \neq 0$, and that we have constructed the line $R = xW$ ($-\infty < x < \infty$). Suppose that $R_0 \neq 0$, and that neither R_0 nor $-R_0$ is in the same direction as W. Where are the points with position vectors $R = R_0 + xW$? As is evident from the diagram, the locus of $R = R_0 + xW$

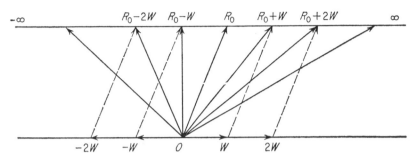

2. Diagram of locus $R = R_0 + xW$.

may be obtained by subjecting each point of the line $R = xW$ to a displacement parallel in direction and equal in magnitude to that displacement which carries O to R_0. We say that the line $R = xW$ is *translated* by the displacement R_0. It would be highly suggestive to designate the line by the symbol $R_0 + \langle W \rangle$, and such formalism occurs, in fact, in the literature; we refrain, however, from formulating the necessary definitions. The equation $R = R_0 + xW$ is called the vectorial equation of the line; note that the line passes through the point R_0 and is parallel to W.

As soon as he has this rather static conception in mind, the student is advised to study the diagram further until he senses the motion, so to speak, of the point R as x varies. (Recall D6–7.) As x increases from $-\infty$, the point $R = R_0 + xW$ appears at the far left on the upper line, moving toward the right, with the vector R rotating (in this particular diagram) clockwise about O. As x takes on the values $-2, -1, 0, 1, 2$, the point R passes through the respective points indicated on the upper line and, as $x \to \infty$, disappears at the far right on the upper line.

EXERCISES

It is to be assumed in these exercises that $P \neq 0$, $Q \neq 0$, and that neither $\pm Q$ has the same direction as P, that is, $\hat{P} \neq \pm\hat{Q}$.

3. Draw the following lines: (a) $R = xP$; (b) $R = Q + xP$; (c) $R = yQ$; (d) $R = 2P + yQ$; (e) $R = -Q + xP$; (f) $R = 2P - 3Q + yQ$; (g) $R = x_0P + yQ$; (h) $R = xP + y_0Q$. Here $-\infty < x, y < \infty$, while x_0 is a fixed value of x and y_0 is a fixed value of y.

4. What can you say about the locus $R = (1 - t)P + tQ$ for $0 \leq t \leq 1$? (Note that $R = P + t(Q - P)$; cf. C5(c) and D7.)

5. Find the vectorial equation of the line through the point P and parallel to the vector Q. (Cf. 3D6 and 3(b).)

6. Find the vectorial equations of the following lines: (a) through the points P and Q; (b) through the points $-2P$ and $3Q$; (c) through the points $3P$ and $-Q$.

7. Show that the vectorial equation of the ray bisecting the angle between P and Q is $R = t(\hat{P} + \hat{Q})$ $(0 \leq t)$.

8. What can you say about the locus of $R = xP + yQ$ as x and y vary independently from $-\infty$ to $+\infty$? (Cf. D5.)

The result of 8 is that, as x and y vary independently from $-\infty$ to $+\infty$, the points $xP + yQ$ all lie in the plane through O containing P and Q, and that the points of the plane are in one-to-one correspondence with the ordered pairs of scalars (x, y). Thus the variable ordered pairs (x, y) may be regarded as the coordinates of a variable point in the plane in a coordinate system determined by P and Q; this system is illustrated in the adjoining diagram (9).

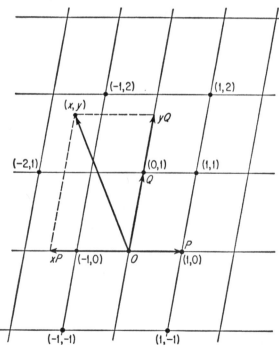

9. Coordinate system determined by P and Q.

The equation $R = xP + yQ$ is the vectorial equation of the plane, and the vectors P and Q are said to *generate* or *span* the plane, which will be denoted by $\langle P, Q \rangle$.

Now let $R_0 \neq 0$ be a given vector not in $\langle P, Q \rangle$. Where are the points with position vectors $R = R_0 + xP + yQ$? By considerations entirely analogous to those connected with the translated line $R_0 + xW$, one sees here that the point R varies over a plane π parallel to $\langle P, Q \rangle$ and containing the point R_0; in other words, π is obtained by translating $\langle P, Q \rangle$ by R_0. If T_0 is any point in π then, of course, $R = T_0 + xP + yQ$ is also a vectorial equation of π.

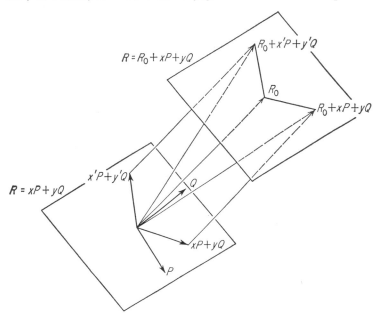

10. Diagram of plane $R = R_0 + xP + yQ$.

It is now a simple matter to obtain vectorial equations for planes determined by various conditions. Suppose, for example, that we desire the vectorial equation of the plane containing the line $R = R_0 + xV$ and the point U not on the line. The desired plane is parallel to the vector V, and to the vector $U - R_0$, and therefore to the plane $xV + u(U - R_0)$. Since the plane contains R_0, its equation is $R = R_0 + xV + y(U - R_0)$, or, equally well, $R = U + xV + y(U - R_0)$.

EXERCISES

11. Obtain a vectorial equation for the plane containing the non-collinear points U, V, and W. What conditions on the scalar coefficients will yield the interior of the triangle UVW?

12. Obtain a vectorial equation for the plane parallel to P and containing distinct points Q and R, neither of which is on the line $\langle P \rangle$. Is there always a unique plane meeting these conditions?

13. Suppose that there exist scalars x and y, neither zero, such that $xU + yV - (x + y)W = 0$. What can be said about the relative positions of the points U, V, and W?

14. Suppose that there exist scalars x, y, and z, not all zero, such that $xU + yV + zW = 0$. What can be said about the relative positions of the points U, V, and W?

15. Suppose that there exist scalars x, y, and z, with $x \neq 0$ and $z \neq 0$, such that $xU + yV + zW = 0$. Show that every linear combination of U and V is a linear combination of V and W, and conversely.

16. Let P and Q be points of $\langle U, V \rangle$. Show that $\langle U, V \rangle$ contains every linear combination of P and Q; in other words, the set of points $pP + qQ$ ($-\infty < p, q < \infty$) is a subset of the set $\langle U, V \rangle$. Do the two sets necessarily coincide? (T)

17. The *centroid* $\overline{P}$ of points P_k ($k = 1, \ldots, n$) with weights $w_k \geq 0$ ($k = 1, \ldots, n$), where some $w_k > 0$, is defined by the formula

$$\overline{P} = \frac{\sum\limits_{k=1}^{n} w_k P_k}{\sum\limits_{k=1}^{n} w_k}.$$

Show that the point $\overline{P}$ is *invariant under change of origin*; in other words, that if a new origin Q is introduced to replace O, and the same formula is used with $\overrightarrow{QP_k}$ instead of $\overrightarrow{OP_k}$, then the same point $\overline{P}$ is obtained as the centroid. (Cf. D10.) What happens to $\overline{P}$ if new weights $w'_k = pw_k$ are introduced with $p > 0$?

F. Linear Dependence and Independence

We have seen (C7) that $U \neq 0$ and $V \neq 0$ generate the same line (in other words, either lies in the line generated by the other) if and only if one (and therefore either) is a non-zero scalar multiple of the other, say $U = tV$. In other words, there exist scalars u and v, not both zero, such that $uU + vV = 0$; for example, $u = 1$, $v = -t$. This relationship between U and V is a special case of the following concept.

1. Linear Dependence and Independence. The set of vectors V_k ($k = 1, \ldots, n$) is said to be (linearly) *dependent* or (linearly) *independent* according as there

do or *do not* exist scalars t_k, *not all zero*, such that $\sum\limits_{k=1}^{n} t_k V_k = 0$.

Let us say that $\sum t_k V_k$ is a *trivial* or *nontrivial* linear combination of the vectors V_k according as $t_k = 0$ ($k = 1, \ldots, n$) or not. If $\sum t_k V_k$ is trivial then $\sum t_k V_k = 0$. The set $\{V_k\}$ is independent if no nontrivial linear combination vanishes; $\{V_k\}$ is dependent if some nontrivial linear combination vanishes.

Although dependence or independence is a property of a set of vectors, we often speak loosely of dependent or independent vectors V_k.

It is convenient to say that a vector V *depends* (linearly) *on* the vectors V_k or is (linearly) *independent* of them, according as V is or is not a linear combination of the V_k.

If one of the vectors V_k is zero, say $V_{k_0} = 0$, then the vectors are dependent, for one may choose $t_k = 1$ for $k = k_0$ and all other $t_k = 0$.

If the vectors V_k are dependent, and the scalar $t_{k_0} \neq 0$, then we see that

$$V_{k_0} = -\frac{1}{t_{k_0}} \sum_{k=1}^{n} t_k V_k \ (k \neq k_0).$$

Thus one of the vectors V_k depends on the others; this condition is also clearly sufficient for the dependence of the vectors V_k.

To say that the vectors V_k are independent is equivalent to saying that if $\sum t_k V_k = 0$ then $t_k = 0$ $(k = 1, \ldots, n)$. In other words, $\sum t_k V_k = 0$ implies $t_k = 0$ $(k = 1, \ldots, n)$. This simple fact has an important consequence. Suppose that the vectors V_k are independent, that $U = \sum u_k V_k$, that $W = \sum w_k V_k$, and that it has been established that $U = W$. From the equation $\sum u_k V_k = \sum w_k V_k$ we obtain $\sum (u_k - w_k)V = 0$, whence $u_k - w_k = 0$ $(k = 1, \ldots, n)$ by virtue of the independence of the vectors V_k. This result may be stated by saying that in the expression of any vector as a linear combination of *independent* vectors the coefficients are *unique*; the condition for independence, indeed, makes exactly this assertion about the zero vector.

It is an appealing idea, when an equation such as $\sum u_k V_k = \sum w_k V_k$ has been established, to conclude that therefore $u_k = w_k$ for each value of k. This step is called "equating coefficients". As we have just seen, the validity of equating coefficients cannot be guaranteed in the present context unless the vectors V_k are *independent*. (See also G3.)

A single vector V is dependent if $V = 0$ and independent if $V \neq 0$. Two vectors are independent if and only if neither is a scalar multiple of the other. The vectors P and Q of E9 are independent. Three vectors, none zero, are independent or dependent according as they do not or do lie in a plane (containing the origin).

What if there are no vectors V_k; in other words, what if the index set (and therefore also the set V_k) is empty? The requirement for independence may be stated as the following disjunction: Either $\sum t_k V_k \neq 0$ or each $t_k = 0$. Since there are no V_k at all, the second alternative is true, the disjunction is therefore true, and we conclude that the empty set is an independent set. By adjoining a vector V to the empty set we obtain a dependent set if and only if $V = 0$; we may say, therefore, that V depends on the empty set if and only if $V = 0$.

EXERCISES

2. Suppose that one can find a dependent subset of the set V_k $(k = 1, \ldots, n)$. Is the set V_k $(k = 1, \ldots, n)$ necessarily dependent? Explain.

3. Suppose that the vectors V_k ($k = 1, \ldots, n$) are independent. Can any conclusion be obtained about subsets of the set V_k? Explain.

4. Let $\langle V_k \rangle$ denote now the set of all linear combinations $\sum t_k V_k$ of the vectors V_k ($k = 1, \ldots, n$). Suppose that, for $j = 1, \ldots, q$, $U_j \in \langle V_k \rangle$. Show that $\langle U_j \rangle$ is a subset of $\langle V_k \rangle$. (T)

5. Suppose that $U \neq 0$, $V \neq 0$, and $uU + vV = 0$ with $u \neq 0$ and $v \neq 0$. Is it always, sometimes, or never possible to choose u and v to be rational?

6. Show that vectors $U \neq 0$ and $V \neq 0$ are dependent if and only if the points U, V, and O are collinear. If $W \neq 0$, can you find a similar necessary and sufficient condition that U, V, and W be dependent?

7. Let U and V be independent. Show that $Y = aU + bV$ and $Z = cU + dV$ are dependent if and only if $ad = bc$. (T)

8. Let the vectors V_k ($k = 1, \ldots, n$) be independent and define $U = \sum t_k V_k$ and $U_k = V_k - U$ ($k = 1, \ldots, n$). Under what conditions will the vectors U_k be dependent?

9. Let the vectors V_k ($k = 1, \ldots, n$) be independent. Show that V_{n+1} depends on or is independent of the V_k according as the vectors V_j ($j = 1, \ldots, n + 1$) are dependent or independent. (T)

10. Let π be a plane through the origin and Q a point not in π. Show graphically that every vector X is the sum of a vector X_Q and a vector X_π where $X_Q = qQ$ for some scalar q and X_π lies in π. Show that X_Q and X_π are unique. For which X is $X_\pi = 0$? For which X is $X_Q = 0$? (X_Q is called the *projection of X onto the line Q* (or *in the direction of Q*) *parallel to π*, while X_π is called the *projection of X onto π parallel to Q*.)

G. Dimension; Basis; Components

The set E_O of which we are thinking consists of all vectors issuing from a point O in the physical space of naive experience. It is a stubborn characteristic of our perceptions that if three such vectors are not coplanar then they span the entire set E_O; any fourth vector is a linear combination of those three. We therefore impose the following assumption.

1. Assumption. The set E_O contains three independent vectors; any set of four vectors in E_O is dependent.

In Chap. 5 we shall define the notions of "linear space" and "dimension", and it will then be a consequence of 1 that E_O is a linear space of dimension 3. In anticipation of this development we shall refer occasionally to "the space E_O". At each point P there is, of course, the space E_P which is similar in every respect to E_O; actually, E_P and E_O are isomorphic in the sense of 4G.

2. Basis for E_O. If three vectors of E_O are independent they are said to form a *basis* for E_O.

Let P_k ($k = 1, 2, 3$) be a basis, and let V be any vector. By 1, the set V, P_k is a dependent set, whence constants v, p_k exist, not all zero, such that $vV + \sum p_k P_k = 0$. If v were to vanish, then $\sum p_k P_k = 0$ would hold with some $p_k \neq 0$, and this would violate the independence of the P_k; hence $v \neq 0$, and we may solve for V.

$$V = -v^{-1} \sum p_k P_k = \sum v_k P_k \qquad (v_k = -p_k/v).$$

Since the P_k are independent, it follows, as noted earlier, that the v_k are unique. Vice versa, the v_k clearly determine a unique vector V. We have therefore established the following result.

3. Theorem. Each basis P_k ($k = 1, 2, 3$) for E_O determines a biunique correspondence between vectors V and ordered triples of scalars (v_k) in such a way that $V = \sum v_k P_k$.

The scalars v_k are called the *components* of V with respect to the basis P_k. The components v_k may be regarded as the coordinates of the point V in a rectilinear (not necessarily orthogonal) coordinate system determined by the basis P_k.

The basis vector P_j ($j = 1, 2, 3$) has jth component 1 and the other two components 0. We introduce a very useful special symbol, called the *Kronecker delta*, denoted by δ_{jk}, and defined as follows:

3.1.
$$\delta_{jk} = \begin{cases} 1 & \text{if } j = k \\ 0 & \text{if } j \neq k \end{cases} \qquad (j, k = 1, 2, 3).$$

Thus

$$P_j = \sum_{k=1}^{3} \delta_{jk} P_k \qquad (j = 1, 2, 3).$$

On examining this indexed equation, one observes that the "free" index j occurs once on each side of the equation, and takes on successively each value in its index set as one writes down successively the three specific equations expressed by the single indexed equation. The bound index k occurs only on the right and occurs there twice. This situation is so typical that it is convenient to agree that a summation sign shall apply to each index appearing twice in the expression to which it applies. Thus we may write $P_j = \sum \delta_{jk} P_k$, it being quite clear that the summation on the right occurs with respect to the repeated index k.

The question of changing from one basis to another is an important one and will be discussed fully in later chapters. For the remainder of this chapter, we work in any specific case with a fixed basis in E_O, chosen for that case, and agree always to denote that basis by P_1, P_2, P_3. Although it will be advantageous later in this chapter to specialize this fixed basis in certain respects, we are assuming for the time being only that the vectors P_k ($k = 1, 2, 3$) are independent.

Whenever, as we are now assuming, the basis is *fixed*, it may be omitted systematically from the notation; we adopt the abbreviation

$$(v_1, v_2, v_3) = v_1P_1 + v_2P_2 + v_3P_3 = \sum v_kP_k = V.$$

It is sometimes convenient, when no confusion can arise, to abbreviate (v_1, v_2, v_3) further, merely writing (v_k).

The linear operations (multiplication by a scalar and addition) may be expressed very simply in terms of components:

$$tV = \sum (tv_k)P_k = (tv_1, tv_2, tv_3) = (tv_k),$$
$$U + V = \sum (u_k + v_k)P_k = (u_1 + v_1, u_2 + v_2, u_3 + v_3)$$
$$= (u_k + v_k).$$

In fact, for any linear combination W of the n vectors $V_\alpha = \sum v_{\alpha k}P_k$ $(\alpha = 1, \ldots, n)$,

$$W = \sum_{\alpha=1}^{n} a_\alpha V_\alpha = \sum_{\alpha=1}^{n} a_\alpha \left(\sum_{k=1}^{3} v_{\alpha k}P_k \right) = \sum_{k=1}^{3} \left(\sum_{\alpha=1}^{n} a_\alpha v_{\alpha k} \right) P_k$$
$$= \left(\sum_{\alpha=1}^{n} a_\alpha v_{\alpha_1}, \sum_{\alpha=1}^{n} a_\alpha v_{\alpha_2}, \sum_{\alpha=1}^{n} a_\alpha v_{\alpha_3} \right),$$

or simply $W = (w_k) = (\sum a_\alpha v_{\alpha k})$. It is often helpful, as we have just done, to use strikingly different symbols for indices having different index sets; here $k = 1, 2, 3$ while α has the index set $1, \ldots, n$, which differs from that of k unless $n = 3$.

The fact that our components with respect to our fixed basis are unique enables us to write down scalar equations corresponding to vectorial equations, and vice versa. To keep the terminology clear, let us speak of a vectorial equation when some vector, especially an "unknown" or "variable" vector appears explicitly in the equation, and of a scalar equation when every vector involved occurs only in terms of its components. Generally speaking, a vectorial equation has the decided advantage of expressing a geometric fact without reference to any coordinate system. The significance of a scalar equation, while obvious in some instances, may appear in much clearer light if one can discover a vectorial equation which is expressed by the scalar equation in the coordinate system in use at the moment. It must also be recognized, as we have already seen in a few cases and shall immediately see again, that a geometric configuration may often be described by each of several rather different vectorial or scalar conditions.

EXAMPLES

4. We have seen (cf. D6 and E2 and the statement accompanying it) that the line through U parallel to V $(\neq 0)$ has the vectorial equation $X = U + tV$ $(-\infty < t < \infty)$. In terms of components, this equation is $\sum x_kP_k = \sum (u_k + tv_k)P_k$, which is *equivalent* to the indexed equation

4.1.
$$x_k = u_k + tv_k \qquad (k = 1, 2, 3).$$

In analytic geometry these scalar equations are often called the *parametric* equations of the line, and the numbers v_k are said to be its *direction numbers*. The equations may be written together in the following *symmetric* form

4.2.
$$\frac{x_1 - u_1}{v_1} = \frac{x_2 - u_2}{v_2} = \frac{x_3 - u_3}{v_3} = t,$$

and here the t is often omitted. It is important to recognize that one or two (but not all three) of the v_k may be zero; an anomalous symbol such as $(x_1 - u_1)/0$ is interpreted, in accordance with 1, to mean that $x_1 = u_1 + t \cdot 0 = u_1$.

5. For instance, if $U = (2, -1, 3) = 2P_1 - P_2 + P_3$ and $V = (-1, 0, 2)$ then the vectorial equation is $X = (2, -1, 3) + t(-1, 0, 2)$, 4.1 becomes

$$x_1 = 2 - t, \qquad x_2 = -1, \qquad x_3 = 3 + 2t,$$

and 4.2 becomes

$$\frac{x_1 - 2}{-1} = \frac{x_2 + 1}{0} = \frac{x_3 - 3}{2} (= t).$$

From these equations one may easily read off, vice versa, that $X = \sum x_k P_k$ varies over a line through $(2, -1, 3) = U$ parallel to $(-1, 0, 2) = V$.

6. Similarly, the vectorial equation of the plane through U and parallel to V and W is $X = U + yV + zW (-\infty < y, z < \infty)$. The equivalent indexed scalar equation is

6.1.
$$x_k = u_k + yv_k + zw_k \qquad (k = 1, 2, 3);$$

the three scalar equations may be referred to as the parametric equations of the plane. For instance the plane through $(-1, 0, 2)$ parallel to $(1, -1, 3)$ and $(2, -3, 0)$ has vectorial equation $X = (-1, 0, 2) + y(1, -1, 3) + z(2, -3, 0)$, and scalar equations

$$x_1 = -1 + y + 2z, \qquad x_2 = -y - 3z, \qquad x_3 = 2 + 3y.$$

From these equations one may easily read off, vice versa, that $X = \sum x_k P_k$ varies over a plane containing $(-1, 0, 2)$ and parallel to $(1, -1, 3)$ and $(2, -3, 0)$.

In the following exercises P_k $(k = 1, 2, 3)$ is a fixed basis, and we use t, y, and z as parameters. They may vary independently from $-\infty$ to $+\infty$. Any appropriate symbol for a variable scalar could be used of course, but a separate statement would then be required in each case. Diagrams will be helpful.

EXERCISES

7. Let $Y = 2P_1 - P_2 - 3P_3 = (2, -1, -3)$ and $Z = -P_1 + 2P_2 + P_3 = (-1, 2, 1)$.

   (a) Calculate the components of $-2Z$, $Y - Z$, $Y + Z$, $2Y - 3Z$, and $4Y + Z$.

   (b) Find vectorial, parametric, and symmetric equations of the line through the point Z parallel to the vector Y.

   (c) Find vectorial and parametric equations of the plane determined by the points O, Y, and Z.

(d) Interpret the vectorial equation $X = (1 - t)Y + tZ$; obtain equivalent parametric and symmetric equations.

(e) Show that Y, Z, and $W = (0, 0, 2)$ are independent.

(f) Calculate the components of $3W - Y + 2Z$ and $W + 2Y - 3Z$.

(g) Where does the line $X = Y + t(W - Z)$ cut the plane $X = W + yY + zZ$?

8. Show that if $X = (x_k)$ and $Y = (y_k)$ then X and Y are dependent if

$$x_2 y_3 - x_3 y_2 = x_3 y_1 - x_1 y_3 = x_1 y_2 - x_2 y_1 = 0.$$

Is this condition also necessary? (The student familiar with determinants of the second order will recognize that the stated conditions may be written in the form

$$\begin{vmatrix} x_2 & x_3 \\ y_2 & y_3 \end{vmatrix} = \begin{vmatrix} x_3 & x_1 \\ y_3 & y_1 \end{vmatrix} = \begin{vmatrix} x_1 & x_2 \\ y_1 & y_2 \end{vmatrix} = 0.$$

Observe that the first ordered pair of indices is 2, 3, and that successive ordered pairs are obtained by cyclic advance: 2 is replaced by 3, 3 by 1, and 1 by 2.) (T)

9. Give vectorial, parametric, and symmetric equations of the following lines, both in general and in the indicated specific instances:

(a) Through W parallel to Y; specifically, let $W = (2, -3, 0)$ and $Y = (-1, 0, 2)$.

(b) Through Z and parallel to the line through the points Q and R; specifically, let $Z = (7, 4, 2)$, $Q = (-3, 1, 5)$, and $R = (6, 0, 2)$.

(c) Through V and W; specifically, let $V = (-2, 5, 0)$ and $W = (6, -1, 3)$.

10. Give parametric and symmetric forms for the lines with the following vectorial equations, and give geometric characterizations of the lines, both in general and in the indicated specific instances:

(a) $X = U + y(V - W)$; specifically, let $U = (3, -1, 2)$, $V = (-2, 0, 3)$, and $W = (5, 2, -1)$.

(b) $X = Y + tZ$; specifically, let $Y = (-1, 2, -2)$ and $Z = (1, 0, -3)$.

(c) $X = (1 - z)U + zV$; specifically, let $U = (3, -2, -2)$ and $V = (1, 1, -1)$.

11. Give symmetric and vectorial forms for the lines with the following parametric equations, and give geometric characterizations of the lines, both in general and in the indicated specific instances:

(a) $x_k = u_k + z(u_k - v_k)$; specifically, let $(u_k) = (0, -1, 3)$ and $(v_k) = (3, -1, 3)$.

(b) $x_k = u_k + y(v_k - w_k)$; specifically, let $(u_k) = (5, 2, -3)$, $(v_k) = (-1, 7, 0)$, and $(w_k) = (-1, -2, 3)$.

(c) $x_k = y_k + tz_k$; specifically, let $(y_k) = (0, 1, -2)$ and $(z_k) = (2, 0, 3)$.

12. Give vectorial and parametric forms for the lines with the following symmetric equations, and give geometric characterizations of the lines, both in general and in the indicated specific instances:

(a) $\dfrac{x_1 - u_1}{v_1 - u_1} = \dfrac{x_2 - u_2}{v_2 - u_2} = \dfrac{x_3 - u_3}{v_3 - u_3}$; specifically, let $(u_k) = (1, 3, -2)$ and $(v_k) = (-1, 3, 2)$.

(b) $\dfrac{x_1 - w_1}{z_1} = \dfrac{x_2 - w_2}{z_2} = \dfrac{x_3 - w_3}{z_3}$; specifically, let $(w_k) = (-1, 3, 0)$ and $(z_k) = (-3, 0, 2)$.

(c) $\dfrac{x_1 - s_1}{v_1 - w_1} = \dfrac{x_2 - s_2}{v_2 - w_2} = \dfrac{x_3 - s_3}{v_3 - w_3}$; specifically, let $(s_k) = (5, 2, -3)$, $(v_k) = (0, 1, -2)$, and $(w_k) = (3, 4, -2)$.

13. Give vectorial and parametric equations for the following planes, both in general and in the indicated specific instances:

(a) Through S and parallel to Y and Z; specifically, let $S = (3, -1, 2)$, $Y = (1, 5, -3)$, and $Z = (0, -2, 3)$.

(b) Through U, V, and W; specifically, let $U = (1, -1, 2)$, $V = (3, 1, -5)$, and $W = (0, 0, 2)$.

(c) Through T and parallel to both $\overrightarrow{VW}$ and $\overrightarrow{YZ}$; specifically, let $T = (2, 1, 3)$, $V = (0, -1, 2)$, $W = (1, -1, 3)$, $Y = (2, 1, -1)$, and $Z = (2, 2, 3)$.

(d) Containing the line $X = U + t(V - U)$ and the point W not on the line; specifically, let $U = (3, -1, 2)$, $V = (-2, -1, 3)$, and $W = (1, 2, -3)$.

14. Give parametric equations for the planes with the following vectorial equations, and give geometric characterizations of the planes, both in general and in the indicated specific instances:

(a) $X = S + t(U - V) + yW$; specifically, let $S = (3, 1, 2)$, $U = (-1, 2, -1)$, $V = (3, 2, 4)$, and $W = (0, 3, -2)$.

(b) $X = V + yY + zZ$; specifically, let $V = (3, -1, 2)$, $Y = (-1, 0, 2)$, and $Z = (3, 0, -2)$.

15. Give vectorial equations for the planes with the following scalar equations and give geometric characterizations of the planes, both in general and in the indicated specific instances:

(a) $x_k = u_k + yy_k + zz_k$; specifically, let $(u_k) = (1, -1, 1)$, $(y_k) = (3, -2, 4)$, and $(z_k) = (1, 2, -3)$.

(b) $x_k = tu_k + y(v_k - w_k)$; specifically, let $(u_k) = (2, 1, 3)$, $(v_k) = (-1, 1, 4)$, and $(w_k) = (-1, 2, -1)$.

16. Find the centroid $\bar{Q}$ of Q_k ($k = 1, 2, 3$) with weights w_k if $Q_1 = (2, -1, 1)$, $Q_2 = (1, 3, -2)$, $Q_3 = (-1, 1, 2)$, $w_1 = \frac{1}{6}$, $w_2 = \frac{1}{3}$, and $w_3 = \frac{1}{2}$. Now keep the Q_k fixed and allow the w_k to vary subject only to the restrictions $w_k \geq 0$ and some $w_k > 0$; what positions may $\bar{Q}$ occupy? In the light of E17 (end), is the correspondence between these positions and ordered triples w_k a one-to-one correspondence?

H. Geometric Problems

Vectors may be applied very usefully to a variety of geometric problems. These applications have been delayed because the notions of dependence, independence, and components are often valuable. Especially if he has had some experience with analytic geometry, the student will be tempted to introduce a coordinate system at once and to work from then on with components in an "analytic" manner, so to speak. This temptation should be resisted, just now, until the student gains some experience of the advantages of using vectors directly in a "synthetic" manner, so to speak. The notions of dependence and independence, and of "equating coefficients" in the latter case, will play an important part, of course, but explicit use of a coordinate system may not be required. A moderate amount of experience will refine the student's judgement as to when to use direct methods and when to introduce coordinates. It should be noted, also, that some of the most powerful "analytic" techniques are not yet available to us; some of them will be developed later in this chapter. In any case, the origin and basis may be adapted to the specific problem, and shrewd choices may bring great simplification.

EXAMPLES

1. The points $OPQR$ form a parallelogram. Lines are drawn from O to the midpoints of PQ and QR. Show that they trisect the diagonal PR.

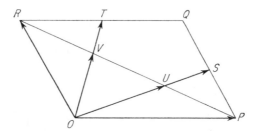

As anticipated by the notation, one places the origin at O. Then

$$S = \tfrac{1}{2}(P + Q) = P + \tfrac{1}{2}R,$$

the line through P and R is

$$P + t(R - P),$$

and one wishes to determine s and t, if possible, so that

$$s(P + \tfrac{1}{2}R) = P + t(R - P).$$

Since P and R are independent, one must have

$$s = 1 - t, \qquad \frac{s}{2} = t,$$

whence $t = \tfrac{1}{3}$, showing that $||\overrightarrow{PU}|| = \tfrac{1}{3}||\overrightarrow{PR}||$. The proof is completed by a similar argument regarding V. Since $s = \tfrac{2}{3}$ one sees, further, that $||U|| = \tfrac{2}{3}||S||$.

66

2. The bisectors of the internal angles of a triangle are concurrent.

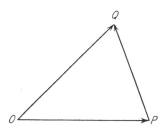

On referring to E7, we see that the vectorial equations of the internal bisectors of the angles at P and Q are, respectively,

$$X = P + t\left(-\frac{P}{||P||} + \frac{Q - P}{||Q - P||}\right),$$

and

$$X = Q + r\left(-\frac{Q}{||Q||} + \frac{P - Q}{||P - Q||}\right).$$

On equating the right members, and rearranging, we see that if these lines intersect they must do so at a point given by t and r satisfying the equation

$$(P - Q)\left(1 - \frac{t + r}{||P - Q||}\right) - \frac{t}{||P||}P + \frac{r}{||Q||}Q = 0.$$

Since P and Q are independent, this equation implies that

$$1 - \frac{t + r}{||P - Q||} = \frac{t}{||P||} = \frac{r}{||Q||},$$

whence

$$t = \frac{||P||\,||P - Q||}{||P|| + ||Q|| + ||P - Q||}.$$

When this value of t is used in the equation for the bisector at P, the result may be written

$$\frac{||P||\,||Q||}{||P|| + ||Q|| + ||P - Q||}\left(\frac{P}{||P||} + \frac{Q}{||Q||}\right);$$

by E7, this point lies on the internal bisector of the angle at O.

3. A man on the ground travelling west at five knots finds that the wind seems to come from the south. On doubling his speed he finds it seems to come from the southwest. Find the vector representing the velocity of the wind with respect to the ground.

Choose for the origin O the point on the ground through which the man is passing, measure all speeds in knots, and let unit distance represent a speed of one knot. Let U denote the unknown wind velocity with respect to the ground, S the velocity of the man with respect to the ground, and V the velocity of the wind with respect to the man (i.e., the velocity of the wind observed by the man). The fundamental relationship then is that $U = S + V$.

One may argue graphically as follows: Draw $\hat{S}$ westward and then $S = 5\hat{S}$. From the observation made at velocity S we know that U is the resultant of S

67

and a vector V_1 with $\hat{V}_1$ directed northward but with $\|V_1\|$ undetermined. From the observation made at velocity $2S$, we know that U is the resultant of $2S$ and a vector V_2 with V_2 directed toward the northeast, but with $\|V_2\|$ undetermined. By virtue of the considerations advanced in connection with D3, we conclude that the terminal point of U lies on the line through S parallel to V_1 and also on the line through $2S$ parallel to V_2. U, therefore, must be as shown in the diagram whence $U = 5\sqrt{2}$ and $\hat{U}$ is directed toward the northwest (i.e., the wind is from the southeast).

Alternatively, one may use S and V_1 as a basis in the plane. Then t_1 and t_2 exist such that

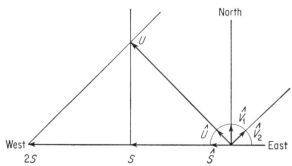

3.1. Graphical solution.

$$U = 5\hat{S} + t_1\hat{V}_1 = 10S + t_2\hat{V}_2.$$

But $\hat{V}_2 = (\hat{V}_1 - \hat{S})/\sqrt{2}$. On substituting this expression for $\hat{V}_2$ and equating coefficients of $\hat{S}$, we find that $t_2 = 5\sqrt{2}$, whence $t_1 = 5$ and $U = 5(\hat{S} + \hat{V}_1)$ as before.

EXERCISES

4. The diagonals of a nondegenerate parallelogram bisect each other.

5. The medians of a nondegenerate triangle intersect in a point which trisects each of them.

6. Prove that the lines joining the midpoints of successive sides of a plane quadrilateral form a parallelogram.

7. The vertices of a triangle are at P, Q, and R, and the midpoints of the sides are X, Y, and Z. Show that for any point U it is true that

$$\overrightarrow{UP} + \overrightarrow{UQ} + \overrightarrow{UR} = \overrightarrow{UX} + \overrightarrow{UY} + \overrightarrow{UZ}.$$

8. The sum of the position vectors of the vertices of a regular polygon with respect to its center is zero. (Choose a basis in the plane so that symmetry can be exploited effectively.)

9. Let the points P and Q vary respectively over two skew (non-parallel non-intersecting) lines. Show that the segments PQ and $P'Q'$ cannot be parallel unless, trivially, they coincide ($P = P'$ and $Q = Q'$). (With the origin on one line, a basis P_k ($k = 1, 2, 3$) can be found such that $P = tP_1$ and $Q = P_2 + uP_3$.)

I. Scalar Product; Orthogonality

Let us begin by defining the angle θ_{YZ} between vectors Y and Z. If either $Y = 0$ or $Z = 0$ then θ_{YZ} is not defined. If $Y \neq 0$ and $Z \neq 0$ then $\theta_{YZ} = 0$ if and only if $\hat{Y} = \hat{Z}$, while $\theta_{YZ} = \pi$ if and only if $\hat{Y} = -\hat{Z}$; in all other cases Y and Z are independent and determine in their plane two unequal angles, and the lesser of these is defined to be θ_{YZ}. It follows that $0 < \theta_{YZ} < \pi$ if and only if Y and Z are independent.

We now define a real-valued function f of ordered pairs of vectors $Y, Z \in E_0$ by agreeing that:

1.   (a) if either $Y = 0$ or $Z = 0$ then $f(Y, Z) = 0$;
  (b) if $Y \neq 0$ and $Z \neq 0$ then $f(Y, Z) = \|Y\| \, \|Z\| \cos \theta_{YZ}$.

Being defined for pairs of vectors, f has the nature of a "product". Since its values lie in the field $\mathfrak{R}$ of scalars, f is called the *scalar product* of Y and Z. Following conventional usage, we abbreviate $f(Y, Z)$ to (Y, Z); thus the symbol (Q, R) will denote, for the time being, not the ordered pair Q, R but rather the value $f(Q, R)$ of f when $Y = Q$ and $Z = R$.

It is left for the exercises (4–7) to prove that if t is a scalar and the capital letters denote elements of E_0 then:

  (a) $(Y, Z) = (Z, Y)$;
2.   (b) $(tY, Z) = t(Y, Z)$;
  (c) $(V + W, Z) = (V, Z) + (W, Z)$.

EXERCISES

3. Prove that $(Y, Z) = 0$ if and only if either $Y = 0$ or $Z = 0$ or $\cos \theta_{YZ} = 0$. Show therefore that if $(Y, Z) = 0$, $Y \neq 0$, and $Z \neq 0$, then $\theta_{YZ} = \pi/2$. (Vectors Y and Z are said to be *orthogonal* if $(Y, Z) = 0$; thus Y and Z are orthogonal if and only if either at least one of them is zero or neither is zero and they form a right angle (are perpendicular).) (T)

4. Prove that $(Y, Z) = (Z, Y)$ for any vectors Y and Z. (T)

5. Prove that $(tY, Z) = t(Y, Z)$ for any scalar t and vectors Y and Z. (T)

6. With Y and Z independent, interpret the following scalars and vectors: $(Y, \hat{Z})$, $(Y, \hat{Z})\hat{Z}$, $(Y, Z)\hat{Z}$, $(Y, \hat{Z})Z$, $(\hat{Y}, Z)$, $(\hat{Y}, Z)\hat{Y}$. (Both the scalar $(Y, \hat{Z})$ and the vector $(Y, \hat{Z})\hat{Z}$ are sometimes referred to as the *resolved part* of Y along Z or the *orthogonal projection* of Y onto $\hat{Z}$ (or, more loosely, along or onto Z). Prove geometrically that, for any vectors U, V, and Z, if $Z \neq 0$ then $(U + V, \hat{Z}) = (U, \hat{Z}) + (V, \hat{Z})$.

7. Prove that $(V + W, Z) = (V, Z) + (W, Z)$ for any vectors V, W, and Z. (If $Z \neq 0$, use 4 and 5 to replace Z by $\hat{Z}$. Then use 6.) (T)

8. Prove that if the index sets for h and k are finite then

$$(\sum v_h V_h, \sum w_k W_k) = \sum_{h,k} v_h w_k (V_h, W_k).$$

In particular, if the vectors P_k ($k = 1, 2, 3$) form a basis (cf. G), then $(Y, Z) = \sum y_h z_k (P_h, P_k)$. (T)

9. Prove that $(X, X) > 0$ unless $X = 0$. (T)

10. Prove that for any vectors Y and Z:

(a) $||Y + Z||^2 + ||Y - Z||^2 = 2||Y||^2 + 2||Z||^2$;

(b) $||Y + Z||^2 - ||Y - Z||^2 = 4(Y, Z)$;

(c) (Pythagoras) Y and Z are orthogonal if and only if $||Y + Z||^2 = ||Y||^2 + ||Z||^2$. (T)

11. Prove that $|(Y, Z)| \leq ||Y|| \, ||Z||$. When does the equality hold? (This is *Schwarz' Inequality* in E_0; it will be proved in much greater generality in a later chapter.) (T)

12. What can be said of X if, with Q fixed, $(X - Q, X - Q) = 0$, ≤ 16, > -4, $= 9$, ≥ 100, < 8, < 0, $= 5$?

13. Suppose that the vectors Q_k ($k = 1, 2, 3$) are pairwise orthogonal, in other words that if $h \neq k$ then $(Q_h, Q_k) = 0$, in which case one says simply that the Q_k are *orthogonal*. Show that the Q_k are independent. What is implied by the equation $(Q_h, Q_k) = \delta_{hk}$ (cf. G3.1)?

14. (Cf. 6 and 13.) Suppose that vectors U, V, and W are independent. Put $P_1 = \hat{U}$. Show that $V_1 = V - (V, P_1)P_1$ is not zero, lies in the plane of U and V, and is perpendicular to U. Put $P_2 = \hat{V}_1$. Show that $W_2 = W - (W, P_1)P_1 - (W, P_2)P_2$ is not zero and is perpendicular to U and V. Put $P_3 = \hat{W}_2$. Show that $(P_j, P_k) = \delta_{jk}$ ($j, k = 1, 2, 3$). What is the geometric significance of the vector $(W, P_1)P_1 + (W, P_2)P_2$? (T)

15. Prove that $2(X, Y) = ||X + Y||^2 - ||X||^2 - ||Y||^2$.

On account of the ease with which they may be used in expressing orthogonality or in writing down orthogonal projections, scalar products are advantageous in formulating and studying vectorial equations or inequalities. In many books, especially those on vector analysis, (Y, Z) is denoted by $Y \cdot Z$ and may then be referred to as the *dot-product*. In some contexts it is helpful to abbreviate $Z \cdot Z = ||Z||^2$ to Z^2, but we do not use this notation. It will be convenient for our discussion, and will help the student to learn both notations to write $Y \cdot Z$ for (Y, Z) during the remainder of this section.

If $N \neq 0$ then the equation $N \cdot X = 0$ will be true if and only if either $X = 0$ or X is perpendicular to N or, in other words, if and only if the point X lies in the plane through the origin perpendicular to the vector N. Thus the plane is the locus of the equation $N \cdot X = 0$, which may therefore be called the (vectorial) equation of the plane.

Any vector or line perpendicular to a plane is said to be *normal* to the plane. Thus $N \cdot X = 0$ is the equation of the plane through the origin with normal N.

Similarly, the equation $N \cdot (X - R) = 0$ states that either $X = R$ or $X - R$ is perpendicular to N, and is therefore the equation of a plane containing R and perpendicular to N. As indicated in the diagram (16), the planes $N \cdot X = 0$ and $N \cdot (X - R) = 0$ are parallel (each having normal N), and the latter may be obtained, in fact, by translating the former in such a way that O is translated onto R (cf. E10 where R is here X and R_0 is here R).

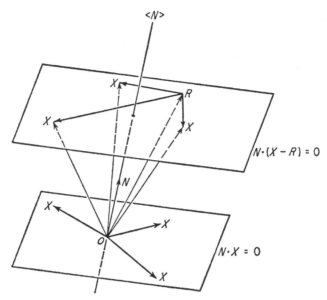

16. Planes $N \cdot X = 0$ and $N \cdot (X - R) = 0$.

Now consider the equation $N \cdot X = p$ with $p \neq 0$. It is evident on inspection that one solution is $Q = pN/||N||^2$, for indeed $N \cdot Q = p$. With Q fixed we arrive by subtraction at the equivalent equation $N \cdot (X - Q) = 0$ already studied.

A more complete geometric interpretation will result from dividing the equation by the positive number $||N||$. If we abbreviate $p/||N||$ to q, the equation will read $\hat{N} \cdot X = q$; here $\hat{N}$ is normalized and the equation itself is said to be *normalized* or *in normal form*. The left member is the orthogonal projection $||X|| \cos \theta_{NX}$ of X on $\hat{N}$, and the equation will be true if and only if X has such a position that this projection has the value q. One such position is clearly $q\hat{N}$ (in the present situation $q\hat{N}$ is the point Q of the preceding paragraph), and the other possible positions constitute a plane through $q\hat{N}$ perpendicular to $\hat{N}$; this relationship is especially evident when the equation is written in the form $\hat{N} \cdot (X - q\hat{N}) = 0$. In the diagram (17), we show, for the sake of simplicity, only a section by a plane containing the vector N. The three-dimensional configuration may be obtained by rotating this diagram about the line $\langle \hat{N} \rangle$ generated by $\hat{N}$.

71

Turning now to inequalities, we wish to show that if $N \cdot Y \neq p$ then $N \cdot Y - p > 0$ or < 0 according as Y lies in one or the other of the two half-spaces determined by the plane $N \cdot X = p$, or $\hat{N} \cdot X = q$ where $q = p/\|N\|$. To begin with, the sign of $N \cdot Y - p$ is the same as the sign of $\hat{N} \cdot Y - q$. This expression, however, is positive or negative according as the orthogonal projection $\hat{N} \cdot Y$ of Y on $\hat{N}$ is greater or less than q. In 17, $\hat{N} \cdot Y > q$ or $< q$ according as Y lies below or above the plane $\hat{N} \cdot X = q$.

We can see from 17, moreover, the meaning of the number $\hat{N} \cdot Y - q$ as well as its sign. Let us first agree that by "the" *distance* between a plane and a point not on it we shall mean the perpendicular distance; this is in fact the distance between the point and the closest point on the plane. If a definite normal is clearly specified by the context, as $\hat{N}$ is in the present situation, let us

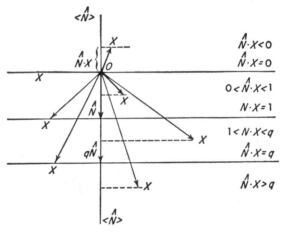

17. Plane $\hat{N} \cdot X = q$ and half-spaces $\hat{N} \cdot Y > q$ and $\hat{N} \cdot Y < q$; here $q > 0$. (Section by plane containing $\hat{N}$.)

agree to measure *directed distance from* the *plane to* the *point positively in the direction of* $\hat{N}$ (and negatively in the opposite direction).

We have seen that $\hat{N} \cdot X = 0$ is the equation of the plane π through the origin parallel to the plane $\hat{N} \cdot X = q$. The number $\hat{N} \cdot Y$, being the projection of Y onto $\hat{N}$, is equal to the directed distance from π to Y, and it follows from our discussion that q is the directed distance (measured positively in the direction of $\hat{N}$) from π to the plane $\hat{N} \cdot X = q$. Hence $\hat{N} \cdot Y - q$ *is the directed distance to* Y *from the plane* $\hat{N} \cdot X - q = 0$.

EXERCISES

18. Observing that $\hat{N} \cdot Y - q = \hat{N} \cdot (Y - q\hat{N})$, show that $\hat{N} \cdot Y > q$ or $< q$ according as the vector $Y - q\hat{N}$ makes an acute or obtuse angle with N. Interpret geometrically (cf. 16 and 17).

19. Obtain vectorial equations for planes parallel to the plane $\hat{N} \cdot X = q$ and at the following directed distances from it: (a) 3, (b) -2, (c) -7, (d) 5.

20. Write down a vectorial equation of the plane through the point R and normal to the line $X = U + tV$.

21. Write down a vectorial equation of the plane through the origin and normal to the line connecting U and V.

22. Where does the line $X = U + tV$ cut the plane $N \cdot X = p$? Are there any exceptional cases?

23. With N, R, and p all different from zero, discuss the equation $N \cdot (X - R) = p$ and the inequalities $N \cdot (Y - R) \geq p$, $\leq p$.

24. Let $Q \neq 0$ be given. Obtain vectorial equations of planes with normal $\hat{N}$ and such that the directed distance from the plane to Q shall have the following values: (a) 2, (b) 5, (c) -3, (d) -7, (e) 0.

25. With $Q \neq 0$ and $r > 0$ given, find the equation of the plane tangent to the sphere $\|X - Q\| = r$ at a point P on the sphere.

J. Vector Product

Let us begin by observing the accompanying diagram. Each figure displays a *triad*, an ordered triple of independent vectors.

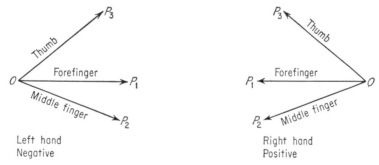

Left hand
Negative

Right hand
Positive

1. Positively and negatively oriented triads.

The reader will notice the difference between these triads if he will compare the diagram with the configuration arising when the fingers of the respective hands are extended, with thumb and forefinger in the indicated position and both parallel to the plane of the paper. Another way to sense the difference is to imagine oneself standing at the origin on the plane $\langle P_1, P_2 \rangle$, with his head on the same side of the plane as P_3; on viewing the plane $\langle P_1, P_2 \rangle$ one will see that in order to rotate P_1, in the plane $\langle P_1, P_2 \rangle$, into the position occupied by P_2, a counterclockwise (positive) rotation will be required for a *right-handed* or *positive* or *positively oriented* triad, while a clockwise (negative) rotation will be required for a *left-handed* or *negative* or *negatively oriented* triad. A triad of either type is changed into one of the other type if the direction of any *one* vector is reversed. The effect of other transformations will be noted later.

This dichotomy of triads rests on the following two intuitively evident facts whose rigorous proof is beyond our reach here; the terms used are to be interpreted intuitively, as they would apply to three rigid arrows with tails attached to a universal joint at O. Suppose first that two triads P_k and Q_k ($k = 1, 2, 3$) are of the same type; then either can be continuously moved into the other in such a way that P_k comes to coincide with Q_k ($k = 1, 2, 3$) and the three vectors of the triad remain independent during the entire motion. On the other hand, neither of two triads of opposite type can be continuously moved into the other, in such a way that P_k comes to coincide with Q_k ($k = 1, 2, 3$), without passing through a configuration in which the three vectors are dependent (coplanar), at which stage they cease, technically speaking, to be a triad.

There are occasionally good practical reasons for using one type of triad rather than the other. When there is no reason for preference, modern writers are almost unanimous in using right-handed triads, and we shall follow this custom. Many books have ambiguous diagrams, sometimes lacking arrows on coordinate axes; the context usually implies that the triad is meant to be right-handed.

We are now in a position to define the vector product of an ordered pair of vectors. The *vector product* of U and V (in that order) is a vector, denoted by $U \times V$, and defined as follows:

(a) if U and V are dependent then $U \times V = 0$;

(b) if U and V are independent then $U \times V$ is a vector perpendicular to both U and V, directed so that U, V, and $U \times V$ in that order form a right-handed triad, and with norm

2.
$$\|U \times V\| = \|U\| \, \|V\| \sin \theta_{UV}.$$

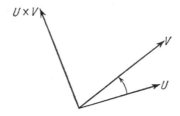

3. Relative directions of U, V, and $U \times V$.

The notations $Y \cdot Z$ for the scalar product and $U \times V$ for the vector product are part of what is commonly called the "Gibbs notation", and the vector product is often called the *cross-product* when this notation is used.

Other notations for $U \times V$ include $[U, V]$ (cf. our (U, V) for $U \cdot V$) and $U \wedge V$.

We leave for the exercises (cf. 5, 10, and 12) proofs of the following results:

4.
(a) $V \times U = -U \times V$;
(b) $(tU) \times V = t(U \times V) = U \times (tV)$;
(c) $U \times (V + W) = U \times V + U \times W$.

EXERCISES

5. Prove that $V \times U = -U \times V$.

6. Prove that $U \times V = 0$ only if U and V are dependent.

7. Prove that if U and V are independent then $\|U \times V\|$ is the area of the parallelogram with U and V as coinitial sides.

8. Prove that if U, V, and W are independent then the scalar $U \cdot V \times W$ is not zero, and is positive or negative according as the triad U, V, W is positively or negatively oriented. Prove also that $|U \cdot V \times W|$ is equal to the volume of the parallelepiped with U, V, and W as coinitial edges.

9. Prove that $U \cdot V \times W = U \times V \cdot W$ and that $U \cdot V \times W = V \cdot W \times U = W \cdot U \times V = -U \cdot W \times V = -W \cdot V \times U = -V \cdot U \times W$.

10. Prove that $(tU) \times V = U \times (tV) = t(U \times V)$ for any scalar t and vectors U and V.

11. Let U and V be independent. Show that $U \times V$ may be constructed as follows: first project V orthogonally onto the plane σ through O perpendicular to U and call the result V_1, then rotate V_1 on σ through $+\pi/2$ as viewed from U and call the result V_2, and, finally, multiply V_2 by $\|U\|$.

12. By using 11, or otherwise, prove that $U \times (V + W) = U \times V + U \times W$.

13. Find a vectorial equation for the line of intersection of the planes $N_1 \cdot (X - Q) = 0$ and $N_2 \cdot (X - Q) = 0$.

14. Suppose that Y and Z are independent. Show that $X = R + yY + zZ$ and $(X - R) \cdot Y \times Z = 0$ are vectorial equations of the same plane.

15. Suppose that $X = R + uU$ and $X = S + vV$ are skew lines. Show that the shortest distance between them is

$$\frac{|(R - S) \cdot U \times V|}{\|U \times V\|}.$$

16. Suppose that $P, Q \in E_0$ with $Q \neq 0$. For which points X is it true that $(X - P) \times Q = 0$?

17. Obtain an expression for the perpendicular distance between the point Q and the line $X = U + tV$.

18. Let U and V be independent. Show that U, $U \times V$, and $U \times (U \times V)$ form, in that order, a right-handed orthogonal triad.

75

19. Let the vectors P_k ($k = 1, 2, 3$) form a basis for E_O. Define

$$Q_1 = P_2 \times P_3, \qquad Q_2 = P_3 \times P_1, \qquad Q_3 = P_1 \times P_2.$$

Prove that if $j \neq k$ then $(Q_j, P_k) = 0$ ($j, k = 1, 2, 3$) and that the vectors Q_k ($k = 1, 2, 3$) form a basis for E_O. The basis Q_k is said to be the basis *reciprocal* to the basis P_k. Could matters be so arranged that $(Q_j, P_k) = \delta_{jk}$? (T)

The formal algebra of the vector product in E_O can be pushed much farther. The student may try, for example, to prove that

20. $$U \times (V \times W) = U \cdot WV - U \cdot VW.$$

(Being perpendicular to $V \times W$, the vector on the left must lie in $\langle V, W \rangle$; try the case $U = V$ first.) It follows from this result that the associative law cannot hold generally for vector products. More complicated examples of non-associative multiplication can be found in the literature.

The vector product has extensive applications in the geometry of curves and surfaces, in mechanics, in the theory of electromagnetic phenomena, and elsewhere.

The student should be explicitly warned, at the same time, that the idea of a vector product of *two* vectors, as it has been presented here, is restricted essentially to $\mathcal{E}_3$. In a linear space of dimension $n \geq 2$, two vectors determine in a simple way an entity with $n(n - 1)/2$ components (technically, a skew tensor of the second order). Only if $n = 3$ does this entity have exactly the n components required for interpretation as a vector. Even in $\mathcal{E}_3$, moreover, the behavior of the components of a vector product under a general change of basis is by no means transparent. We shall see later that whenever $n \geq 3$ there is a very natural way of associating a non-zero vector with $n - 1$ independent vectors.

We have nevertheless included a brief discussion of the vector product in order to cover the elements of classical "vector algebra" found in books on vector analysis, and because of the great utility of the vector product in expressing some picturesque relationships in $\mathcal{E}_3$.

K. Bases; Orthonormal Bases

Little was said in I and J regarding the use of components in calculating scalar or vector products. The reason is that unless the basis is specialized in certain respects the necessary calculations, while in principle entirely feasible, are rather awkward without methods which involve tensor algebra and are therefore beyond the scope of this chapter. We proceed to develop arrangements facilitating calculation with components.

Let the vectors P_k ($k = 1, 2, 3$) form a basis for E_O. In I8 we showed that

1. $$(Y, Z) = \sum y_h z_k (P_h, P_k),$$

the sum being formed, of course, for h, $k = 1, 2, 3$ and therefore involving nine terms if no coefficients are zero. One sees similarly, by virtue of J10–12, that

2. $$U \times V = \sum u_h v_k P_h \times P_k.$$

On using the fact (J5) that $P_k \times P_h = -P_h \times P_k$, we see that 2 may be written out as (cf. G8),

3. $U \times V = (u_2 v_3 - u_3 v_2) P_2 \times P_3 + (u_3 v_1 - u_1 v_3) P_3 \times P_1 + (u_1 v_2 - u_2 v_1) P_1 \times P_2.$

On referring to J18, moreover, we see that the vectors on the right in 3 are the members Q_k ($k = 1, 2, 3$) of the basis reciprocal to P_k. In order to find the components of $U \times V$ referred to P_k we would need to express the Q_k in terms of the P_k by formulas such as $Q_h = \sum q_{hk} P_k$ ($h = 1, 2, 3$), which are in general by no means obvious.

It is most fortunate that both 1 and 3 can be greatly simplified by requiring (cf. I13) that

4. $$(P_h, P_k) = \delta_{hk} \qquad (h, k = 1, 2, 3).$$

A set of three vectors with this property is independent, by I13, and therefore a basis. The triad is orthogonal and also normalized in the sense that $\|P_k\| = 1$ ($k = 1, 2, 3$). Its scalar multiplication table has the very simple form shown in 5; the tabular entry is the scalar product of the vector appearing at the left of its (horizontal) row and the vector at the top of its (vertical) column.

	P_1	P_2	P_3
P_1	1	0	0
P_2	0	1	0
P_3	0	0	1

5. Scalar multiplication table for orthogonal normalized basis $P_k(k = 1, 2, 3)$.

With such a basis the expression I8 reduces to the sum of three terms:

6. $$(Y, Z) = \sum y_k z_k.$$

On referring again to J19 one sees there that if P_k is an orthogonal normalized basis and Q_k is the reciprocal basis, then either $Q_k = P_k$ ($k = 1, 2, 3$) or $Q_k = -P_k$ ($k = 1, 2, 3$) according as P_k is positively or negatively oriented, and 3 simplifies accordingly with only an ambiguous sign on the right. Now a basis satisfying condition 4 will still satisfy that condition if the directions of any or all of the vectors are reversed. By reversing one direction, if necessary, we may therefore secure a basis consisting of a right-handed triad which is orthogonal and normalized. Such a basis is said to be *orthonormal*. If the basis is orthonormal then the ambiguous sign on the right in the simplified form of 3 is "$+$", and it then reads

7.
$$(u_k) \times (v_k) = (u_2v_3 - u_3v_2, \; u_3v_1 - u_1v_3, \; u_1v_2 - u_2v_1).$$

A very simple form is assumed by the table of vector products for the vectors of an orthonormal basis, in which the tabular entry is the vector product, in this order, of the vector at the left of its row and the vector at the top of its column.

	P_1	P_2	P_3
P_1	0	P_3	$-P_2$
P_2	$-P_3$	0	P_1
P_3	P_2	$-P_1$	0

8. Vector multiplication table for orthonormal basis P_k ($k = 1, 2, 3$).

A negatively oriented triad satisfying 4 might be called "anti-orthonormal", but we anticipate no need for this term. The table 5 for such a basis would be identical with 5, while the table 8 would have the sign of every entry changed.

Orthonormal bases are so advantageous that in many applications they are used almost exclusively, and many discussions in the literature, especially in physics and technology, are based on the *tacit* assumption that a *fixed* orthonormal basis is in use. An orthonormal basis is frequently indicated by "*i, j, k*" either with superscript arrow or in boldface type.

It is most important to know, intuitively obvious, and fortunately very easy to prove, that orthonormal bases exist. The construction of J18 yielded a right-handed orthogonal triad; if each vector is normalized, the result will be an orthonormal basis. Depending as it does on the vector product, however, that construction may not generalize readily.

A construction that does generalize easily is known in the literature as the *Schmidt orthogonalization* (more properly, orthonormalization) *process*. Except for the question of orientation, details of this process in E_0 are given in I14, where geometric argument shows readily that if U, V, and W are positively (negatively) oriented then the same is true of P_k ($k = 1, 2, 3$). In order to arrive at an orthonormal basis, therefore, one may either arrange to have U, V, and W right-handed at the outset or pay no attention to orientation until the last step of the process and then put $P_3 = \pm W_2$, with the sign chosen so that P_k is right-handed. A practical test is afforded (cf. J8) by the sign of $P_1 \cdot P_2 \times P_3$.

For the remainder of this section we *assume that E_0 is referred to a fixed orthonormal basis P_k* ($k = 1, 2, 3$).

A most important advantage of an orthonormal basis lies in the fact that the components of a vector are its resolved parts (cf. I6) along the basis vectors. If $X = \sum x_k P_k$, in fact, then $(X, P_j) = \sum x_k (P_k, P_j) = \sum x_k \delta_{kj} \neq x_j$. Therefore

9.
$$X = \sum (X, P_k)P_k.$$

It follows from I8 that

10.
$$(Y, Z) = \sum y_k z_k = \sum (Y, P_k)(Z, P_k),$$

11.
$$\|X\|^2 = (X, X) = \sum x_k^2 = \sum (X, P_k)^2,$$

and

12.
$$\|U - V\|^2 = \sum (u_k - v_k)^2 = \sum (U - V, P_k)^2.$$

The equation of a sphere, for example, with center at $(3, -1, 2)$ and radius 4 is

$$(x_1 - 3)^2 + (x_2 + 1)^2 + (x_3 - 2)^2 = 16.$$

The components u_k of a unit vector U have the property that $\|U\|^2 = \sum u_k^2 = 1$. For $k = 1, 2, 3$, moreover, $u_k = (U, P_k) = \cos \theta_{UP_k}$. The numbers u_k are therefore called the *direction cosines* or, more briefly, the cosines of U or of any vector V such that $\hat{V} = U$ (cf. G4.1). More generally, the line $X = R + xW$ is parallel to W, hence to $\hat{W}$, and the components of $\hat{W}$ are called (direction) *cosines* of the line. The line $X = (3, 2, -4) + x(-2, 3, 4)$ has direction numbers $-2, 3, 4$ and cosines $-2/\sqrt{29}, 3/\sqrt{29}, 4/\sqrt{29}$. If we abbreviate θ_{UP_k} to θ_k $(k = 1, 2, 3)$, then the line through $V = (v_k)$ parallel to U has cosines $\cos \theta_k$ and its symmetric equations are

13.
$$\frac{x_1 - v_1}{\cos \theta_1} = \frac{x_2 - v_2}{\cos \theta_2} = \frac{x_3 - v_3}{\cos \theta_3}.$$

In I we studied vectorial equations of the form $N \cdot X = p$, $N \cdot (X - R) = 0$, $\hat{N} \cdot X = q$, and interpreted the number $\hat{N} \cdot Y - q$. Let us work out a few examples.

If $N = (2, 3, -1)$ and $p = 4$ then the equation $N \cdot X = p$ takes the form

$$2x_1 + 3x_2 - x_3 = 4.$$

If $S = (2, 0, 0)$ then clearly $N \cdot S = 4$, and the equation may be written as $N \cdot (X - S) = 0$ or

$$2(x_1 - 2) + 3x_2 - x_3 = 0;$$

this is seen to be the equation of the plane through $(2, 0, 0)$ perpendicular to N.

The point S on the plane was obtained by inspection. We could equally well have sought t so that tN would lie on the plane, requiring, therefore, that

$$t[2^2 + 3^2 + (-1)^2] = 4,$$

whence $t = \frac{2}{7}$ and one point on the plane is $R = tN = (4, 6, -2)/7$. Thus the equation may be written as $N \cdot (X - R) = 0$, or

$$2(x_1 - \tfrac{4}{7}) + 3(x_2 - \tfrac{6}{7}) - (x_3 + \tfrac{2}{7}) = 0,$$

an equation that differs only in form, of course, from the earlier versions.

Since $||N|| = \sqrt{14}$, the normal form for the equation is $N \cdot X = q$ with $q = 4/\sqrt{14}$, or

$$\frac{2x_1 + 3x_2 - x_3}{\sqrt{14}} = \frac{4}{\sqrt{14}}.$$

Where is the point $Y = (4, -3, 5)$ situated with respect to the plane? We calculate $N \cdot Y - q$,

$$\frac{2 \cdot 4 + 3(-3) - 5 - 4}{\sqrt{14}} = -\frac{10}{\sqrt{14}} = -\frac{5\sqrt{14}}{7},$$

and conclude that Y is $5\sqrt{14}/7$ units (perpendicularly) away from the plane in the direction opposite to that in which N points.

If we seek a point $Y = (y_k)$ whose directed distance from the plane is 6 units, then we are looking for y_k such that

$$\frac{2y_1 + 3y_2 - y_3 - 4}{\sqrt{14}} = 6$$

or

$$2y_1 + 3y_2 - y_3 = 4 + 6\sqrt{14}.$$

By inspection, one such point is $(2 + 3\sqrt{14}, 0, 0)$; others are, for example, $(2, 2\sqrt{14}, 0)$ and $(2, 0, -6\sqrt{14})$.

In J we studied the vector product $U \times V$. Since we are using an orthonormal basis, 7 is valid. A few examples will illustrate the use of the vector product. To begin with,

$$(3, -8, 2) \times (-2, -3, 1)$$
$$= ((-8) \cdot 1 - 2(-3), 2(-2) - 3 \cdot 1, 3(-3) - (-8)(-2))$$
$$= (-2, -7, -25).$$

Suppose now that we wish a scalar equation for the plane containing $U = (2, -1, 3)$, $V = (-3, 2, 4)$, and $W = (5, 0, -3)$ (cf. E11). The vectors $V - U = (-5, 3, 1)$ and $W - U = (3, 1, -6)$ are parallel to the plane. Any vector perpendicular to both of them, such as their vector product $N = (-19, -27, -14)$, will be normal to the plane. Since U is on the plane, an equation for the plane is $N \cdot (X - U) = 0$ or

$$-19(x_1 - 2) - 27(x_2 + 1) - 14(x_3 - 3) = 0$$

or

$$-19x_1 - 27x_2 - 14x_3 = -53$$

or

$$19x_1 + 27x_2 + 14x_3 = 53.$$

It should be noted, however, that while the last two equations are equivalent *equations*, and the planes have the same normal *line* $\langle N \rangle$, the directions of the unit normal *vectors* $\hat{N}$ (as we have interpreted the coefficients) are opposite to each other; this circumstance must be observed in interpreting directed distances and linear inequalities associated with the equation.

When using an orthonormal basis in E_O, it is customary to avoid subscripts by writing (x, y, z) instead of (x_1, x_2, x_3). We follow this usage, in order to illustrate it, in the next example and in a few of the exercises.

In J13 suppose that $N_1 = (2, -1, 3)$, $N_2 = (-1, 2, -1)$ and $R = (3, -5, 4)$; thus the scalar equations of the planes are

$$2(x - 3) - (y + 5) + 3(z - 4) = 0$$

or

$$2x - y + 3z = 23,$$
$$-(x - 3) + 2(y + 5) - 1(z - 4) = 0$$

or

$$-x + 2y - z = -17.$$

We know, of course, that the line has the vectorial equation $X = R + tN_1 \times N_2$, and could simply substitute for R and the N's. If merely the two scalar equations are given, however, we can still get the N's readily enough from the coefficients, but how shall we find the coordinates of some (any) point R common to both planes?

One way is simply to assign a value to one of the variables and solve the resulting equations for the others. With $z = 0$, for example, our equations yield $x = \frac{29}{3}$ and $y = -\frac{11}{3}$. A possible difficulty is indicated by the equations

$$ax + by + (c + 1)z = 1$$
$$ax + by + cz = 0.$$

If one puts $z = 0$, he arrives at the clearly inconsistent pair $ax + by = 1$, $ax + by = 0$. (Difficulties of this kind will be discussed more fully when we study linear algebraic equations.) By subtraction, however, we see that the equations imply that $z = 1$. If this value of z is used, then both equations reduce to $ax + by + c = 0$. If, say, $a \neq 0$, then for any t the numbers $x = -(c/a) + tb$, $y = -ta$ satisfy the equation. The line in question must therefore be given by

$$\left(-\frac{c}{a}, 0, 1\right) + t(b, -a, 0).$$

More generally, one would treat one of the variables as a parameter, solving for the others in terms of it. In this way, in fact, simple manipulations can be made to yield the parametric equations of the line. In our example we find

$$x = \tfrac{29}{3} - \tfrac{5}{3}z, \qquad y = -\tfrac{11}{3} - \tfrac{1}{3}z, \qquad z = z.$$

Each of the first two of these equations is the equation of a plane containing the desired line. By writing $z = 3t$ we arrive at these three equations,

$$x = \tfrac{29}{3} - 5t, \qquad y = -\tfrac{11}{3} - t, \qquad z = 3t.$$

Thus the line passes through $(\frac{29}{3}, -\frac{11}{3}, 0)$ and is parallel to $(-5, -1, 3)$. As a check, we note that $N_1 \times N_2 = (-5, -1, 3)$; any non-zero multiple of this vector would have provided an equally convincing check.

The ideas and methods developed in this chapter are adequate for a discussion of most elementary problems involving points, lines, and planes in $\mathcal{E}_3$. After the further examples included in the following exercises, the student should be able to solve most problems of that nature occurring in standard texts on solid analytic geometry. The concepts used here have been so formulated as to carry over (except for the vector product) almost verbatim to the more general situations to be studied later. We therefore have in E_O a rich source of examples and illustrations for the more abstract theory. That theory, at the same time, will be more extensive in its aims, and will include as special cases results applying to problems in E_O not studied in this chapter, such as change of basis, linear transformations (for example, rotations), systems of linear algebraic equations, bilinear and quadratic forms, and so on. These applications will be noted as they occur.

EXERCISES

In all these exercises it is assumed that E_O is referred to a fixed orthonormal basis P_k $(k = 1, 2, 3)$, with $X = \sum x_k P_k = x P_1 + y P_2 + z P_3$.

14. Let $Q_1 = (2, -1, 3)$, $Q_2 = (0, 2, -1)$, and $Q_3 = (1, -3, 2)$.

(a) Form the scalar multiplication table (Q_j, Q_k).

(b) Form the vector multiplication table $Q_j \times Q_k$.

(c) Find a scalar equation of the plane through Q_1 perpendicular to Q_2.

(d) Find where the plane of (c) is cut by the line $X = Q_2 + t Q_3$.

(e) Find the scalar equation of the plane through Q_2 and parallel to Q_1 and Q_3.

(f) Find a linear combination of Q_1 and Q_2 that is perpendicular to Q_2.

(g) Find a vector in $\langle Q_2, Q_3 \rangle$ that is perpendicular to Q_1. Find also the orthogonal projection of Q_1 on $\langle Q_2, Q_3 \rangle$.

(h) Find the equation of the sphere with center at Q_3 and radius 5.

(i) Find the interior angles of the triangle with vertices at Q_k $(k = 1, 2, 3)$.

(j) Find the equation of the plane containing 0, Q_1, and Q_2. How far is Q_3 from this plane, and in what direction?

(k) Find the (direction) cosines of the line $X = Q_3 + t(Q_1 - Q_2)$.

(l) Find a scalar equation of the plane determined by Q_1, Q_2, and Q_3.

(m) Apply the orthonormalization process (I14) to the Q_k.

15. Let the plane π_1 have the equation $3x - 2y + 2z = 6$.

(a) Find the unit normal N_1 to π_1.

(b) Find where π_1 is cut by the line of 14(k).

(c) Find the equation of a plane parallel to π_1 and containing the point $(2, 0, -2)$.

(d) Find the directed distance from π_1 to $(6, 3, -1)$.

(e) Find the resolved parts of $V = (2, -1, 5)$ normal to π_1 and parallel to π_1.

(f) Find the equation of the plane parallel to π_1 and $+8$ units of distance from it.

(g) Find the points where π_1 is cut by each of the coordinate axes. (The coordinates are called the *intercepts* on the respective axes.)

(h) Find an equation of a plane whose intercepts are three times those of π_1.

(i) Find equations for a line through $(1, 1, -4)$ parallel to π_1.

(j) For which points is it true that $(3x - 2y + 2z - 6)^2 = 7$?

16. Keep π_1 as in 15 and let π_2 have the equation $x + y - 3z = 5$.

(a) Show that π_1 and π_2 are not parallel and find a vector parallel to their line of intersection.

(b) Find vectorial and (parametric) scalar equations of their line of intersection.

(c) Find an equation for a plane through $(3, -5, 4)$ normal to the line of intersection of π_1 and π_2.

(d) Find an equation for the locus of a point equidistant from π_1 and π_2. Interpret geometrically.

(e) Find an equation for the locus of a point that is three times as far from π_1 as from π_2.

(f) Show that if not both of u and v are zero then the equation $u(3x - 2y + 2z - 6) + v(x + y - 3z - 5) = 0$ is the equation of a plane π containing the line of intersection of π_1 and π_2.

(g) Try to choose u and v so that the plane π in (f) will:

    (i) contain the origin;

    (ii) contain the point $(3, 3, -5)$;

    (iii) be parallel to the plane $4x - 8y + 7z = 6$;

    (iv) have $(3, -1, 4)$ at a directed distance of -5 from it.

17. Let λ_1 and λ_2 denote respectively the lines $(x_k) = (-1, 2, 4) + t(3, -2, 1)$ and $(x_k) = (2, -3, -1) + u(3, 0, -2)$.

(a) Find the direction cosines of λ_1 and λ_2.

(b) Find the direction of their common perpendicular.

(c) Find an equation for the plane through $(1, 1, 7)$ and parallel to both lines.

(d) Find the perpendicular distance between λ_1 and $(3, 3, 2)$.

(e) Find the perpendicular distance between λ_1 and λ_2 (cf. J15).

(f) Find the angle between the directions of the two lines.

(g) Try to find a line through the origin meeting both lines.

(h) Where does λ_2 cut the plane which is normal to λ_1 at the point on λ_1 for which $t = -3$?

(i) Find equations for two planes containing λ_1.

18. Let λ denote the line $X = R + tV$. Write down a condition that the vector $\overrightarrow{RY}$ shall make an angle α $(0 < \alpha < \pi/2)$ with V. Use this condition to find a scalar equation for a cone with vertex R, axis λ, and vertex angle 2α. Can you adjust your equation so as to describe both nappes of the cone? Specialize your work to find the equation of a cone with vertex at $(3, 2, -1)$, axis parallel to $(2, -3, 2)$, and vertex angle 2α with $\cos \alpha = \frac{3}{4}$.

19. The line $x - 2y = 3$, $z = 0$ is revolved about the x-axis. Find an equation for the cone it generates. What can you say about the curve in which the cone is cut by the plane $y = 0$?

20. With λ as in 18, write down a condition that the point Q shall be at distance $r > 0$ from λ (cf. J17). Hence obtain a scalar equation for a right circular cylinder with axis λ and radius r. Specializing, find an equation for the right circular cylinder with axis $(3, 2, -1) + t(2, -3, 2)$ and radius 5.

21. The line $X = (4, -3, 2) + t(6, -1, -4)$ is revolved about a parallel line through $(4, 2, -3)$. Find an equation for the cylinder generated. What can you say about the curve in which the cylinder is cut by the plane $z = 0$?

22. Let the direction cosines of U and V be denoted respectively by $\cos \theta_k$ and $\cos \varphi_k$ $(k = 1, 2, 3)$. Prove that $\cos \theta_{UV} = \sum \cos \theta_k \cos \varphi_k$.

23. Find the endpoints of the orthogonal projection on the plane $3x - y + 2z = 4$ of the segment joining the points $(1, 2, -1)$ and $(2, 3, -1)$.

24. Does the inequality
$$[\sum (u_k + v_k)^2]^{1/2} \leq [\sum u_k^2]^{1/2} + [\sum v_k^2]^{1/2}$$
follow from the triangle inequality (D8)? In any event, try to devise a direct proof. (This is the form taken in E_0 by Minkowski's Inequality, which we shall prove in a more general situation later on.) (T)

25. Does the inequality
$$|\sum y_k z_k|^2 \leq (\sum y_k^2)(\sum z_k^2)$$
follow from Schwarz' Inequality (I11)? In any event, try to devise a direct proof. (T)

26. Let Q_h $(h = 1, 2, 3)$ be a right-handed orthonormal triad, and suppose that $Q_h = \sum q_{hk} P_k$ $(h = 1, 2, 3)$. Prove that:

(a) $q_{hk} = (Q_h, P_k)$ $(h, k = 1, 2, 3)$;

(b) (cf. 10) $P_k = \sum q_{hk} Q_h$ $(k = 1, 2, 3)$;

(c) $\sum q_{hk} q_{jk} = \delta_{hj}$ $(h, j = 1, 2, 3)$;

(d) $\sum q_{hk} q_{hj} = \delta_{kj}$ $(k, j = 1, 2, 3)$;

(e) $q_{11} = q_{22} q_{33} - q_{23} q_{32}$, $q_{12} = q_{23} q_{31} - q_{21} q_{33}$, $q_{13} = q_{21} q_{32} - q_{22} q_{31}$.

What other relations similar to (e) are valid? Explain. (T)

L. Concluding Remarks

Our principal object of study in this chapter has been the space E_O of all vectors issuing from a fixed point O in $\mathcal{E}_3$. In these concluding remarks we wish first to describe the idea of a free vector and then to mention briefly the connection between our work and some uses of vectors in mechanics and physics.

1. **Translations; Free Vectors.** A *translation* is a displacement of $\mathcal{E}_3$ in which every point moves the same distance in the same direction. A translation is therefore a function T on $\mathcal{E}_3$ onto $\mathcal{E}_3 : P \to T(P) = P'$ such that the vectors $\overrightarrow{PP'}$ all agree in length and direction. We also accept as a translation the *identity* displacement in which each point is fixed, moving a distance zero.

Now suppose, vice versa, that at each point P of $\mathcal{E}_3$ there is a vector $\overrightarrow{PP'}$, where P' is determined by P, and that if P and Q are any two points of $\mathcal{E}_3$ then $\overrightarrow{PP'}$ and $\overrightarrow{QQ'}$ agree in length and direction; the set of all these vectors is called a *free vector*, and a particular vector $\overrightarrow{PP'}$ is called the *representative* of the free vector at P. If for each $P \in \mathcal{E}_3$ it is true that $P' = P$, then we speak of the *zero* (free) *vector*.

We have just seen that a translation determines a unique free vector whose representative at each point P is the directed segment from P to its image $T(P)$ under the translation. A free vector, conversely, determines a unique translation T such that if $\overrightarrow{PP'}$ is the representative of the free vector at P then $T(P) = P'$.

On account of the biunique correspondence just established between free vectors and translations, we shall denote a free vector by the letter T.

There is an algebra of free vectors that is similar in every respect to the algebra of the set E_O of all vectors localized at O. Let T be a free vector. If the representative $\overrightarrow{PP'}$ of T at each point P is multiplied by the same scalar a then (cf. C) the resulting vectors $a\overrightarrow{PP'}$ all agree in length and direction and therefore constitute a free vector; we denote this free vector by aT and call it the *product of T by the scalar a*. Let T_1 and T_2 be free vectors. If the respective representatives $\overrightarrow{PP_1}$ and $\overrightarrow{PP_2}$ at each point P are added, then (cf. D) the resulting vectors $\overrightarrow{PP_1} + \overrightarrow{PP_2}$ all agree in length and direction and therefore constitute a free vector; we denote this free vector by $T_1 + T_2$ and call it the *sum* or *resultant* of T_1 and T_2. So defined, the operations of addition of free vectors and multiplication of a free vector by a scalar have all the properties of addition of vectors and multiplication of a vector by a scalar in E_O (cf. C2, D2, and D4).

The process of adding vectors in E_O, as defined in D, may be called the coinitial process, for the vectors to be added necessarily have the same initial point. When adding free vectors, however, we are naturally led to a slightly different process that yields the same result. If T_1 and T_2 are translations, and $P \to T_1(P) = P_1$ and $P_1 \to T_2(P_1) = P_2$, then it is natural to think of P as displaced by T_1 to P_1 and then displaced from P_1 by T_2 to P_2. The resultant

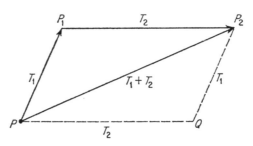

1.1. Resultant of translations; addition of free vectors.

$T_1 + T_2$ is that single translation which carries P onto P_2. This process for adding free vectors may be called the "tail-to-tip" process. It is formulated in the equation

1.2.
$$\overrightarrow{PP_1} + \overrightarrow{P_1P_2} = \overrightarrow{PP_2},$$

which says that if the free vector whose representative at P is $\overrightarrow{PP_1}$ is added to the free vector whose representative at P_1 is $\overrightarrow{P_1P_2}$, then the result is the free vector whose representative at P is $\overrightarrow{PP_2}$.

The tail-to-tip method is often used in mechanics. If there are several vectors, each representing a force, the construction yields a polygon which is called the "polygon of forces". The polygon will be closed (i.e., the terminal point of the last vector will coincide with the initial point of the first vector) if and only if the resultant of the forces is zero.

We shall see in the next chapter (4G8) that the set of all free vectors, with its algebraic structure, is in a certain precise technical sense equivalent (isomorphic) to the set E_P of all vectors issuing from a point P, with its algebraic structure.

2. **Remarks on Vectors in Physics.** While an exhaustive statement is clearly out of the question, a few observations of an illustrative nature may be helpful. For details the student is referred to books on vector or tensor analysis, theoretical mechanics, and theoretical physics.

Let us consider first a *rigid motion*, that is, a displacement of $\mathcal{E}_3$ in which each point P is carried onto a point P' in such a way that orientation (positive or negative) of triads is preserved and all distances are preserved:

$||\overrightarrow{PQ}|| = ||\overrightarrow{P'Q'}||$ for every pair of points P, Q and the points P', Q' onto which they are displaced. Suppose, to begin with, that the displacement has at least one fixed point: $O' = O$. It can then be shown geometrically (Euler did so in 1776) that the displacement consists of a rotation of $\mathcal{E}_3$ about a suitably chosen line through O. Even if there is no fixed point, we can first translate $\mathcal{E}_3$ so as to carry some point O directly to its final position O'; the residual displacement will then have O' as a fixed point and will therefore consist of a rotation about a suitable line through O'. The most general rigid motion of $\mathcal{E}_3$ can therefore be expressed as the resultant of a translation and a rotation.

As a second example, let us consider a system of moving particles. For $j = 1, \ldots, n$ let the jth particle have mass m_j, be located instantaneously at Q_j, have velocity V_j and be acted on by a resultant force Z_j. Now the velocities V_j and forces Z_j are quite naturally considered to have their initial points at Q_j, in other words, to be *localized* at the instantaneous positions of the particles. It turns out, however, to be advantageous to act *as if* they were free vectors with V_j and Z_j as representatives at Q_j. One can then go to any fixed point P_0 and construct there the representatives V_j^0 of the free vectors V_j and the representatives Z_j^0 of the free vectors Z_j. The linear combination $Y = \sum m_j V_j^0$ is called the linear momentum of the system of particles. The vector Y has in most cases a derivative $\overset{\circ}{Y}$ with respect to time; $\overset{\circ}{Y}$ is a vector whose exact definition, which need not concern us here, is entirely similar to that of the derivative $\overset{\circ}{y}$ of a scalar function y of the time, and whose interpretation as a rate of change is also entirely similar. The vector $Z = \sum Z_j^0$ is called the resultant force on the system. The fundamental result, which can be obtained from Newton's laws of motion, is that $\overset{\circ}{Y} = Z$. This equation states that the time-derivative of the linear momentum is equal to the resultant force, a statement which reduces in the case of a single particle to the familiar "mass times acceleration equals force".

It may also be of interest to recognize that the instantaneous centroid $W = m^{-1} \sum m_j Q_j$ of the system, where $m = \sum m_j$ is the total mass of the system, moves in such a way that $m\overset{\circ}{W} = Y$. Hence $m\overset{\circ\circ}{W} = Z$; this equation says that the centroid W moves as though the entire mass m of all the particles were concentrated at W and acted on there by the resultant Z of all the forces Z acting on the separate particles. In other words, Newton's equation "mass times acceleration equals force" is true if "mass" means total mass, "acceleration" means acceleration of the centroid, and "force" means resultant of all forces applied to the system. In this sense Newton's equation is true of a very general class of isolated mechanical systems.

We have seen that the set E_P of all vectors issuing from a point P in $\mathcal{E}_3$ is a satisfactory mathematical model or representation for, say, the set of all possible forces applicable to a moving particle which is instantaneously at P. Is this model equally valid if the particle is not moving independently but is, for example, a point of a rigid body?

Now a non-zero force will be represented by a non-zero vector V. This vector will determine a line $\langle V \rangle$ containing it. If the force is to have any effect at all on the rigid body B, then $\langle V \rangle$ must intersect B. Let us denote by $[V]$ the set of points common to $\langle V \rangle$ and B, assume that V is applied at a point P of $[V]$, and represent this fact by localizing V at P. The essential point is that the effect of V on the behavior of B does not depend on the point P of $[V]$ at which V is localized. The force V may therefore be said to be localized in the set $[V]$. Accepted terminology neglects the fact that many points of the line $\langle V \rangle$ may not be rigidly connected with B and says merely that V is *localized in* its *line* of action $\langle V \rangle$. Sometimes V is described as a *sliding vector*, and any localized vector is sometimes called a *bound* vector. It can be shown that the instantaneous angular velocity of a rigid body may be represented, similarly, by a vector localized in the instantaneous axis of rotation.

Various attempts have been made to use vectorial methods to devise a special mathematical model adequate for a complete study of the dynamics of rigid bodies. The calculus of "motors" is an example; cf., e.g., Frank, P., and R. Von Mises, *Die Differential-und Integralgleichungen der Mechanik und Physik*, 2nd ed. (reprint), Rosenberg, N.Y. (1943), Vol. II, pp. 161–5. No special model, however, has gained widespread acceptance. While vectors are very useful in rigid dynamics, especially in practical problems, some theoretical problems in rigid dynamics may be approached most effectively by the methods of tensor analysis, and these more powerful methods become practically indispensable for a complete analysis of the internal forces and displacements of an elastic body under stress.

3. Vector Fields in $\mathcal{E}_3$. The notion of vectors localized at points is especially prominent in situations in which there is a vector defined at every point of a region of $\mathcal{E}_3$, thus constituting a *vector field*.

To begin with an example, let us regard the earth as a sphere of radius r_0 and mass m, and let us seek to represent the gravitational force exerted by the earth on a unit mass situated at a point distant $r > r_0$ from its center. Newton's law of gravitation says that magnitude of this force, in an appropriate system of units, is m/r^2, and that the force is directed toward the center of the earth. If the origin is taken at the center of the earth, and the point in question has position vector R, so that $\|R\| = r$, then the force may be represented by a vector at R agreeing in direction and norm with

3.1.
$$-\frac{m}{r^2}\hat{R} = -\frac{m}{r^3}R.$$

At every point R outside the surface of the earth, therefore, there is localized a vector, given explicitly by 3.1, which represents the gravitational attraction of the earth on unit mass at R. These vectors constitute a vector field which is defined in the region exterior to the earth. This field is called the *gravitational field* of the earth.

A moving fluid occupying a certain region of space may be said, in a certain sense, to have an instantaneous velocity vector at each point of the region. The class of all these localized vectors forms a vector field, which is called the velocity field of the fluid.

Other examples of fields of velocities, accelerations, forces, and so on, can readily be imagined. Vector fields play an indispensable role in the theory of electromagnetic phenomena.

Let us suppose, as a final example, that we have a scalar point-function F defined over a region. In other words, at each point X of the region there is an associated real number $F(X)$, for example, the temperature at X. If we choose an origin O and an orthonormal basis there, then F will be expressible as a definite function $f(x, y, z)$ of the coordinates of X. If we assume further that f is differentiable then the three numbers

3.2.
$$\frac{\partial f}{\partial x}, \quad \frac{\partial f}{\partial y}, \quad \frac{\partial f}{\partial z},$$

where the derivatives are evaluated at X, can be shown to be the components of a vector at X. This vector is called the *gradient* of F (or of f) at X, and is commonly denoted by ∇F (or ∇f). By carrying through this construction at every point of a region in which f is differentiable we arrive at a vector field. The student may find it entertaining to show, for example, that the gravitational field of the earth given in 3.1 is the gradient of

$$f(x, y, z) = \frac{m_0}{r} = \frac{m_0}{(x^2 + y^2 + x^2)^{1/2}}.$$

It can be shown quite generally that ∇F at a point P is perpendicular to the level surface $F(X) = F(P)$, that it points in the direction in which F increases, and that $\|\nabla F\|$ is equal to the rate of increase of F per unit increase in distance in the direction of ∇F. If F denotes temperature, for example, then under certain circumstances it is a physical law that the flow of heat per unit area normal to ∇F is $-k\,\nabla F$, where k is a positive physical constant.

A vector field, then, consists of a vector $V(Q)$ localized at each point Q of a region of $\mathcal{E}_3$. The vector $V(Q)$, being localized at Q, is an element of the set (three-dimensional linear space) E_Q of all vectors issuing from Q. Now we shall see (4G8) that all these spaces have the same structure. Suppose, however—and this is an important question—that we wish to introduce bases into the various spaces E_Q. Is there any choice of these local bases, one at each point Q, that is clearly convenient or appropriate? Is there any reason to try to relate the local bases at various points in any way to each other?

We can suggest here only a very partial answer to this question. There is, to begin with, no *a priori* overriding reason for insisting on any particular choice of local bases, but calculations involving several points at once would quickly become quite unmanageable if local bases were not assigned in some orderly manner. In many investigations there will be an underlying coordinate system for the region in which the field is defined. It turns out to be convenient, in most such cases, to use at each point vectors tangent at that point to the coordinate curves through the point; that these vectors, except possibly at certain special points, will be independent and therefore useful as a local basis, is a fundamental requirement for a satisfactory underlying coordinate system.

There are three very important special coordinate systems for $\mathcal{E}_3$, each using a fixed origin O. If one has an orthonormal and therefore a rectangular Cartesian coordinate system for $\mathcal{E}_3$, then at every point Q the unit vectors tangent to the coordinate curves constitute a local orthonormal basis; it is this local basis at each point to which the components 3.2 of the gradient are referred. These local bases are all mutually parallel; the one at P will be carried into the one at Q by the translation $\overrightarrow{PQ}$ of $\mathcal{E}_3$.

To set up a spherical coordinate system one constructs the surface of the unit sphere with center at O and sets up coordinates of latitude and longitude on the sphere. Then the coordinates of a point in $\mathcal{E}_3$ may be found by constructing its position vector R with respect to O and then using as coordinates the number $r = \|R\|$ along with the colatitude Q and east longitude φ of the point where the line $\langle R \rangle$ cuts the unit sphere; see 3.3(a). The local bases formed by the unit tangents to the coordinate curves are orthonormal bases.

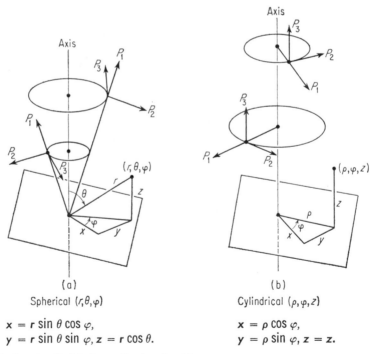

(a)
Spherical (r, θ, φ)

(b)
Cylindrical (ρ, φ, z)

$x = r \sin \theta \cos \varphi,$
$y = r \sin \theta \sin \varphi, z = r \cos \theta.$

$x = \rho \cos \varphi,$
$y = \rho \sin \varphi, z = z.$

3.3. Spherical and cylindrical coordinates; local bases.

One may be visualized for a point on the surface of the earth, with O at its center, as follows: P_1 points toward the zenith while P_2 and P_3 are tangent to the surface of the earth with P_2 pointing south and P_3 east. No local bases are defined on the polar axis of the sphere. Local orthonormal bases at different points cannot, in general, be carried onto each other by the same translation of $\mathcal{E}_3$.

To set up a cylindrical coordinate system, one may start with a rectangular Cartesian coordinate system and set up polar coordinates ρ, φ in the x-y plane. Then the point whose Cartesian coordinates are (x, y, z) has the cylindrical coordinates (ρ, φ, z); see 3.3(b). The local bases formed by unit tangents to the coordinate curves are again orthonormal. P_1 is parallel to the x-y plane and perpendicular to and directed away from the z-axis; P_3 is parallel to and has the same positive direction as the z-axis; $P_2 = P_3 \times P_1$ is parallel to the x-y plane, tangent to the cylinder $\rho = $ constant through the point in question, and points in the direction in which φ increases. No local bases are defined on the z-axis, and local bases at different points cannot, in general, be carried onto each other by the same translation of $\mathcal{E}_3$.

An underlying coordinate system for $\mathcal{E}_3$ (or for a region in $\mathcal{E}_3$) which leads in this way to orthogonal local bases is said to be an orthogonal coordinate system. Such systems are of the very greatest utility in the mathematical study of problems arising in physics and technology.

With local bases related in the indicated manner to an underlying coordinate system, it is natural to ask what change in the local bases is produced by a change in the underlying coordinate system. While the answer is geometrically quite evident, actual calculations turn out to involve the partial derivatives of old and new coordinates with respect to each other. Efforts to systematize these and other calculations led originally to the invention of tensor analysis.

For the extremely interesting and important analysis of vector fields the reader is referred to books on vector and tensor analysis.

FOUR
Systems and Structures

The object of this chapter is to describe further ideas and relationships that will be useful later on. Many examples will be drawn from earlier chapters.

In presenting the idea of a set in 1A we insisted that the term implied a specification of members or a meaningful criterion of membership and nothing more. Examples quickly arose of sets in which an operation of addition was defined, or an operation of multiplication, or both, and we spoke accordingly of the systems N, I, $\Re^*$, and $\Re$. Each of these systems was also ordered (cf. 2D1.1). Let us say quite generally and loosely (technical precision is out of the question here) that a set along with some such organizing principle is a *system*.

The words *structure* and *space* are also used for specific systems. While precise distinctions are not feasible, we may observe that current usage has a tendency to speak of a "structure" when referring (A) to a set in which an operation of an algebraic nature is defined, and of a "space" in referring (B) to a set in which there is a notion of nearness such as, for example, that provided by a way of measuring distances. The set E_P of vectors issuing from a point P in $\mathcal{E}_3$, for example (and the symbol E_P will always have this meaning), is a structure in the sense (A) by virtue of the definition of addition. The same set is a space in sense (B) by virtue of the possibility of measuring the length of each vector. The anomalies of usage are such, however, that the structure E_P, with the further operation of multiplication of a vector by a real number, is called a real linear space!

Several important specific types of systems will be described in this chapter.

A. Products of Sets

We have already encountered the notion of an ordered pair. Suppose now, more generally, that we are given n sets S_k ($k = 1, \ldots, n$), none void. The *product* (sometimes called "Cartesian product") of these sets, in the given order, is defined and denoted as follows:

1. $S_1 \times S_2 \times \ldots \times S_n = \{(x_1, x_2, \ldots, x_n) : x_k \in S_k, k = 1, 2, \ldots, n\}$;

that is, the product consists of all *ordered n-tuples* $x = (x_1, \ldots, x_n)$ with each x_k an element of the respective set S_k. An ordered n-tuple is often written $x = (x_k)$ $(k = 1, \ldots, n)$, and is called a *point* of the product. Equality of points is defined as follows: $(x_k) = (y_k)$ if and only if $x_k = y_k$ $(k = 1, \ldots, n)$.

If $n = 2$ and the sets S_1 and S_2 are represented, in some figurative sense, by the horizontal and vertical sides of a rectangle, then the set $S_1 \times S_2$ is represented in the same sense by the plane area covered by the rectangle, for the points of that area are in 1-1 correspondence with the ordered pairs (x_1, x_2) constituting $S_1 \times S_2$. With this motivation the element x_k is called the *kth coordinate* of $x = (x_1, x_2, \ldots, x_n)$.

If the sets S_k are identical, $S_k = S$ $(k = 1, \ldots, n)$, then we write S^n instead of $S_1 \times \ldots \times S_n$. The *diagonal* of S^n consists of those points $x = (x_k)$ such that $x_k = s \in S$ $(k = 1, \ldots, n)$; that is, each coordinate x_k of x has the same value s.

If f is a function on X into Y then the *graph* of f is that subset of $X \times Y$ consisting of points $(x, f(x))$ with $x \in X$.

B. Binary Operations

A *binary operation* on a set S is a function f on $S \times S$ into S. With each ordered pair (x_1, x_2) with $x_1, x_2 \in S$ there is associated by f a unique element $f(x_1, x_2)$ of S. It is usual to denote the value $f(x_1, x_2)$ of f by some symbol such as $x_1 \circ x_2$, $x_1 \cdot x_2$, $x_1 + x_2$, or simply $x_1 x_2$; we agree to use "$\circ$" as the generic symbol, reserving "$\cdot$", "$+$", and mere juxtaposition for appropriate special purposes.

If $\circ$ is a binary operation on S one speaks of the *system* or *structure* "S with $\circ$" and writes $\{S, \circ\}$; when it is entirely clear what $\circ$ is, one speaks loosely of the system S, implying the presence of $\circ$, as well as of the set S, the latter designation ignoring $\circ$ or not implying its presence.

EXAMPLES

1. In the sets N, I, R^*, and R, addition $a + b$ is a binary operation, and one may therefore speak of the systems or structures $\{N, +\}, \ldots, \{R, +\}$. Similarly, vectorial addition $X + Y$ is a binary operation on E_P, and one may speak of the structure $\{E_P, +\}$.

2. In the sets N, I, R^*, and R, multiplication $a \cdot b$ is a binary operation, and we therefore have the structures $\{N, \cdot\}, \ldots, \{R, \cdot\}$.

3. The operation of forming the vector or cross product $X \times Y$ is a binary operation on E_P, constituting the system $\{E_P, \times\}$. The scalar product $X \cdot Y$, on the contrary, is not a binary operation on E_P; although $E_P \times E_P$ is the domain of $X \cdot Y$, its range is R rather than E_P.

Among the most important properties which a binary operation ∘ may or may not have are those listed in 2C1.1 for numerical addition and multiplication. There is no question about the closure (cf. A1 and M1) of a system $\{S, \circ\}$ under a binary operation ∘, for if x_1, $x_2 \in S$, then the definition of a binary operation implies that $x_1 \circ x_2 \in S$ and closure is automatic.

Many binary operations are associative (cf. A2 and M2), but we saw in the preceding chapter that the cross-product $X \times Y$ of vectors is not, for $(X \times Y) \times Z$ is ordinarily not the same as $X \times (Y \times Z)$. Similarly, $X \times Y$ is perpendicular to both X and Y, whence the existence (cf. A3 and M3) of a single vector U such that $X \times U = X$ for every X is out of the question; it is therefore unreasonable to seek an inverse (cf. A4 and M4). Moreover, $X \times Y \neq Y \times X$ except in very special cases, and the cross-product is therefore not commutative (cf. A5 and M5); in fact, since $X \times Y = -Y \times X$ the cross-product is said to be *anticommutative*.

EXERCISES

4. Let X and Y be nonvoid subsets of a set S and Z a nonvoid subset of T. Prove that, as subsets of $S \times T$:

   (a) $(X \times Z) \cup (Y \times Z) = (X \cup Y) \times Z$;

   (b) $(X \times Z) \cap (Y \times Z) = (X \cap Y) \times Z$.

   What happens to (b) if one side or the other is $\square$; how, in fact, might one define $\square \times U$ for any set U?

5. Let G denote the graph in $X \times Y$ of $f : X \to Y$. Show that $(x, y) \in G$ if and only if $y = f(x)$. Show also that $y \in f(X)$ if and only if $G \cap (X \times \{y\}) \neq \square$. (T)

6. Let S and T denote variable subsets of a set X, that is, $S, T \in 2^X$. Which of the following are binary operations on 2^X: $S \cup T$, $S \cap T$, $S \times T$, $S \cap T'$? Of those that are binary operations, which are associative? Commutative? What is the identity element (if any) for each? When an identity exists, is there necessarily an inverse for each element of 2^X?

7. Define f on X into $X \times X$ as follows: $x \to f(x) = (x, x)$. Show that f sets up a biunique correspondence between X and the diagonal D of $X \times X$. Find a function $h : X \to X$ whose graph is D.

8. Suppose that $E \subset X \times Y$. Show that E is the graph of a (single-valued) function $f : X \to Y$ if and only if for each $x \in X$ there exists a unique corresponding $y \in Y$ such that $E \cap (\{x\} \times Y) = \{(x, y)\}$. (T)

9. Is there any particular vector X in the system $\{E_P, \times\}$ (cf. Example 3) for which there exists a vector Y such that $X \times Y = X$? If so, can there be more than one such Y?

10. In the system $\{E_P, \times\}$, let A and B be given vectors and consider the problem of finding a vector X such that $A \times X = B$. (Note that X must be perpendicular to B. Try a linear combination of $A \times B$ and A. Examine special cases.)

11. Given $f : R \to S$ and $g : S \to T$, define $g \circ f$ on R into T : $(g \circ f)(x) = g(f(x))$. Show that if f and g are both 1–1 then so is $g \circ f$. (This result has already occurred, e.g., just after 1I19.) Bearing in mind that f and g are single-valued, determine whether the converse is true or false. (T)

12. In the context of 11, suppose that $S = T = X$. Show that $\circ$ is an associative binary operation on X^X (cf. 1I26). Produce a set X and mappings f and g on X into X such that $g \circ f \neq f \circ g$.

13. In the context of 11 let $h : T \to U$ also be given. Prove that each member of the following equation is meaningful and that the equation is true.

13.1
$$(h \circ (g \circ f))(x) = ((h \circ g) \circ f)(x).$$

The operation $\circ$ of 11 is often called *composition*, and $g \circ f$ is the *composite* or the *resultant* of f and g in the order (f, g). Composition is a mapping on $T^S \times S^X$ into T^X, and is therefore not a binary operation in the sense of this section except when $X = S = T$ as in 12. In view of 13.1, however, composition is still said to be associative, and the fact expressed in 13.1 is invoked in rather loose language as the *associativity* of *mappings* or of *transformations*. (T)

C. Groups

The technical noun "group" is applied to any structure $\mathcal{G} = \{G, \circ\}$ in which the binary operation $\circ$ is associative, G has an identity element, and each element of G has an inverse. This idea is so important that we write out the details.

1. Properties of a Group. A *group* $\mathcal{G}$ is a system $\{G, \circ\}$ consisting of a set G and a binary operation $\circ$ defined on G in such a way as to have the following properties:

Associativity

A. If $p, q, r \in G$ then $p \circ (q \circ r) = (p \circ q) \circ r$.

Identity Element

E. G has an element e such that if $x \in G$ then $x \circ e = e \circ x = x$.

Inverse

I. For each $x \in G$ there is an element x^{-1} of G such that $x \circ x^{-1} = x^{-1} \circ x = e$.

It can be shown (cf. 4) that e is unique and that x^{-1} is uniquely determined by x. By virtue of E, G is not empty.

A group $\mathcal{G}$ is said to be *commutative* or *abelian* if it has the following further property:

Commutativity

C. If $p, q \in G$ then $p \circ q = q \circ p$.

The system $\{N, +\}$ is not a group; it has property A and, since $0 \in N$, property E, but if $x \in N$ and $x \neq 0$ then x has no inverse in N. The systems $\{I, +\}$, $\{R^*, +\}$ and $\{R, +\}$ are commutative groups, and one speaks of the *additive group* of the integers, rationals, or reals. The use of the sign "$+$" for the binary operation of addition is usual but not mandatory.

None of the systems $\{N, \cdot\}, \ldots, \{R, \cdot\}$ is a group. Each is associative and has an identity element, namely 1, but the particular element 0 has no inverse. If $0 \in S$ let us in this context denote by S_0 the result of deleting 0 from S, i.e., $S_0 = \{0\}'_S$. The systems $\{R_0^*, \cdot\}$ and $\{R_0, \cdot\}$ are commutative groups, and are called respectively the *multiplicative groups* of the rationals and of the reals.

If $G = \{a_1, \ldots, a_n\}$ and $\mathcal{G} = \{G, \circ\}$ is a group, it is sometimes helpful to display the effect of the operation $\circ$ in tabular form, in the manner of a multiplication table. If the element on the left margin is a_p and that on the top margin is a_q, then the entry in the table in the pth row and qth column is $a_p \circ a_q$ *in that order*. If $G = \{e, a, b\}$, then one may verify that $\mathcal{G} = \{G, \circ\}$ is a commutative group if the table for $\circ$ is this:

	e	a	b
e	e	a	b
a	a	b	e
b	b	e	a

As a further example of a group, let us consider the set of those displacements of three-dimensional space $\mathcal{E}_3$ which leave fixed a given point O and have the further property of being *rigid* motions in the sense that orientation of triads is preserved and the distance between any pair of points is the same before and after the displacement. It is proved in books on mechanics, and was mentioned in 3L2, that each such motion consists, unless every point is fixed and the displacement is the identity, of a rotation through a definite angle about a definite axis through the fixed point O. It follows that the image of a straight line is a straight line, that the image of a plane is a plane, that points of intersection are preserved, and that angles are preserved. If we perform a motion, m_1, and follow it by another, m_2, then in the final position the point O is still fixed and distances between pairs of points are still unchanged. It follows that the displacement from the position before m_1 to the position after m_2 is another rigid motion with O fixed. There is therefore a single motion m_3 that accomplishes by one rotation about one axis the whole effect of the rotation demanded by m_1 about its axis followed by the rotation demanded by m_2 about its axis. We call m_3 the resultant of m_1 followed by m_2 and write $m_3 = m_2 \circ m_1$ in that order. If M is the set of all rigid motions of $\mathcal{E}_3$ leaving O fixed then the operation $\circ$ of taking the resultant of m_1 followed by m_2 is a binary operation on M. It is easy to see (cf. B10) that $\circ$ is associative. The identity motion e is that leaving every point fixed; the axis of this "rotation" is undefined, but this is of no consequence since the angle of the "rotation" is zero. The inverse of e is e, while if $m \neq e$ and m consists of rotation through an angle α about a certain axis, then m^{-1} consists of a rotation through an angle $-\alpha$ about the same axis. We conclude that $\{M, \circ\}$ is a group; this group is not abelian (cf. 6).

EXERCISES

2. Why is $\{N_0, \cdot\}$ not a group? Is $\{I_0, \cdot\}$ a group? Why?

3. Prove that the system $\{E_P, +\}$ is an abelian group (cf. 3D2).

4. Let $\mathcal{G} = \{G, \circ\}$ be a group.
  (a) Prove that $e^{-1} = e$, that $(a^{-1})^{-1} = a$, and that $(a \circ b)^{-1} = b^{-1} \circ a^{-1}$.
  (b) Prove that if $a \circ x = a \circ y$ then $x = y$.
  (c) With $a, b \in G$ given, show how to solve the equation $a \circ x = b$. Is the solution unique? Study similarly the equation $y \circ a = b$. (T)

5. Let $\circ$ be a commutative binary operation on a set S. Suppose (cf. property E) that there are elements $f, g \in S$ such that if $s \in S$ then $s \circ f = s$ and $s \circ g = s$. Does it follow, or not, that $f = g$?

6. At the point O in $\mathcal{E}_3$ introduce rectangular Cartesian coordinates (x, y, z). Let m_1 and m_2 denote rotations of 90° about the x-axis and the y-axis respectively. Show that the map of the point $(0, 0, 1)$ under $m_2 \circ m_1$ is $(0, -1, 0)$, while its map under $m_1 \circ m_2$ is $(1, 0, 0)$. The *group* $\{M, \circ\}$ *is therefore not commutative*.

7. In a given plane π let us associate with each pair P, Q of points of π the point $f(P, Q)$ defined to be the midpoint of the segment joining P and Q. Show that f is a binary operation on π. Is this operation commutative? Associative? Is there an identity element?

8. In a plane π let O be a fixed point and if $P \neq Q$ define $P * Q$ to be the perpendicular projection of O onto the line through P and Q; if $P = Q$ define $P * Q$ to be P. Show that $*$ is a binary operation on π. Is it commutative? Associative?

9. In the context of B12 show that if X has at least two elements, then $\{X^X, \circ\}$ is not a group. Produce a mapping $e : X \to X$ such that if $f \in X^X$ then $e \circ f = f \circ e = f$.

10. Still in the context of B12 let B denote that subset of X^X consisting of those mappings f that are 1–1 on X onto X. Prove that $\{B, \circ\}$ is a group. Is this group generally abelian?

D. Subgroups

Let $\mathcal{G} = \{G, \circ\}$ be a group and let H be a nonvoid subset of G. If $f, g \in H$ then $f, g \in G$ and $f \circ g$ is defined and is an element of G; it is clear that $\circ$ will be a binary operation on H if and only if $f, g \in H$ imply $f \circ g \in H$, in other words, H is closed under $\circ$. If this condition is met, then $\{H, \circ\}$ will be called a *substructure* or a *subsystem* of $\{G, \circ\}$.

If $\{H, \circ\}$ is a subsystem of $\{G, \circ\}$ then the operation $\circ$ must naturally be associative on H as it is on G. If the subsystem $\{H, \circ\}$ is itself a group then we say that $\mathcal{K} = \{H, \circ\}$ is a *subgroup* of $\mathcal{G}$. When will $\{H, \circ\}$ be a group? Since the identity element e of G is unique, H must contain e. From this fact it follows that if $b \in H$, then the inverse b^{-1}, calculated in G, must, since it is unique, also belong to H. Vice versa, if $b \in H$ implies that $b^{-1} \in H$, then by closure $e = b \circ b^{-1} \in H$ and $\{H, \circ\}$ is a group. In order that $\{H, \circ\}$ be a group, and hence a subgroup of $\mathcal{G}$, it is therefore necessary and sufficient that H be closed under $\circ$ and that if $b \in H$ then $b^{-1} \in H$, where b^{-1} is the element inverse to b in $\mathcal{G}$.

The groups $\{I, +\}$ and $\{R^*, +\}$ are subgroups of $\{R, +\}$; the trivial group $\{\{0\}, +\}$ is a subgroup of each of these groups. The group $\{R_0^*, \cdot\}$ is a subgroup of the group $\{R_0, \cdot\}$.

EXERCISES

1. If $\{H, \circ\}$ is a subgroup of $\mathcal{G} = \{G, \circ\}$, then $a, b \in H$ clearly imply that $a \circ b^{-1} \in H$. Prove conversely that if this condition is satisfied then $\{H, \circ\}$ is a subgroup of $\mathcal{G}$. (T)

2. In the additive group $\{E_0, +\}$ show that each subset xP ($P \neq 0$, $-\infty < x < \infty$) and each subset $xP + yQ$ (P and Q independent, $-\infty < x, y < \infty$) is a subgroup.

3. Since G is a subset of G, $\{G, \circ\}$ is a subgroup of $\mathcal{G} = \{G, \circ\}$ which is, so to speak, the "largest" subgroup of $\mathcal{G}$. Show that $E = \{\{e\}, \circ\}$ is a subgroup of $\mathcal{G}$; this is the "smallest" subgroup of $\mathcal{G}$, and may be called the trivial subgroup. Consider the group $\mathcal{G}$ with $G = \{e, a, b\}$ whose table is displayed in C; does it have any subgroups other than $\mathcal{G}$ and E?

4. Let P denote the set of positive rational numbers. Show that if $\cdot$ denotes numerical multiplication then $\{P, \cdot\}$ is a group and is a subgroup of $\{R_0^*, \cdot\}$ and of $\{R_0, \cdot\}$.

5. In the group M_O of rigid motions of $\mathcal{E}_3$ leaving O fixed, let L denote the subset of those rigid motions consisting of rotations about a fixed line ℓ through O. Prove that L is a subgroup of M_O. It is evident that each point of ℓ is fixed under each motion of L. Is there any point not on ℓ that is fixed under each motion of L?

6. In 5 each point on ℓ is fixed under each motion of L, and ℓ is therefore said to be *pointwise invariant under L*. A configuration C is said to be *invariant under L* if each point of C is mapped by each motion of L onto some point of C (not necessarily itself). Exploit the fact that distances and angles are preserved under each transformation of L to find some configurations that are invariant under L, for example, planes perpendicular to ℓ.

7. In the context of C10, let S be a subset of X and let B_S consist of those elements of B that leave each point of S fixed. Is $\{B_S, \circ\}$ a subgroup of $\{B, \circ\}$? Let G_S consist of those elements of B that map S onto itself (that is, $f(S) = S$, each point of S is mapped onto a point of S). Is $\{G_S, \circ\}$ a subgroup of $\{B, \circ\}$?

E. Permutations

Let X be a given set and let B denote the set of all biunique correspondences of X with itself. If f, $g \in B$ and we define $g \circ f$, calling it the *product* of g and f in that order, to be that function h on X into X whose value for $x \in X$ is $h(x) = g(f(x))$, then $h \in B$, $\circ$ is a binary operation on B, and $\{B, \circ\}$ was shown in C10 to be a group.

We are interested here in the special case in which X is *finite*. If X has n distinct elements, we label them $a_1, \ldots, a_n$. Then $f : X \to X$ tells us for instance that $f(a_k) = a_l$, and this information is equivalent to the information that the value l of the index corresponds to the value k. We therefore lose nothing by assuming that $X = \{1, \ldots, n\}$, and that f is one-to-one on X onto $X : k \leftrightarrow f(k)$ $(k = 1, \ldots, n)$. Each such mapping is called a *permutation* or a *reordering* of the elements of X or of n objects. We develop here certain properties of permutations that will be needed later.

Let P denote the set of all permutations of X. The group $\{P, \circ\}$ is called the *symmetric group of order n* and is denoted by S_n or $\{S_n, \circ\}$. Since $f(1)$ may be chosen in n ways, then $f(2)$ in $n - 1$ ways, and so on, we see that S_n has $n!$ elements. The groups S_1 and S_2 are rather trivial; S_3 is not abelian and it follows that neither is S_n in general.

We abbreviate $f(k)$ to f_k and display the values of f as follows: $f_1, \ldots, f_n$. The ordered n-tuple $f_1, \ldots, f_n$ is a rearrangement of X, and the name "permutation" is sometimes given to the n-tuple instead of to f. Since f and the ordered n-tuple determine each other uniquely, the resulting ambiguity is harmless so long as we keep in mind that an element f of S_n is the correspondence $k \to f_k$ and not really the result of that process (the ordered n-tuple). At the same time, it is often briefer and more picturesque to describe a permutation in terms of its effect on the n-tuple rather than in functional notation.

Suppose, for example, that $n = 4$, that the values of f are 3, 1, 4, 2, and that the values of g are 2, 4, 1, 3. If $h = g \circ f$ then $h(1) = g(f(1)) = g(3) = 1$, $h(2) = g(f(2)) = g(1) = 2$, $h(3) = 3$, and $h(4) = 4$. It turns out therefore that h is the identity mapping e, with $e_k = k$ $(k = 1, \ldots, 4)$; hence $g = f^{-1}$ and $f = g^{-1}$. We may also describe $h = g \circ f$ by examining the effect of g on the ordered quadruple f_k of values of f as follows: For $k = 1, \ldots, 4$, the value of h_k is obtained by putting into the kth position that integer occupying the f_kth position in g; thus $h(k) = g(f(k))$.

An *inversion* is said to occur in a permutation $f_1, \ldots, f_n$ whenever $j < k$ and $f_j > f_k$. Let us count the inversions in the permutation g whose values are 2, 6, 4, 1, 3, 5; since 2 precedes 1, 6 precedes 4, 1, 3, and 5, and 4 precedes 1 and 3, this permutation has seven inversions. Similarly, the permutation h with values 4, 1, 3, 5, 6, 2 has six inversions. We denote by J_f the number of inversions occurring in the permutation f; thus $J_g = 7$ and $J_h = 6$.

The *sign* of a permutation f is denoted by $sg(f)$ and is defined to be

1.
$$sg(f) = (-1)^{J_f}.$$

Thus $sg(f) = +1$ or -1 according as the number of inversions occurring in f is even or odd, and f itself is said to be *even* or *odd* in the respective cases. For the permutations g and h of the preceding paragraph we have $sg(g) = (-1)^7 = -1$ and $sg(h) = (-1)^6 = +1$; thus g is odd and h is even.

The value of $sg(f)$ depends only on f. At the same time, $sg(f)$ is connected in an important way with the possibility of factoring or decomposing f into permutations that may be simpler. No permutation except the identity can be simpler than the interchange of two integers. In fact, S_2 has only two elements, the identity e, with values 1, 2, and the permutation f with values 2, 1, and f consists of interchanging 1 and 2. A permutation that leaves fixed all but two elements of X (not necessarily adjacent) and interchanges those two is called a *transposition*.

We have seen that each permutation in S_2 except the identity can be accomplished by transposition (indeed, by one transposition). If t is any transposition, moreover, then $t^2 = e$ so that even the identity e can be accomplished by repeating the same transposition twice.

Now assume, arguing by induction, that each permutation belonging to S_n can be accomplished by transpositions, and let f be a permutation belonging to S_{n+1} with the values $f_1, \ldots, f_n, f_{n+1}$. Either $n + 1$ is in the $(n + 1)$th position, so that $f_{n+1} = n + 1$, or it may be placed there by one transposition. If $n + 1 \neq f_{n+1}$, in fact, then $n + 1 = f_h$ for some h in the range $1, \ldots, n$; when f_h and f_{n+1} are interchanged, then $n + 1$ is in the $(n + 1)$th position. With $n + 1$ in the $(n + 1)$th position the positions $1, \ldots, n$ are occupied by a rearrangement of $1, \ldots, n$. Since this rearrangement is the result of a permutation belonging to S_n, and by hypothesis can therefore be accomplished by transpositions, it follows that f can be accomplished by transpositions. If $n \geq 2$ then *every permutation belonging to S_n can be accomplished by transpositions*.

Let us try by transpositions to rearrange the integers $1, \ldots, 6$ in the order resulting from the permutation h, mentioned earlier, having values 4, 1, 3, 5, 6, 2. The following four transpositions performed in turn lead to the desired result: 2 and 1, 2 and 4, 2 and 5, and 2 and 6. The following six transpositions performed in turn give the same result less quickly (cf. 12): 5 and 4, 4 and 3, 3 and 6, 3 and 2, 4 and 1, and 1 and 3. The number of transpositions in each case, however, is even, corresponding to the fact that h is even as defined above. We shall prove the following theorem.

2. **Theorem.** If $t_1, \ldots, t_T$ are transpositions and $f \in S_n$ is a permutation such that $f = t_T \circ \ldots \circ t_1$ then $(-1)^T = (-1)^{J_f}$.

Since the identity e has no inversions, $J_e = 0$ and $sg(e) = 1$. It will suffice to show that if $h \in S_n$ and t is any transposition then $sg(t \circ h) = -sg(h)$.

Let the result of h be $h_1, \ldots, h_n$, and let t consist in interchanging h_p and h_{p+q} ($q \geq 1$). We shall analyze t into *steps* in which two *adjacent* elements are interchanged. If h_p takes q successive steps to the right then it is in position $p + q$, and each of the terms $h_{p+1}, \ldots, h_{p+q}$ has taken one step to the left. If h_{p+q}, now in position $p + q - 1$, takes $q - 1$ steps to the left, then, as desired, it arrives at position p and the elements $h_{p+1}, \ldots, h_{p+q-1}$ are restored to their initial positions, completing the transposition t.

Now each step either creates or destroys a single inversion involving the two adjacent elements interchanged and leaves each other inversion unaltered. Hence each step changes the sign of the permutation. Since the number of steps required to effect t is $2q - 1$, it follows as claimed that $sg(t \circ h) = (-1)^{2q-1} sg(h) = -sg(h)$ and the proof is complete.

3. Corollary. If $f \in S_n$ and f is the product of T transpositions then $(-1)^T = sg(f)$.

We see, therefore, that a decomposition of a permutation f into transpositions will involve the product of an even or an odd number of transpositions according as f is even or odd. In other words, if $f \in S_n$ and $f = t_T \circ \ldots \circ t_1 = u_U \circ \ldots \circ u_1$, where the t's and u's are transpositions, then T and U have the same parity, that of f. The product of two permutations of like sign is accordingly an even permutation, while the product of two permutations of unlike sign is odd; in other words, $sg(g \circ f) = sg(g) \cdot sg(f)$.

EXERCISES

4. Enumerate the elements of S_3, determine the sign of each, and write out their multiplication table. Obtain all subgroups of S_3.

5. List all even permutations of four objects.

6. Prove that every transposition is an odd permutation.

7. For each of the following elements f of S_5, calculate J_f and $sg(f)$, and express f as a product of transpositions: 3, 2, 5, 1, 4; 4, 2, 1, 5, 3; 2, 5, 1, 4, 3.

8. Let A_n be the set of even permutations of n objects; prove that $\{A_n, \circ\}$ is a subgroup of $\{S_n, \circ\}$. (A_n is often called the *alternating group* on n objects.) (T)

9. Let $f \in S_n$ and suppose that φ_f integers are fixed under f, that is, $f_k = k$ for φ_f values of k. Prove that f can be expressed as the product of at most $n - \varphi_f - 1$ transpositions.

10. Let $X = \{1, 2, 3, 4\}$, let e denote the identity, let (p, q) denote the transposition which interchanges p and q, and let $a = (1, 2) \circ (3, 4)$, $b = (1, 3) \circ (2, 4)$, and $c = (1, 4) \circ (2, 3)$. Prove that $F = \{\{e, a, b, c\}, \circ\}$ forms a subgroup of S_4. Write out the multiplication table of F. Is F a subgroup of A_4 (cf. 8)? (The group F, often called the *four group*, is the group of symmetries of a non-square rectangle with its vertices labelled 1, 2, 3, and 4.)

11. *The alternating function* of variables x_k ($k = 1, \ldots, n$) is $\prod\limits_{q>p} (x_q - x_p)$ ($p, q = 1, \ldots, n$). For $f \in S_n$ define $A(n; f) = \prod\limits_{q>p} (f_q - f_p)$. Prove that $|A(n; f)| = 1! \, 2! \ldots (n-1)!$ and that $A(n; f) = (-1)^{J_f} |A(n, f)|$.

F. Fields

The familiar systems N, I, $\mathcal{R}^*$, and $\mathcal{R}$ each involve two binary operations, addition and multiplication. With these operations the sets R^* and R constitute structures having the properties 2C1.1. Each of these structures is called a field; we proceed to define this concept precisely.

Let F be a set with at least two elements on which a binary operation $\circ$ is defined in such a way that $\{F, \circ\}$ *is an abelian group*. Let e_0 denote the identity element of $\{F, \circ\}$, and let F_0 denote F with e_0 omitted: $F_0 = \{e_0\}'_F$. Let there be defined on F a second binary operation, denoted by $*$, in such a way that $\{F_0, *\}$ *is an abelian group*. Suppose further that $*$ *is distributive with respect to* $\circ$ in the sense that for each a, b, $c \in F$ it is true (cf. 2C1.1, MDA) that

1.
$$a * (b \circ c) = (a * b) \circ (a * c).$$

The structure constituted by F, $\circ$, and $*$ is called a *field* and is denoted by $\mathcal{F} = \{F, \circ, *\}$.

The group $\{F, \circ\}$ is called the *additive group* of $\mathcal{F}$; the symbol "$+$" is ordinarily used instead of "$\circ$", and the additive group is then denoted by $\{F, +\}$. The group $\{F_0, *\}$ is called the *multiplicative group* of $\mathcal{F}$; the symbol "$\cdot$" is ordinarily used instead of "$*$", and the multiplicative group is then denoted by $\{F_0, \cdot\}$. The multiplicative "$\cdot$" is often omitted, $a \cdot b$ being abbreviated to ab.

A set with two elements, say 0 and 1, may be made into a field by defining "$+$" and "$\cdot$" as follows:

$$0 + 0 = 0, \quad 0 + 1 = 1, \quad 1 + 1 = 0;$$
$$0 \cdot 0 = 0, \quad 0 \cdot 1 = 0, \quad 1 \cdot 1 = 1.$$

This field may be called the *trivial* field; it has nontrivial applications.

The structures $\{R^*, +, \cdot\}$ and $\{R, +, \cdot\}$ are fields by virtue of 2C and 2D; one speaks respectively of the *rational field* $\mathcal{R}^*$ and the real field $\mathcal{R}$. The additive group of the field $\mathcal{R}^*$, for example, is $\{R^*, +\}$; the multiplicative group of the field $\mathcal{R}$ is $\{R_0, \cdot\}$.

The structures $\{N, +, \cdot\}$ and $\{I, +, \cdot\}$ are not fields, for they do not have property M4 of 2C1.1. These structures nevertheless have interesting algebraic properties into which we shall not go. The structure I, for example, is an instance of the general concept of a "ring" and has, moreover, certain further properties by virtue of which it is an "integral domain". The structure $\mathcal{R}^*$ can be constructed from the structure I by a process that can be generalized so as to generate from any integral domain D a field that contains D in the same sense that $\mathfrak{R}^*$ contains I; for details see [A6, Chap. 2].

The theory of rings, domains of integrity, and fields has been developed extensively and is discussed in books on modern algebra. We must be content here to use the real field $\mathfrak{R}$ to construct the field $\mathcal{C}$, or $\{C, +, \cdot\}$, of complex numbers and to develop a few of its properties. Our later work will use primarily the fields $\mathfrak{R}$ and $\mathcal{C}$.

EXERCISES

2. Prove that $\{R^*, +\}$ is a subgroup of $\{R, +\}$ and that $\{R_o^*, \cdot\}$ is a subgroup of $\{R_o, \cdot\}$. In view of these facts the field $\{R^*, +, \cdot\}$ is said to be a *subfield* of $\{R, +, \cdot\}$.

3. Let S_2 denote the set of all numbers $s \in R$ such that $s = a + b\sqrt{2}$ with $a, b \in R^*$. Let $+$ and $\cdot$ have the same meanings on S_2 that they have in $\mathfrak{R}$. Prove that the structure $S_2 = \{S_2, +, \cdot\}$ is a field. Is S_2 a subfield of $\mathfrak{R}$?

4. For $n = 3, 4, 5, \ldots$, and $S_n = \{s : s = a + b\sqrt{n} \text{ with } a, b \in R^*\}$, study the structure $S_n = \{S_n, +, \cdot\}$.

5. Let $\{F, \circ, *\}$ be a field and let e_o denote the identity element of the group $\{F, \circ\}$. Prove that if $a \in F$ then $a * e_o = e_o * a = e_o$.

G. Isomorphism

Our understanding of the field of complex numbers, as well as of certain structures already introduced, will be facilitated by using biunique mappings which have the further property of relating to each other in a special way the structures of the domain and codomain.

Consider, for example, the set I and the set I_2 of even integers, displayed as follows:

$$\ldots, -n, \ldots, -3, -2, -1, 0, 1, 2, 3, \ldots, p, \ldots$$
$$\ldots, -2n, \ldots, -6, -4, -2, 0, 2, 4, 6, \ldots, 2p, \ldots.$$

The structures $\mathcal{I} = \{I, +\}$ and $\mathcal{I}_2 = \{I_2, +\}$ are both groups; in fact, $\mathcal{I}_2$ is a subgroup of $\mathcal{I}$. The correspondence $q \leftrightarrow 2q$ on I onto I_2 is clearly biunique. How does the group operation behave under this correspondence?

Suppose that $p \leftrightarrow 2p$ and $q \leftrightarrow 2q$; what is the map of $p + q$? Evidently, $2(p + q)$. But $2(p + q) = (2p) + (2q)$, and this is the sum of the images $2p$ of p and $2q$ of q; *the sum of the maps is the map of the sum.*

A second example may be based on the additive group $\{R, +\}$ of real numbers and the multiplicative group $\{P, \cdot\}$ of positive real numbers; here $x \in P$ if $x \in R$ and $x > 0$. Fix $b > 1$ and take logarithms always to the base b. Let $r \in R$ and $p \in P$ correspond to each other if $r = \log p$. This correspondence between R and P is biunique. If $s = \log q$, moreover, then $r + s = \log(p \cdot q)$; *the sum in* $\{R, +\}$ *of the maps is the map of the product in* $\{P, \cdot\}$.

Motivated by these two instances, we define groups $\{G, \circ\}$ and $\{H, *\}$ to be *isomorphic* (literally, same in structure) if there exists a biunique correspondence between G and H of such a nature that if $g, g' \in G$ and $h, h' \in H$ and $g \leftrightarrow h$ and $g' \leftrightarrow h'$, then

1.
$$g \circ g' \leftrightarrow h * h'.$$

$\mathcal{G}$ and $\mathcal{G}_2$ are isomorphic by virtue of the correspondence $q \leftrightarrow 2q$; $\{P, \cdot\}$ and $\{R, +\}$ are isomorphic by virtue of the correspondence $p \leftrightarrow \log p$.

Similarly, fields $\{G, +, \cdot\}$ and $\{H, \circ, *\}$ are said to be *isomorphic* if there exists a biunique correspondence between G and H of such a nature that if $g \leftrightarrow h$ and $g' \leftrightarrow h'$, then

2.
$$g + g' \leftrightarrow h \circ h' \qquad \text{and} \qquad g \cdot g' \leftrightarrow h * h'.$$

Quite generally, but rather loosely, we call two structures isomorphic if there exists a biunique structure-preserving correspondence between them. The correspondence itself is also said to be an *isomorphic* correspondence and is called an *isomorphism*. An isomorphism between a structure and itself is called an *automorphism*.

When choosing a specific structure for a specific purpose one may first settle upon a desired pattern of structural characteristics. There may then exist several mutually isomorphic structures having the desired characteristics, and a choice may be made between them on grounds of simplicity or some other advantage. In arithmetical computation, for example, one may pass at will from multiplication to addition by using logarithms, reverting to multiplication by exponentiation.

The same point may be stated a little differently by observing that it is enough to study *one* of a family of isomorphic structures in order to learn the common structural characteristics of all. As an illustration we state without proof a famous theorem of Cayley: *Every finite group is isomorphic with a group of permutations*; more precisely, if G is a group having n elements, then the symmetric group S_n (cf. 4E) has a subgroup isomorphic with G (see 7). Instead of studying a particular finite group, therefore, one may study the isomorphic group of permutations. By studying all groups S_n and their subgroups one is really studying all finite groups.

EXERCISES

3. Let I_m denote the set of all integral multiples of a fixed positive integer m, and let $\mathcal{G}_m$ denote the group $\{I_m, +\}$. Prove that $\mathcal{G}_m$ and $\mathcal{G} = \{I, +\}$ are isomorphic.

4. Let $\{G, \circ\}$ and $\{H, *\}$ be isomorphic groups. Prove that in any isomorphism between them the respective identity elements must correspond to each other. Do corresponding elements necessarily have corresponding inverses? (T)

5. With $\{R, +\}$ and $\{P, \cdot\}$ as in the second example in the text, and with fixed $b > 1$, study the mapping $x \to b^x$ on R onto P. Is it biunique? Is it an isomorphism?

6. Suppose that the groups $\{F, \circ\}$ and $\{G, *\}$ are isomorphic and that the groups $\{G, *\}$ and $\{H, \#\}$ are isomorphic. Prove that the groups $\{F, \circ\}$ and $\{H, \#\}$ are isomorphic.

7. Let $\{A, \circ\}$ be a finite group with identity $e = a_1$ and other elements $a_2, \ldots, a_n$. Associate with a_k ($k = 1, \ldots, n$) the mapping $g_k : A \to A$ such that $x \to g_k(x) = a_k \circ x$. Show that each g_k is a permutation of A. Let $G = \{g_k : a_k \in A\}$ and define a binary operation $*$ on G by agreeing that if $x \in A$ then $(g_h * g_k)(x) = g_h(g_k(x))$. Prove that $\{G, *\}$ is a group and is isomorphic to $\{A, \circ\}$.

8. It was shown in 3D2ff. that the structure $\{E_P, +\}$ is an abelian group and in 3L1 that the same is true of the structure $\{V, +\}$ where V denotes the set of all free vectors in $\mathcal{E}_3$. Prove that for each $P \in \mathcal{E}_3$ the structures $\{E_P, +\}$ and $\{V, +\}$ are isomorphic. Prove also that if $P, Q \in \mathcal{E}_3$ then the structures $\{E_P, +\}$ and $\{E_Q, +\}$ are isomorphic.

9. Let $\{G, \circ\}$ denote a group. Show that if $a \in G$ then the mapping $f_a : x \to a \times a^{-1}$ is an automorphism of G.

H. The Complex Field; Polynomials

In high school one studies quadratic equations of the form $ax^2 + bx + c = 0$ where $a, b, c \in R$. Some such equations, for example, the equation $x^2 + 1 = 0$, have no real solution. By introducing (perhaps in a somewhat mysterious way) an entity i, with the rather startling property that $i^2 = -1$, one is able to show that every quadratic equation with real coefficients such that $b^2 - 4ac < 0$ has two solutions of the form $p \pm qi$ with $p, q \in R$.

Starting with the system $\mathfrak{R}$ of Chap. 2 as given, we here *define* a complex number as an ordered pair of real numbers, so that the complex numbers are in biunique correspondence with the points of a plane having a rectangular Cartesian coordinate system. The algebraic operations on complex numbers are so defined as to have certain very natural geometric interpretations. That $i^2 = -1$ is not at all startling, but rather an unavoidable consequence of the definition of i and the algebraic operations.

Let C denote the set of ordered pairs $z = (x, y)$ with $x, y \in R$ and $z' = (x', y') = z$ if and only if $x = x'$ and $y = y'$; each ordered pair is called a *complex number*. Thus $C = R \times R$ in the sense of 1I24. Let x and y be interpreted as rectangular Cartesian coordinates in a plane, with the same unit of distance on both axes. Then the points of the plane are in biunique correspondence with the ordered pairs (x, y) and therefore with the elements z of the set C. We may therefore speak without confusion of the point z

(in the plane) and in this context the plane itself is often called the *complex plane*.

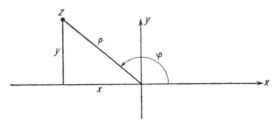

The name "complex number" implies that numerical operations can be defined for complex numbers. This anticipation is confirmed by the following definitions. Let $z = (x, y)$ and $z' = (x', y')$; then we define

1.
$$z + z' = (x + x', y + y'),$$

2.
$$z \cdot z' = (xx' - yy', xy' + yx').$$

For example,

$$(2, -1) + (-5, 3) = (2 - 5, -1 + 3) = (-3, 2)$$

$$(2, -1) \cdot (-5, 3) = (2(-5) - (-1)3, 2(3) + (-1)(-5)) = (-7, 11).$$

Both addition and multiplication are clearly binary operations on C (cf. B). The geometric interpretation of addition is evidently this: $z + z'$ is the point whose position vector with respect to the origin is the vectorial sum of the position vectors of z and of z' with respect to the origin. An equally illuminating interpretation of multiplication will be given presently.

That the structure $\{C, +\}$ is an abelian group is almost obvious. The associative law follows from the associative law for addition in $\{R, +\}$. The identity element of $\{C, +\}$ is evidently $(0, 0)$ (cf. the "zero vector"), and $(x, y) + (-x, -y) = (0, 0)$ so that $(-x, -y)$ is the additive inverse of (x, y).

Similarly, $\{C_0, \cdot\}$ is an abelian group. Its identity element is $(1, 0)$ and the multiplicative inverse of $z = (x, y)$ is (when $z \neq 0$)

3.
$$z^{-1} = \left(\frac{x}{x^2 + y^2}, \frac{-y}{x^2 + y^2} \right).$$

It is easy to verify that if u, v, $w \in C$ then $u \cdot (v + w) = u \cdot v + u \cdot w$. Hence *the structure* $\mathcal{C} = \{C, +, \cdot\}$ *is a field*.

Having recorded the conceptual distinction between the set R and the field $\mathcal{R} = \{R, +, \cdot\}$, and that between the set $C = R \times R$ and the field $\mathcal{C} = \{C, +, \cdot\}$, we simplify notation by discarding the script letters. The letter "R" (or "C") may mean either the set of real (or complex) numbers or the real (or complex) field.

Now let us examine the set S of all $z = (x, y)$ having $y = 0$. It follows at once from 1 that $\{S, +\}$ is a group and a subgroup of $\{C, +\}$. From 2 it follows similarly that $\{S_0, \cdot\}$ is a group and a subgroup of $\{C_0, \cdot\}$. Multi-

106

plication in S is distributive with respect to addition because it is distributive in C. Hence $\{S, +, \cdot\}$ is a field; it may be called a subfield of $\{C, +, \cdot\}$ (cf. F2).

In the complex plane each point $(x, 0) \in S$ lies on the x-axis; conversely, to each point on the x-axis there corresponds a unique complex number $(x, 0) \in S$. We have already seen in 2D3, however, that the points of the x-axis are in biunique correspondence with the real numbers. It follows, and is indeed evident directly, that the correspondence

4.
$$x \leftrightarrow (x, 0)$$

between $x \in R$ and $(x, 0) \in S$ is biunique.

In order to see that this correspondence is an isomorphism let us denote addition and multiplication in R by $\oplus$ and $\circ$. If $x \leftrightarrow (x, 0)$ and $y \leftrightarrow (y, 0)$ then

5.
$$x \oplus y \leftrightarrow (x, 0) + (y, 0),$$

6.
$$x \circ y \leftrightarrow (x, 0) \cdot (y, 0).$$

To prove the second relation, for example, we observe first that the map of $x \circ y$ is $(x \circ y, 0) \in S$; by 2, $(x \circ y, 0) = (x, 0) \cdot (y, 0)$; 6 follows because the mapping is biunique.

Since $\{R, +, \circ\}$ and $\{S, +, \circ\}$ are isomorphic, we simply say that the complex number $(x, 0)$ is real, denote it by x, and observe that if $z = (u, v)$ then

$$xz = (x, 0) \cdot (u, v) = (xu, xv).$$

It follows that

$$(x, y) = x(1, 0) + y(0, 1),$$

or, since we are replacing $(1, 0)$ by 1, and $x \circ 1 = x$,

$$(x, y) = x + y(0, 1).$$

The great algebraic advantage of C over R can be traced to the behavior of the element $(0, 1)$. It is easy to verify that

$$(0, 1)^2 = (0, 1) \cdot (0, 1) = (-1, 0) = -1.$$

We introduce the special symbol i as an abbreviation for $(0, 1)$ (electrical engineers use j instead of i). Thus $i^2 = -1$. We may now write

7.
$$z = (x, y) = x + yi.$$

The real numbers x and y are called respectively the *real part* and the *imaginary part* of z, and are denoted, as functions of z, by $Re(z)$ and $Im(z)$. A complex number $x + iy$ is said to be *real* if $y = 0$ and *imaginary* if $x = 0$. In the complex plane the x-axis is called the *real axis* and the y-axis is called the *imaginary axis*. The adjective "imaginary", regrettably sanctioned by enduring usage, has a strictly technical meaning and not the slightest connotation of the visionary or fanciful.

Now let ρ and φ denote the usual radial and angular polar coordinates of the point z in the complex plane. Then

8. $$z = x + iy = \rho \cos \varphi + i\rho \sin \varphi = \rho(\cos \varphi + i \sin \varphi).$$

The non-negative real number $\rho = \sqrt{x^2 + y^2}$ is called the *modulus*, or *norm*, or *absolute value* of z and is denoted by $|z|$. If $z = 0$ then $|z| = 0$ and the corresponding angle φ is not defined; if $z \neq 0$ the angle φ is defined up to an integral multiple of 2π, is called the *phase* or the *amplitude* of z, and is denoted by ph z or am z.

It is easy to verify that

9. $\rho(\cos \varphi + i \sin \varphi) \cdot \rho'(\cos \varphi' + i \sin \varphi') = \rho\rho'[\cos (\varphi + \varphi') + i \sin (\varphi + \varphi')].$

The geometric interpretation of multiplication of complex numbers is now evident: *the norm of the product is the product of the norms, while the phase of the product is the sum of the phases.* In symbols, $|zz'| = |z| |z'|$ and ph $zz' = $ ph $z + $ ph z'. The effect of multiplying by a complex number of norm ρ and phase φ is therefore to stretch radially by the factor ρ and rotate about the origin through the angle φ.

It is possible to give a precise definition of exponentiation for complex numbers. The general definition requires, however, ideas that we cannot develop here, and one consequence of the definition, moreover, is that if $a, b \in C$ and $a \neq 0$, then there are infinitely many values of a^b unless b is real and rational. We need, fortunately enough, only a very special result, namely Euler's formula

10. $$e^{it} = \cos t + i \sin t \qquad (t \text{ real})$$

and its consequences. It is agreed here that the functions appearing are the sums of the familiar power series for e^x, $\sin \theta$, and $\cos \theta$ when x is replaced by it and θ by t; it can be shown that the series converge for all values of the variables. It can be shown, moreover, if u is also real, that

11. $$e^{it} \cdot e^{iu} = e^{i(t+u)}, \ (e^{it})^u = e^{itu}.$$

Euler's equation can be used with 8 to write

12. $$z = \rho e^{i\varphi} = |z| e^{i \, \text{ph} \, z}.$$

Either of the equivalent representations 8 or 12 is called the *polar representation* of z, while $x + iy$ is called its *Cartesian representation*.

If $z = x + iy = \rho e^{i\varphi}$ then the complex number *conjugate* to z is denoted by $\bar{z}$ and is defined to be

13. $$\bar{z} = x - iy = \rho e^{-i\varphi}.$$

It is easy to show that

14. $$\text{Re} \, (z) = \frac{1}{2}(z + \bar{z}), \qquad \text{Im} \, (z) = \frac{1}{2i}(z - \bar{z}),$$

15. $$z\bar{z} = |z|^2, \qquad \overline{z \cdot w} = \bar{z} \cdot \bar{w}.$$

We have already observed that while the equation $x^2 + 1 = 0$ has no solution $x \in R$, the equation $z^2 + 1 = 0$ has the solution $z = i \in C$ and, of course, the solution $z = -i$ as well. It is remarkable that the ability to solve this simple equation brings with it the ability to solve, not merely the quadratic equations mentioned earlier, but any algebraic equation having coefficients in C.

The field C *cannot* be ordered in the sense of 2D1.1; the proof of this result is beyond our means here.

A *polynomial* is a function f on C into C whose value $f(z)$ for each z in C is given by a formula

16.
$$f(z) = a_0 + a_1 z + a_2 z^2 + \ldots + a_{n-1} + a_n z^n = {}_k\sum_0^n a_k z^k$$

where the coefficients $a_0, \ldots, a_n$ are complex constants. If all the a's are zero then $f(z) = 0$ for all values of z and we may write $f = 0$. If $f \neq 0$ then $a_k \neq 0$ for some value of k; if n is the greatest value of k such that $a_k \neq 0$, then n is the *degree* of f and a_n is its *leading coefficient*. If $f = 0$ then the degree of f is undefined. An *algebraic equation* of degree n is an equation

17.
$$f(z) = 0,$$

where f is a polynomial of degree n. A complex number r such that $f(r) = 0$ is called a *root* of the equation or a *zero* of the polynomial.

If f is of degree zero then its value is the constant $a_0 \neq 0$ and the equation $f(z) = 0$ is inconsistent. *If f is of degree $n \geq 1$ and has complex coefficients then f has a complex zero.* Most proofs of this "Fundamental Theorem of Algebra", due originally to Euler and Gauss, involve non-algebraic concepts.

Accepting the preceding theorem without proof, we base upon it deductions involving the notion of divisibility of polynomials: if f, g, and h are polynomials and it is true for each $z \in \mathcal{C}$ that $f(z) \cdot g(z) = h(z)$ then we say that f and g are *divisors* or *factors* of h. For example, since (cf. 2C1.6)

$$(z - r)(z^{n-1} + z^{n-2}r + \ldots + zr^{n-2} + r^{n-1}) = z^n - r^n,$$

$z - r$ is a factor of $z^n - r^n$ $(n = 1, 2, 3, \ldots)$.

Now let f be a polynomial of degree $n \geq 1$ and suppose that $f(r) = 0$. Then, for each $z \in C$,

$$f(z) = f(z) - f(r) = {}_k\sum_1^n a_k(z^k - r^k) = (z - r) \sum_{k=1}^{n} a_k \sum_{j=1}^{k} z^{k-j} r^{j-1}.$$

We conclude that *if r is a zero of a polynomial f of degree $n \geq 1$ then $z - r$ is a factor of f.* This result is often called the *Factor Theorem*. In the coefficient of $z - r$ the coefficient of z^{n-1} is simply a_n, so that $f(z) = (z - r_1)g(z)$, where $r_1 = r$ and $g(z)$ is of degree $n - 1$.

Proceeding now inductively, let us suppose that

$$f(z) = (z - r_1) \ldots (z - r_k) g(z)$$

where $g(z)$ is of degree $n - k$ and has leading coefficient a_n. If $n - k > 1$ then by the Fundamental Theorem and the Factor Theorem $g(z) = (z - r_{k+1}) h(z)$ where $h(z)$ is of degree $n - k - 1 \geq 1$ and has leading coefficient a_n. Proceeding in this manner we arrive at a situation in which $k = n - 1$ and $f(z) = (z - r_1) \ldots (z - r_{n-1})(a_n z - b_0)$, where b_0 is some constant. Then $f(r_n) = 0$ where $r_n = b_0/a_n$, and we may write

$$f(z) = a_n(z - r_1) \ldots (z - r_n).$$

Grouping together equal roots in the manner of 2B2, we arrive at the following theorem:

18. Theorem. Let $f(z) = {}_k\sum_0^n a_k z^k$ be a polynomial with complex coefficients of degree $n \geq 1$. Then there exist a unique positive integer m, unique positive integers $p_1, \ldots, p_m$, and distinct complex numbers $r_1, \ldots, r_m$, unique except for the order in which they occur, such that ${}_j\sum_1^m p_j = n$ and

$$f(z) = a_n(z - r_1)^{p_1} \cdot \ldots \cdot (z - r_m)^{p_m}.$$

The integer p_j is called the *multiplicity* of r_j as a zero of f or as a root of the equation $f(x) = 0$.

A polynomial whose coefficients are real is said to be a *real polynomial*. If f is real and $z \in R$, then clearly $f(z) \in R$. Now let f be real and suppose that $f(r_1) = 0$ with $r_1 \in C$ and $\in' R$. Since $f(\bar{z}) = \overline{f(z)}$ (because $(\bar{z})^n = \overline{z^n}$), we see that $f(\bar{r}_1) = 0$ and, moreover, that r_1 and $\bar{r}_1$ must have the same multiplicities as roots of $f(z) = 0$. Arrange the notation so that $r_2 = \bar{r}_1$; then $p_2 = p_1$ and

$$f(z) = a_n[(z - r_1)(z - \bar{r}_1)]^{p_1} g(z)$$

where $g(z)$ is of degree $n - 2p_1$ and has leading coefficient 1. Now

$$(z - r_1)(z - \bar{r}_1) = z^2 - 2z \operatorname{Re}(r_1) + |r_1|^2,$$

and this is a quadratic polynomial with real coefficients. By repeating this argument with each non-real zero of f we see that *every real polynomial can be expressed as the product of real linear and quadratic factors.*

EXERCISES

19. Prove that if $zz' = 0$ then either $z = 0$ or $z' = 0$. (T)

20. Prove that if $u, v, w \in C$ then $u \cdot (v + w) = u \cdot v + u \cdot w$. (T)

21. Prove 5. (T)

22. Verify 9. (T)

23. Use 11 and Euler's formula to prove the familiar addition theorems for the sine and cosine function. (Cf. also 9.)

24. Prove 14 and 15. Prove also that $2 \cos \varphi = e^{i\varphi} + e^{-i\varphi}$, while $2i \sin \varphi = e^{i\varphi} - e^{-i\varphi}$. (T)

25. Prove that if t is real then $|e^{it}| = 1$. (T)

26. Prove that if $z_1, \ldots, z_n \in C$ then $\sum \operatorname{Re}(z_k) \leq |\sum z_k| \leq \sum |z_k|$.

27. Express in the form $x + iy$ and in the form $\rho e^{i\varphi}$:

(a) $\dfrac{1}{1+i}$, (b) $\dfrac{2-3i}{4+5i}$, (c) $2e^{\pi i/3}$, (d) $\dfrac{(2+i)^2}{(3-2i)^3}$.

28. Let α be a fixed real number. Study the transformation on C into C such that $z \rightarrow z' = e^{i\alpha}z$.

29. For which values of z, respectively, is each of the following relationships true:

(a) $|z| = |\bar{z}|$,

(b) $|z| = 4$,

(c) $|z| < 2$,

(d) $|z - 3| \le 3$,

(e) $|z - i| \ge 1$,

(f) $|4z + 5| \le 20$,

(g) $z^2 = 4i$,

(h) $0 \le \text{ph } z \le \pi/4$,

(i) $|z - a| = p|z - b|$, with $a, b \in C$ and $p > 0$?

30. Let n be a positive integer. Use the fact that $(\cos \theta + i \sin \theta)^n = \cos n\theta + i \sin n\theta$ and the binomial theorem to express $\cos n\theta$ and $\sin n\theta$ as polynomials in $\cos \theta$ and $\sin \theta$.

31. Let $z = \rho e^{i\varphi}$. What must be true respectively of ρ and φ if $z^3 = 1$? If $z^4 = 16$? If $z^m = p$, where p is real and m is a positive integer? If $z^3 = pe^{i\alpha}$, α real and fixed? If $z^m = pe^{i\alpha}$?

32. Let p be real and positive. Study the transformation T defined by $z \rightarrow z' = p^2/\bar{z}$. Is T defined on all of C? What is the range of T? Is T one-to-one on its domain onto its range? Does T have any fixed points?

33. Let $z_1, \ldots, z_n, c_1, \ldots, c_n \in C$, with the z_k all distinct, and let

$$f_k(z) = \frac{(z - z_1) \ldots (z - z_{k-1})(z - z_{k+1}) \ldots (z - z_n)}{(z_k - z_1) \ldots (z_k - z_{k-1})(z_k - z_{k+1}) \ldots (z_k - z_n)}$$

and

$$g(z) = {}_k\sum_1^n c_k f_k(z).$$

Calculate $f_k(z_j)$ $(j = 1, \ldots, n)$; also $g(z_j)$. What is the degree of g? (This is the Lagrange Interpolation Formula.) (T)

34. Suppose that $p, q, r, s \in R$. Study the roots of the equation $z^2 + 2(p + iq)z + r + is = 0$, obtaining a condition for the roots to be equal, a condition that there be a real root, and a condition that there be a pair of conjugate complex roots.

I. Equivalence Relations and Partitions

A relation between the elements of an ordered pair of objects is a *binary* relation. Examples include equality or inequality between pairs of numbers,

111

divisibility of one integer by another, equipotence of two sets, inclusion of one set in another, and isomorphism of two structures. Although a formal definition of "relation" can be given (cf. 12–14) the intuitive idea is sufficient for our purposes. If a particular binary relation is denoted by ρ then we write $a\,\rho\,b$ to indicate that a is in the relation ρ to b; special relations are often denoted, of course, by special symbols, such as "$=$", "$\leq$", and so on. We shall be interested only in binary relations.

This section and the next are devoted to two very important types of relations between elements of a given set. Those of the type discussed in this section are called equivalence relations; numerical "$=$" is a special case. Those of the type discussed in the next section are called partial orderings; numerical "$\leq$" is a special case.

Let ρ be a relation between ordered pairs of elements of a set X. We say that ρ is an *equivalence relation on* X if and only if the following three statements are true for all $x, y, z \in X$:

1.

R.	$x\,\rho\,x$	(Reflexive Law)
S.	$x\,\rho\,y$ implies $y\,\rho\,x$	(Symmetric Law)
T.	$x\,\rho\,y$ and $y\,\rho\,z$ imply $x\,\rho\,z$	(Transitive Law)

Examples: equality of numbers, equivalence of propositions, equipotence of sets, isomorphism of structures, and congruence of geometric configurations. It is an entertaining exercise to count the frequency with which these properties of numerical equality are used tacitly in even a short calculation; the result may be astonishing.

A further example is of interest in its own right. Let m be a fixed integer ≥ 2. One says that integers a and b are *congruent modulo* m (or mod m), and writes $a \equiv b \pmod{m}$, if and only if $m|(a - b)$ or, in other words, there exists an integer q such that $a = b + mq$. Examples: $-3 \equiv 7 \pmod 5$, $21 \equiv 0 \pmod 7$, and $38 \equiv 2 \pmod 4$. That congruence (mod m) is reflexive and symmetric is obvious. Now suppose that $a \equiv b \pmod m$ and $b \equiv c \pmod m$. Then there exist integers q and r such that $a = b + mq$ and $b = c + mr$, whence $a = c + m(q + r)$ and we conclude that $a \equiv c \pmod m$. The relation of congruence (mod m) is therefore also transitive and, consequently, an equivalence relation. The expression "(mod m)" is abbreviated occasionally to "(m)".

If ρ is an equivalence relation on a set X, then the set $S(x) = \{y : y \in X$ and $x\,\rho\,y\}$ is called the *equivalence-set* determined by x. By H1.S, $y \in S(x)$ if and only if $x \in S(y)$.

For example, if $m = 5$ then the set $S(13) = \{x : x \in I$ and $x \equiv 13(5)\}$ may be listed as follows: $\ldots, -7, -2, 3, 8, 13, \ldots$. Now for $k = 0, 1, 2, 3, 4$ write S_k; thus $S_3 = S(3) = S(13)$ is the set just listed. It is evident that the entire class of equivalence-sets is the class S_k ($k = 0, \ldots, 4$). Observe moreover that the sets S_k are nonvoid and disjoint and that their union is the entire set I of integers. This situation is typical.

Let us say that a class S_e ($e \in E$) of subsets of a set I is a *partition* of T if and only if the following three requirements are met:

(a) No S_e is empty;
(b) The S_e are disjoint;
(c) T is the union of the S_e.

As indicated by the case $m = 5$ examined above, it is true for any value of $m \geq 2$ that congruence (mod m) determines a partition of the integers into a class of m equivalence-sets, two elements of the same set being congruent to each other and not congruent to any element of the complement of that set. The general situation lends itself to explicit formulation.

2. Theorem. Let ρ be an equivalence relation defined on a set X. Let C be a set in 1-1 correspondence with the class of equivalence-sets $S(x)$ for $x \in X$, and for $c \in C$ let T denote the equivalence-set corresponding to c. Then $\{T_c : c \in C\}$ is a partition of X. Conversely, let $\{T_a : a \in A\}$ be a partition of X and define the relation ρ on X by agreeing that $x \rho y$ if and only if there exists an $a \in A$ such that both $x \in T_a$ and $y \in T_a$; then ρ is an equivalence relation on X such that $\{T_a : a \in A\}$ is the class of equivalence-sets determined by ρ.

Since $S(x) = S(y)$ whenever $x \rho y$, we note, $x \neq y$ does not imply that $S(x) \neq S(y)$. Hence x cannot be used as an index for the class of sets $S(x)$ although it is true that $\{S(x) : x \in X\} = \{T_c : c \in C\}$. In the example of congruence (mod 5), if the class of equivalence-sets is denoted by $\{S_k\}$ ($k = 0, 1, 2, 3, 4$), then the set C is $\{0, 1, 2, 3, 4\}$.

We must prove that $\{T_c : c \in C\}$ is a partition of X. First of all, since $x \rho x$ (because ρ is reflexive) $x \in S(x)$; we conclude both that no T_c is empty and that $\bigcup_{c \in C} T_c = X$. That the sets T_c are disjoint is proved indirectly. Suppose that $b, c \in C$, that $b \neq c$, and that $w \in T_b \cap T_c$. Choose any $x \in T_b$ and any $y \in T_c$. Since x and w are both in T_b, $x \rho w$; since y and w are both in T_c, $y \rho w$. By symmetry, $w \rho y$ and then, by the transitive law, $x \rho y$. By symmetry again, $y \rho x$. Hence $y \in T_b$ and $x \in T_c$. Since x and y were arbitrary, $T_b = T_c$, contradicting our assumption that $b \neq c$ and the fact that C is in 1-1 correspondence with the class of equivalence-sets.

In the converse we are given the partition $\{T_a : a \in A\}$ of X and a corresponding definition of ρ. Since $x \in T_a$ for some $a \in A$, $x \rho x$ and ρ is reflexive. If $x \rho y$ then x and y both belong to T_a for some $a \in A$ and therefore $y \rho x$; hence ρ is symmetric. Now suppose that both $x \rho y$ and $y \rho z$. Then for some $b \in A$ and $c \in A$ both x and y belong to T_b and both y and z belong to T_c. Unless $b = c$ we would have disjoint sets T_b and T_c with the common element y; hence $b = c$, $T_b = T_c$, and $x \rho z$ as required. Thus ρ is indeed an equivalence relation, and the sets T_a are clearly the equivalence-sets determined by ρ.

In order to give a final example, let us return to $\mathcal{E}_3$ and say that vectors $\overrightarrow{PP'}$ and $\overrightarrow{QQ'}$ are *equipollent* if they agree in length and direction. It is easy to verify that equipollence is an equivalence relation. The equivalence-set $S(\overrightarrow{PP'})$ is simply the free vector (cf. 3L1) whose representative at P is $\overrightarrow{PP'}$. Had the notion of an equivalence relation been available in 3L a free vector could have been *defined* as an equivalence-set for the relation of equipollence. Our definitions of addition and multiplication by a scalar would then have applied, quite literally, to equivalence-sets, but the practical effect on the representatives would have been the same. The idea of defining an algebraic structure on a partition of a given set has been applied with great success in more advanced work.

EXERCISES

3. For points on a horizontal line, let $A \rho B$ mean "A is to the left of B". Which of the properties R, S, T does ρ have? Study similarly the relation "A is not to the right of B".

4. Which of the properties R, S, T are possessed by each of the following relations between human beings: (a) A is a descendant of B, (b) A is older than B, (c) A loves B, (d) A is married to B, (e) A is not richer than B?

5. Let E denote this property of a relation ρ : $a \rho b$ and $a \rho c$ imply $b \rho c$; if ρ means "$=$" then E says that things equal to the same thing are equal to each other. Prove that if ρ has properties R and E then it has properties S and T and is therefore an equivalence relation. Verify properties R and E for the following relation between pairs of decimal fractions: the third digit after the decimal point is the same. (T)

6. List the equivalence-sets for congruence of integers (mod 2), (mod 3), and (mod 4).

7. Let S denote the set of all ordered pairs (a, b) with $a, b \in I$ and $b \neq 0$. Define a relation ρ on S by agreeing that $(a, b) \rho (c, d)$ if and only if $ad = bc$. Show that ρ is an equivalence relation. What are the equivalence-sets?

8. Given sets S and T, define a relation ρ on the set $S \times T$ by agreeing that $(s, t) \rho (s', t')$ if and only if $s = s'$. Show that ρ is an equivalence relation and specify the equivalence-sets. Specify the corresponding partition of $S \times T$. (T)

9. Determine whether or not the following relations between integers are equivalence relations: $a \rho b$ if and only if $a - b$ is odd; $a \rho b$ if and only if $a + b$ is composite.

10. Given $f : X \to Y$. For $x, x' \in X$ define $x \rho x'$ to hold if and only if $f(x) = f(x')$. Show that ρ is an equivalence relation on X and determine the corresponding partition of X.

11. Consider the following relations with respect to the properties R, S, T where $a, b \in N$: (a) $a \geq b$; (b) a and b are both positive; (c) $|a - b| \leq 1$. In the light of these results, is there any way of deriving one of the properties R, S, T from the other two? Show why or why not.

114

12. Let variables s and t have respective domains S and T. If ρ is a relation between values of s and values of t, then define a corresponding subset W_ρ of $S \times T$ by agreeing that $(s, t) \in W_\rho$ if and only if $s \rho t$. Vice versa, if W is any subset of $S \times T$, define ρ_W by agreeing that $s \rho_W t$ if and only if $(s, t) \in W$. Show that this correspondence between subsets of $S \times T$ and relations of elements of S and T is biunique. (A relation may therefore be defined as a subset of a product set.) (T)

13. Let ρ be a binary relation between elements of a set A. What geometric properties of the corresponding subset of $A \times A$ are implied respectively by properties R and S of ρ? (The interpretation of properties T and E (cf. 5) is less picturesque.)

14. Let $J = \{x : x \in \Re$ and $0 \leq x \leq 1\}$. Which subsets of $J \times J$ correspond, respectively, to the following relations: $x \leq y$, $y = (x + 1)/2$, $x^2 + y^2 \leq 1$, $x + y = 1$, $y > x^2$, and $y^2 = x$?

15. In the context of 3G16, let triples w_k and w'_k be in the relation ρ if and only if there exists a number $p > 0$ such that $w'_k = pw_k$. Show that ρ is an equivalence relation and that the positions of $\overline{Q}$ correspond biuniquely with the equivalence-sets of the partition produced by ρ in the set of all ordered triples.

16. Let P denote the set of all polynomials with real coefficients. If f, $g \in P$ let us say that $f \sim g$ if $f(z) - g(z)$ is divisible by $z^2 + 1$. Show that $\sim$ is an equivalence relation on P and determine the equivalence-sets. Show that if $f \sim g$ and $f' \sim g'$ then $f + f' \sim g + g'$ and $ff' \sim gg'$. These facts suggest definitions of binary operations $\oplus$ and $\odot$ on the set Q of equivalence-sets. Show that $\{Q, \oplus, \odot\}$ is isomorphic with $C = \{C, +, \cdot\}$. (T)

J. Partial Order

A binary relation between variables x and y having the same domain X is said to define or to be a *partial order* on X, or to *partially order* X, or to be a *partial ordering* of X if and only if it is reflexive and transitive and is *antisymmetric* in this sense: if $x \rho y$ and $y \rho x$ then $y = x$. The set of positive integers is partially ordered by the divisibility relation $x|y$. The set of real numbers is partially ordered by the relation $x \leq y$. The class 2^X of subsets of a given set X is partially ordered by the relation $S \subset T$.

If ρ is a partial order on X and particular elements x, $y \in X$ have either the property that $x \rho y$ or the property that $y \rho x$, then x and y are said to be *comparable*. If every pair is comparable, that is, if for each x, $y \in X$ it is true that either $x \rho y$ or $y \rho x$, then X is said to be *totally* or *linearly ordered* (by ρ) and is called a *chain*. The set of real numbers with the relation $x \leq y$ is a chain (cf. 2D1.1).

If a set has more than one element, then the class of its subsets is not linearly ordered by the inclusion relation. If $X = \{a, b, c\}$ then we may display 2^X as in the accompanying illustration, where a line rising from one set to another indicates that the lower set is a subset of the upper. The sets $\{a, b\}$ and $\{c\}$ are not comparable.

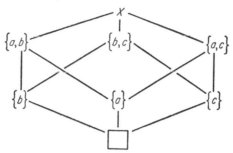

On account of the analogy between any partial order ρ on any set X and the special partial order $\leq$ on the set of real numbers, it is often highly suggestive to think in terms of $\leq$, and most authors replace "ρ" by "$\leq$" when no confusion can arise; we shall accept this convention. With this agreement, the inclusion relation $S \subset T$ could equally well be written $S \leq T$.

Given a partial order $\leq$ on a set X one can define "$>$" to mean "not $\leq$", "$\geq$" to mean "$>$ or $=$", and "$<$" to mean "not $\geq$".

If $x \leq y$, one conventionally speaks of y as a greater of the two and of x as a lesser; in particular x is both the greater and lesser number of the pair (x, x). More generally, suppose that a subset S of a partially ordered set X *contains* an element s^* such that if $s \in S$ then $s^* \leq s$. If t is another such element of S, so that if $s \in S$ then $t \leq s$, then clearly both $s^* \leq t$ and $t \leq s^*$, whence $t = s^*$. Such an element s^*, if it exists, is therefore *unique*; it is called the *minimum* or *least element* of S and is denoted by min S. Similarly, an element s^{**} of S such that if $s \in S$ then $s \leq s^{**}$ is easily shown, if it exists, to be *unique*; it is called the *maximum* or *greatest element* of S and is denoted by max S. In R, for example, consider the subset $Y = \{y : 0 \leq y < 1\}$. Here min $Y = 0$ but max Y does not exist.

If x and y are not comparable, then there may or may not exist a z such that $x \leq z$ and $y \leq z$; such a z is called an upper bound of x and y. More generally, if Y is any subset of a partially ordered set X, and $z \in X$ has the property that if $y \in Y$ then $y \leq z$, then z is said to be an *upper bound* of Y. Similarly, $z \in X$ is said to be a *lower bound* of Y if $y \in Y$ implies $z \leq y$. In the subset Y above of the set of real numbers, 1 (or any larger number) is an upper bound of Y, while 0 (or any smaller number) is a lower bound. In the class of subsets of $\{a, b, c\}$ displayed above, the subclass consisting of $\{a, b\}$ and $\{b, c\}$ has the lower bounds $\{b\}$ and $\square$, and the upper bound X. Note with extreme care that max S and min S, if they exist, *must belong to S*, while $x \in X$ is *not required* to belong to S in order to qualify as an upper or lower bound of S.

Let us denote by $L(S)$ and $U(S)$ respectively the sets of lower and upper bounds of S. We define the *infimum* or *greatest lower bound* of S, denoted by inf S or glb S, and the *supremum* or *least upper bound* of S, denoted by sup S or lub S, respectively as follows:

$$\text{inf } S = \text{max } L(S), \qquad \text{sup } S = \text{min } U(S).$$

The set Y of the example above has inf $Y = 0$ and sup $Y = 1$. In the class of subsets of $X = \{a, b, c\}$ the subclass S consisting of $\{a, b\}$ and $\{b, c\}$ has inf $S = \{b\}$ and sup $S = X$. Of course, if $L(S) = \square$ then inf S does not exist; if $U(S) = \square$ then sup S does not exist.

The foregoing definitions apply in an amusing way to the void subset of a partially ordered set X. It is true of any $x \in X$ that if $y \in \square$, then both $x \leq y$ and $y \leq x$; hence $L(\square) = X = U(\square)$. It follows that inf $\square$ = max X, if it exists, and that sup $\square$ = min X, if it exists.

With the terminology just introduced we may say that a *Dedekind cut* (cf. 2D3) in R^* or R is a partition into two sets, L and U, such that $x \in L$ and $y \in U$ imply that $x < y$. A Dedekind cut in either R^* or R cannot have the property that both max L and min U exist. A Dedekind cut in R may have the property that neither max L nor min U exists. In R however, and this is the "completeness" property of 2D3, it is true of any Dedekind cut that either max L or min U exists.

We close this section with three definitions that will occasionally be helpful. Let sets X and Y be partially ordered, respectively, by relations ρ and σ and let f map X into Y. If and only if, for each $x_1, x_2 \in X$, $x_1 \rho x_2$ implies $f(x_1) \sigma f(x_2)$ we say that f is *isotonic*; if $x_1 \rho x_2$ implies $f(x_2) \sigma f(x_1)$ we say that f is *antitonic*. If f is a real-valued function of a real variable and "$\leq$" has its usual meaning, then f is isotonic if and only if $f(x)$ does not decrease as x increases and f is antitonic if and only if $f(x)$ does not increase as x increases. If either f is isotonic or f is antitonic, then we say that f is *monotonic*.

For the extensive theory of partially ordered sets and many applications, the reader may consult *Lattice Theory*, by Garrett Birkhoff (rev. ed., Am. Math. Soc. Colloq. Pub., N.Y., 1948, Vol. 25), from which the first two definitions of the preceding paragraph are taken.

EXERCISES

Here $x \leq y$ if a line rises from x to y; thus $\alpha \leq \beta \leq \delta$, but it is false that $b \leq f$ and false that $q \leq p$.

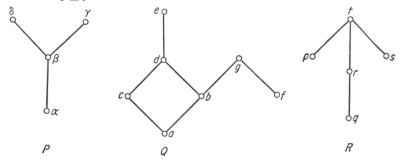

$A = \{\alpha, \beta\} \subset P,$ $B = \{b, c, d\} \subset Q,$ $C = \{c, b, f\} \subset Q,$
$D = \{p, q, r\} \subset R.$

1. Specify L, U, inf, sup, max, and min for each of the sets A, B, C, D, P, Q, and R.

2. The partially ordered sets P, Q, and R have nine chains, each having at least two elements, which are maximal in the sense of not being contained in any longer chain. List them.

3. Let functions f, g, and h on P into R be defined as in the accompanying table. Which are isotonic? Which are antitonic?

	α	β	γ	δ
f	q	r	t	t
g	t	r	p	s
h	r	q	q	q

4. In the set I of positive integers, partially ordered by the relation $a|b$, show that inf S and sup S are respectively the greatest common divisor and the least common multiple of the elements of S (cf. 2B).

5. Let S be a nonempty subset of a partially ordered set X and assume that $y = $ inf S exists.

   (a) Show that if $x \in S$ then $y \leq x$.

   (b) Show also that, if $z \in X$ has the property that if $x \in S$ then $z \leq x$, then $z \leq y$.

   (c) Suppose that $y \in X$ has the properties stated in (a) and (b); does it follow that $y = $ inf S?

   (d) Study sup S similarly.

6. Show that a partially ordered set is a chain if and only if the Trichotomy Law (cf. 2D1.1A) is valid in it. (T)

7. In the set P of partitions of a given set S, call a partition π' a *refinement* of a partition π, and write $\pi' \rho \pi$, if every element of π' is a subset of just one element of π. Prove that ρ partially orders P. If $\pi, \sigma \in P$, describe inf $\{\pi, \sigma\}$. Show by an example that sup $\{\pi, \sigma\}$ may be the partition whose only set is S itself.

8. Assuming the existence of the elements in question, prove the following weaker analogues of the distributive laws for elements x, y, z of a partially ordered set:

$$\sup \{\inf \{x, y\}, \inf \{x, z\}\} \leq \inf \{x, \sup \{y, z\}\}$$
$$\sup \{x, \inf \{y, z\}\} \leq \inf \{\sup \{x, y\}, \sup \{x, z\}\}.$$

9. Let X and Y be given sets, and consider the set F of functions f having domains contained in X and ranges contained in Y. If the domain S of f is a subset of the domain T of g, and $x \in S$ implies that $f(x) = g(x)$, then we say that g is an *extension* of f from S to T and that f is the *restriction* of g to S. Let $f \rho g$ mean that g is an extension of f; prove that F is partially ordered by ρ. (T)

10. Suppose that ρ partially orders X. Define ρ^* on $X \times X$ by agreeing that $(u, v) \rho^* (x, y)$ if and only if both $u \rho x$ and $v \rho y$. Show that ρ^* partially orders $X \times X$. Use this result to set up a partial order in $C = R \times R$.

FIVE
Linear Spaces

Our principal aim in this book is to study the theory of finite-dimensional linear spaces. In this chapter we first say what a "linear space" is and give several examples. Then we develop the ideas of basis and dimension along lines very close to those followed in Chap. 3. After obtaining properties of subspaces we study changes of basis and are led to nonsingular square matrices.

A. External Operations on Abelian Groups

Let $\mathcal{G} = \{G, +\}$ be an Abelian group (see 4C) and $\mathcal{F} = \{F, \circ, \cdot\}$ a field (see 4F). An *external operation* by $\mathcal{F}$ on $\mathcal{G}$ is a function on $F \times G$ (see 4A) into G, with values denoted by $f * g$ ($f \in F, g \in G$) having the following properties: If $f_1, f_2 \in F$ and $g_1, g_2 \in G$ then,

E_1. $f_1 * (g_1 + g_2) = (f_1 * g_1) + (f_1 * g_2)$,
E_2. $(f_1 \circ f_2) * g_1 = (f_1 * g_1) + (f_2 * g_1)$,
E_3. $f_1 * (f_2 * g_1) = (f_1 \cdot f_2) * g_1$,
E_4. $1 * g_1 = g_1$.

EXAMPLES

1. Let $\mathcal{G}$ be $\{R, +\}$ (the additive group of real numbers), let $\mathcal{F}$ be the rational field R^*, and let the external operation consist of multiplying a real number r by a rational number ρ to get $\rho \cdot r$. E_1 requires that $\rho(r_1 + r_2) = \rho r_1 + \rho r_2$, E_2 that $(\rho_1 + \rho_2)r = \rho_1 r + \rho_2 r$, and E_3 that $\rho_1(\rho_2 r) = (\rho_1 \rho_2)r$; each of these requirements is evidently met.

2. Let $\mathcal{G}$ be $\{R, +\}$ or $\{C, +\}$, let $\mathcal{F}$ be R or C in the respective cases, and let the "external" operation be numerical multiplication.

3. In the example of typical interest to us let $\mathcal{G}$ be the additive group $\{E_P, +\}$ of vectors at a point P in $\mathcal{E}_3$, let $\mathcal{F} = R$, and let the external operation be multiplication of a vector by a scalar. The requirements E_k ($k = 1, 2, 3$) are respectively 3D4b, 3D4a, and 3C2, while E_4 is mentioned in the paragraph preceding 3C2.

It is convenient for our purposes to accept a symbol such as $g * f$ ($f \in F$, $g \in G$), if it should arise, as identical in meaning to $f * g$ (cf. 3C following 1).

B. Linear Spaces

A *linear space* (or *vector space*) *over a field* $\mathfrak{F}$ is a structure consisting of a commutative group $\mathcal{G} = \{X, +\}$, a field $\mathfrak{F}, = \{F, +, \cdot\}$ and an external operation $\cdot$ by $\mathfrak{F}$ on $\mathcal{G}$ (see A). We adopt $\mathfrak{X} = \{X, +; \mathfrak{F}, \cdot\}$ as the complete symbol for the linear space. When it is perfectly evident from the context what the group operation "$+$" is, and what $\mathfrak{F}$ and the external operation are, we speak briefly of the space X. In our work the field $\mathfrak{F}$ will almost always be either the real field R (see 2D) or the complex field C (see 4F) and $\mathfrak{X}$ will be said to be a *real* or a *complex* linear space in the respective cases.

The elements of X will be called *points* or *vectors* and will be denoted by small Latin letters. The elements of F will be called *scalars* and will be denoted by small Greek letters. The dot denoting multiplication of a vector by a scalar will ordinarily be omitted. In this notation, if α, $\beta \in F$ and $x, y \in X$ then the requirements E_1–E_4 of A become these:

1. $$\alpha(x + y) = \alpha x + \alpha y,$$
2. $$(\alpha + \beta)x = \alpha x + \beta x,$$
3. $$\alpha(\beta x) = (\alpha\beta)x,$$
4. $$1x = x.$$

It will be observed that in 2 the "$+$" on the left denotes numerical addition of α and β in $\mathfrak{F}$, while the "$+$" on the right denotes vectorial addition in $\{X, +\}$ of the vector αx and the vector βx. This ambiguity is frequent but entirely harmless, for the meaning of the "$+$" will always be quite evident from the context. The symbol "0" is affected by a similar harmless ambiguity; according to context it denotes either the number zero of F or the identity element (*zero-vector*) of $\{X, +\}$.

5. Theorem. If $\alpha \in F$ then $\alpha 0 = 0$. If $x \in X$ then $0x = 0$.

Fix $y \in X$. By 1, $\alpha y + \alpha 0 = \alpha(y + 0) = \alpha y$; now add the inverse of αy in $\{X, +\}$ to get $\alpha 0 = 0$. Similarly, fix $\beta \in F$. By 2, $\beta x + 0x = (\beta + 0)x = \beta x$; add the inverse of βx to get $0x = 0$.

6. Corollary. If $x \in X$ then $x + ((-1)x) = 0$.

It follows that $(-1)x$ is the (unique, cf. 4C1I) inverse of x in $\{X, +\}$. We abbreviate $(-1)x$ to $-x$, and $x + (-y)$ to $x - y$, and speak of subtracting y from x.

Two linear spaces $\{X, +; \mathfrak{F}, \cdot\}$ and $\{Y, +'; \mathfrak{F}, \cdot'\}$ over the same field $\mathfrak{F}$

are said to be *isomorphic* (cf. 4G) if there is a biunique correspondence $x \leftrightarrow y$ between them of such a nature that the operations of addition and scalar multiplication are preserved; more explicitly, if $x_1 \leftrightarrow y_1$ and $x_2 \leftrightarrow y_2$ then $x_1 + x_2 \leftrightarrow y_1 +' y_2$, and if $\alpha \in \mathfrak{F}$ then $\alpha \cdot x_1 \leftrightarrow \alpha \cdot' y_1$.

If X and Y are isomorphic, then $0 \leftrightarrow 0$. Otherwise, if $0 \leftrightarrow e$, then

$$x + 0 = x \leftrightarrow y = y + e;$$

since this is true for all mated pairs, hence for all $y \in Y$, $e = 0$ in Y.

EXAMPLES

7. From A3 it follows that $\{E_P, +; R, \cdot\}$ is a real linear space. This space will be a rich source of ideas, illustrations, and terminology.

8. If $\mathfrak{F} = \{F, +, \cdot\}$ is a field, and the "$\cdot$" in $\{F, +; \mathfrak{F}, \cdot\}$ is interpreted as numerical multiplication, then $\{F, +; \mathfrak{F}, \cdot\}$ is a linear space over $\mathfrak{F}$ or, to simplify the notation, over F; it is denoted by F_1. Special cases: R_1^*, R_1, C_1.

9. Let $\{F, +, \cdot\}$ be a field. Let us denote elements of F^n (cf. 4A) by $x = (\xi_k)$ ($k = 1, \ldots, n$). For $x, y \in F^n$ and $\alpha \in F$ define

$$x + y = (\xi_k + \eta_k) \quad \text{and} \quad \alpha \cdot x = (\alpha \xi_k).$$

Then $\{F^n, +; F, \cdot\}$ is a linear space; it will be denoted by F_n. The number ξ_k is called the kth *coordinate* or *component* of x.

10. Let P_n consist (cf. 4H) of polynomials $\alpha \to x(\alpha) = \sum_{k=0}^{n} \xi_k \alpha^k$ having coefficients $\xi_k \in C$ and of degree not exceeding n, along with the zero-function $x(\alpha) \equiv 0$, and define addition and multiplication by a scalar in the obvious (usual) way; then $\{P_n, +; C, \cdot\}$ is a linear space.

11. Let J denote the interval $0 \leq \xi \leq 1$. Consider all functions $x : J \to R$ with addition and multiplication by scalars defined pointwise: for x, y on J into R, $\xi \in J$, and $\alpha \in R$, $(x + y)(\xi) = x(\xi) + y(\xi)$, $(\alpha x)(\xi) = \alpha x(\xi)$. The resulting linear space is designated by R^J (cf. 1I26). If we look, instead, only at those x which are continuous (or differentiable) on J, we find again in each case a linear space.

12. Let S be any nonvoid set and F a field. Let F^S denote the set of all functions $x : S \to F$, with addition and multiplication defined pointwise as in 11; this structure is a linear space. Special cases:

(a) With $S = \{1, \ldots, n\}$, F^S is the linear space F_n of 9.

(b) With $S = J$ and $F = R$, F^S is the space R^J of 11.

(c) With $S = N$ and $F = R$ (or C), F^S is the space of all infinite sequences of real (or complex) numbers, with addition and multiplication by scalars defined component-wise; these spaces may be denoted, respectively, by R_∞ and C_∞.

We note that in many instances there is a natural built-in zero-vector; in C_n and R_n, for example, $0 = (0, \ldots, 0)$, while in any space of functions such as 11, the zero-vector is the function that vanishes identically on S. This is one reason for emphasizing in $\mathcal{E}_3$ the space E_P with the fixed origin P rather than the isomorphic space of free vectors.

EXERCISES

13. Show from 1 that $\{R, +; R^*, \cdot\}$ is a linear space. Show similarly that $\{C, +; R, \cdot\}$ is a linear space. (In each case the "$\cdot$" denotes numerical multiplication.)

14. Let $X = \{e\}$, define $e + e = e$ and, for $\alpha \in F$ (a field), define $\alpha \cdot e = e$; verify that $\{X, +; F, \cdot\}$ is a linear space. This space, or any space (over F) isomorphic with it, will be called the *trivial* space over F, and will often be denoted by $\langle 0 \rangle$. (T)

15. In R_4 (cf. 9) let $x = (2, -1, 3, 0)$ and $y = (3, 1, -2, 2)$. Calculate $u = 2x - 3y$ and $v = x + 4y$. Find $z \in R_4$ such that $3x - 4z = 2y$.

16. In C_3 let $x = (i, 2 - i, 3 + 5i)$ and $y = (1 + i, -2, -3 + 2i)$. Calculate $u = (1 - i)x + (3 - 4i)y$ and $v = (2 + i)x - (1 - 3i)y$. Find $z \in C_3$ such that $(2 - i)x + (3 - 4i)z = -iy$.

17. In R_∞, let $x = (\xi_n)$ and $y = (\eta_n)$ where, for $n = 1, 2, 3, \ldots, \xi_n = (-1)^n + 2^{-n}$ and $\eta_n = 1 + 3^{-n}$. Calculate $u = x + y$ and $v = 2x - 3y$.

18. Let X be a linear space, and let $a, b \in X$. Prove that there exists a unique $x \in X$ such that $a + x = b$. (T)

19. Prove (cf. 5) that $\alpha x = 0$ only if either $\alpha = 0$ or $x = 0$. (T)

20. In the space R^J of 11, which of the following subsets are themselves linear spaces:

(a) $\{x : x(0) = x(\frac{1}{2}) = x(1) = 0\}$,

(b) $\{x : x(0) = 2\}$,

(c) $\{x : 2x(\frac{1}{2}) = 3x(1)\}$,

(d) $\{x : x(\alpha) > 0 \text{ for } 0 < \alpha < 1\}$,

(e) $\{x : x \text{ is continuous and } \int_0^1 x(\alpha)\, d\alpha = 0\}$,

(f) $\{x : x \text{ is continuous and } \int_0^1 x(\alpha)\, d\alpha = 1\}$?

21. Verify in detail the isomorphism between the space E_P, with P fixed (cf. 7), and the space F of all free vectors in $\mathcal{E}_3$ (cf. 3L1).

22. Let $\mathcal{X}_1 = \{X_1, +_1; F, \cdot_1\}$ and $\mathcal{X}_2 = \{X_2, +_2; F, \cdot_2\}$ be linear spaces over the same field F. Define $Y = X_1 \times X_2$ and denote its elements by $y = (x_1, x_2)$ with $x_1 \in X_1$ and $x_2 \in X_2$. Define a binary operation "$+$" on Y as follows:

$$y + y' = (x_1, x_2) + (x_1', x_2') = (x_1 +_1 x_1', x_2 +_2 x_2').$$

Prove that $\{Y, +\}$ is an abelian group. Define an external operation $\cdot$ by F on $\{Y, +\}$ by defining $\alpha \cdot y$ for $\alpha \in F$ and $y \in Y$ as follows:

$$\alpha \cdot y = \alpha \cdot (x_1, x_2) = (\alpha \cdot_1 x_1, \alpha \cdot_2 x_2).$$

Prove that this operation has properties 5B1-4. It follows that $\mathcal{Y} = \{Y, +; F, \cdot\}$

is a linear space. We say that $\mathcal{Y}$ is the *direct sum* of $\mathcal{X}_1$ and $\mathcal{X}_2$ and write $\mathcal{Y} = \mathcal{X}_1 \oplus \mathcal{X}_2$ or, when no confusion is possible, we say that the space Y is the direct sum of the spaces X_1 and X_2, writing $Y = X_1 \oplus X_2$. (T)

22.1. For example, $F_{p+q} = F_p \oplus F_q$. Observe that we seem to be making here the patently false statement that

$$(\xi_1, \ldots, \xi_{p+q}) = ((\xi_1, \ldots, \xi_p), (\xi_{p+1}, \ldots, \xi_{p+q})).$$

At the same time, the two structures are obviously isomorphic. We may regard the equality between spaces as asserting merely an isomorphism, in which case the equality between the vectors should be replaced by "$\leftrightarrow$", meaning that the vectors are mated with each other by this "natural" isomorphism. An alternative is to regard the equality between the vectors as one of those conventions which is accepted, for the sake of simplicity, when no confusion is possible; after this identification of the vectors, the equality between the spaces means, as it ordinarily does, that the spaces are identical.

C. Linear Combinations; Dependent and Independent Sets

If $x_k \in X$ and $\alpha_k \in F$ $(k = 1, \ldots, n)$, then the vector $\sum \alpha_k x_k$ is said to be a *linear combination* of the vectors x_k. The combination is *trivial* if $\alpha_k = 0$ $(k = 1, \ldots, n)$ and otherwise *nontrivial*. The restriction to finite sets is essential, for we have no way of adding infinitely many vectors.

A set of $x_k \in X$ $(k = 1, \ldots, n)$ is said to be *dependent* or *independent* according as it *has* or *does not have* a nontrivial linear combination that vanishes, in other words, according as there *do* or *do not* exist scalars α_k, *not all zero*, such that $\sum \alpha_k x_k = 0$. We often say loosely that the vectors x_k are dependent or independent according as the set $\{x_k\}$ is dependent or independent.

If $0 \in \{x_k\}$ then $\{x_k\}$ is dependent, for we may form a nontrivial linear combination that vanishes by giving 0 a non-zero coefficient and taking all other coefficients to be zero.

The set $\square$ is (vacuously) independent (cf. 3F).

The vector $y = \sum \alpha_k x_k$ is said to *depend* (linearly) on the vectors x_k; if y does not depend on the vectors x_k then y is said to be *independent* of them.

Suppose now that $\sum \alpha_k x_k = 0$. If $\{x_k\}$ is independent then each $\alpha_k = 0$. If, on the other hand, $\sum \alpha_k x_k$ is nontrivial, then the equation may be solved for any x_j for which $\alpha_j \neq 0$, expressing x_j as a linear combination of the x_k with $k \neq j$. A finite set of vectors is dependent or independent, therefore, according as there is or is not at least one of its vectors which depends on the others.

We establish now a nontrivial result that will be useful in the next section.

1. **Theorem.** If in a linear space X an independent subset B has $n \geq 1$ elements, then there cannot exist more than n independent linear combinations of the vectors of B.

The situation is trivial if $n = 1$, so assume that the assertion is true for $n = p - 1$. Let $B = \{b_k\}$ $(k = 1, \ldots, p)$ be an independent set and suppose that the vectors

$$a_j = {}_k\textstyle\sum_1^p \alpha_{jk}b_k \; (j = 1, \ldots, p + 1)$$

are $p + 1$ independent linear combinations of the b_k. Since $a_{n+1} \neq 0$, $\alpha_{n+1\,k} \neq 0$ for some value of k. Reorder B, if necessary, so that $\alpha_{n+1\,n} \neq 0$ and write $\beta = \alpha_{n+1n}^{-1}$.

Consider now the p vectors

$$u_h = a_h - \beta\alpha_{hn}a_{n+1} \qquad h = 1, \ldots, p.$$

These vectors are independent. Any combination $\sum \beta_h u_h$ is a combination of the independent a_j $(j = 1, \ldots, n + 1)$, and if $\sum \beta_h a_h = 0$ it is seen at once that then $\beta_h = 0$ $(h = 1, \ldots, p)$.

Now let us calculate. For $h = 1, \ldots, p$,

$$u_h = {}_k\textstyle\sum_1^p \alpha_{hk}b_k - \beta\alpha_{hn}\,{}_k\textstyle\sum_1^p \alpha_{n+1\,k}b_k$$

$$= {}_k\textstyle\sum_1^p (\alpha_{hk} - \beta\alpha_{hn}\alpha_{n+1\,k})b_k.$$

The coefficient of b_n in the expression for u_h is

$$\alpha_{hn} - \alpha_{hn}\beta\alpha_{n+1n} = \alpha_{hn} - \alpha_{hn} = 0.$$

Since all the coefficients of b_n vanish, the vectors u_h $(h = 1, \ldots, p)$ are p independent combinations of the $p - 1$ independent vectors b_k $(k = 1, \ldots, p - 1)$. This contradicts the inductive hypothesis and the theorem is proved.

Let us recall that the definitions adopted above are precisely those of 3E and 3F. Which part of the ideas developed there will still be valid here? We can still draw diagrams in which a vector x can be represented by an arrow with tail at the *origin* (point representing the zero-vector) and tip at the point x. We offer further heuristic considerations, by analogy with 3E.

If a and b are fixed vectors and $a \neq 0$, we may still refer to the loci $x = \tau a$ and $x = \tau a + b$ as τ varies over F as *lines*, calling the former the line *generated by a* and denoting it by $\langle a \rangle$.

Now let a and b be independent and consider the locus $\pi : x = \sigma a + \tau b$ as σ and τ vary independently over F. If x and $y = \lambda a + \mu b$ are both on π, then the line joining them should be the locus of $z = x + \theta(y - x)$ as θ varies over F and we see that

$$z = [\sigma + \theta(\lambda - \sigma)]a + [\tau + \theta(\mu - \tau)]b$$

also belongs to π. In other words, if two points lie in π then so does the entire line they determine. It is natural therefore to call π a *plane*, to say that it is *generated* by a and b, and to denote it by $\langle a, b \rangle$.

Now let us try to find a point common to the lines $x = \sigma a$ and $x = \tau a + b$. If there is such a point x_0 then there will exist scalars σ_0 and τ_0 such that $(\tau_0 - \sigma_0)a + b = 0$, whence a and b are dependent. If a and b are independent, therefore, then the two lines, both of which are clearly in the plane $\langle a, b \rangle$, do not intersect and may therefore be said to be *parallel*. We may accordingly say, if $a \neq 0$, that the line $x = \tau a + b$ passes through b (when $\tau = 0$) and is parallel to a or to $\langle a \rangle$. It follows that the sum $x + y$ may be represented in a diagram as the "diagonal" of a "parallelogram" with x and y as coinitial sides.

All the ideas and results developed in 3A–G can be and are taken over, with obvious slight changes in notation and terminology and with one essential reservation. There we used the concepts of length of a vector and of the angle between vectors; these concepts are not available here.

The diagrams drawn in Chap. 3 were regarded as faithful models of spatial relationships in $\mathcal{E}_3$. In studying a general linear space we lack this "spatial" reference, especially in a complex linear space, but diagrams may still be highly suggestive. Their value lies principally in their power to suggest relationships, and terminology and language in which to express a valid proof. It is a remarkable fact that many properties of a linear space, regardless of its dimension (cf. D), relate primarily to its two-or-three-dimensional subspaces and can therefore be displayed, in a figurative sense, by simple diagrams of the kind used in Chap. 3.

In a later chapter we shall see that a notion of "length of a vector" can be introduced into a finite-dimensional linear space in many ways. It will always be true that the length of αx will be $|\alpha|$ times the length of x. We may therefore say, anticipating that result, that we can now measure ratios of lengths without, indeed, knowing what the lengths themselves might be.

EXERCISES

2. In B15, determine whether the vectors u and v are independent or dependent. Similarly for u and v in B16.

3. In the space P_2 of B10, let $x = \alpha$ and $y = 2 + 3\alpha^2$. Are x and y independent or not? Do there exist scalars β and γ such that $\beta x + \gamma y = 4 - \alpha - \alpha^2$? Such that $\beta x + \gamma y = -2 + 3\alpha - 3\alpha^2$?

4. Let X be a given linear space over F, let $a_k \in X$ ($k = 1, \ldots, p$) be fixed, and consider all $y = \sum \alpha_k a_k$ as the scalars α_k vary independently over F. We know that in X, $\beta y = \sum \beta \alpha_k a_k$, and if $y' = \sum \alpha'_k a_k$ then $y + y' = \sum (\alpha_k + \alpha'_k) a_k$. If Y is the set of all such y, show that $\{Y, +; F, \cdot\}$ is a linear space over F; this space, which consists of all linear combinations of the vectors a_k, is said to be *generated* or *spanned* by the vectors a_k ($k = 1, \ldots, p$) and is denoted by $\langle a_1, \ldots, a_p \rangle$. (T)

5. Define spaces $\langle a_1, a_2, a_3 \rangle$ (cf. 3) as follows:

(a) in R_3, $a_1 = (1, -2, 1)$, $a_2 = (2, 1, -1)$, $a_3 = (-1, -13, 8)$;

(b) In C_3, $a_1 = (3 - i, 2i, -1 + i)$, $a_2 = (2 + i, -1 + i, -1)$, $a_3 = (-1 + 2i, -1 - i, -i)$;

(c) in P_2 (of B10) with θ and φ fixed,

$$a_1 = -3e^{-i\varphi}\alpha - 4e^{i\varphi}\alpha^2, \quad a_2 = e^{i\theta} + 2e^{i\varphi}\alpha^2, \quad a_3 = 2e^{i\theta} - 3e^{i\varphi}\alpha.$$

In each case the vectors a_1, a_2, and a_3 are dependent. Find in each space an independent set that has as few elements as possible and spans the space.

6. For $\lambda = 1, \ldots, p$ let $x_\lambda = (\xi_{\lambda k}) \in C_n$. Prove that the set $\{x_\lambda\}$ is independent if and only if the solution of the equations $\sum_\lambda \eta_\lambda \xi_{\lambda k} = 0$ $(k = 1, \ldots, n)$ is the trivial one $\eta_\lambda = 0$ $(\lambda = 1, \ldots, p)$. (T)

D. Basis; Dimension

Let X be a linear space. A set $\{v_k\}$ $(k = 1, \ldots, p)$ is said to *span* or *generate* X if every $x \in X$ is a linear combination of the v_k, in other words, if for each $x \in X$ there exist scalars α_k such that $x = \sum \alpha_k v_k$. Thus $\{v_k\}$ spans X if and only if $X = \langle v_1, \ldots, v_p \rangle$ in the sense of C3. In C3 the set $\{a_k\}$ generates Y.

Let us say for the moment that a basis for X is an independent set that spans X. In F_n of B9, for example, consider the n vectors e_k $(k = 1, \ldots, n)$ having, respectively, the kth coordinate 1 and each other coordinate 0. Observe that $x = (\xi_1, \ldots, \xi_n) = \sum \xi_k e_k$. The set $\{e_k\}$ obviously spans F_n and the set is independent because $x = 0$ (if and) only if $\xi_k = 0$ for $k = 1, \ldots, n$. The set $\{e_k\}$ is therefore a basis for F_n. It is called the *natural* basis for F_n (not that other bases are in any way unnatural).

If $b_1, \ldots, b_k$ is an independent subset of X then either there does not exist or there does exist a vector $c \in X$ such that with $b_{k+1} = c$ the set $b_1, \ldots, b_k, b_{k+1}$ is an independent set. In the first case each $c \in X$ is a linear combination of $b_1, \ldots, b_k$, these vectors span X, $B = \{b_j\}$ $(j = 1, \ldots, k)$ is a basis for X, and $X = \langle b_1, \ldots, b_k \rangle$. In the second case there does not or does exist $c \in X$ such that, with $b_{k+2} = c$, the set $b_1, \ldots, b_{k+2}$ is an independent set. Proceeding recursively, we obtain a sequence of subsets S_k such that S_k has k elements, $S_k \subset S_{k+1}$, and each S_k is an independent set.

The process will terminate if for some value of k, say $k = n$, every $c \in X$ is a linear combination of the elements of $S_n = \{b_j\}$ $(j = 1, \ldots, n)$. In that case S_n spans X and, being independent, constitutes a basis for X having n elements.

1. Theorem. If X has a basis having n elements, then every basis for X has n elements.

This is a consequence of C1. Suppose that $\{p_j\}$ $(j = 1, \ldots, n)$ and $\{q_k\}$ $(k = 1, \ldots, n)$ were both bases for X, with $m \neq n$. If $m < n$, then, by C1, the m vectors p_j cannot have n independent combinations q_k $(k = 1, \ldots, n)$; in other words the set $\{p_j\}$ cannot span X and cannot, therefore, be a basis. A similar argument applies if $n < m$ and we conclude that $m = n$.

If X has a basis consisting of n elements, then X is said to have *dimension n*, or to be *n-dimensional*, and we write dim X for the dimension of X. For example, dim $F_n = n$. We will often write X_n to indicate that dim $X = n$.

If X does not have a finite basis then X is said to be *infinite-dimensional*. Such a space has a basis; for details see [C5]. Without explicit notice or evidence to the contrary, any space occurring in our study will be assumed to be finite-dimensional.

The space E_p of B7 has dimension 3. The spaces of B8 have dimension 1. The space P_n of B10 has dimension $n + 1$, for the elements $1, \alpha, \alpha^2, \ldots, \alpha^n$ form a basis. The space of B11 is infinite-dimensional; so are R_∞ and C_∞.

The trivial space $\langle 0 \rangle$ of B14 deserves a word. We know that $\square$ is independent. Moreover, $\square$ spans $\langle 0 \rangle$ in the sense that $x \in \langle 0 \rangle$ depends on $\square$ if and only if $x = 0$. We recognize $\square$ as a basis for $\langle 0 \rangle$; dim $\langle 0 \rangle = 0$.

If $B = \{p_k\}$ $(k = 1, \ldots, n)$ is a basis for X and $C = \{p_j\}$, where $j = f_k$ is a permutation of $1, \ldots, n$, then C is seen easily to be also a basis for X. It turns out to be important to regard B and C as distinct. A *basis* for a space X is an *ordered independent* set that *spans* X.

Now let X have a basis $B = \{b_k\}$ $(k = 1, \ldots, n)$. If $x \in X$ then, since B spans X there exist $\xi_k \in F$ such that $x = \sum \xi_k b_k$. An argument used in 3F may be repeated to show, moreover, that the ξ's are uniquely determined by x. Just as in 3F, therefore, if $\sum \xi_k b_k = \sum \eta_k b_k$ and the b's are *independent*, then $\xi_k = \eta_k$ for each value of k (equating coefficients).

Suppose, conversely, that an ordered set $A = \{a_h\}$ $(h = 1, \ldots, q)$ has the property that for *each* $x \in X$ there exist *uniquely* determined $\xi_h \in F$ such that $x = \sum \xi_h a_h$. Since the ξ's exist, A spans X. Since $x = 0$ only if $\xi_h = 0$ $(h = 1, \ldots, q)$, the set A is independent and is therefore a basis for X. We have proved the following theorem.

2. Theorem. An ordered set $B = \{b_k\}$ $(k = 1, \ldots, n)$ of vectors is a basis for a linear space X if and only if for each $x \in X$ there exist scalars ξ_k, uniquely determined by x, such that $x = \sum \xi_k b_k$.

The scalar ξ_k in 2 is called the kth *component* or *coordinate* of x with respect to the basis $\{b_k\}$. At the same time (ξ_k) is a point of F_n, and one conclusion of 2 is that (ξ_k) is uniquely determined by $x \in X_n$. Vice versa, given $(\xi_k) \in F_n$ we have a uniquely determined $x = \sum \xi_k b_k \in X_n$. The basis $B = \{b_k\}$ $(k = 1, \ldots, n)$ therefore determines a biunique correspondence $x \leftrightarrow (\xi_k)$ between X_n and F_n. This correspondence, moreover, is an isomorphism, for if $y \leftrightarrow (\eta_k)$ and $\alpha \in F$, then

$$x + y \leftrightarrow (\xi_k + \eta_k) \text{ and } \alpha x \leftrightarrow (\alpha \xi_k).$$

When it is entirely clear what the basis is, therefore, we may write $x = (\xi_k)$. These results are stated in the following theorem (cf. 3G3).

3. Theorem. Each basis $\{b_k\}$ $(k = 1, \ldots, n)$ for X_n determines an isomorphic correspondence between X_n and F_n in such a way that $x \leftrightarrow (\xi_k)$ if and only if $x = \sum \xi_k b_k$.

In this particular isomorphism, of course, $b_k \leftrightarrow e_k$.

In view of our remarks in 4G about the essential identity of isomorphic structures we might be tempted to restrict attention to the space F_n as the prototype of all n-dimensional linear spaces over F. By such a step, however, we would lose any suggestions that might arise from the concrete nature of the vectors in a specific space. It is true, for example, that a space E_P in Chap. 3 is isomorphic to R_3, but in E_P our thinking may be guided by geometrical considerations that are not quite so evident in R_3 (even if R_3 is endowed, as we shall see that it can be, with metric properties).

Precisely those properties of a linear space will be of special interest, moreover, which are truly geometric in the sense of being independent of any basis for the space. In different bases, in fact, such a property may be expressed by quite different relationships among components. Now each specific isomorphism between X_n and F_n produced in the above theorem was produced by means of a specific basis in X_n. In carrying a property established in F_n over to X_n, we would therefore have to show that, as a property of X_n, it was independent of the basis in X_n or, in other words, of the particular isomorphic correspondence implied by the basis. There is accordingly still some merit in studying an arbitrary space X_n.

Many of our theorems can be proved without appealing to the existence of a basis. Such theorems are valid in linear spaces of any dimension. In a specific problem a specific basis may bring great simplification and much of our later work will be concerned with the search for appropriate bases in specific instances.

In order to see that spaces of dimension greater than three are of practical interest, let us begin by observing that the instantaneous "state" of a moving particle consists of its position and velocity. If these are represented respectively, in suitable coordinate systems, by points (ξ, η, τ) and (α, β, γ) of R_3, then a state is represented by a point $(\xi, \eta, \tau; \alpha, \beta, \gamma)$ of the six-dimensional space $R_6 = R_3 \oplus R_3$ (cf. B9, B22), and this space is often called the *phase-space* of the particle. A cubic centimeter of air contains a very large number N of individual particles, and will have a phase-space of $6N$ dimensions. Suppose, as another example, that a psychologist administers t tests to p persons. He will have tp scores and can consider them either as p points in a t-dimensional space (one point for the t scores of one person) or as t points in a p-dimensional space (one point for the p scores on one test).

We do not present a practical application of infinite-dimensional linear spaces; extensive preliminaries would be required. Such applications have thrown much light on many important problems which arise in mathematical analysis and involve differential equations or other functional equations. Our presentation has been strongly motivated by the application of algebraic and geometric ideas to the solution of problems arising in analysis; this extensive branch of modern mathematics is often called "functional analysis".

It is there, too, that complex linear spaces are most extensively exploited. It should be observed, at the same time, that finite-dimensional complex spaces are used in connection with various aspects of electromagnetic phenomena and also, for example (cf. 10B, C, 14B, C), in connection with an important class of matrices called Hermitian.

A basis as defined at the beginning of this section is usually of little practical value in an infinite-dimensional space. There may be available, however, a notion of convergence which makes it possible to deal with infinite series of vectors. When "infinite linear combinations" are permissible, the term "basis" is used with different meanings by different writers. We have no occasion to use a meaning other than that adopted above.

EXERCISES

4. For which values of α will $x = (1, -2)$ and $y = (\alpha, -1)$ form a basis for R_2?

5. With $\alpha = 1$ in 3, show that x and y form a basis for R_2 and determine (a) λ and μ so that $\lambda x + \mu y = (1, 0)$, and (b) ρ and σ so that $\rho x + \sigma y = (0, 1)$. Then find β and γ such that $\beta x + \gamma y = (\xi, \eta)$, where ξ and η are given.

6. Find a necessary and sufficient condition in order that vectors (α, β) and (ξ, η) in C_2 be independent. Find a similar condition for two vectors in C_3.

7. Suppose that a, b, and c are independent. What can you say about the three vectors $b - c$, $c - a$, and $a - b$?

8. In R_3, let $b_1 = (1, 2, 3)$, and $b_2 = (0, 1, 2)$, and $b_3 = (0, 0, 1)$. Prove that b_k ($k = 1, 2, 3$) form a basis for R_3 and determine α_k such that $\sum \alpha_k b_k = (2, 0, -3)$.

9. In R_3, let $c_1 = (1, 0, 0)$, $c_2 = (-1, 1, 0)$, and $c_3 = (-2, -1, 1)$, and keep b_k ($k = 1, 2, 3$) as in 8. Determine scalars α_{hk} such that $c_h = \sum \alpha_{hk} b_k$ ($h = 1, 2, 3$) and scalars γ_{kh} such that $b_k = \sum \gamma_{kh} c_h$ ($k = 1, 2, 3$). If $a = \sum \xi_k b_k = \sum \eta_h c_h$ find equations connecting ξ_k and η_h ($h, k = 1, 2, 3$).

10. In R_3 let $u = (1, 2, 3)$, $v = (3, 2, 1)$, $w = (0, -1, 2)$, $x = (1, 1, 1)$, $y = (-1, -2, -3)$, and $z = (6, 12, 18)$. Determine the dimensions of the following spaces (cf. C3): $\langle u, v \rangle$, $\langle u, v, w \rangle$, $\langle u, x \rangle$, $\langle u, v, x \rangle$, $\langle u, v, y \rangle$, $\langle u, z \rangle$, $\langle u, y, z \rangle$, and $\langle v, w, x \rangle$.

11. Prove that an independent set of vectors is a basis for X_n if and only if it is not a proper subset of an independent set, in other words, if and only if the set has n vectors. (T)

12. Suppose that the set S of vectors spans X_n. Prove that S is a basis for X_n if and only if S has no proper subset that spans X_n. (T)

13. Let X_n and Y_n be linear spaces over the same field and let f be an isomorphic mapping on X_n onto Y_n such that $x \leftrightarrow y = f(x)$. Show that if b_k ($k = 1, \ldots, n$) form a basis for X_n, then the vectors $f(b_k)$ form a basis for Y_n. It is evident, by the same token, that if c_k is a basis for Y_n then $f^{-1}(c_k)$ is a basis for X_n. It follows that *an isomorphism on X_n onto Y_n sets up a biunique correspondence between bases for X_n and bases for Y_n.* (T)

14. Suppose that $\{b_k\}$ and $\{c_k\}$ ($k = 1, \ldots, n$) are bases for X_n and Y_n (over the same field). Define f on X_n into Y_n by agreeing that, for $k = 1, \ldots, n, f(b_k) = c_k$, and that $f(\sum \xi_k b_k) = \sum \xi_k c_k$. Prove that f is an isomorphism on X_n onto Y_n. (T)

129

15. Prove that two finite-dimensional linear spaces over the same field are isomorphic if and only if they have the same dimension. (T)

16. In the space of polynomials in B10, let us remove the restriction that the degree not exceed n, arriving at the set X of all polynomials and the zero-function. Show that $\{X, +; C, \cdot\}$ is a linear space. Is its dimension finite? Explain.

17. Let $\{b_k\}$ be a basis for X_n. Show that $b_j = \sum \delta_{jk} b_k$, where $\delta_{jk} = 1$ if $j = k$ or $= 0$ if $j \neq k$ (Kronecker's delta; cf. 3G). (T)

18. Prove that the set $A = \{a_h\}$ $(h = 1, \ldots, q)$ is a basis for the space $\langle A \rangle$ if and only if A is independent. (T)

E. Subspaces; Flats

Let $\mathfrak{X} = \{X, +; F, \cdot\}$ be a linear space and let S be a subset of X. If x and y are arbitrary elements of S and α is an arbitrary scalar, then of course $x + y$ and αx are well-defined elements of X. If $x + y$ and αx belong always *to S itself*, if, in other words, S is closed under addition and under multiplication by scalars, then, as we shall show, $\{S, +; F, \cdot\}$ is a linear space in its own right. The associative and commutative laws of vector addition, as well as the identities B1–4 hold in S because they hold in $\mathfrak{X}$. If $x \in S$ then $-x = (-1)x \in S$, whence $x - x = x + (-x) = 0 \in S$. We conclude that $\{S, +\}$ is indeed an abelian group with the same addition as in $\mathfrak{X}$ and the same external operation as in $\mathfrak{X}$ of multiplication by elements of F. The linear space $\mathcal{S} = \{S, +; F, \cdot\}$ is called a *subspace* of $\mathfrak{X}$, and we write $\mathcal{S} \leq \mathfrak{X}$; we also say, when no confusion is possible, that S is a subspace of X, writing $S \leq X$.

If $S \leq X$ then S is clearly closed under the formation of linear combinations in the sense that any linear combination of elements of S is again an element of S. The converse is obvious from the definition.

Of course, $X \leq X$ and (cf. B14) $\langle 0 \rangle \leq X$. If Y is any subspace of X then $\langle 0 \rangle \leq Y \leq X$ and in this sense we may say that $\langle 0 \rangle$ is the "smallest" and X the "largest" subspace of X.

The space $\langle a_1, \ldots, a_k \rangle$ spanned by a set of vectors $a_1, \ldots, a_k$ (see C3) is a subspace of any space containing them. If Y is any sub*set* of X then the set of all linear combinations of elements of Y is a sub*space* which is said to be generated by Y; this subspace will be denoted by $\langle Y \rangle$. Other examples of subspaces are given in B11 and B20; it is to examples of this kind that the theory of linear spaces owes much of its importance in analysis.

A *subset* obtained by translating a subspace by a vector not in it, or trivially by 0, is called a *flat*. If $Y \leq X$ and either $u = 0$ or $u \in' Y$ then we denote by $u + Y$ the flat consisting of all vectors of the form $u + y$ with $y \in Y$; this flat is a subspace if and only if $u = 0$, and if $u = 0$ then the flat reduces to Y.

If $B = \{b_k\}$ $(k = 1, \ldots, n)$ is a basis for X_n and $A = \{a_h\}$ $(h = 1, \ldots,$

$m \leq n$) is a subset of B, then the vectors a_h, being independent, form a basis for the subspace $\langle a_1, \ldots, a_m \rangle$ they span (cf. C3), whence this subspace has dimension m.

Vice versa, suppose now that $Y_m \leq X_n$ and that $A = \{a_h\}$ ($h = 1, \ldots, m$) is a basis for Y_m. We wish to define a basis $B = \{b_k\}$ ($k = 1, \ldots, n$) for X_n such that A shall be a subset of B. For $k = 1, \ldots, m$, put $b_k = a_k$. If $m = n$ the problem is finished, so assume that $m < n$. Since $m < n$, the vectors $b_1, \ldots, b_m$ are not a basis for X_n. By D11 these vectors constitute a proper subset of an independent set. In some such set choose a vector, designated by b_{m+1}, such that the set $b_1, \ldots, b_m, b_{m+1}$ is an independent set. If $m + 1 = n$ the problem is finished. If $m + 1 < n$ we repeat the process, arriving after $n - m$ steps at an independent set $B = \{b_k\}$ ($k = 1, \ldots, n$) which is a basis for X_n and has A as a subset. We have proved the following theorem.

1. **Theorem.** Suppose that $Y_m \leq X_n$ and that $\{a_h\}$ ($h = 1, \ldots, m$) is a basis for Y_m. There exists a basis $\{b_k\}$ ($k = 1, \ldots, n$) for X_n such that, for $h = 1, \ldots, m$, $a_h = b_h$.

The basis $\{b_k\}$ ($k = 1, \ldots, n$) for X_n supplied by the theorem is said to be *adapted to* the subspace Y_m. If, for example, Y_2 is the subspace of C_3 spanned by the vectors $a_1 = (3 - i, 2, -1)$ and $a_2 = (1, 2 + i, 0)$, then a_1, a_2, and $a_3 = (0, 0, 1)$ form a basis for C_3 that is adapted to Y_2.

The theorem may be stated briefly by saying that any independent set in a space X can be augmented, if necessary, to obtain a basis for X.

EXERCISES

2. Find bases for R_4 adapted to the respective subspaces spanned by the following sets of vectors:

(a) $(1, -1, 2, 2)$, $(0, 1, 0, 1)$, and $(-1, 2, 2, 1)$;
(b) $(2, 1, 3, 2)$ and $(1, -1, 1, 0)$;
(c) $(2, -1, 1, -2)$.

3. Find bases for C_3 adapted to the respective subspaces spanned by the following sets of vectors:

(a) $(2 - i, 0, 1 + i)$ and $(3 + i, 1 - i, i)$;
(b) $(-3 + 2i, 0, 2 - i)$ and $(1, 0, 4 + 3i)$;
(c) $(-1 + i, -1 - i, 2 + 3i)$.

4. Prove that a subset S of a linear space X is a subspace of X if and only if $x, y \in S$ and $\alpha \in F$ imply that $x - y \in S$ and $\alpha x \in S$. (T)

5. In R_2 consider the equations (a) $\alpha_1 \xi_1 + \alpha_2 \xi_2 = 0$, (b) $\beta_1 \xi_1 + \beta_2 \xi_2 = 0$, (c) $\gamma_1 \xi_1 + \gamma_2 \xi_2 = 0$. Is the set S_a of all solutions $x = (\xi_1, \xi_2)$ of (a) a linear space? What about the set S_b of all vectors satisfying both (a) and (b)? What is the conclusion if equations (a), (b), and (c) are all required to be satisfied? How do the results change if the right members of the equations are not zero but are instead, respectively, λ, μ, and ν? Are the results, in each case, the same in C_2?

6. In R_n, consider the equations $\sum_k \alpha_{jk}\xi_k = 0$ $(j = 1, \ldots, p)$. Is the set of all solutions $x = (\xi_k)$ of these equations a linear space? Does it make any difference if $p < n$, $p = n$, or $p > n$? Do the results change if some of the right members of the equations are not zero? Are the results the same in C_n? (T)

7. Let S be a subspace of a linear space X, and for $x, y \in X$ say that x *is congruent to* y *modulo* S, writing $x \equiv y$ (mod S), if and only if $x - y \in S$. Prove that the relation $x \equiv y$ (mod S) is an equivalence relation on X (cf. 4I). What are the equivalence-sets? (Examine the situation in a space E_P of Chap. 3.) (T)

8. Prove that the relation $X \leq Y$ partially orders the class of subspaces of a given linear space Z (cf. 4J). If $X \leq Z$ and $Y \leq Z$, what would be the meaning of inf (X, Y) and of sup (X, Y)? Naturally, min $\{X : X \leq Z\} = \langle 0 \rangle$ and max $\{X : X \leq Z\} = Z$. (T)

F. Intersection and Sum of Subspaces

Let X and Y be subspaces of a linear space Z. If $a, b \in X$ and $a, b \in Y$ then $a, b \in X \cap Y$, where $X \cap Y$ is the set-theoretic intersection of X and Y (cf. 1E). Moreover, $a - b$ and, if $\alpha \in F$, αa both belong to both X and Y and therefore to $X \cap Y$. It follows by E4 that $X \cap Y$ is a subspace of Z; it is called the *intersection* or *meet* of X and Y. This subspace is inf (X, Y) in E8. Since $\langle 0 \rangle \leq W$ for every subspace W, $\langle 0 \rangle \leq X \cap Y$; $X \cap Y$ may be trivial, but it is *never empty*.

It is obvious that the set-theoretic union $X \cup Y$ is not a subspace of Z unless, indeed, either $X \leq Y$ or $Y \leq X$. In a two-dimensional space Z, for example, let x and y be independent vectors and define $X = \langle x \rangle$ and $Y = \langle y \rangle$. Then $x + y \in' X \cup Y$.

Let us therefore consider, in the general case, the set $W = \{w : w \in Z, w = x + y, x \in X, y \in Y\}$ of all vectors $x + y$ with $x \in X$ and $y \in Y$. Now if $x' \in X$ then $-x' \in X$ and if $y' \in Y$ then $-y' \in Y$. If $w' = x' + y' \in W$ and $w \in W$, then $w - w' = x + y - (x' + y') = (x - x') + (y - y') \in W$. Since also $\alpha w \in W$ if $\alpha \in F$, we see from E4 that W is a subspace. The subspace W is called the *sum* of X and Y; we write $W = X + Y$. This subspace is sup (X, Y) in E8.

What can we say about dim $(X + Y)$? Let $A = \{a_j\}$ be a basis for X and $B = \{b_k\}$ be a basis for Y. It is evident that $A \cup B$ spans $X + Y$ and, therefore, that dim $(X + Y) \leq$ dim $X +$ dim Y. Let us assume first that $X \cap Y = \langle 0 \rangle$. Then $A \cup B$ is a basis for $X + Y$ and dim $(X + Y) =$ dim X + dim Y. Each $w \in X + Y$ has an expression $w = x + y$ with $x \in X$ and $y \in Y$ and the vectors x and y are uniquely determined by w. It follows, in view of B22, that the correspondence $(x, y) \leftrightarrow x + y$ between $X \oplus Y$ and $X + Y$ is an isomorphism. For the sake of brevity we shall say, whenever $X \cap Y = \langle 0 \rangle$ and only then, simply that $X + Y = X \oplus Y$.

If $X \leq Z$ and $Y \leq Z$ and $X \oplus Y = Z$ (that is, $X + Y = Z$ and $X \cap Y = \langle 0 \rangle$), then we say that X and Y are *complementary* subspaces of Z, and that each of X and Y is a *complement* of the other (in Z). For example, X and $\langle 0 \rangle$ are complementary subspaces of a space X, and each is the only complement of the other. That no other subspace has a *unique* complement will be a consequence of an argument to which we now turn.

Let us revert for a moment to the proof of E1. We had $Y_m \leq X_n$ and a basis $A = \{a_h\}$ $(h = 1, \ldots, m)$ for Y_m. As just observed, the situation is entirely clear if $m = 0$ or $m = n$, so we assume that $0 < m < n$. In proving E1 we produced a set $C = \{b_j\}$ $(j = m + 1, \ldots, n)$ such that the set $B = A \cup C$ was a basis for X_n. Let us denote by W_{n-m} the subspace spanned by C. Since B is a basis for X_n, we conclude both that $W_{n-m} + Y_m = X_n$ and that $W_{n-m} \cap Y_m = \langle 0 \rangle$. It follows that $X_n = Y_m \oplus W_{n-m}$; thus Y_m and W_{n-m} are complementary subspaces of X_n. That W_{n-m} is not uniquely determined by Y_m is evident from the arbitrariness, in the proof of E1, in the choice of the vectors $b_{m+1}, \ldots, b_n$.

1. **Theorem.** If $Y_m \leq X_n$ and $m < n$, then Y_m has a complementary subspace W_{n-m} in X_n and $X_n = Y_m \oplus W_{n-m}$.

It is also true that each subspace of an infinite-dimensional space has a complement; see [C5].

Suppose that $Y_m \leq X_n$. The common dimension $n - m$ of each complement of Y_m may be called the *codimension* of Y_m. A subspace with codimension 1 has itself dimension $n - 1$ and is called a *hyperspace*; a *hyperplane* is a flat (cf. E5) obtained by translating a hyperspace. A hyperplane is therefore a hyperspace if and only if it contains the origin.

The operation of adding subspaces is obviously commutative and is easily seen (cf. 8) to be associative. We may therefore define the sum of any finite set of subspaces; if the subspaces are X^j $(j = 1, \ldots, p)$ we denote their sum by $\overset{p}{\underset{j=1}{+}} X^j$. A set of subspaces is said to be *independent* if each has only the trivial intersection with the sum of all the others. If the subspaces X^j $(j = 1, \ldots, p)$ are independent and their sum is the space X, then we say that X is the *direct sum* of the subspaces X^j and write $X = \overset{p}{\underset{j=1}{\oplus}} X^j$; evidently $\dim X = \overset{p}{\underset{j=1}{\sum}} \dim X^j$. For example, let X_n have a basis $\{b_k\}$ $(k = 1, \ldots, n)$ and for $k = 1, \ldots, n$ denote by B^k the one-dimensional space $\langle b_k \rangle$ spanned by b_k. Since the vectors b_k are independent, so are the spaces B^k, and their sum is evidently X_n; hence $X_n = \overset{n}{\underset{k=1}{\oplus}} B^k$.

We prove, finally, in the finite-dimensional case the following important theorem.

2. **Theorem.** If $Y \leq X$ and $Z \leq X$, then $\dim Y + \dim Z = \dim (Y \cap Z) + \dim (Y + Z)$.

Let U and V be complements of $Y \cap Z$ in Y and Z respectively. Thus $Y = (Y \cap Z) \oplus U$ and $Z = (Y \cap Z) \oplus V$. We shall show that the sub-spaces U, V, and $Y \cap Z$ are independent. Since $U \leq Y$, we see that $U \cap Z \leq Y \cap Z$; since $U \cap (Y \cap Z) = \langle 0 \rangle$, we conclude that $U \cap Z = \langle 0 \rangle$. Similarly, $V \cap Y = \langle 0 \rangle$. A vector of $U + V$, moreover, will be of the form $u + v$ with $u \in U$ and $v \in V$. If $u + v = w \in Y \cap Z$ then u, $w \in Y$, whence $v \in Y$; since also $v \in Z$, it follows that $v \in Y \cap Z$ and hence, by the definition of V, $v = 0$. Similarly, $u = 0$ and we conclude that $(Y \cap Z) \cap (U + V) = \langle 0 \rangle$. Hence the subspaces $Y \cap Z$, U, and V are independent, and therefore

$$Y + Z = [(Y \cap Z) \oplus U] + [(Y \cap Z) \oplus V].$$

Since addition of subspaces is associative (cf. 8), and $W + W = W$, it follows that
$$Y + Z = (Y \cap Z) \oplus U \oplus V.$$

Hence

$$\dim (Y + Z) = \dim (Y \cap Z) + (\dim Y - \dim (Y \cap Z))$$
$$+ (\dim Z - \dim (Y \cap Z)),$$

and the theorem follows.

EXERCISES

3. For each subspace in E2–3 find a basis for a complementary subspace. Then find in each case a basis for a complementary subspace other than the one just found.

4. Suppose that $X \leq Z$ and $Y \leq Z$. Show that the set-theoretic union $X \cup Y$ is closed under multiplication by scalars. Show also that $X \cup Y$ is a subspace of Z if and only if either $X \leq Y$ or $Y \leq X$. (T)

5. Let X_a $(a \in A)$ be any set of subspaces of Y. Prove that $\cap_a X_a \leq Y$. (T)

6. Let $X \leq Z$ and $Y \leq Z$. Prove that $X + Y$ is the intersection (cf. 5) of all $W \leq Z$ such that $X \leq W$ and $Y \leq W$. Hence show that $X + Y = \sup (X, Y)$ of E8. What is $\inf (X, Y)$? (T)

7. Suppose that a *subset* A spans X and a subset B spans Y. Show that $A \cup B$ spans $X + Y$, i.e., $\langle A \cup B \rangle = X + Y$. In particular, $\langle X \cup Y \rangle = X + Y$. (T)

8. Prove that addition of subspaces is associative. Prove also that there is an identity element for the operation of addition. Is the set of all subspaces with the binary operation of addition a group?

9. Suppose that $Z = X \oplus Y$ and that $z \in Z$. Prove that there exist vectors $x \in X$ and $y \in Y$ such that $z = x + y$ and that these vectors are uniquely determined by z. (When no confusion is possible we shall not distinguish between $x \in X$ and $x + 0 \in Z$, where $0 \in Y$ and, in fact, $x + 0$ is $(x, 0)$ of B22.) (T)

10. Suppose that $X \leq Z$ and $Y \leq Z$ and that for each $z \in Z$ there exist vectors $x \in X$ and $y \in Y$, uniquely determined by z, such that $z = x + y$. Prove that $X \cap Y = \{0\}$ and hence that $Z = X \oplus Y$.

11. An element of R^R (cf. B12) is a real-valued function $\alpha \to x(\alpha)$ of a real variable α. We say that x is *even* or *odd* if for every α it is true respectively that $x(-\alpha) = x(\alpha)$ or $x(-\alpha) = -x(\alpha)$. Prove that the set of all even functions is a subspace of R^R, and that the same is true of the set of all odd functions. Are there subspaces complementary? (It is always true that

$$x(\alpha) = \tfrac{1}{2}[x(\alpha) + x(-\alpha)] + \tfrac{1}{2}[x(\alpha) - x(-\alpha)].)$$

12. Suppose that $Y_7 \leq X_{13}$ and $Z_9 \leq X_{13}$. What conclusion can you draw from 2 about $\dim (Y_7 \cap Z_9)$?

13. Suppose that $Y_7 \leq X_{13}$, that $Z \leq X_{13}$, and that we have learned that $\dim (Y_7 \cap Z) = 2$. What conclusion can we draw about $\dim Z$? Is there a similar conclusion if $\dim (Y_7 \cap Z) \leq 2$ or ≥ 2?

14. Suppose that $Y = X \oplus V$ and $Y = X \oplus U$. Show by an example that $U \cap V$ is not necessarily trivial. What can be said about $\dim (U \cap V)$?

15. There is a relation similar to that of F2 involving codimension instead of dimension. What is it? Prove it.

16. Let X be a proper subspace of Z and suppose that $u \in' X$. Show that $\langle u \rangle$ has a complement that contains X.

17. If $X \leq Z$ and $\dim X < \dim Z$, prove that X is the intersection of all the hyperspaces of Z which contain X.

18. Let $S \leq X$ and (cf. E7) for the purpose of this exercise denote by (x) the equivalence-set of all vectors y such that $y \equiv x \pmod S$, and denote by E the class of all equivalence-sets. Define addition and multiplication by scalars on E as follows: $(x) + (y) = (x + y)$ and $\alpha(x) = (\alpha x)$. Prove that $\{E, +; F, \cdot\}$ is a linear space of dimension $\dim X - \dim S$. It follows that this space is isomorphic to any complement of S in X; for this reason the space is often denoted by $X - S$ or by X/S, and is called the *difference-space* or *quotient space* of X and S.

19. Let $S \leq X$, let $a \in X$ but $a \in' S$ and consider the set $[a]$ of all vectors of the form $x = a + s$ with $s \in S$. Show that any two such vectors are congruent $\pmod S$. With the set (a) as defined in 18, is it true that $(a) = [a]$? Prove your answer. The set $[a]$ is a flat in the sense of E. If $c \in [a]$ then $c + S = a + S$. If $\{b_k\}$ $(k = 1, \ldots, n)$ is a basis for S then S consists of all vectors $\sum \xi_k b_k$ and the flat $a + S$ consists of all vectors $a + \sum \xi_k b_k$. (T)

20. Let X denote the space of all functions $\alpha \to x(\alpha)$ defined for $a \leq \alpha \leq b$ and such that the kth derivative $x^{(k)}(\alpha)$ is continuous for $k = 1, \ldots, n$. Suppose that $\xi_k(\alpha)$ are continuous for $k = 1, \ldots, n$ and for $x \in X$ define $Lx = \sum_{k=0}^{n} \xi_k(\alpha) x^{(k)}(\alpha)$. Then Lx is continuous for $a \leq \alpha \leq b$ and it makes sense to seek $x \in X$ such that $Lx = 0$; this equation is a homogeneous linear ordinary differential equation of order n, and we assume for simplicity that $\xi_n(\alpha) \neq 0$. Prove that the set of all $x \in X$ such that $Lx = 0$ is a subspace of X; denote it by N_L. (It is shown in the theory of differential equations that $\dim N_L = n$.) Now let $\alpha \to y(\alpha)$ be continuous for $a \leq \alpha \leq b$ and consider the nonhomogeneous equation $Lx = y$. Prove that if u and v are two solutions of the nonhomogeneous equation and $w = u - v$, then $Lw = 0$. Let x_0 be any particular solution of the equation $Lx = y$. Prove that the set of all solutions constitutes the flat $x_0 + N_L$. (If $x_1, \ldots, x_n$ are n independent solutions of the equation $Lx = 0$, then (cf. 18) the flat may be represented parametrically as $x_0 + \sum \beta_k x_k$; the x_0 is a "particular integral" and $\sum \beta_k x_k$ is the "complementary function".)

21. Is it necessarily true that $X \cap (Y + Z) = (X \cap Y) + (X \cap Z)$? That $X \cap (Y \oplus Z) = (X \cap Y) \oplus (X \cap Z)$? Prove by examples that the answer to each question is negative. Study the possibility of replacing one or the other of the equality signs by $\leq$ or $\geq$.

22. Suppose that $X \leq U, Y \leq U, Z \leq U$ and that $X \leq Z$. Prove that $X + (Y \cap Z) = (X + Y) \cap Z$. This result is sometimes called the *modular* law. Show by an example with $U = R_3$, that the hypothesis $X \leq Z$ cannot be omitted.

23. Let $\{b_k\}$ be a basis for X_n and suppose that the vectors a_h ($h = 1, \ldots, m < n$) are independent. Show that $n - m$ of the vectors b_k can be chosen so as to form, along with the vectors a_h, a basis for X_n. (In other words, the other m b's can be replaced by the a's. For this reason this result is often called the *Exchange Theorem*.)

24. Prove that the intersection of two flats is a flat, unless it is empty.

G. Change of Basis; Nonsingular Matrices of Order n

Suppose that we are using a basis $\{p_k\}$ for X_n and wish to introduce a new basis $\{q_k\}$; see D8 for an example. We know that there exist uniquely determined scalars α_{jk} and β_{jk} such that

1.
$$p_k = \sum \alpha_{jk} q_j, \qquad q_k = \sum \beta_{jk} p_j.$$

It follows that
$$p_k = \sum_j \alpha_{jk}\left(\sum_h \beta_{hj} p_h\right) = \sum_h \left(\sum_j \beta_{hj}\alpha_{jk}\right)p_h.$$

Now the p_k are independent and $p_k = \sum_h \delta_{hk} p_h$ (cf. SE17), whence

2.
$$\sum_j \beta_{hj}\alpha_{jk} = \delta_{hk} \qquad (h, k = 1, \ldots, n).$$

Using the q's, we obtain similarly

3.
$$\sum_j \alpha_{hj}\beta_{jk} = \delta_{hk} \qquad (h, k = 1, \ldots, n).$$

How are the old and new components ξ_h and η_k of a vector $x = \sum \xi_h p_h = \sum \eta_k q_k$ related to each other? From the equations
$$x = \sum \xi_h p_h = \sum_{h,j} \xi_h \alpha_{jh} q_j = \sum \eta_j q_j = \sum_{h,j} \eta_j \beta_{hj} p_h$$

and the independence of the p's and q's, we draw these conclusions:

4.
$$\eta_j = \sum \alpha_{jh}\xi_h, \qquad \xi_h = \sum \beta_{hj}\eta_j.$$

In order to emphasize the exact relationship between 4 and 1 let us rewrite 1 as follows:

5.
$$p_k = \sum q_j \alpha_{jk}, \qquad q_k = \sum p_j \beta_{jk}.$$

Here is an example in a real X_3:

6. $\begin{cases} p_1 = \quad q_1 + 2q_2 - 2q_3 \\ p_2 = -q_1 + 3q_2 \\ p_3 = \qquad\; - 2q_2 + \; q_3 \end{cases}$ $\qquad \begin{aligned} q_1 &= 3p_1 + 2p_2 + 6p_3 \\ q_2 &= \; p_1 + \; p_2 + 2p_3 \\ q_3 &= 2p_1 + 2p_2 + 5p_3 \end{aligned}$

Equations 2 and 3 are easily verified. Equations 4 become these:

7. $\begin{cases} \eta_1 = \quad \xi_1 - \; \xi_2 \\ \eta_2 = \quad 2\xi_1 + 3\xi_2 - 2\xi_3 \\ \eta_3 = -2\xi_1 \qquad\;\; + \; \xi_3 \end{cases}$ $\qquad \begin{aligned} \xi_1 &= 3\eta_1 + \; \eta_2 + 2\eta_3 \\ \xi_2 &= 2\eta_1 + \; \eta_2 + 2\eta_3 \\ \xi_3 &= 6\eta_1 + 2\eta_2 + 5\eta_3. \end{aligned}$

The function of x whose expression in terms of the η's is $5\eta_1^2 + 2\eta_1\eta_2 + 4\eta_1\eta_3$ has, in terms of the ξ's, the expression $\xi_1^2 - \xi_2^2$. The function of x whose expression in terms of the ξ's is $2\xi_1^2 - 3\xi_2^2 + \xi_1\xi_2 + 2\xi_2\xi_3 - 2\xi_3\xi_1$ has, in terms of the η's, the very simple expression $\eta_1\eta_2$.

Much information is latent in equations such as 1 and 4 which relate to each other bases and sets of coordinates. We illustrate by asking and answering a few questions concerning the foregoing example in X_3.

What are the old coordinates of q_2? By inspection, from 6 (right) they are $(\xi_k) = (1, 1, 2)$. The same result follows on substituting $(\eta_k) = (0, 1, 0)$ into 7 (right).

What are the new coordinates of the point whose old coordinates are $(\xi_k) = (2, -1, 1)$? On substituting into 7 (left) we find $(\eta_k) = (3, -1, -3)$. The same result can be obtained by using 6 (left) to form the linear combination $2p_1 - p_2 + p_3$ and picking off the coefficients of the q's.

What is the old expression for $2\eta_1 + 3\eta_2 - \eta_3$? On substituting from 7 (left) we find $10\xi_1 + 7\xi_2 - 7\xi_3$.

The new equation of a line is $x = -2q_2 + q_3 + \lambda(q_1 + 2q_2 - 2q_3)$, $(-\infty < \lambda < \infty)$; what was its old equation? On substituting from 6 (right) we obtain $x = p_3 + \lambda p_1$.

What are the new symmetric equations for a line whose old symmetric equations were

$$\frac{\xi_1 - 3}{4} = \frac{\xi_2 + 1}{0} = \frac{\xi_3 + 5}{-2}?$$

One method is to substitute from 7 (right) and reduce the result to symmetric form. An easier way is to go back to the vectorial form, writing

$$x = (3, -1, -5) + \lambda(4, 0, -2).$$

On calculating new coordinates from 7 (left), we obtain the new equation $x = (4, 13, -11) + \lambda(4, 12, -10)$ and the symmetric equations

$$\frac{\eta_1 - 4}{4} = \frac{\eta_2 - 13}{12} = \frac{\eta_3 + 11}{-10}.$$

In a practical situation we may be given simply the values of a function expressed in terms of coordinates with respect to a known basis, the problem being to find another basis with respect to which the expression of the function becomes appreciably simpler—preferably, indeed, "as simple as possible". We shall obtain detailed results on this problem later, and our work will be greatly facilitated by concepts that we mention now on a preliminary informal basis.

In the right members of 7 let us detach the coefficients, write them down in the same square arrangement, and enclose the array in brackets. Each of the respective results

8.
$$A = [\alpha_{jk}] \quad \text{and} \quad B = [\beta_{jk}]$$

is called an nth order *matrix*, and these matrices are said to be, respectively, the matrix A of the η's with respect to the ξ's, and the matrix B of the ξ's with respect to the η's. They are:

9.
$$A = \begin{bmatrix} 1 & -1 & 0 \\ 2 & 3 & -2 \\ -2 & 0 & 1 \end{bmatrix} \quad \text{and} \quad B = \begin{bmatrix} 3 & 1 & 2 \\ 2 & 1 & 2 \\ 6 & 2 & 5 \end{bmatrix}.$$

The scalars α_{jk} are called the *elements* or *entries* of A. The horizontal lines are called *rows* and the vertical lines are called *columns*. The matrices of 8 are of *order n* because they have n rows and columns; in 9, A and B are of order three. The position of the element α_{jk} is indicated by the subscripts; α_{jk} is in the jth row and the kth column. In A of 9, for example, $\alpha_{22} = 3$, while $\beta_{31} = 6$ in B; the second row of B is 2, 1, 2, and its third column has, in order, the elements 2, 2, 5. The fourth row of $[\alpha_{jk}]$ is $\alpha_{41}, \ldots, \alpha_{4n}$, while its fifth column has, in order, the elements $\alpha_{15}, \ldots, \alpha_{n5}$.

Similarly, the matrices of detached coefficients in 6 are said to be, respectively, the matrix P of the p's with respect to the q's, and the matrix Q of the q's with respect to the p's. They are:

10.
$$P = \begin{bmatrix} 1 & 2 & -2 \\ -1 & 3 & 0 \\ 0 & -2 & 1 \end{bmatrix} \quad \text{and} \quad Q = \begin{bmatrix} 3 & 2 & 6 \\ 1 & 1 & 2 \\ 2 & 2 & 5 \end{bmatrix}.$$

The manner of summation should be noted with extreme care. In 4 (see also 7) the summation in the right member runs across the respective *rows* of $[\alpha_{jk}]$ and $[\beta_{jk}]$ (see 9, A and B). In 1 and 5, on the other hand (see also 6) the summation in the right member runs down the respective *columns* of $[\alpha_{jk}]$ and $[\beta_{jk}]$ (see 10, P and Q). Although this fact is connected with the idea of duality (see Chap. 7), we may regard it here as a reflection of our invariable habit of writing equations horizontally instead of vertically.

The student may seek a relation, which we do not exploit now, between A and P, and between B and Q. We shall also see later that 2 and 3 express a highly important relation between A and B, that either of these equations is a consequence of the other, and that they are equivalent to similar relations between P and Q; in fact, any *one* of A, B, P, Q determines all the others.

We have seen that the bases $\{p_k\}$ and $\{q_k\}$ determine the matrices P, Q, A, and B. It is tempting to choose some one of them and call it *the* matrix of the change of basis. Such a step would invite mnemonic disaster, and we prefer, therefore, always to speak quite explicitly of the matrix of the old or new basis or components with respect to the new or old basis or components.

Suppose now, vice versa, merely that we are given an nth order matrix $C = [\gamma_{jk}]$ $(j, k = 1, \ldots, n)$ with elements in F. We can say that each row and each column is a vector of F_n referred to the natural basis E of F_n, or to some other preassigned basis for F_n. What information does C give about our space X_n?

The answer, quite simply, is NONE! Until, that is, a basis is specified for X_n. With a basis $\{p_k\}$ specified, the matrix C enables us to write down (cf. D2) an ordered set of vectors $c_h = \sum \gamma_{kh} p_k$ $(h = 1, \ldots, n)$. It is natural to ask under what circumstances $\{c_h\}$ will be a basis for X_n; this will evidently be true (cf. D) if and only if the vectors c_h are independent. This in turn will be true if and only if $\sum \lambda_h c_h = \sum_k (\sum_h \lambda_h \gamma_{kh}) b_k = 0$ implies $\lambda_h = 0$ $(h = 1, \ldots, n)$. This in turn will be true if and only if the equations $\sum \lambda_h \gamma_{kh} = 0$ imply that $\lambda_h = 0$ $(h = 1, \ldots, n)$ or, in other words (cf. C6), if and only if the n vectors (γ_{kh}) of F_n formed by the columns of C are independent in F_n.

Let us call an nth order matrix with elements in F *nonsingular* or *regular* if and only if the n vectors of F_n formed by its columns are independent in F_n. Our results may be summarized in the following theorem.

11. **Theorem.** Let $\{p_h\}$ and $\{q_k\}$ be bases for an n-dimensional linear space X_n. Then the matrix of either with respect to the other is a nonsingular nth order matrix. If $C = [\gamma_{kh}]$ is an nth order matrix, then the following conditions are equivalent:

(a) C is nonsingular;

(b) considered as vectors in F_n, the columns of C are independent;

(c) the only solution of the equations $\sum \lambda_h \gamma_{kh} = 0$ $(k = 1, \ldots, n)$ is the trivial one, $\lambda_h = 0$ $(h = 1, \ldots, n)$;

(d) if $c_h = \sum \gamma_{kh} p_k$ $(h = 1, \ldots, n)$, then $\{c_h\}$ is an independent set and therefore a basis for X_n, and $[\gamma_{kh}]$ is the matrix of the basis $\{c_h\}$ with respect to the basis $\{p_k\}$.

EXERCISES

12. Prove 3. (T)

13. In the example of 6–7, as in the illustrations in the text, refer to $\{q_k\}$ and η_k as "new" and to $\{p_k\}$ and ξ_k as "old". Obtain answers to the following questions:

(a) What are the new coordinates of $(\xi_k) = (3, 2, 3)$?

(b) What is the old expression for a function whose new expression is $4\eta_1 - 5\eta_2 + 2\eta_3$?

(c) What is the old expression for a function whose new expression is $13\eta_1^2 + 2\eta_2^2 + 8\eta_3^2 + 10\eta_1\eta_2 + 8\eta_2\eta_3 + 20\eta_1\eta_3$?

(d) What is the new representation of the plane whose old representation is $x = \lambda p_1 + \mu p_2 (-\infty < \lambda, \mu < \infty)$?

(e) What is the new representation of the flat (cf. E) whose old representation is $x = 2p_1 - p_2 + p_3 + \lambda(p_1 + p_3) + \mu(2p_2 + 3p_3), (-\infty < \lambda, \mu < \infty)$?

14. In a real X_4 we have a basis $\{b_k\}$ and coordinates ξ_k. We wish to introduce a new basis $\{c_k\}$ with $c_1 = b_1$, $c_2 = b_2$, and $c_h = \sum \xi_{kh} b_k$ $(h = 3, 4)$. Find conditions on ξ_{kh} $(h = 3, 4; k = 1, 2, 3, 4)$ necessary and sufficient for $\{c_k\}$ to be a basis. Choose particular ξ_{kh} meeting these conditions and write out the matrix of the resulting basis $\{c_k\}$ with respect to $\{b_k\}$.

15. In a real X_3 we have a basis $\{b_k\}$ and coordinates ξ_k. We wish to introduce a new basis $\{a_k\}$ and coordinates η_k in such a way that $\xi_1 = 4\eta_1 - 3\eta_2 + 2\eta_3$ while $\xi_h = \sum \beta_{hk}\eta_k$ $(h = 2, 3)$. Find conditions on $\beta_{hk} = (k = 1, 2, 3; h = 2, 3)$ necessary and sufficient for $\{a_k\}$ to be a basis if $b_k = \sum \beta_{kk}a_h$ (cf. 1). Choose particular β_{hk} meeting these conditions and write out the matrix of the ξ's with respect to the η's.

16. In the text we obtained 4 from 1 and an appeal to the independence of the p's and q's. Suppose now that we are given bases $\{p_k\}$ and $\{q_k\}$ and are told that each $x = \sum \xi_k p_k = \sum \eta_k q_k$, where the ξ's and η's are related as in 4. Can we conclude that the p's and q's are related as in 1? Explain. (T)

17. In the contexts of 1 and 4 suppose that we have functions f and g whose respective expressions are $\sum \gamma_k \eta_k$ and $\sum \delta_k \xi_k$. Obtain an expression for f in terms of the ξ's and for g in terms of the η's. If the results are $\sum \gamma'_k \xi_k$ and $\sum \delta'_k \eta_k$, obtain equations connecting γ'_k and γ_k and equations connecting δ'_k and δ_k.

18. Let $X_{p+q} = Y_p \oplus Z_q$, let $\{a_k\}$ and $\{b_k\}$ $(k = 1, \ldots, p)$ be bases for Y_p and let $\{a_{p+h}\}$ and $\{b_{p+h}\}$ $(h = 1, \ldots, q)$ be bases for Z_q. Show that $\{a_j\}$ and $\{b_j\}$ $(j = 1, \ldots, p + q)$ are bases for X_{p+q}. Let the matrix of $\{a_k\}$ with respect to $\{b_k\}$ be $[\alpha_{rk}]$ and let the matrix of $\{a_{p+h}\}$ with respect to $\{b_{p+h}\}$ be $[\alpha_{p+h\, p+s}]$. Write down the matrix $[\alpha_{jt}]$ $(j, t = 1, \ldots, p + q)$ of $\{a_t\}$ with respect to $\{b_j\}$. Noting the special form of $[\alpha_{jt}]$, prove conversely that if $\{a_j\}$ and $\{b_j\}$ are bases of X_{p+q} and are connected by a matrix of this special form, then $X_{p+q} = Y_p \oplus Z_q$ where $Y_p = \langle a_1, \ldots, a_p \rangle = \langle b_1, \ldots, b_p \rangle$ and $Z_q = \langle a_{p+1}, \ldots, a_{p+q} \rangle = \langle b_{p+1}, \ldots, b_{p+q} \rangle$.

19. Let $\{b_j\}$ be a basis for X_{p+q}. We wish to introduce a new basis $\{a_j\}$, requiring only that it be adapted, as $\{b_j\}$ is, to the subspace $\langle b_1, \ldots, b_p \rangle$ (cf. F1). Obtain an equivalent condition on the matrix $[\alpha_{jt}]$ $(j, t = 1, \ldots, p + q)$ of $\{a_t\}$ with respect to $\{b_j\}$. (T)

20. It is sometimes desirable to use only bases having certain special properties, and it is natural to ask how these properties may be reflected in the matrix connecting two such bases. In the three-space E_P of Chap. 3, for example, suppose that $\{b_k\}$ and $\{a_k\}$ are orthonormal bases and that $a_k = \sum \alpha_{hk}b_h$ $(h, k = 1, 2, 3)$. What special properties does the matrix $[\alpha_{hk}]$ have? (See 3K26.)

SIX
Linear Transformations

We saw in Chap. 4 that a structure is determined by designating its elements and defining certain operations on them. A proposed structure may be studied by comparing it with structures whose properties are already known from previous study; it may be possible, for example, to discern in the proposed structure a sub-structure isomorphic (see 4G) with a known one. The comparison between structures will ordinarily consist in establishing correspondences between elements of one and elements of the other, or, in other words, mapping one structure into the other. Those correspondences will be of special interest, naturally enough, under which structural operations correspond or are "preserved" in the sense of this example: let a structure S with elements $a, b, \ldots$ and a binary operation "$\circ$" be mapped by a function f into a structure T with a binary operation "$*$"; then "$\circ$" and "$*$" correspond if $f(a \circ b) = f(a) * f(b)$ for all $a, b \in S$.

Since we are concerned primarily with the linear spaces defined in the preceding chapter, we shall take special interest in those mappings of one linear space into another which preserve the linear operations. The effect of such a mapping may be described briefly by saying (see A6) that the map of any particular linear combination of vectors is the same linear combination of the maps of the vectors. Such mappings are said to be linear, and are called linear transformations. The ideas and results developed in this chapter underlie all our later work.

A. Definitions and Examples

Let $\{X, +; F, \cdot\}$ and $\{Y, +'; F, \cdot'\}$ be two linear spaces over the same field F of scalars. A function (cf. 1I) or transformation or mapping L on X into $Y : x \to L(x)$ (often abbreviated to Lx) is said to be *linear* if for each $x_1, x_2 \in X$ and $\alpha_1, \alpha_2 \in F$ it is true that

$$L(\alpha_1 \cdot x_1 + \alpha_2 \cdot x_2) = \alpha_1 \cdot' Lx_1 +' \alpha_2 \cdot' Lx_2.$$

Since it is clear from the context whether or not the primes are needed they may be omitted. As usual, we also omit the dots and write the condition as

1.
$$L(\alpha_1 x_1 + \alpha_2 x_2) = \alpha_1 L x_1 + \alpha_2 L x_2.$$

Capital Latin letters H, I, J, K, L, and M will always denote linear mappings (or, later, matrices). We agree that $K = L$ if and only if $x \in X$ implies $Kx = Lx$.

It is sometimes convenient to deal separately with each of two conditions which are together equivalent to 1. A mapping T on X into $Y : x \to Tx$ is said to be *homogeneous* if $x \in X$ and $\alpha \in F$ imply that

2.
$$T(\alpha x) = \alpha Tx,$$

and to be *additive* if x, $x' \in X$ imply that

3.
$$T(x + x') = Tx + Tx'.$$

The interchangeability of vectorial operations and mapping implied by these requirements may be displayed as follows:

	Vectorial operations in domain, then map	Map first, then vectorial operations in codomain
Homogeneity	$T(\alpha x) = \alpha Tx$	
Additivity	$T(x + x') = Tx + Tx'$	

The proof of the following theorem is left to the reader.

4. Theorem. A mapping $T : X \to Y$ is linear (1) if and only if it is both homogeneous (2) and additive (3).

Observe that if T is homogeneous, then $T(0) = 0$. Hence a translation (cf. 3L1) is not linear unless, trivially, it is the identity.

As in 1I we denote by LS the image in Y of a subset S of X. The image LX of X is the *range* of L; we write $R_L = LX$. If $Y \le X$ then L maps X into itself and is called an *endomorphism* of X or a (linear) *operator* on X or in X. If $R_L = Y$ then L maps X *onto* Y.

As a first example, fix $\beta \in F$ and define an endomorphism $T_\beta : x \to \beta x$. Such a mapping is called a *scalar* mapping and is easily seen (cf. 8) to be linear. If $\beta = 0$ then $T_\beta X = \langle 0 \rangle$; this transformation is called the zero-transformation and is denoted by the numeral 0. If $\beta = 1$ then $x \to x$ and each $x \in X$ is fixed; T_1 is called the *identity* and is denoted by I_X or merely I or, sometimes, by the numeral 1. If $\beta = -1$ then T_β merely reverses the "direction" of each vector and hence is called a *reflection in the origin*. We recall that in E_P (cf. 3C) T_p had the effect, for any $p > 0$, of a radial stretching by a factor p. In the present more general situation we cannot speak of lengths, of course, but we shall not be misled if we think of ratios of lengths.

As a second example let us reconsider a rotation M of E_P about P (see 3L2). A parallelogram with one vertex at P is carried by M onto a congruent parallelogram, the vertex at P being fixed. Hence (in present notation) the image $M(\alpha x + \beta y)$ of $\alpha x + \beta y$ is $\alpha M x + \beta M y$ and M is linear by 1. (Cf. 14H4.)

In this example the plane π perpendicular to the axis of M is mapped into itself. We may conclude that the rotation of a plane π about an axis perpendicular to it through a point P on it is an endomorphism of the two-dimensional linear space Z_2 of vectors in π issuing from P. This result may be obtained directly by regarding Z_2 as the complex plane (cf. 4H). Rotation through an angle φ about the origin is the mapping $z \rightarrow e^{i\varphi}z$. This mapping is linear because $e^{i\varphi}(\alpha_1 z_1 + \alpha_2 z_2) = \alpha_1(e^{i\varphi}z_1) + \alpha_2(e^{i\varphi}z_2)$.

The linear functionals of Chap. 7 are linear transformations on X into the space F_1 of scalars.

As a final example, for the moment, let us introduce a few general ideas by studying briefly endomorphisms L of a two-dimensional space X_2 with a fixed basis p_1, p_2. By 1, $Lx = L(\xi_1 p_1 + \xi_2 p_2) = \xi_1 L p_1 + \xi_2 L p_2$.

Let us express Lp_1 and Lp_2 in terms of p_1 and p_2:

$$Lp_1 = \alpha p_1 + \gamma p_2 \qquad \text{and} \qquad Lp_2 = \beta p_1 + \delta p_2.$$

Then

$$Lx = \xi_1(\alpha p_1 + \gamma p_2) + \xi_2(\beta p_1 + \delta p_2) = (\alpha\xi_1 + \beta\xi_2)p_1 + (\gamma\xi_1 + \delta\xi_2)p_2.$$

Since p_1 and p_2 are independent, the components of the image vector $Lx = y = \eta_1 p_1 + \eta_2 p_2$ are therefore given in terms of the components ξ_1, ξ_2 of x by these equations:

5.
$$\eta_1 = \alpha\xi_1 + \beta\xi_2, \qquad \eta_2 = \gamma\xi_1 + \delta\xi_2.$$

In a real X_2, for example, if $Lp_1 = (3, -1)$ and $Lp_2 = (-5, 2)$, then

$$\eta_1 = 3\xi_1 - 5\xi_2, \qquad \eta_2 = -\xi_1 + 2\xi_2.$$

We are often told, instead, merely that a mapping T has the property that if $x = \xi_1 p_1 + \xi_2 p_2$, then $Tx = \eta_1 p_1 + \eta_2 p_2$ where η_1 and η_2 are given by 5. That T is linear is nearly obvious (see 9) and it is evident that $Tp_1 = T(1, 0) = (\alpha, \gamma)$ and $Tp_2 = T(0, 1) = (\beta, \delta)$.

The essential feature of $L : X \rightarrow Y$ is that linear combinations in X map onto linear combinations in Y, while linear combinations in Y are the images of linear combinations in X. These facts result from reading from left to right or from right to left the equation

6.
$$L(\textstyle\sum \alpha_k x_k) = \sum \alpha_k L x_k = \sum \alpha_k y_k,$$

where $y_k = Lx_k$; this equation follows (see 10) by an easy induction from 1.

Now suppose that $S \leq X$, that is, S is a subspace of X. If S is generated by vectors x_k then it follows from 6 that LS is the subspace of Y generated by the vectors Lx_k. If, on the other hand, $W \leq Y$ is generated by vectors y_k, and $y_k = Lx_k$, then it follows from 6 that $W = LV$, where $V \leq X$ and V is generated by the vectors x_k. We have proved the following theorem.

7. **Theorem.** Let L map X linearly into Y. If $S \leq X$ then $LS \leq Y$. If $W \leq LX$ then $W = LV$ for some $V \leq X$.

Since $LX \leq Y$ it follows that $\dim R_L \leq \dim Y$. If p_k $(k = 1, \ldots, n)$ is a basis for X, moreover, then the vectors Lp_k span R_L, whence $\operatorname{sim} R_L \leq \dim X$. Hence $\dim R_L \leq \min(\dim X, \dim Y)$.

We spell out, finally, the definitions of 4J9 as they apply to linear transformations. Given $S \leq X$, $K : S \to Y$, and $L : X \to Y$, such that $x \in S$ implies $Kx = Lx$, we say that L is an *extension* of K to X and that K is the *restriction* of L to S, or that L *induces* K on S.

EXERCISES

8. With $\beta \in F$ fixed, define $T : x \to \beta x$. Prove that T is linear.

9. In X_2 with a fixed basis p_1, p_2, $x = \xi_1 p_1 + \xi_2 p_2 \to Tx = \eta_1 p_1 + \eta_2 p_2$ where the η's are calculated from the ξ's by 5. Prove that T is linear.

10. Prove 6. Does this condition imply, conversely, that L is linear? (T)

11. In E_2 (a Euclidean plane) with an orthonormal basis p_1, p_2 investigate the geometric effect of the following endormorphisms $(\xi, \eta) \to (\lambda, \mu)$, and find in each case the images of p_1 and p_2:

(a) $\begin{aligned} \lambda &= \alpha\xi \\ \mu &= \beta\eta \end{aligned}$; (b) $\begin{aligned} \lambda &= \xi \\ \mu &= \gamma\xi + \eta \end{aligned}$; (c) $\begin{aligned} \lambda &= \dfrac{\xi - \eta}{\sqrt{2}} \\ \mu &= \dfrac{\xi + \eta}{\sqrt{2}} \end{aligned}$;

(d) $\begin{aligned} \lambda &= \xi \\ \mu &= -\eta \end{aligned}$; (e) $\begin{aligned} \lambda &= -3\xi + 2\eta \\ \mu &= -6\xi + 4\eta \end{aligned}$.

(These examples and those of 12 will be used again; calculations may be saved for later reference.)

12. In a real X_2 with basis p_1, p_2 endomorphisms are determined by Lp_1 and Lp_2 as follows:

(a) $Lp_1 = 2p_1$, $\quad Lp_2 = 3p_2$;

(b) $Lp_1 = p_1 - p_2$, $\quad Lp_2 = 2p_2 - p_1$;

(c) $Lp_1 = 2p_1 + p_2$, $\quad Lp_2 = 3p_1 - 2p_2$;

(d) $Lp_1 = 3p_1 - 4p_2$, $\quad Lp_2 = p_1 - p_2$.

If $L(\xi_1 p_1 + \xi_2 p_2) = \xi_1 Lp_1 + \xi_2 Lp_2 = \eta_1 p_1 + \eta_2 p_2$, find in each case equations giving the η's in terms of the ξ's.

13. E_2 (cf. 11) is to be rotated about the origin through an angle φ. Use Euler's formula (4H10) or a geometric argument to show that if $(\xi, \eta) \to (\xi', \eta')$ and the basis is orthonormal then $\xi' = \xi \cos \varphi - \eta \sin \varphi$ and $\eta' = \xi \sin \varphi + \eta \cos \varphi$. Prove also that every linear transformation which leaves the lengths of vectors in E_2 unchanged and preserves the sense of angles is a rotation. What other possibilities exist if the restriction on the sense of angles is removed?

14. If T is linear on X into X and ℓ is a straight line through 0 then, unless $Tx = 0$ for each $x \in \ell$, $T\ell$ is a straight line through 0. Give an example in an X_2 to prove that this condition is not sufficient to insure that T be linear.

15. Suppose that $X = S \oplus T$ and that we are given $K : S \to Y$. Define $L : X \to Y$ as follows: if $x = s + t$ with $s \in S$ and $t \in T$, let $x \to Lx = Ks$. Prove that L is linear and that $LT = \langle 0 \rangle$. (This L is the trivial extension of K to X.) (T)

16. Vectors $x_1, \ldots, x_k \in X$ are dependent. Prove that $Lx_1, \ldots, Lx_k \in Y$ are dependent. (T)

17. Vectors $x_1, \ldots, x_k \in X$ have the property that their images $Lx_1, \ldots, Lx_k \in Y$ are independent. Use 16 to prove indirectly that $x_1, \ldots, x_k$ are independent. Give also a direct proof. (T)

18. Let p be a positive real number. On the space of all real-valued $x(t)$ defined for $-\infty < t < \infty$ define $K : x \to Kx$, where $Kx(t) = x(t + p) - x(t)$. Prove that K is linear and that if x is continuous then so is Kx. For which x is $Kx = 0$ (the zero-function)?

19. Let C^0 denote the space of real-valued functions x that are continuous for $0 \le t \le 1$, and let $x \in C^n$ if its nth derivative $x^{(n)} \in C^0$. For $n = 1, 2, 3, \ldots$, define D on C^n into $C^{n-1} : x \to Dx$, where $Dx(t) \equiv x'(t)$. Prove that D is linear. For which x is $Dx = 0$? For $n = 0, 1, 2, \ldots$, define S on C^n into $C^{n+1} : x \to Sx$ where $Sx(t) = \int_0^t x(u)\, du$. Prove that S is linear. (Observe that $x \to \int x(t)\, dt$ is not linear in the strict sense, for $\int 0\, dt = c$ where c is any constant; for this reason, in fact, $\int x(t)\, dt$ is not a specific element of C^{n+1} so that $x \to \int x(t)\, dt$ is not a mapping in our sense of the word. In order to retain the advantages of linearity for indefinite integration one may deal in C^{n+1} with equivalence-sets in which x and y are equivalent if $x(t) - y(t)$ is constant. We omit details.)

20. In the space $\{X, +; C, \cdot\}$ of 5B10 define M on X into $X : x \to Mx$, where, for $\alpha \in C$, $Mx(\alpha) = \alpha x(\alpha)$. Prove that M is linear. How is the degree of Mx related to the degree of x?

B. Algebraic Operations with Linear Transformations

Since linear transformations are functions, it is entirely natural that the sum $L + M$ of two transformations and the product αL of a mapping L by a scalar α should be specified, as in 5B, by pointwise operations in the domain.

Given linear mappings L and M on X into Y we define T on X into $Y : x \to Tx = Lx + Mx$. We verify in 2 that T is linear and denote it by $L + M$. We verify in 3 that

$$L + M = M + L$$

$$K + (L + M) = (K + L) + M$$

$$L + 0 = L.$$

Given $\alpha \in F$ and a linear mapping $L : X \to Y$ we define T on X into

$Y : x \to Tx = \alpha(Lx)$. We verify in 2 that T is linear and denote it by $\alpha \cdot L$. We verify in 3 that

$$(\alpha + \beta)L = \alpha L + \beta L$$
$$\alpha(L + M) = \alpha L + \alpha M$$
$$\alpha(\beta L) = (\alpha\beta)L$$
$$1L = L.$$

Let us denote by $\mathcal{L}(X, Y)$ the set of all linear mappings L on X into Y. With addition $(+)$ and multiplication by a scalar $(\cdot)$ as just defined, we prove in 3 the following theorem:

1. $\{\mathcal{L}, + ; F, \cdot\}$ is a linear space.

Given K on X into Y and L on Y into Z, let us define a mapping T on X into $Z : x \to Tx = L(Kx)$. We see in 2 that T is linear, denote it by LK, and call it the *product* or *resultant* of K by L or of K and L in that order. In order for the resultant LK to be defined, it is sufficient (and necessary) for L to be defined on R_K. (Note 7 below.)

The resultant of two endomorphisms is always defined; hence powers L^n ($n = 1, 2, 3, \ldots$) may be formed for an endomorphism L. We agree that $L^0 = I$. It then makes sense to speak of a polynomial in L : $\sum_{k=0}^{m} \alpha_k L^k$.

Although the study of "linear algebras" as such is beyond our scope, there are so many examples close at hand that we take the opportunity to give and illustrate the definition. The set $\mathcal{L}(X, X)$ of all endomorphisms of a given linear space X is by 1 a linear space. The operation of forming the product LK of an ordered pair of elements of $\mathcal{L}$ is a binary operation on $\mathcal{L}$. This operation is associative by 4B10.1 (see also 4B9); it is right-and-left-distributive with respect to addition in $\mathcal{L}$ by 7 (below); it has the further property that if $K, L \in \mathcal{L}$ and $\alpha \in F$, then

$$\alpha(LK) = (\alpha L)K = L(\alpha K).$$

A structure with these properties is called a linear algebra.

A *linear algebra* is a linear space $\{Y, + ; \mathcal{F}, \cdot\}$ on which there is defined an associative binary operation $\circ$ which is right-and-left-distributive with respect to addition in Y and has the further property that if $y, z \in Y$ and $\alpha \in \mathcal{F}$, then

$$\alpha(y \circ z) = (\alpha y) \circ z = y \circ (\alpha z).$$

If there is an identity e for the binary operation of the linear algebra, then e is an *identity* for the algebra. By 2, I_X is an identity for the algebra $\mathcal{L}(X, X)$ with the operation $\circ$.

The spaces R_1, C_1, and F_1 are linear algebras, and so are most linear spaces of functions with scalar values; the binary operation is simply multiplication of values: $(xy)(\alpha) = x(\alpha)y(\alpha)$. As a particular example, the space 5B10 of all polynomials with complex coefficients is a linear algebra; the identity of this algebra is the constant $x(\alpha) \equiv 1$.

EXERCISES

2. Under the conditions stated in the text, verify that αL, $L + M$, and LK are linear on their domains into their codomains. Prove also that $LI_X = L$ and $I_Y L = L$. (T)

3. Prove 1. (Lengthy but straightforward.) What is the dimension of this space? (Answer in 8A8.) (T)

4. We are given a real space X_2 with basis b_1, b_2. Endomorphisms $x = (\xi_1, \xi_2) \rightarrow Tx = (\eta_1, \eta_2)$ are defined as follows:

$$L\begin{cases}\eta_1 = 2\xi_1 + 3\xi_2 \\ \eta_2 = \xi_1 + 2\xi_2\end{cases}, \quad M\begin{cases}\eta_1 = -3\xi_1 + 2\xi_2 \\ \eta_2 = -6\xi_1 + 4\xi_2\end{cases}.$$

(a) Find the images of b_1, b_2, and $(2, 3)$.

(b) Of what vectors are b_1 and b_2 the images?

(c) Obtain equations $x \rightarrow Tx$ for $3L$, $-2M$, $3L - 2M$, L^2, $L^2 - 4L + I$, M^2, $M^2 - M$, LM, and ML. Observe that $LM \neq ML$.

(d) A point or vector x is *fixed* or *invariant* under an endomorphism T if $Tx = x$. Does either L or M have any fixed points other than $x = 0$?

(e) A subspace S is invariant under an endomorphism T if $TS \leq S$. The whole space X is invariant; so is the trivial space $\langle 0 \rangle$. Does either L or M have any invariant one-dimensional subspaces? (Seek a scalar λ and a vector $x \neq 0$ such that, respectively, $Lx = \lambda x$ or $Mx = \lambda x$.)

5. For the endomorphisms of E_2 given in A11, find equations for the resultants of the following pairs, in the stated order: (a) and (b), (b) and (a), (b) and (d), (e) and (a), (a) and (e).

6. For the endomorphisms of X_2 given in A12, find the maps of p_1 and p_2 under the resultants of the following pairs, in the stated order: (b) and (a), (c) and (b), (d) and (c).

7. Stating clearly the context underlying the equations, prove that the operation of forming the resultant is both associative and right-and-left-distributive: $K(LM) = (KL)M$, (cf. 4B10.1) $(K + L)M = KM + LM$, and $M(K + L) = MK + ML$. (T)

8. Prove that R_{KL} is a subspace of R_K. Prove also that if both K and L are biunique, then so is KL. (T)

9. Given $K : X \rightarrow Y$ and $L : Y \rightarrow Z$, we know that LK maps X into Z. Show that KL is defined if and only if $Z \leq X$. If it is true that $Z \leq X$, what can you say about the range and domain of KL? What must be true of X, Y, and Z in order for the equation $KL = LK$ to make sense (quite apart from its truth or falsehood)? (T)

10. In the context of A19 prove that if $x \in C^0$ then $DSx = x$. Is it necessarily true that $SDx = x$? Explain.

11. For each ordered pair $K, L \in \mathcal{L}(X, X)$ define $[K, L] = KL - LK$. Prove that if J, $K, L \in \mathcal{L}(X, X)$ and $\alpha \in \mathfrak{F}$, then

$$[J + K, L] = [J, L] + [K, L],$$
$$\alpha[K, L] = [\alpha K, L] = [K, \alpha L],$$
$$[K, L] = -[L, K], \qquad [L, L] = 0,$$
$$[[J, K], L] + [[K, L], J] + [[L, J], K] = 0.$$

Show that the binary operation $(K, L) \to [K, L]$ is not associative. With this binary operation, sometimes called the *bracket product* or the *commutator* of K and L, $\mathcal{L}(X, X)$ is an example of a Lie algebra; the study of Lie algebras is beyond our scope.

C. Projections; Reflections

Two special types of endomorphism have particular interest. Each can be understood quite readily in terms of a direct sum (cf. 5F).

Suppose that $X = Y \oplus Z$. Then for each $x \in X$ there exist unique vectors $y \in Y$ and $z \in Z$ such that $x = y + z$. Define mappings H and J on X into X as follows:

$$x \to Hx = H(y + z) = y;$$
$$x \to Jx = J(y + z) = y - z.$$

We verify readily (4) that these mappings are linear and therefore are endomorphisms of X. For reasons that will soon be clear we call H the *projection of X onto Y along Z*, and we call J the *reflection of X in Y along Z*. In the accompanying diagram (1) the solid lines with no tips represent the

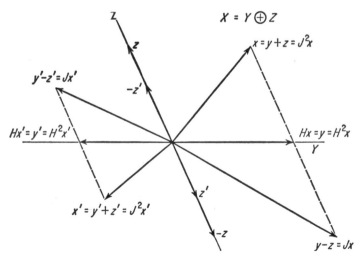

Projection H of X onto Y along Z: $x = y + z \to Hx = y$.
Projection J of X in Y along Z: $x = y + z \to Jx = y - z$.
1. Symbolic diagram.

subspaces Y and Z, and $X = Y \oplus Z$ is represented by the plane. The diagram is valid in detail if dim $Y = 1 = $ dim Z, and has symbolic value otherwise.

First let us take a closer look at H. Since $y = y + 0$ with $0 \in Z$, $H^2x = H(y + 0) = y = Hx$; since x is arbitrary, $H^2 = H$. An endomorphism H such that $H^2 = H$ is said to be *idempotent*, and we have just seen that a projection is idempotent.

Now suppose, conversely, that H is an idempotent endomorphism: $H^2 = H$. If $x \in X$ then clearly $x = Hx + x - Hx = Hx + (I - H)x$, whence $X = HX + (I - H)X$. We shall prove that the sum is direct by showing that $W = HX \cap (I - H)X = \langle 0 \rangle$. If $w \in W$ then $w = Hu = (I - H)v$ for some $u, v \in X$. It follows on the one hand that $Hw = H^2u = Hu = w$ and on the other hand that $Hw = Hv - H^2v = 0$, whence $w = 0$ and $W = \langle 0 \rangle$. Hence $X = HX \oplus (I - H)X$, and we see readily that H projects X onto HX along $(I - H)X$. These results are summarized in the following theorem.

2. Theorem. If an endomorphism H of a linear space X is a projection, then $H^2 = H$. Conversely, if H has the property that $H^2 = H$ then $X = HX \oplus (I - H)X$ and H projects X onto HX along $(I - H)X$.

In order to arrive at analogous results for J, let us observe first that $J^2x = J^2(y + z) = J(y - z) = y + z = x$; since x is arbitrary, $J^2 = I$. An endomorphism J such that $J^2 = I$ is called an *involution* and is said to be *involutory*, and we have just seen that a reflection is involutory.

Now suppose, conversely, that J is an involutory endomorphism: $J^2 = I$. For $x \subset X$ we now write

$$x = \tfrac{1}{2}(x + Jx) + \tfrac{1}{2}(x - Jx) = \tfrac{1}{2}(I + J)x + \tfrac{1}{2}(I - J)x.$$

On defining $Y = \tfrac{1}{2}(I + J)X$ and $Z = \tfrac{1}{2}(I - J)X$ we see that $X = Y + Z$. We wish to show that $X = Y \oplus Z$ by showing that $W = Y \cap Z = \langle 0 \rangle$. If $w \in W$ then $w = \tfrac{1}{2}(I + J)u = \tfrac{1}{2}(I - J)v$ for some $u, v \in X$. It follows on the one hand that $Jw = \tfrac{1}{2}J(I + J)u = \tfrac{1}{2}(J + I)u = w$ and on the other that $Jw = \tfrac{1}{2}J(I - J)v = \tfrac{1}{2}(J - I)v = -w$. Since we are assuming that $1 + 1 \ne 0$, it follows that $w = 0$ and hence that $W = \langle 0 \rangle$ and $X = Y \oplus Z$. We have just observed, essentially, that if $y = \tfrac{1}{2}(x + Jx)$ then $Jy = y$, while if $z = \tfrac{1}{2}(x - Jx)$ then $Jz = -z$, whence $J(y + z) = y - z$ and J is a reflection of X in Y along Z. These results are summarized in the following theorem.

3. Theorem. If an endomorphism J of a linear space X is a reflection, then $J^2 = I$. Conversely, if J has the property that $J^2 = I$, then $X = (I + J)X \oplus (I - J)X$ and J reflects X in $(I + J)X$ along $(I - J)X$.

If J reflects X in Y along Z then J leaves points of Y fixed and interchanges all other points in pairs; if $x = y + z \to x' = Jx = y - z$, in fact, then $x' = y - z \to Jx' = y + z = x$. For this reason X or any configuration invariant under J may be said to be *symmetric* about Y (along Z). In most applications the notion of angle is available, Z is orthogonal to Y, and the qualification "along Z" is tacitly understood. In E_P, if Y is a plane and Z a line then we have "plane symmetry", while if Y is a line and Z a plane then we have "axial symmetry". The apparently trivial special case $Y = \langle 0 \rangle$, $Z = X$ is of great practical importance; then the reflection J is the scalar transformation $x \rightarrow -x$ (cf. A), the phrase "along Z" is redundant, and a configuration invariant under J is said to have "point symmetry" about the origin or to be "symmetric in the origin".

It must be clearly observed, of course, that a reflection "in" Y is not a mapping "into" Y. An interesting connection between idempotents and involutions is given below in 7.

It is reasonable to expect that similar results can be obtained if (see 5F) $X = {}_k\bigoplus_1^p X_k$; here the subscript k is a mere index, devoid of dimensional significance. For example, let $Y_h = {}_k\bigoplus_1^p X_k$ ($k \neq h$). Then $X = X_h \oplus Y_h$ and it makes sense to project X onto X_h along Y_h (cf. 11) or to reflect X in X_h along Y_h. More generally, if $x = \sum x_k$ (for unique $x_k \in X_k$) and for $k = 1, \ldots, p$ each ϵ_k is $+1$, or 0, or -1, then the mapping $x \rightarrow \sum \epsilon_k x_k$ is linear and may be regarded in a natural way as the resultant of a projection and a reflection. We forego a detailed development.

EXERCISES

4. Prove that the mappings H and J of the text are linear.

5. Which of the mappings in A11 and A12 are projections? Which are involutions? (The answer to the question may depend on the values of parameters in the equations.) If the mapping is a projection H, determine HX and $(I - H)X$. If the mapping is an involution J, determine those x for which $Jx = x$.

6. Let $X = Y \oplus Z$. Prove that H is the projection of X onto Y along X if and only if $I - H$ is the projection of X onto Z along Y. (T)

7. Prove that if H is an idempotent, then $J = 2H - I$ is an involution. Prove also that if J is an involution, then $H = \frac{1}{2}(I + J)$ is a projection. (T)

8. Does there exist an endomorphism which is both a projection and an involution?

9. Let $J : X \rightarrow X$ be an endomorphism such that, for each $x \in X$, if $x \rightarrow Jx = x'$ then $x' \rightarrow Jx' = x$. Does it follow that J is an involution?

10. Let $X = Y_q \oplus Z_r$, let y_k ($k = 1, \ldots, q$) be a basis for Y_q and let z_k ($k = q + 1, \ldots, q + r$) be a basis for Z_r. Determine the images of the basis vectors under the projection of X onto Y along Z. Determine their images also under the involutions $x = y + z \rightarrow y - z$ and $x = y + z \rightarrow -y + z$. (T)

11. In the notation of the paragraph preceding 4 let L_h denote the projection of X onto X_h along Y_h. Prove that $\sum L_h = I$ and that if $h \neq j$ then $L_h L_j = L_j L_h = 0$. It is true, conversely, that if L_h ($h = 1, \ldots, p$) are projections such that $\sum L_h = I$ and $L_h L_j = L_j L_h = 0$ if $h \neq j$ then $X = {}_k\bigoplus_1^p X_k$ where $X_k = L_k X$ and L_k is the projection of X onto X_k along $_j\oplus_1^n X_j$ $(j \neq k)$. (The proof is essentially simple but rather laborious.)

12. Given $L_1 : X' \to Y'$ and $L_2 : X'' \to Y''$, let $X = X' \oplus X''$ and $Y = Y' \oplus Y''$ and define $L : X \to Y$ by $x \to y = Lx$ where $x = (x', x'') \to (y', y'') = (L_1x', L_2x'') = y = Lx$. Prove that L is an extension of L_1 from X' to X and an extension of L_2 from X'' to X, while L_1 and L_2 are the respective restrictions of L to X' and X''. Prove also that if P_1 is the projection of X onto X' along X'', then $L_1 = LP_1$. (T)

D. Nonsingular Transformations; the Inverse

Given $L : X_n \to Y_m$, with $m \geq n$, and a basis p_k $(k = 1, \ldots, n)$ for X, we know (see the proof of A7) that the vectors Lp_k generate R_L. These vectors will be a basis for R_L if and only if they are independent; in that event $\dim R_L = \dim X$ and L is said to be *nonsingular* (on X), while otherwise $\dim R_L < \dim X$ and L is said to be *singular*. This section is devoted to nonsingular transformations.

The integer $\dim R_L$ is called the *rank* of L, and is denoted by $\rho(L)$. Thus L is nonsingular if and only if $\rho(L) = \dim X$.

If L is nonsingular then L must be biunique on X onto R_L. If not, then $Lx = Lx'$ with $x, x' \in X$ and $x \neq x'$. If $x = \sum \alpha_k p_k$ and $x' = \sum \alpha'_k p_k$ then $0 = L(x - x') = \sum (\alpha_k - \alpha'_k)Lp_k$; since $\alpha_k \neq \alpha'_k$ for some value of k, the vectors Lp_k would not be independent. If L is biunique, conversely, then $\dim R_L = \dim X$ and L is nonsingular.

It follows that L is nonsingular if and only if L establishes an isomorphic correspondence between X and R_L. A nonsingular endomorphism of X is called an *automorphism* of X.

If L is biunique then, since $L0 = 0$, $Lx = 0$ implies $x = 0$. Now suppose, conversely, that $Lx = 0$ implies $x = 0$. Then, we claim, L must be biunique. If, in fact, $Lx = y = Lx'$, then $L(x - x') = 0$, whence $x - x' = 0$ or $x = x'$; hence L is biunique.

Now we know by A7, since $\langle 0 \rangle \leq Y$, that $N_L = \{x : Lx = 0\} \leq X$. This subspace of X is called the *nullspace* or *kernel* of L, its elements are said to be *annulled* by L, and its dimension, denoted by $\nu(L)$, is called the *nullity* of L. The result of the preceding paragraph is that L is nonsingular if and only if $N_L = \langle 0 \rangle$ or, equivalently, $\nu(L) = 0$.

These equivalent conditions are listed, along with one further condition (h) in the following theorem; we recall that I_Z denotes the identity on the space Z.

1. **Theorem.** Given $L : X_n \to Y_m$, with $m \geq n$, and a basis p_k $(k = 1, \ldots, n)$ for X_n, the following conditions on L are equivalent:

(a) The vectors Lp_k are independent;

(b) L is nonsingular;

(c) L is 1-1 on X onto R_L;

(d) L is an isomorphic correspondence between X and LX;

(e) $Lx = 0$ implies $x = 0$, or $N_L = \langle 0 \rangle$;

(f) $\rho(L) = \dim R_L = \dim X$;

(g) $\nu(L) = \dim N_L = 0$;

(h) if $K : R_L \to X$ is so defined that $y \to Ky$, where $Ky = x$ if and only if $Lx = y$, then K is linear and nonsingular and $KL = I_X$ and $LK = I_{LX}$.

It is clear that (h) implies (e), for if $Lx = 0$ then (h) yields $KLx = x = 0$, establishing (e) for L. Now suppose that L is nonsingular and observe first of all that Ky is determined uniquely by y.

Since $L\alpha x = \alpha Lx = \alpha y$, it follows that $K\alpha y = \alpha x = \alpha Ky$ and K is *homogeneous*.

If $Lx = y$ and $Lx' = y'$, then $L(x + x') = y + y'$ and therefore $K(y + y') = x + x' = Ky + Ky'$; hence K is also *additive* and therefore *linear*.

Since $x = 0$ implies $y = Lx = 0$, $x = Ky = 0$ implies that $y = 0$; hence K is *nonsingular* by condition (e).

If $Lx = y$ then $KLx = Ky = x$; since this is true for each $x \in X$ we conclude that $KL = I_X$. In particular, K maps R_L onto X. Similarly, if $Ky = x$ then $LKy = Lx = y$; since this is true for each $y \in R_L$, $LK = I_{R_L}$.

The mapping K is called the *inverse* to L and is denoted by L^{-1}.

Let us look at a few examples. If $\alpha \neq 0$ then the scalar transformation $x \to \alpha x$ annuls no $x \neq 0$ and is therefore nonsingular; its inverse is $x \to \alpha^{-1}x$. A rotation of E_P about P (see 3L2) annuls no non-zero vector and is therefore nonsingular; the inverse of a rotation through an angle φ about a line ℓ consists of a rotation through $-\varphi$ about ℓ. In the complex plane the inverse of $z \to e^{+i\varphi}z$, is $z \to e^{-i\varphi}z$. The mapping given by A5 will be nonsingular, by condition (e) of 1, if and only if we are able to show, on putting $\eta_1 = \eta_2 = 0$, that then both ξ_1 and ξ_2 must vanish; we see in a line or two that the mapping is nonsingular or singular according as $\alpha\delta - \beta\gamma \neq 0$ or $= 0$. In B4 we see easily that L is nonsingular, while M is singular; in fact, $M(2, 3) = 0$. In A19 D is singular, for $Dc = 0$ if c is a constant even if $c \neq 0$. On the other hand, S is nonsingular; on recalling that $x \in C^0$ we see that $\int_0^t x(u)\, du = 0$ implies $x = 0$ (cf. B10). The only nonsingular projection (cf. 3) is the identity. Every involution is nonsingular; indeed, since $J^2 = I$ an involution is its own inverse.

The operation of forming the inverse is not related in any very pleasant way to the linear space $\mathfrak{L}$ (cf. B1) of transformations on a space X into a space Y. One sees readily that αL is nonsingular if and only if $\alpha \neq 0$ and L is nonsingular, and in the favorable case that $(\alpha L)^{-1} = \alpha^{-1}L^{-1}$. Even if L and M are nonsingular we can say nothing, in general, about $L + M$; for example, if $M = -L$ then the sum is zero (an extremely singular mapping). The set of nonsingular elements of $\mathcal{L}$ is therefore not a subspace of $\mathcal{L}$, and this fact is reflected in the absence of any relation between L^{-1}, M^{-1}, and $(L + M)^{-1}$, even when they all exist.

The product behaves more agreeably. The result of B8 can be stated in our present terminology as follows: if L is nonsingular on X into Y and K is nonsingular on Y into Z then KL is nonsingular on X into Z. Hence $(KL)^{-1}$ is defined on R_{KL} onto X and is linear and nonsingular. Now K^{-1} is nonsingular on R_K onto Y, and L^{-1} is nonsingular on R_L onto X. Let us examine the effect of $L^{-1}K^{-1}$ on an arbitrary $z \in R_{KL}$, recalling (cf. B8) that R_{KL} is a subspace of R_K. Since $z \in R_{KL}$, $K^{-1}z \in Y$, and since $z = KLx$ for some $x \in X$, we conclude that $K^{-1}z = K^{-1}KLx = Lx$. Hence $K^{-1}z \in R_L$ and $L^{-1}K^{-1}z = L^{-1}Lx = x$. But also $(KL)^{-1}z = x$ because $z = KLx$. Hence $(KL)^{-1} = L^{-1}K^{-1}$, and we have the following theorem.

2. **Theorem.** If L is nonsingular on X into Y and K is nonsingular on R_L into Z then KL is nonsingular on X into Z and $(KL)^{-1} = L^{-1}K^{-1}$ on R_{KL} onto X.

In order to develop some ideas that will be useful in studying singular transformations let us revert for a moment to 1(h) and examine separately the two conditions $KL = I_X$ and $LK = I_{LX}$ which are there stated to be jointly sufficient for L to be nonsingular.

If the range LX of L is a proper subspace of Y and if $M : Y \to X$ is a candidate to be L^{-1}, then it is evident from (h) that only the restriction of M to LX is significant; in fact, if L^{-1} exists its domain is precisely LX.

The attentive reader will have noticed, moreover, that in proving that (h) implies (e) we used only the equation $KL = I_X$. The other equation, $LK = I_{LX}$, must therefore be a consequence.

Let us say that $J : LX \to X$ is a *left-inverse* of L if $JL = I_X$. We show that *if L has a left-inverse J then L is nonsingular and $J = L^{-1}$ on LX.* That L is nonsingular was shown in the first few lines following the statement of 1. For each $y \in LX$ it follows, if $y = Lx$, that $x = L^{-1}y$, whence $x = JLx = JLL^{-1}y = Jy = L^{-1}y$; since y is arbitrary in LX, $J = L^{-1}$ as claimed.

In this situation, of course, $\dim LX = \dim X$. If $\dim LX < \dim Y$ and J is defined on all of Y onto X then J is necessarily singular because $\dim JY < \dim Y$. The restriction of J to LX, however, is biunique on LX onto X.

As an example, let a real X_2 have basis p_1, p_2, with $x = \lambda p_1 + \mu p_2$, and let Y_3 have basis q_1, q_2, q_3, with $y = \xi q_1 + \eta q_2 + \xi q_3$. Define $L : X \to Y$ by the equations

2.1. $$\xi = 3\lambda - 4\mu, \qquad \eta = \lambda - \mu, \qquad \tau = 3\lambda - 5\mu$$

and $J : Y \to X$ by the equations

2.2.
$$\lambda = -\xi + 4\eta, \qquad \mu = -\xi + 3\eta.$$

We see easily that $Lx = 0$ implies $x = 0$ and that $JY = R_J$ is all of X. One can verify that R_L is the plane $2\xi - 3\eta = \tau$. Now with ξ and η *fixed*, the entire line (ξ, η, ζ) with $-\infty < \zeta < \infty$ is mapped onto the point $(\lambda, \mu) = (-\xi + 4\eta, -\xi + 3\eta) \subset X_2$; hence J is singular on Y. Since R_L is pierced by such a line in the unique point $(\xi, \eta, 2\xi - 3\eta)$, the correspondence established between X_2 and R_L by J (more properly, by the restriction of J to R_L) is biunique; hence J is nonsingular on R_L. This result can also be established by choosing a basis for R_L, for example $e_1 = (3, 2, 0)$ and $e_2 = (0, -1, 3)$; for $y = \alpha e_1 + \beta e_2 \subset R_L$ one then has the 1-1 mapping $\lambda = 5\alpha - 4\beta$, $\mu = 3\alpha - 3\beta$ on R_L onto X_2.

With the equation $LK = I_{LX}$ of 1(h) in mind, let us say that $K : LX \to X$ is a *right-inverse* of L if $LK = I_{LX}$. We have seen that if L has a left-inverse J, then J is also a right-inverse and $L^{-1} = J$. Can a similar conclusion be reached if L has a right-inverse?

As an example, let X_3 and Y_2 have bases such that $x = (\xi, \eta, \zeta)$ and $y = (\lambda, \mu)$. Define $L : X \to Y$ by the equations

3.
$$\lambda = -\xi + 4\eta, \qquad \mu = -\xi + 3\eta.$$

Since $L(\xi, \eta, \zeta) = L(\xi, \eta, \zeta')$ for any values of ζ and ζ', L is clearly singular. Let us define K on Y into X (actually into the subspace $\{x : \zeta = 0\}$ of X) by the equations

4.
$$\xi = 3\lambda - 4\mu, \qquad \eta = \lambda - \mu, \qquad \zeta = 0.$$

We verify easily that $LK(\lambda, \mu) = (\lambda, \mu)$, whence $LK = I_Y = I_{LX}$ and K is a right-inverse of L.

From the existence of a right-inverse K for L, therefore, we cannot conclude that L is nonsingular. We can conclude, however, that $K : LX \to X$ is nonsingular, for if $y = Lx \subset LX$ and $Ky = 0$ then $0 = LKy = y$. By 1(c) K is 1-1 on LX into X, in fact, onto KLX. The same result follows from the fact that $L : KLX \to LX$ is a left-inverse of K; the restriction of L to KLX is K^{-1}.

EXERCISES

5. In A11–13, determine which transformations are nonsingular, and find the inverse of each nonsingular one.

6. In X_2 with basis b_1, b_2, let $x = (\xi_1, \xi_2) \to Lx = (\eta_1, \eta_2)$, where $\eta_1 = \alpha \xi_1 + \beta \xi_2$, $\eta_2 = \gamma \xi_1 + \delta \xi_2$. Prove that L is nonsingular if and only if $\Delta = \alpha\delta - \beta\gamma \neq 0$; if $\Delta \neq 0$ find equations for L^{-1}.

7. Let H be an endomorphism of X with the property that there exist endomorphisms J and K of X such that $JH = I$ and $HK = I$. Show that H is nonsingular and that $H^{-1} = J = K$. (T)

8. Suppose that $L : X \to Y$ is nonsingular and that $S \leq X$, and let L_S denote the restriction of L to S. Prove that $L_S : S \to Y$ is nonsingular.

9. Prove that $L : X \to Y$ is singular if dim $Y <$ dim X. Is this condition necessary in order that L be singular? (T)

10. Show that the set of all nonsingular endomorphisms with the binary operation of forming the resultant constitutes a group. (T)

11. Suppose that $L : X \to Y$ and $K : Y \to X$ have the property that $LK = I_Y$. What conclusions can you draw concerning K and L, and concerning dim X and dim Y? (T)

E. Singular Transformations; Pseudo-Inverses

If $L : X_n \to Y_m$ $(m \geq n)$ is nonsingular then $\rho(L) = n$ and $\nu(L) = 0$. If L is singular then $\rho(L) < n$ and $\nu(L) > 0$. It is still true, as we shall see, that $\rho(L) + \nu(L) = n$ or, in words, that rank plus nullity equals the dimension of the domain.

If $x \in' N_L$ then $Lx \neq 0$. Let W be (cf. 5F) any complement of N_L in X. Then $X = N_L \oplus W$ and dim $N_L +$ dim $W =$ dim X, or $\nu(L) +$ dim $W = n$.

The relation between W and R_L is quite simple; they are isomorphic. Let us show first that L (more properly, the restriction of L to W) maps W onto R_L. If $y \in R_L$ then $y = Lx$ with $x \in X$. Since $X = N_L \oplus W$, $x = u + w$ for unique vectors $u \in N_L$ and $w \in W$. Then $y = Lx = Lu + Lw = Lw$, because $Lu = 0$. Hence $y = Lw$ with $w \in W$, and R_L is covered by LW. That $L : W \to R_L$ is biunique follows either from the fact that w is the unique element of W such that $x = u + w$, or from the fact that, since $w \in W$, $w \in' N_L$ unless $w = 0$, whence $Lw = 0$ implies $w = 0$.

Since $L : W \to R_L$ is 1-1, dim $W =$ dim $R_L = \rho(L)$ and we conclude that $\nu(L) + \rho(L) = n$.

1. Theorem. Given $L : X_n \to Y$, let W be any complement in X_n of the null-space of L. Then L establishes a 1-1 correspondence between W and R_L and

$$\nu(L) + \rho(L) = n = \dim X.$$

In the example of D3, $N_L = \langle\langle(0, 0, 1)\rangle\rangle$, that is, $N_L = \{x : \xi = \eta = 0\}$, and $\nu(L) = 1$. A complement of N_L is $W = \{x : \zeta = 0\}$. Here $R_L = Y_2$, L is nonsingular (as claimed) on W onto Y_2, dim $W =$ dim $Y_2 = 2 = \rho(L)$ and $\nu(L) + \rho(L) = 1 + 2 = 3 = n =$ dim X.

Let us denote by L_W the restriction of L to W. By 1, L_W is nonsingular on W onto R_L. It follows by D1 that L_W has an inverse L_W^{-1} on R_L onto W. In D3, again, let $W = \{x : \zeta = 0\}$; then the mapping K on $Y_2 = R_L$ onto W given by equations D4 is 1-1 and $L_W K = I_Y$. Since also $L_W L_W^{-1} = I_Y$, we have $L_W(K - L_W^{-1}) = 0$. Hence $L_W(K - L_W^{-1})y = 0$ for each $y \in Y$. Since L_W is nonsingular, we conclude that $(K - L_W^{-1})y = 0$ for each $y \in Y$, whence $K = L_W^{-1}$.

The conclusion is general. The mapping $L_W^{-1} : LX \to W$ has the property that $LL_W^{-1} = I_{LX}$. Hence L_W^{-1} is a right-inverse of $L : X \to LX$.

Given $L : X \to Y$, and a linear mapping $M : Y \to X$, let us say that M is a *pseudo-inverse* of L if the restriction $K = M_{LX}$ of M to LX is a right-inverse of $L : X \to LX$; that is, $LK = I_{LX}$. It may happen that M is defined only on Z, where $LX \leq Z \leq Y$; one may then first extend M trivially from Z to Y and arrive at the situation just contemplated.

If L is nonsingular, of course, then any extension of L^{-1} to Y is a pseudo-inverse of L. It is evident from the remarks following 1 that any extension to Y of any right-inverse of $L : X \to R_L$ is a pseudo-inverse of L. We obtained a right-inverse of $L : X \to R_L$ as L_W^{-1}, where L_W was the restriction of L to a complement W of N_L. The problem of calculating a pseudo-inverse is equivalent to the problem of solving linear equations and will be treated fully later; meanwhile we keep our examples and exercises so simple that the calculations offer no difficulty.

Now suppose, conversely, that M is a pseudo-inverse of L and let K denote the restriction of M to R_L. We claim that $R_K = KR_L$ is a complement of N_L; that is, $X = N_L \oplus R_K$.

First of all, if $x \in X$ then $Lx \in R_L$, $KLx \in X$, the vector $u = x - KLx \in X$ and, since $LK = I_{R_L}$, $Lu = Lx - LKLx = Lx - Lx = 0$, whence $u \in N_L$. The conclusion is that $x = (x - KLx) + KLx$, with $x - KLx \in N_L$ and $KLx \in KR_L$, whence $X = N_L + KR_L$.

In order to see that the sum is direct we must show that $N_L \cap KR_L = \langle 0 \rangle$. If $x \in N_L \cap KR_L$ then $Lx = 0$ and $x = KLv$ for some $v \in X$. Since $LK = I_{R_L}$ it follows from the second equation that $Lx = LKLv = Lv$, then from the first that $Lv = 0$, and then from the second that $x = 0$.

Our results are summarized by the following theorem, from which it is evident, incidentally, that a pseudo-inverse is not unique; one can say only that for each complement of N_L in X there is a uniquely determined right-inverse of L, and conversely.

2. **Theorem.** Given $L : X \to Y$, let W be any complement in X of the null-space of L. Then the restriction L_W of L to W is 1-1 on W onto R_L, L_W^{-1} on R_L onto W is a right inverse of $L : X \to R_L$, and any extension M of L_W^{-1} from R_L to Y is a pseudo-inverse of L. Conversely, if $M : Y \to X$ is a pseudo-inverse of L and K is the restriction of M to R_L, then $W = R_K = KR_L$ is a complement of N_L and K is the right-inverse L_W^{-1} of $L : X \to R_L$ corresponding to W.

In D we mentioned that the singularity or nonsingularity of $L + M$ could not be predicted, in general, from similar knowledge regarding L and M separately. It is somewhat remarkable, therefore, that information on ranks and nullities is not wholly lacking; see 7–10 below. We give similar information, which has long been known, on the rank and nullity of a resultant.

3. Theorem. Sylvester's Law of Nullity. Given $L : X \to Y$ and $K : Y \to Z$, it is always true that

(a) $\rho(KL) \leq \min(\rho(K), \rho(L))$,

(b) $\nu(KL) \leq \nu(K) + \nu(L)$.

By the remark following A7, $\rho(KL) \leq \dim R_L \leq \rho(L)$. By B8, moreover, $R_{KL} \leq R_K$, whence $\rho(KL) \leq \rho(K)$ and (a) is proved.

The proof of (b) is less immediate. We begin by choosing a complement T of R_L in Y. Then

$$Y = R_L \oplus T, \qquad KY = KR_L + KT,$$

$$\dim Y = \dim R_L + \dim T, \qquad \dim KY \leq \dim KR_L + \dim KT.$$

In the last relation we use the fact that

$$\dim KT \leq \dim T = \dim Y - \dim R_L$$

to arrive at

$$\dim KY \leq \dim KR_L + \dim Y - \dim R_L.$$

On adding $\dim X$ to each side and observing that $\dim KR_L = \dim KLX = \rho(KL)$, and that $\dim KY = \rho(K)$, we have

$$\dim X - \rho(KL) \leq \dim Y - \rho(K) + \dim X - \rho(L)$$

or

$$\nu(KL) \leq \nu(K) + \nu(L).$$

We defend, finally, our distinction between $L : X \to Y$ and $L : X \to R_L$. It is an appealing idea, if R_L is a proper subspace of Y, to discard all of Y except R_L. There is this difficulty, however, that in some applications we may know X, and know L, and be able to calculate Lx for each particular $x \in X$, and be able to designate a linear space Y of which it can be said that $x \in X$ implies $Lx \in Y$ without being able, unfortunately, to specify R_L precisely or even, in some cases, being able to say whether or not R_L is a proper subspace of Y.

If both X and Y are finite-dimensional, as will be the case in our work, then there are constructive methods (see 8D1) of specifying R_L precisely when $L : X \to Y$ is known. A valid finite-dimensional example is therefore, in principle, out of the question. To see the point at issue we consider the space X of real-valued functions $x : t \to x(t)$ defined for $0 \leq t \leq 1$ and integrable in some sense or other. Define J on X so that $x \to Jx$, where $Jx(t) = \int_0^t x(u)\, du$. It is easy to show that, for each $x \in X$, Jx is a continuous function of t for $0 \leq t \leq 1$; hence J maps X into the space C of functions x that have $x(0) = 0$ and are continuous for $0 \leq t \leq 1$. Hence $R_J \leq C$; does $R_J = C$, or is R_J a proper subspace of C? The student will doubtless have heard that there exist functions $x \in C$ that are not differentiable for any value of t, and he will be willing to accept our assurance that Jx is differentiable for some value of t. It follows that R_J is a proper subspace of C. But what further property of

$y \in C$ will be both necessary and sufficient to guarantee that $y \in R_J$? The answer depends on which definition of the integral is used and cannot be given in full here. (If X consists, for example, of the space of functions x that are integrable in the Lebesgue sense (ordinarily studied in early graduate courses) then R_J consists of that subspace of C consisting of those $x \in C$ that have a certain stronger type of continuity called "absolute continuity".) Even in the finite-dimensional case, moreover, the constructive specification of the range may in a particular case be by no means trivial. We wish in any case, therefore, to be able to say as much as possible without being obliged to determine R_L exactly. That is the reason for speaking, according to context, of $L : X \to Y$ or $L : X \to R_L$; it should be observed, of course, that L always maps X onto R_L.

EXERCISES

4. In A11 and A12 determine the rank and nullity of the transformations when they are singular.

5. Determine the rank and nullity of a projection and of a reflection (cf. C).

6. Given $\alpha \neq 0$ and $L : X \to Y$, prove that $\rho(\alpha L) = \rho(L)$.

7. Given $K : X \to Y$ and $L : X \to Y$, prove that $R_{K+L} \leq R_K + R_L$ (cf. 5F). Hence show that $\rho(K + L) \leq \rho(K) + \rho(L)$.

8. Apply 7 to $\rho(K) = \rho(K + L - L)$ and use 6 with $\alpha = -1$ to show that $\rho(K) - \rho(L) \leq \rho(K + L)$. Hence show that $|\rho(K) - \rho(L)| \leq \rho(K + L)$ and therefore that
$$\max{(\rho(K), \rho(L))} \leq \rho(K + L) + \min{(\rho(K), \rho(L))}.$$

9. Prove from 7 that $\nu(K) + \nu(L) - \dim X \leq \nu(K + L)$.

10. Show that $\dim X = \min{(\nu(K), \nu(L))} + \max{(\rho(K), \rho(L))}$. Use this fact and the last result of 8 to show that
$$\nu(K + L) \leq \min{(\nu(K), \nu(L))} + \min{(\rho(K), \rho(L))}.$$

11. Use 3(b) to prove that $\rho(L) + \rho(K) - \dim Y \leq \rho(KL)$, i.e., that $\rho(L) \leq \rho(KL) + \nu(K)$. It follows that if $KL = 0$ then $\rho(K) + \rho(L) \leq \dim Y$.

12. Suppose that K and L are endomorphisms of X and that L is nonsingular. Prove that
$$\rho(KL) = \rho(LK) = \rho(K).$$

In 13–16 we are given $L : X \to Y$ and $M : Y \to X$.

13. Prove that if M is a pseudo-inverse of L, then $LML = L$ on X, and conversely. (For this reason, some authors *define* a pseudo-inverse of L as a mapping M on Y into X such that $LML = L$ on X.) (T)

14. Prove that if M is a pseudo-inverse of L, then $X = R_{ML} \oplus N_L$, and that ML projects X onto R_{ML} along N_L while $I - ML$ projects X onto N_L along R_{ML}. (T)

15. Prove that if M is a pseudo-inverse of L, then $MLM = M$ on R_L. Prove conversely that if M is nonsingular on R_L and $MLM = M$, then M is a pseudo-inverse of L. (T)

16. Let M be a pseudo-inverse of L. Prove that LM projects Y onto R_L while $I - LM$ annuls R_L. (T)

F. Linear Equations

Given $L : X \rightarrow Y$ and $y \in Y$, the equation $Lx = y$ is a *linear equation*. It is said to be *homogeneous* or *nonhomogeneous* according as $y = 0$ or $y \neq 0$. If $y \neq 0$ then the equation $Lx = 0$ is called the *corresponding homogeneous* equation or the *reduced* equation. Our knowledge of linear transformations makes possible a comprehensive result, in which the solution of a consistent nonhomogeneous equation is made to depend on finding a single solution of the equation and all solutions of the reduced equation.

1. Theorem. Given $L : X \rightarrow Y$ and $y \in Y$, the equation $Lx = y$ is consistent if and only if $y \in R_L$. If L is nonsingular and $y \in R_L$, then the equation has the unique solution $x = L^{-1}y$. If L is singular and $y \in R_L$ and M is any pseudo-inverse of L, then My is a solution, and x is a solution if and only if $x = My + w$ with $w \in N_L$ or, in other words, if and only if the point x lies in the flat $My + N_L$.

The first two statements are evident from their meanings. Since by E2 the restriction of M to R_L is a right-inverse of L, if $y \in R_L$, then $L(My) = (LM)y = I_{R_L}y = y$ and My is a solution. If x is any solution then $L(x - My) = 0$, whence $x - My = w \in N_L$. Vice versa, if $w \in N_L$ then $L(My + w) = LMy = y$ and $My + w$ is a solution.

This theorem is theoretically quite satisfying. But what shall we do when confronted with specific spaces X and Y, a specific mapping L, and a specific vector y? How shall we determine R_L, N_L, and M? We have answered such questions only for quite simple mappings, such as those of A11 and A12 (cf. also A5).

Even those examples, however, suggest fruitful procedures. The science we are studying has a highly developed technology. The hardware of that technology consists of bases and components and its processes involve linear algebraic equations and matrices. Although complete details will be delayed, we give next a preliminary discussion of these fundamental ideas, leading to biunique correspondences (in the presence of bases, always) between transformations, ordered n-tuples of vectors in the codomain, matrices, and systems of linear algebraic equations.

G. Matrix and Equations of a Transformation

We are given X_n with a basis $\{p_k\}$ ($k = 1, \ldots, n$) and vectors $x = \sum \xi_k p_k$, and Y_μ with a basis $\{q_\lambda\}$ ($\lambda = 1, \ldots, \mu$) and vectors $y = \sum \eta_\lambda q_\lambda$, and a linear transformation $L : X \to Y$. In connection with A6 and A7 we saw that the vectors $Lp_k \in Y$ generate R_L. As soon, in fact, as Lp_k ($k = 1, \ldots, n$) have been specified we can calculate $Lx = L(\sum \xi_k p_k) = \sum \xi_k Lp_k$. Conversely, let y_k be any ordered n-tuple of vectors in Y and define $T : X \to Y$ by $x \to Tx = \sum \xi_k y_k$. It is easily verified that T is linear and that $Tp_k = y_k$. If $M : X \to Y$ also has $Mp_k = y_k$, then $M = T$. We see, therefore, that *there is a biunique correspondence $L \leftrightarrow (y_k)$ ($k = 1, \ldots, n$) between linear transformations $L : X \to Y$ and ordered n-tuples of vectors $y_k \in Y$ in such a way that $y_k = Lp_k$ ($k = 1, \ldots, n$).*

We now use the basis $\{q_\lambda\}$ available in Y. Since $Lp_k \in Y$ there exist unique scalars $\alpha_{\lambda k}$ such that $Lp_k = {}_\lambda\sum_1^\mu \alpha_{\lambda k} q_\lambda$. The order of the indices λ and k of $\alpha_{\lambda k}$ is important, for it is connected by a rigid convention with a universally accepted way of displaying the scalars $\alpha_{\lambda k}$ in a bracketed rectangular array:

$$[\alpha_{\lambda k}] = \begin{bmatrix} \alpha_{11} & \alpha_{12} & \cdots & \alpha_{1n} \\ \alpha_{21} & \alpha_{22} & \cdots & \alpha_{2n} \\ \cdots & \cdots & \cdots & \cdots \\ \alpha_{\mu 1} & \alpha_{\mu 2} & \cdots & \alpha_{\mu n} \end{bmatrix}.$$

Any bracketed rectangular array of elements of F is called a *matrix* (over F). The vertical (horizontal) lines of scalars are called *columns* (*rows*). A matrix with μ rows and n columns is said to be a $\mu \times n$ matrix. We agree that $[\alpha_{\lambda k}] = [\beta_{\lambda k}]$ if and only if $\alpha_{\lambda k} = \beta_{\lambda k}$ for $\lambda = 1, \ldots, \mu$ and $k = 1, \ldots, n$. Each individual scalar $\alpha_{\lambda k}$ is called an *element* or an *entry* of $[\alpha_{\lambda k}]$.

The matrix $[\alpha_{\lambda k}]$ above is called *the matrix of L with respect to, or referred to, the bases $\{p_k\}$ and $\{q_\lambda\}$.*

We observe that the kth column of $[\alpha_{\lambda k}]$ is the μ-tuple of scalars constituting the components of Lp_k with respect to the basis $\{q_\lambda\}$ of Y. A similar interpretation of the rows will become apparent later on.

It is now evident that, in the presence of a fixed basis $\{q_\lambda\}$ for Y_μ, *there is a biunique correspondence between ordered n-tuples of vectors of Y_μ and $\mu \times n$ matrices*, in which the kth column of the matrix consists of the μ components with respect to $\{q_\lambda\}$ of the kth vector of the n-tuple.

If $\{p_k\}$ and $\{q_\lambda\}$ are bases, respectively, for X_n and Y_μ, it follows that *there is a biunique correspondence between $\mu \times n$ matrices and linear transformations $L : X \to Y$* in which for $k = 1, \ldots, n$ the kth column of the matrix corresponding to L consists of the μ components of Lp_k.

It is not at all surprising that we can calculate the components η_λ of the image $y = Lx$ of x when the components ξ_k of x are known. Here are the essential equations:

$$Lx = L(\sum \xi_k p_k) = \sum_k \xi_k Lp_k = \sum_k \xi_k (\sum \alpha_{\lambda k} q_\lambda)$$
$$= \sum_\lambda (\sum_k \alpha_{\lambda k} \xi_k) q_\lambda = \sum \eta_\lambda q_\lambda = y.$$

Since the q_λ are independent,

1.
$$\eta_\lambda = {}_k\sum_1^n \alpha_{\lambda k} \xi_k \qquad (\lambda = 1, \ldots, \mu),$$

and we have arrived at a system of μ linear algebraic equations in the n variables ξ_k. The matrix $[\alpha_{\lambda k}]$ is called the *matrix of the system*, and it is evident that the matrix and the system of equations determine each other uniquely.

As a consequence, in the presence of the bases $\{p_k\}$ and $\{q_\lambda\}$ the mapping L and the equations 1 determine each other uniquely (cf. A5). The linear equation $Lx = y$ of 6 and the linear algebraic equations 1 are therefore equivalent. We shall exploit this fact later.

If $X = Y$ then L is an endomorphism of X, $\mu = n$, the matrix of L is square, and it is usually understood tacitly that the basis $\{q_k\}$ is the same as the basis $\{p_k\}$, i.e., that $q_k = p_k$ ($k = 1, \ldots, n$).

We identify the scalar α and the 1×1 matrix $[\alpha]$, although they are conceptually distinct, because their properties are identical.

In dealing with matrices it is customary not to insert commas between the elements unless they are required for clarity. Instead of $[-1, 2, -5]$ one writes $[-1 \quad 2 \quad -5]$.

At the expense of a mild pun we record the foregoing results, which provide a framework for much of our later work, as the "Basic Principle".

2. Theorem. Basic Principle. Given X_n with basis $\{p_k\}$ ($k = 1, \ldots, n$) and Y_μ with basis $\{q_\lambda\}$ ($\lambda = 1, \ldots, \mu$), there is a biunique correspondence between mappings $L : X \to Y$, ordered n-tuples of vectors of Y, $\mu \times n$ matrices $[\alpha_{\lambda k}]$, and systems of μ equations in n variables, according to the following table:

Transformation $L : X_n \to Y_\mu$	$x \to Lx = y$
$\updownarrow$	$\updownarrow$
Ordered n-tuple in Y	Lp_k ($k = 1, \ldots, n$)
$\updownarrow$	$\updownarrow$
$\mu \times n$ matrix	$[\alpha_{\lambda k}]$ with $Lp_k = \sum \alpha_{\lambda k} q_\lambda$
$\updownarrow$	$\updownarrow$
μ linear equations $\Big\}$ in n variables	$\begin{cases} \eta_\lambda = \sum \alpha_{\lambda k} \xi_k \quad (\lambda = 1, \ldots, \mu) \\ \text{where } L(\sum \xi_k p_k) = \sum \eta_\lambda q_\lambda \end{cases}$

EXAMPLES

3. Let X_2 and Y_3 both be real. Let $Lp_1 = (2, 1, 3)$ and $Lp_2 = (-1, 2, -2)$. Then

$$[\alpha_{\lambda k}] = \begin{bmatrix} 2 & -1 \\ 1 & 2 \\ 3 & -2 \end{bmatrix} \quad \text{and} \quad \begin{aligned} \eta_1 &= 2\xi_1 - \xi_2 \\ \eta_2 &= \xi_1 + 2\xi_2 \\ \eta_3 &= 3\xi_1 - 2\xi_2 \end{aligned}$$

4. Let X_3 and Y_2 be complex. Suppose that

$$\eta_1 = (1 + i)\xi_1 - 2\xi_2 + (3 - 2i)\xi_3$$

and

$$\eta_2 = (2 - i)\xi_1 + (1 - i)\xi_2 - 3\xi_3.$$

Then

$$[\alpha_{\lambda k}] = \begin{bmatrix} 1+i & -2 & 3-2i \\ 2-i & 1-i & -3 \end{bmatrix}$$

and $Lp_1 = (1+i, 2-i)$, $Lp_2 = (-2, 1-i)$, and $Lp_3 = (3-2i, -3)$.

5. Here is a real 2×3 matrix:

$$\begin{bmatrix} 2 & -1 & 1 \\ -3 & 0 & \sqrt{2} \end{bmatrix}.$$

Is it the matrix of a transformation? What are the domain and the codomain? Which bases are in use? We can say that the domain is a space X_3 and the codomain is a space Y_2, each over the same field F (perhaps R), of which R is a subfield. Choose now *any* basis $\{p_{kj}\}$ $(k = 1, 2, 3)$ for X and *any* basis (q_λ) $(\lambda = 1, 2)$ for Y. Define a mapping $T : X \to Y$ by either of the following two equivalent prescriptions:

(a) $T(\sum \xi_k p_k) = \sum \eta_\lambda q_\lambda$, where
$$\eta_1 = 2\xi_1 - \xi_2 + \xi_3$$
$$\eta_2 = -3\xi_1 + \sqrt{2}\xi_3;$$

(b) $Tp_1 = (2, -3)$, $Tp_2 = (-1, 0)$, $Tp_3 = (1, \sqrt{2})$ and $T(\sum \xi_k p_k) = \sum \xi_k Tp_k$.

It is now trivial to verify that T is linear on X into Y and that the matrix of T referred to the chosen bases is the given matrix.

As the last example indicates, given any $\mu \times n$ matrix with elements in a field F (or a subfield of F), any X_n and Y_μ both over F, any basis for X, and any basis for Y, we can use these bases and a prescription similar to (a) or (b) to define a linear mapping on X into Y whose matrix with respect to the given bases is the given matrix.

But do we know a linear mapping if we know its effect only when a single specific basis is used in X and a single specific basis is used in Y? We must find some means to assure ourselves that to each $x \in X$ there shall correspond the same $Lx \in Y$ regardless of which bases are in use. This we achieve by one further understanding: When bases are changed then the transformation is to be expressed with respect to the new bases by a new matrix calculated in a perfectly definite way (see 8F5) from the old matrix and the relations between the bases (cf. 5G).

An isolated matrix over a field F can always be interpreted, therefore, as the matrix of any one of a vast collection of transformations with domain and codomain each a linear space over F (or any superfield of F). If the matrix is a $\mu \times n$ matrix, then the domain has dimension n and the codomain has dimension μ. Beyond that there is complete ambiguity. Only when the spaces and bases in them are specified does the interpretation become definite and concrete. Having recognized this, we shall still speak of *the* transformation corresponding to a given matrix, for all those corresponding to it are abstractly identical.

EXERCISES

6. Develop the correspondences of 2 in full detail for scalar transformations and for the transformations of A11, A12, A13, and C9. For those which are nonsingular develop the details also for the inverse (cf. D3).

7. We are given real spaces X_2 with basis p_1, p_2, and Y_3 with basis q_1, q_2, q_3; each mapping L below has domain X and codomain Y.

(a) $Lp_1 = 3q_2 - q_3$, $Lp_2 = 2q_1 + q_2 + 2q_3$. Find the matrix and the equations of L.

(b) $\eta_1 = 3\xi_1 + \xi_2$, $\eta_2 = -\xi_1 + 2\xi_2$, $\eta_3 = \xi_1 - 3\xi_2$. Find Lp_1, Lp_2, and the matrix of L.

(c) The matrix of L is $\begin{bmatrix} 2 & 3 \\ -1 & 0 \\ 0 & 2 \end{bmatrix}$. Find Lp_1, Lp_2, and the equations of L.

Prove that each mapping L is nonsingular. Try to specify R_L and L^{-1}.

8. Prove that the prescriptions (a) and (b) of 5 *are* equivalent. What are the prescriptions (a) and (b) for a $\mu \times n$ matrix $[\alpha_{\lambda k}]$ over a field F when bases $\{p_k\}$ over X_n and $\{q_\lambda\}$ for Y_μ are given?

9. What is the effect of a transformation having a $1 \times n$ matrix? A $\mu \times 1$ matrix? What are the ranks of these transformations? (T)

10. The matrix of a transformation K is $\begin{bmatrix} L & 0 \\ 0 & M \end{bmatrix}$, where L and M are given matrices and the zeros indicate zero-matrices of the appropriate order. What can be said about the effect of K? (T)

11. Let $\{p_k\}$ be a basis for X and, with h fixed so that $1 < h < n$, let $Y = \langle p_1, \ldots, p_h \rangle$ and $Z = \langle p_{h+1}, \ldots, p_n \rangle$; hence $X = Y \oplus Z$. What is the matrix of the projection of X onto Y along Z? Of the reflection of X in Y along Z? (T)

SEVEN
Linear Functionals; Duality

Let X, meaning $\{X, +; F, \cdot\}$, be a linear space over a field F. A linear transformation with domain X can have as codomain any linear space over F. The simplest such space is the trivial space $\langle 0 \rangle$, but the only mapping L with this codomain is $L = 0$. The next simplest codomain is the one-dimensional space $F_1 = \{F, +; F, \cdot\}$ (cf. 5B8). The step from $\langle 0 \rangle$ to F_1 brings with it a wealth of notable possibilities.

A. Linear Functionals

If X is a linear space over a field F then any mapping $f : X \to F$ is commonly called a *functional*; thus a functional is simply a scalar-valued function on X.

In the space E_P of Chap. 3, for example, the length $\|X\|$ of a vector X is a functional. Again, in E_P, if W is a fixed vector then the value (W, X) of the scalar product (cf. 3I) of W with X is a functional.

A linear mapping $f : X \to F_1$ is called a *linear functional*. In accordance with 6A1, the requirement that a functional f be linear is that

1.
$$f(\alpha x + \beta y) = \alpha f(x) + \beta f(y).$$

Of the preceding examples $\|X\|$ is not linear, while (W, X) is, for in fact $(W, \alpha X + \beta Y) = \alpha(W, X) + \beta(W, Y)$. For the duration of this chapter the word "functional" shall be understood, with a few clearly noted exceptions, to be an abbreviation for "linear functional". Lower case letters from the early part of the Latin alphabet $(a, b, c, \ldots, f, g)$ will always denote (linear) functionals. Just as Lx is a common abbreviation for $L(x)$, so fx is a common abbreviation for $f(x)$. We agree further, just as for L, that if S is a subset of X then fS shall denote the set of images of elements of S, that is, the set $\{fx : x \in S\}$ of images fx of elements x of S.

Let us mention some examples. On C_n, define $a_k x = a_k(\xi_1, \ldots, \xi_n) = \xi_k$, or, more generally, in X_n with a basis p_k define $a_k x = a_k \sum \xi_i p_i = \xi_k$; in either case a_k is called the kth *coordinate* functional. More generally still, in the same context, let $\alpha_k \in F$ and define $fx = \sum \alpha_k \xi_k$. In all these examples the functional is defined by using components with respect to a fixed basis, and it is not immediately clear what modifications are required if the basis is changed; we shall return to this question later (see 7B4–5). In one case, namely $fx = 0$ for each $x \in X$, the expression is the same in all bases; we call this functional the *zero-functional* and denote it by 0.

In the space X of real sequences $x = (\xi_k)$ $(k = 1, 2, 3, \ldots)$ the mapping $x \to fx = \sum \xi_k$ is a functional defined on the subspace S consisting of those x for which fx exists in the sense that the series converges; the problem of "summing divergent series" is the problem of extending f to subspaces of X larger than S.

Here are examples of types to which the notions of linear functional and duality owe much of their importance in functional analysis. Let X denote the space of real functions $x(t)$ so defined for $0 \leq t \leq 1$ as to have a derivative there; here are three functionals:

(1) $x \to fx = \alpha x'(0) + \beta x(0)$ with α, β real;
(2) with t_0 fixed, $x \to f_{t_0}x = x(t_0)$;
(3) with $y(t)$ integrable, $x \to f_yx = \int_0^1 y(t)x(t)\, dt$.

Since a functional is a linear mapping on X into F_1 the results of Chap. 6 can be applied. Some of those results are trivial and others have only limited interest in the present context. Since $\dim fX \leq \dim F_1 = 1$, for example, the mapping f is necessarily singular unless $\dim X \leq 1$. We shall depart somewhat from the order in Chap. 6, and shall occasionally give a direct proof.

Theorem 6A7 contains two statements. It is a consequence of the first that $fX \leq F_1$. Since the only subspaces of F_1 are $\langle 0 \rangle$ and F_1, we conclude that either $f = 0$ or $fX = R_f = F_1$; in the latter case the equation $fx = \alpha$ has a solution for each $\alpha \in F$. A direct proof is almost trivial. If $f \neq 0$, choose $x_0 \in X$ so that $fx_0 \neq 0$ and then, given $\alpha \in F$, define $y = \alpha x_0/fx_0$. Since f is linear, $fy = f(\alpha x_0)/(fx_0) = \alpha(fx_0/fx_0) = \alpha$; thus fx takes on the value α when $x = y$.

The second statement of 6A7 specializes here as follows: if $W \leq F_1$ then $W = fV$ for some $V \leq X$. If $W = F_1$ then, as we have just seen, $fX = W$ if and only if $f \neq 0$. The other subspace of F_1 is $\langle 0 \rangle$, and this subspace is in fact the image of the nullspace N_f of f. If $f \neq 0$ and $\dim X = n$ then $fX = F_1$ and $\rho(f) = 1$; it follows from 6E1 that $\nu(f) = n - 1$. *The nullspace N_f of a non-zero functional f is therefore a hyperspace of the domain.*

It is evident from the foregoing argument that if $f \neq 0$ and $fx_0 \neq 0$ then $X = \langle x_0 \rangle \oplus N_f$, and that the mapping $J : F_1 \to \langle x_0 \rangle$ where $\alpha \to J\alpha = \alpha x_0/(fx_0)$ is a right-inverse of f (cf. 6E2). Bearing 6F1 in mind, we summarize most of the foregoing results in the following theorem.

2. **Theorem.** Let $f : X \to F_1$ be a (linear) functional. If $f = 0$ then the equation $fx = \alpha$ is true identically if $\alpha = 0$ and inconsistent if $\alpha \neq 0$. If $f \neq 0$ then the solutions of the equation $fx = 0$ form a hyperspace N_f. If $fx_0 \neq 0$ then $X = \langle x_0 \rangle \oplus N_f$ and, if $\alpha \in F$ then the solutions of the equation $fx = \alpha$ constitute the flat $\alpha x_0/(fx_0) + N_f$.

The illustrative diagram 3 is valid if $F = R$, $f \neq 0$, and $n = 3$ and has symbolic interest for other fields and other values of n.

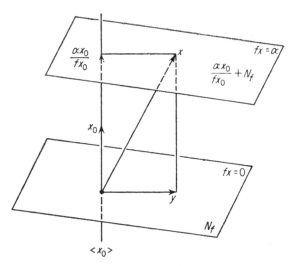

3. $X = \langle x_0 \rangle \oplus N_f$; flat $\alpha x_0 / f x_0 + N_f$ of solutions of $fx = \alpha$.

It is easy to see, conversely, that if Y_{n-1} is a hyperspace in X_n then there exists a functional f such that $N_f = Y_{n-1}$. In fact, choose $x_0 \in' Y_{n-1}$. Then $X = \langle x_0 \rangle \oplus Y_{n-1}$, and for each $x \in X$ there exist a unique scalar ξ and a unique vector $y \in Y_{n-1}$ such that $x = \xi x_0 + y$. Now define $f : X_n \to F_1$ by the stipulation that

$$x = \xi x_0 + y \to fx = f(\xi x_0 + y) = \xi.$$

We omit the trivial verification that f is linear. Observe next that $fx = 0$ if and only if $\xi = 0$; since $\xi = 0$ if and only if $x \in Y_{n-1}$ it follows that $N_f = Y_{n-1}$. Moreover, $fx_0 = 1$. Can there be another functional, say, g, such that $N_g = Y_{n-1}$ and $gx_0 = 1$? It would follow for each $x \in X$ that $gx = g(\xi x_0 + y) = \xi g x_0 = \xi = fx$, whence $f = g$. We have proved the following theorem.

4. Theorem. Given a hyperspace $Y_{n-1} \leq X_n$ and a vector $x_0 \in' Y_{n-1}$ there exists a unique linear functional f such that $fx_0 = 1$ and $N_f = Y_{n-1}$.

In spelling out the specialization of the basic principle 6G2 (with $\mu = 1$) let us agree to use in F_1 only the natural basis consisting simply of the scalar 1.

5. Theorem. Given X_n with basis $\{p_k\}$ $(k = 1, \ldots, n)$, there is a biunique correspondence between functionals $f : X \to F_1$, ordered n-tuples of scalars, $1 \times n$ matrices, and single linear equations in n variables as follows: $f \leftrightarrow fp_k \leftrightarrow [\alpha_k]$ with $fp_k = \alpha_k \leftrightarrow \eta = \sum \alpha_k \xi_k$, where $f(\sum \xi_k p_k) = \eta$.

Let us denote by $[f]$ the $1 \times n$ matrix $[\alpha_k]$ associated with f by a basis $\{p_k\}$ for X. Thus $[f] = [\alpha_k]$; can we write $f = [f]$? Since $f \in X_n$ and $[f] \in F_n$, f and $[f]$ are obviously not identical objects, unless $X_n = F_n$. We can still accept the equation $f = [f]$ if we understand that $[f]$ is the coordinate vector of f with respect to the basis in use at the moment; if the basis is changed then f will not change at all, but $[f]$ will change in an entirely predictable way (see B5).

Similarly, if $x = \sum \xi_k p_k \in X_n$, then we have a coordinate vector $[x] = [\xi_k]$, and we accept the equation $x = [x]$ in a sense similar to that just explained for the equation $f = [f]$. When the basis for X is changed, $[x]$ changes as indicated in 5G4.

We seem now to have a notational ambiguity. Is $[2 \quad 1 \quad -3]$ the vector $x = 2p_1 + p_2 - 3p_3$ or the functional f with $fp_1 = 2, fp_2 = 1$, and $fp_3 = -3$? A way out is suggested in 6G2. There the maps of the basis vectors are the columns of the matrix of the transformation. Let us agree, therefore, to represent $x \in X_n$ by an $n \times 1$ matrix or column vector $[x]$, and to represent a functional f on X_n by a $1 \times n$ matrix or row vector $[f]$.

If a column vector $[x] = [\xi_k]$ and a row vector $[f] = [\alpha_k]$, and if $\alpha_k = \xi_k$ $(k = 1, \ldots, n)$ then each of the two vectors is said to be the *transpose* of the other, and we write $[x]^t = [f]$ and $[f]^t = [x]$. For example,

$$\begin{bmatrix} 2 \\ 1 \\ -3 \end{bmatrix}^t = [2 \quad 1 \quad -3], \qquad [2 \quad 1 \quad -3]^t = \begin{bmatrix} 2 \\ 1 \\ -3 \end{bmatrix}.$$

Now it is typographically inconvenient to display column vectors frequently. We shall therefore often *represent* a column vector as the transpose of a row vector, writing $x = [x] = [2 \quad 1 \quad -3]^t$ instead of the column vector on the right in the last example. With our present understanding and notation it would be correct in 6G3 to write $Lp_1 = [2 \quad 1 \quad 3]^t$ and $Lp_2 = [-1 \quad 2 \quad -2]^t$; observe that these vectors are the columns of $[\alpha_{\lambda k}]$. It must be kept in mind when there are two indices, as in $[\alpha_{\lambda k}]$, that the left index (λ) runs down the columns while the right index (k) runs across the rows.

We are now in a position, in the context of 5, to write

5.1.
$$fx = [f][x] = [\alpha_k][\xi_k]^t = \sum \alpha_k \xi_k.$$

The expression $\sum \alpha_k \xi_k$ is called a *linear form*; except in the trivial case in which each $\alpha_k = 0$, it is a homogeneous polynomial of degree one. It follows from 5 that a basis for X sets up a 1-1 correspondence between functionals and linear forms:

$$f \leftrightarrow [f] = [\alpha_k] \leftrightarrow \sum \alpha_k \xi_k,$$

where $\alpha_k = fp_k$ $(k = 1, \ldots, n)$. It will turn out in 8B that the expressions $[f][x] = [\alpha_k][\xi_k]^t$ are actually products of the matrices $[f]$ and $[x]$, in that order.

EXERCISES

6. In a real X_3 with a fixed basis p_k ($k = 1, 2, 3$) let $fx = 2\xi - \eta + 3\zeta$.

    (a) Calculate $f[1, -1, 5]^t, f[0, 0, 2]^t, f[1, 2, 0]^t, f[0, 3, 1]^t$.

    (b) Find (perhaps by inspection) a solution of the equation $fx = 6$; obtain also a vector x such that $fx = 1$.

    (c) Obtain a parametric representation (cf. 7) of the flat of all solutions of the equation $2\xi - \eta + 3\zeta = 6$.

    (d) What can you say about the following sets: $\{x : fx > 6\}$, $\{x : fx \le -2\}$, $\{x : fx \ge 0\}$?

    (e) Where is the flat $fx = 6$ cut by the line $x = [2, 0, -1]^t + \tau[3, 1, -2]^t$? By the line $x = [2, 0, -1]^t + \tau[1, -1, -1]^t$?

7. Given $y = [\eta_k]^t$ and $z = [\zeta_k]^t$ in a real X_3, define (cf. 3G8, 3K8):

7.1.
$$\alpha_1 = \eta_2\zeta_3 - \eta_3\zeta_2, \qquad \alpha_2 = \eta_3\zeta_1 - \eta_1\zeta_3, \qquad \alpha_3 = \eta_1\zeta_2 - \eta_2\zeta_1,$$

and put $f = [\alpha_k]$. Verify that $fy = 0 = fz$. Show that if r is a fixed vector then the flat $x = r + \sigma y + \tau z$ has the equation $fx = fr$. Find in this way an equation for the flat $x = [3, 1, -2]^t + \sigma[2, 0, -1]^t + \tau[-1, 2, 3]^t$. Supposing now that $X_3 = E_P$, examine possible relationships between f and the vector product $y \times z$ of 3J.

8. Given distinct functionals $f = [\alpha_k]$ and $g = [\beta_k]$ on a real X_3, write down formulas analogous to 7.1 ($\xi_1 = \alpha_2\beta_3 - \alpha_3\beta_2, \ldots$), put $x_0 = [\xi_k]$, and show that $fx_0 = gx_0 = 0$. Let a fixed vector u have the property that $fu = \alpha$ and $gu = \beta$. Show that the line of intersection of the planes (flats) $fx = \alpha$ and $gx = \beta$ is given by $x = u + \tau x_0$ ($-\infty < \tau < \infty$). Use this method to find the line of intersection of the planes $3\xi - 2\eta + \zeta = 4$ and $\xi + \eta - 2\zeta = -3$.

9. Let $f \ne 0$ on a real X_3. Choose $u \in X_3$ so that $fu \ne 0$ and $v, w \in X_3$ so that u, v, and w are independent. Determine ρ, σ, τ, and φ in such a way that $y = \rho u + \sigma v$ and $z = \tau u + \varphi w$ shall be independent and shall have $fy = fz = 0$. (The last two conditions require that $\rho fu + \sigma fv = 0$ and $\tau fu + \varphi fw = 0$.)

10. In 4 is either the condition $fx_0 = 1$ or the condition $N_f = Y_{n-1}$ enough by itself to determine f uniquely? Explain. (T)

11. Given a functional b on X_n, define a relation ρ for $x, y \in X_n$ by agreeing that $x \rho y$ if and only if $bx = by$. Show that ρ is an equivalence relation and specify the equivalence-sets in the partition of X_n set up by ρ. (T)

12. Given $u \in X_n$, $u \ne 0$. In order that a functional f defined on $\langle u \rangle$ be linear it is necessary that f be homogeneous: $f(\alpha u) = \alpha(fu)$. Prove that if f is homogeneous on $\langle u \rangle$ then f is also additive and hence linear on $\langle u \rangle$ (cf. 6A2–3). Does it follow, or not, that if f is linear on $\langle u \rangle$ then f is completely determined by its value fu at u?

13. Given $u, v \in X_n$ ($n \ge 2$) with u and v independent. Given (cf. 12) f linear on $\langle u \rangle$ and g linear on $\langle v \rangle$, define c on $\langle u, v \rangle$ by setting $c(\alpha u + \beta v) = \alpha fu + \beta gv$. Prove that c is linear on $\langle u, v \rangle$.

14. Given $f \neq 0$ on a real X_n, let z_q $(q = 2, \ldots, n)$ be a basis for N_f and choose z_1 so that $fz_1 \neq 0$. Show that z_k $(k = 1, \ldots, n)$ form a basis for X_n. If $x = \sum \xi_k z_k$ then the sign of fx is determined entirely by the signs of ξ_1 and fz_1. What can you say (cf. 6(d)) about the sets $\{x : fx > 0\}$ and $\{x : fx \leq 0\}$?

15. Verify in E_P that each linear functional f is the mapping which takes $X \in E_P$ onto the scalar product of X with a fixed vector W, depending on $f : fX = (W, X)$. Prove that the correspondence between functionals f and vectors W is biunique.

B. The Dual Space; Dual Bases; the Bidual

The set of all (linear or nonlinear) functionals $f : X \to F_1$ on a linear space X is itself a linear space F (cf. 5B12). The subset of F consisting of all *linear* functionals is a subspace of F; this subspace of F may be denoted in the notation of 6B1 by $\mathcal{L}(X, F_1)$. Explicitly, $\mathcal{L}(X, F_1)$ consists of all (linear) functionals on X with addition of functionals and multiplication of a functional by a scalar defined pointwise. The space $\mathcal{L}(X, F_1)$ will be called the space *dual* or *conjugate* to X, and will be designated by X^d; in its relation to X^d, X is said to be the *primal* space.

It is natural to expect that dim X^d is determined by dim X. While this is true in general, we shall show only that, in the finite-dimensional case, dim $X^d =$ dim X. In the infinite-dimensional case the result is that dim $X^d = (\text{card } F)^{\dim X}$, where card F is the cardinal number of the field F (cf. 1I19 ff. and [C5, p. 247]).

If $X = \langle 0 \rangle$ then a functional $f : X \to F_1$ can take on only the value 0, and we have agreed that if $x \in X$ implies $fx = 0$ then by definition $f = 0$. Hence $X^d = \langle 0 \rangle$ and dim $X^d = 0 =$ dim X.

It is also true for $n = 1, 2, 3, \ldots$ that if dim $X = n$, then dim $X^d = n$. Let $\{p_k\}$ $(k = 1, \ldots, n)$ be a basis for X. Then $X = {}_k\bigoplus_1^n \langle p_k \rangle$. Define hyperspaces P_k as follows:

$$P_k = {}_j\bigoplus_1^n \langle p_j \rangle \qquad (j \neq k).$$

Then $X = \langle p_k \rangle \oplus P_k$. With k arbitrary but fixed we apply A4 (with p_k for x_0 and P_k for Y_{n-1}) to obtain a unique functional a_k such that

1.
$$a_k p_k = 1 \quad \text{and} \quad N_{a_k} = P_k.$$

Thus $a_k p_j = 0$ if $j \neq k$, and therefore

2.
$$a_k p_j = \delta_{kj} = a_j p_k \qquad (j, k = 1, \ldots, n).$$

We now maintain that the functionals a_k $(k = 1, \ldots, n)$ form a basis for X^d. If $\sum \alpha_k a_k = 0$ then, for $j = 1, \ldots, n$,

$$0 = (\sum \alpha_k a_k) p_j = \sum \alpha_k \delta_{kj} = \alpha_j;$$

hence the a's are independent. Given now $b \in X^d$ we shall show that

169

$b = \sum (bp_k)a_k$, proving that the a's span X^d and therefore form a basis for it. If $x = \sum \xi_j p_j$, then on one hand

$$bx = b(\sum \xi_j p_j) = \sum \xi_j(bp_j),$$

and on the other

$$\sum_k (bp_k)a_k(\sum_j \xi_j p_j) = \sum_k (bp_k) \sum_j \xi_j a_k p_j = \sum_k (bp_k) \sum_j \xi_j \delta_{jk} = \sum \xi_k(bp_k);$$

since the results are the same and x is arbitrary, we see that, as desired, $b = \sum (bp_k)a_k$.

3. **Theorem.** If dim $X = n$ $(n = 0, 1, 2, \ldots)$ then dim $X^d = n$. If $n \geq 1$ and p_k $(k = 1, \ldots, n)$ is a basis for X, then there is a unique basis a_k for X^d such that

$$a_k p_j = \delta_{jk} \qquad (j, k = 1, \ldots, n).$$

If $b \in X^d$ then $b = \sum (bp_k)a_k$.

The basis a_k for X^d is said to be *dual* to the basis p_k for X, which in its relation to a_k is called the *primal* basis. It will turn out in 7 that each basis for X^d is the dual of a basis for X. There is thus a 1-1 pairing $\{p_k\} \leftrightarrow \{a_k\}$ between bases for X and bases for X^d in such a way that equations 2 hold between elements of the two bases. Such a pair is called a *dual pair* of bases, or they are said simply to be *dual bases*. Coordinates with respect to dual bases will be called *dual* (systems of) *coordinates*.

It is reassuring to observe in retrospect that the numbers $\alpha_k = fp_k$ of A5 are precisely the components of $f = [\alpha_k]$ with respect to the basis a_k dual to p_k. Indeed, since the bases are dual, it follows from 2 that

$$fx = (\sum (fp_k)a_k)(\sum \xi_j p_j) = \sum_{j,k} \alpha_k \xi_j a_k p_j = \sum \alpha_k \xi_k.$$

Dually, $a_k x = a_k \sum \xi_j p_j = \xi_k$.

According to the convention adopted toward the end of A, if $\{p_k\}$ is a basis for X and $\{a_k\}$ is a basis for X^d, then

$$f = \sum \alpha_k a_k = [\alpha_k]$$

$$x = \sum \xi_k p_k = [\xi_k]',$$

the former being a row vector and the latter a column vector. The general expression for fx is

$$fx = (\sum_j \alpha_j a_j)(\sum_k \xi_k p_k) = \sum_{j,k} \alpha_j \xi_k(a_j p_k)$$

and cannot be reduced to A5.1 unless relations 2 hold. That is why dual bases are advantageous, and we shall always assume that bases for X and X^d form a dual pair.

Given two spaces of the same dimension, such as X and X^d, and a basis for each, we have seen in 5D13 that there is an isomorphism between them in which a vector and its mate simply have the same respective kth components. It is interesting to observe that just this isomorphism between X and X^d is established by the operation of transposition described toward the end of A:

$$x \leftrightarrow x^t, \qquad f \leftrightarrow f^t.$$

It must be emphasized that this mapping depends upon the bases in use and therefore has, in general, no intrinsic or invariant significance.

The space F_n of ordered n-tuples of field elements was introduced in 5B9. We agree henceforth to interpret vectors in F_n as *column* vectors, and the dual space, F_n^d, consists of n-component *row* vectors. Accordingly,

$$[f] = [\alpha_k] \in F_n^d,$$

while

$$[x] = [\xi_k]^t \in F_n.$$

Let us suppose now that the basis $\{p_k\}$ for X is to be replaced by a basis $\{q_k\}$ with (cf. 5G5) $p_k = \sum q_j \alpha_{jk}$. Can we find the basis $\{b_k\}$ dual to $\{q_k\}$ without repeating the construction used in proving 3? The answer is affirmative if the basis $\{a_k\}$ dual to $\{p_k\}$ is known.

One method of argument uses bases. By 3, since $\{a_k\}$ is dual to $\{p_k\}$, $b_j = \sum_k (b_j p_k) a_k$. Hence

$$b_j = \sum_k (b_j \sum_h q_h \alpha_{hk}) a_k = \sum_{k,h} \alpha_{hk} (b_j q_h) a_k.$$

Since $\{b_k\}$ is to be dual to $\{q_k\}$, we must have $b_j q_h = \delta_{jh}$, whence

4.
$$b_j = \sum \alpha_{jk} a_k, \qquad a_k = \sum \beta_{kj} b_j,$$

where we have used 5G2 to obtain the last relation.

Another argument uses linear forms. If

$$x = \sum \xi_k p_k = \sum \eta_k q_k \qquad \text{and} \qquad a = \sum \gamma_k a_k = \sum \delta_k b_k,$$

then we wish to have, by 5G4,

$$\sum \gamma_k \xi_k = \sum \gamma_k \beta_{kh} \eta_h = \sum \delta_h \eta_h.$$

Since this is to hold for each $[\eta_h]^t$, it follows that

5.
$$\delta_h = \sum \gamma_k \beta_{kh}, \qquad \gamma_k = \sum \delta_h \alpha_{hk},$$

where we have used 5G3 to obtain the last relation.

Either 4 or 5 can be obtained, of course, from the other. They are companions to 5G4–5; it will be noted that components here transform like basis vectors there, while basis vectors here transform like components there.

Being a linear space in its own right, X^d has a dual space $(X^d)^d$ consisting of the (linear) functionals defined on X^d. This space is denoted by X^{dd} and is called the *bidual* of X. It is a consequence of 3 that if dim X is finite then dim $X^{dd} = \dim X^d = \dim X$; thus X, X^d, and X^{dd} are isomorphic. If X and X^{dd} are isomorphic, X is said to be (algebraically) *reflexive*; we have just seen that every finite-dimensional linear space is reflexive. It can be shown that if dim X is not finite then dim $X^d > \dim X$; hence dim $X^{dd} > \dim X$ and (algebraic) reflexivity is out of the question. Topological considerations enter into the idea of reflexivity for infinite-dimensional topological linear spaces;

reflexivity turns out, as modified, to be a rather strong property, bringing with it notable simplifications in the theory.

When confronted with several isomorphic spaces (here X, X^d, and X^{dd}), one asks, since they all have the same fundamental structure, whether there is any reason to keep them conceptually distinct. In the present situation we can display a most natural and intimate isomorphic correspondence between X and X^{dd}, independent of any bases, while there is no such immediate general relationship, if $n > 1$, between X^d and either X or X^{dd}.

An element φ of X^{dd} is a linear functional defined on X^d, on the space, that is, of all linear functionals on X; thus φ is a linear functional of linear functionals. That each $\varphi \in X^{dd}$ determines a unique vector $x \in X$ may therefore seem rather bizarre, but the reason is very simple.

Let z denote a fixed vector in X. We shall define a corresponding φ_z on X^d into F_1 as follows: $f \to \varphi_z(f) = fz$; thus the value of φ_z at the element f of its domain is the scalar fz. That φ_z depends linearly on f is immediate, for

$$\varphi_z(\alpha f + \beta g) = (\alpha f + \beta g)z = \alpha fz + \beta gz = \alpha\varphi_z(f) + \beta\varphi_z(g).$$

With each $x \in X$ we have therefore associated a uniquely determined $\varphi_x \in X^{dd}$, and it is easy to verify that the mapping $x \to \varphi_x$ is linear. If $\varphi_x = 0$ then $fx = 0$ for each $f \in X^d$ and it follows that $x = 0$; otherwise, in fact, we could use A4 (with $x_0 = x$ and Y_{n-1} any complement of $\langle x \rangle$) to obtain an $f \in X$ with $fx = 1$. The correspondence $x \to \varphi_x$ is therefore biunique; it is the "natural" isomorphism between X and X^{dd} mentioned above.

Putting the matter a little differently we may say that the scalar fx, viewed as a function defined on $X^d \times X$ into F_1 has these properties: with f fixed it is linear in x while with x fixed it is linear in f. The latter property amounts to this: with x fixed and f a variable with domain X^d, fx is precisely the element φ_x of X^{dd}. We therefore simply abandon the distinction between X and X^{dd}, identifying $x \in X$ and $\varphi_x \in X^{dd}$; thus $x = \varphi_x$ and $X = X^{dd}$. We record this result as a theorem:

6. **Theorem.** If dim X is finite then $X = X^{dd}$.

There is no such compelling reason to identify X and X^d; there are indeed other reasons (beyond our scope here) for insisting on the conceptual distinction between X and X^d.

Given now a basis $\{a_k\}$ for X^d, we return to the problem of obtaining for X a basis $\{p_j\}$ such that equations 2 hold. We apply 3 to X^d and a_k, obtaining for X^{dd} a basis $\{\varphi_k\}$ such that

$$\varphi_k a_j = \delta_{jk} = \varphi_j a_k \qquad (j, k = 1, \ldots, n).$$

By virtue of the isomorphism just established between X and X^{dd} there exist vectors $p_k \in X$ such that $\varphi_k = \varphi_{p_k} (k = 1, \ldots, n)$. The vectors p_k form a basis for X and have the property, finally, that

$$\varphi_k a_j = \varphi_{p_k} a_j = a_j p_k = \delta_{jk} \qquad (j, k = 1, \ldots, n).$$

The other of equations 2 follows when j and k are interchanged, and the following result is established.

7. Corollary. If dim $X = n$ $(n = 1, 2, 3, \ldots)$ and $\{a_k\}$ $(k = 1, \ldots, n)$ is a basis for X^d, then X has a unique basis $\{p_k\}$ such that

$$a_k p_j = \delta_{jk} = a_j p_k \qquad (j, k = 1, \ldots, n).$$

A final word may be devoted to a situation arising in reflexive spaces from the fact that $X^{dd} = X$, that the dual of the dual is the primal. There is no way of telling abstractly—apart from the nature of their elements—whether one is dealing with X and its dual X^d or with X^d and its dual $X^{dd} = X$. The spaces occur in dual pairs, and it really makes no difference which is designated as primal so long as the designation, once made, is carefully observed. In a practical situation one is usually interested in a specific space, calls it the primal space X, and uses the dual space X^d in order to study properties of X. It is then customary to refer to elements of X as vectors and to elements of X^d as functionals, although the latter are "vectors" in the space X^d and the former are "functionals" on X^d.

EXERCISES

In these exercises we have a real X_n $(n \geq 1)$ and its dual space X^d with dual bases p_k for X and b_k for X^d.

8. Let $n = 4$ and define

$$f = [2, -1, 0, 3] \in X^d, \qquad u = [1, 3, 0, 1]^t \in X,$$
$$g = [-2, 4, 1, -1] \in X^d, \qquad v = [-1, 1, 3, -3]^t \in X.$$

(a) Calculate $2f$, $f + 3g$, $3f - 2g$.

(b) Calculate fu, gv, $(f + 3g)u$, $(3f - 2g)(u + v)$.

(c) Show that f and g are independent.

(d) Obtain an $x \in X$ such that $(3f - 2g)x = 0$.

(e) Obtain an $x \in X$ such that $fx = gx = 0$; try to find all such $x \in X$.

(f) Obtain a $c \in X^d$ such that $cu = cv = 0$; try to find all such $c \in X^d$.

(g) For $k = 2$ and $k = 4$; calculate fp_k, gp_k, $b_k u$, and $b_k v$.

9. In C_3 with $x = [\xi_1, \xi_2, \xi_3]^t$ where $\xi_k \in C$ $(k = 1, 2, 3)$, which of the following expressions are linear forms:

(a) ξ_2,

(b) $\bar{\xi}_3$,

(c) $(1 - i)\xi_1 - \xi_2 + (3 - 4i)\xi_3$,

(d) $\text{Re}(\xi_1)$,

(e) $\sqrt{\xi_1\bar{\xi}_1 + \xi_2\bar{\xi}_2 + \xi_3\bar{\xi}_3}$,

(f) $\xi_1 - \xi_2 + 2i$,

(g) $\xi_2\bar{\xi}_3 - \xi_3\bar{\xi}_2$?

10. With $f, g \in X^d$ fixed, consider the families of level surfaces of f and g, i.e., the families of flats $fx = \alpha$ and $gx = \beta$ with $\alpha, \beta \in F$. Obtain a necessary and sufficient condition that each level surface of either f or g be a level surface of the other. (T)

11. With $f, g \in X^d$ fixed, prove that the conditions $fx = 0$ and $gx = 0$ are equivalent if and only if there is a scalar α such that $f = \alpha g$. Try to specify the scalar α. (T)

12. Given a fixed $z \in X$ define a relation for $f, g \in X^d$ by agreeing that $f \rho g$ if and only if $fz = gz$. Show that ρ is an equivalence relation. What are the equivalence-sets in the partition of X^d set up by ρ? (T)

13. Given independent $f, g \in X^d$, show that if not both $\alpha = 0$ and $\beta = 0$, then the flat φ of solutions of $(\alpha f + \beta g)x = 0$ is a hyperspace containing the intersection of N_f and N_g. Find values of α and β such that φ will contain a given point $z \in X$ not on $N_f \cap N_g$. Apply this result in a real X_3, with given basis, to find an equation for the plane containing the point $[3, -2, 1]'$ and the line of intersection of the planes $\xi + 2\eta - 3\zeta = 0$ and $2\xi + \zeta = 0$.

14. Assume that $n > 1$, that $1 \leq m < n$, and that $a_\mu \in X^d$ ($\mu = 1, \ldots, m$). Prove that there exists a vector $x \neq 0$ such that $a_\mu x = 0$ ($\mu = 1, \ldots, m$). What can you conclude about the system $\sum_{k=1}^{n} \alpha_{\lambda k}\xi_k = 0$ ($\lambda = 1, \ldots, m$)? (T)

15. Prove that if $X = U \oplus V$ then $X^d = U^d \oplus V^d$. (Use dual bases, with that for X adapted to U and V.) (T)

16. (Outline of direct proof of 7; interpretation in a real X_3 is suggestive). For $k = 1$, $\ldots$, n let N_k denote the nullspace of a_k and define $Q_k = \bigcap_{j=1}^{n} N_j$ ($j \neq k$). Let k be arbitrary but fixed. Prove that $Q_k \neq \langle 0 \rangle$ (cf. 11). Prove that if $x \in Q_k$ and $x \neq 0$, then $a_k x \neq 0$. Prove that if $p, q \in Q_k$ then p and q are dependent. Hence $Q_k = \langle q_k \rangle$ for some $q_k \in X$ with $q_k \neq 0$. Define $p_k = q_k/(a_k q_k)$. Prove that $\{p_k\}$ forms a basis for X and that $a_k p_j = \delta_{kj}$.

C. Orthogonal Subspaces of Dual Spaces

Given a linear space X of dimension $n \geq 1$, let us say that $f \in X^d$ and $x \in X$ are *orthogonal* if $fx = 0$. This notion is quite distinct, of course, from that of the orthogonality of two vectors in E_P, but the ideas are related in such a way, as we shall see in Chap. 12, as to justify the use of the term "orthogonal" in the present context. The terms *normal*, *perpendicular*, and *incident* are also used, and it is said that f and x *annul* or *annihilate* each other.

Given $f \in X^d$, we know that if $f \neq 0$ then the set of those $x \in X$ such that $fx = 0$ is the hyperspace N_f of X. More generally, given subsets B of X^d and W of X we define associated subsets B° of X and W° of X^d as follows:

$$B° = \{x : \text{If } g \in B \text{ then } gx = 0\},$$

$$W° = \{f : \text{If } w \in W \text{ then } fw = 0\}.$$

It is obvious that if $x_j \in B°$ then $\sum \alpha_j x_j \in B°$; hence $B°$ is a subspace of X. Similarly, $W° \le X^d$. Recalling that $\langle B \rangle$ denotes the subspace of X^d generated by B, we verify easily that $B° = \langle B \rangle°$. Similarly, $W° = \langle W \rangle°$. We therefore confine attention to subspaces but allow ourselves the liberty of abbreviating $\langle x \rangle°$ to $x°$ and $\langle f \rangle°$ to $f°$. The subspaces $B°$ and $W°$ are the *subspaces orthogonal to B and W* respectively; they are also called *annihilators* of B and W.

Clearly $X° = \langle 0 \rangle \le X^d$ and $X^{d°} = \langle 0 \rangle \le X$. Also, for $0 \in X$, $\langle 0 \rangle° = X^d$; for $0 \in X^d$, $\langle 0 \rangle° = X$. We know too that if $f \ne 0$ then $\dim f° = n - 1$. These are all special instances of the following theorem, which is not necessarily valid if $\dim X$ is infinite.

1. Theorem. If $\dim X = n \ge 1$, $Y \le X$, and $B \le X^d$, then

$$\dim Y + \dim Y° = n, \qquad \dim B + \dim B° = n,$$

and moreover, $Y°° = Y$ and $B°° = B$.

We shall prove the statements regarding Y; the proofs of those regarding B are entirely analogous. Let $X = Y \oplus Z$ and let $\{p_k\}$ $(k = 1, \ldots, n)$ be a basis for X such that $\{p_j\}$ $(j = 1, \ldots, m = \dim Y)$ is a basis for Y while $\{p_h\}$ $(h = m + 1, \ldots, n)$ is a basis for Z. Let $\{b_k\}$ be a basis for X^d dual to the basis $\{p_k\}$ for X, and consider an arbitrary $f = \sum \alpha_k b_k \in X^d$. We must require that $y = \sum_{j=1}^{m} \eta_j p_j \in Y$ shall imply that $fy = 0$; this will hold if and only if $\alpha_k = 0$ $(k = 1, \ldots, m)$. Hence

$$Y° = \left\{ f : f = \sum_{h=m+1}^{n} \alpha_h b_h \right\};$$

since the vectors b_h $(h = m + 1, \ldots, n)$ are clearly a basis for $Y°$, we conclude that $\dim Y° = n - m = n - \dim Y$, proving the dimensional assertion of the theorem.

By $Y°°$ we mean, of course, $(Y°)°$; this is the subspace of X orthogonal to $Y°$. Clearly $Y \le Y°°$, for if $y \in Y$ then $f \in Y°$ implies that $fy = 0$, whence $y \in (Y°)°$. It is also true that $\dim Y°° = n - \dim Y° = \dim Y$. Since $Y°°$ is a subspace containing Y and having the same dimension as Y we conclude that $Y°° = Y$, for any basis for Y is a basis for $Y°°$.

The operation $Q \to Q°$ of passing from a subspace Q of X or X^d to the orthogonal subspace $Q°$ of X^d or X is involutorial in the sense that two performances of the operation on a subspace yield the original subspace: $Q°° = Q$. It follows that the correspondence $Q \leftrightarrow Q°$ is a biunique correspondence in which each $Q \le X$ is mated with a unique $Q° \le X^d$ and conversely. This correspondence is related to the inclusion, intersection, and union of subspaces as follows.

2. **Theorem.** If P and Q are both subspaces of X, or both subspaces of X^d, then:

(a) if $P \leq Q$ then $Q^\circ \leq P^\circ$;

(b) $(P \cap Q)^\circ = P^\circ + Q^\circ$;

(c) $(P + Q)^\circ = P^\circ \cap Q^\circ$.

Assertion (a) is obvious, for any element of Q° is orthogonal to every element of Q and hence, since $P \leq Q$, to every element of P. In order to prove (b) we recall first (cf. 5E8, 5F) that $P \cap Q$ is that subspace S (of X or X^d) such that $S \leq P$ and $S \leq Q$ and, if $R \leq P$ and $R \leq Q$ then $R \leq S$. It follows at once that $(P \cap Q)^\circ = S^\circ$ has the property that both $P^\circ \leq S^\circ$ and $Q^\circ \leq S^\circ$. Now suppose that a subspace T has the property that $P^\circ \leq T$ and $Q^\circ \leq T$. Then $T^\circ \leq P$ and $T^\circ \leq Q$, whence $T^\circ \leq S$ and, therefore, $S^\circ \leq T$. It follows from 5F6 that S° is precisely $P^\circ + Q^\circ$, and (b) is proved.

A second proof of (b) will use (a) and slightly different lines of argument. Since $P \cap Q \leq P$, Q, it follows that P°, $Q^\circ \leq (P \cap Q)^\circ$, whence $P^\circ + Q^\circ \leq (P \cap Q)^\circ$. Also, P°, $Q^\circ \leq P^\circ + Q^\circ$, whence $(P^\circ + Q^\circ)^\circ \leq P$, Q, and $(P^\circ + Q^\circ)^\circ \leq P \cap Q$, whence $(P \cap Q)^\circ \leq P^\circ + Q^\circ$, completing the proof.

A direct proof of (c) along similar lines is easy. We give instead a proof which starts with (b) and exploits the correspondence $S \to S^\circ$. From (b) we have

$$(P \cap Q)^{\circ\circ} = P \cap Q = (P^\circ + Q^\circ)^\circ.$$

Now denote P° by R and Q° by S. Then $P = P^{\circ\circ} = R^\circ$ and $Q = Q^{\circ\circ} = S^\circ$ and, as desired, we have

$$R^\circ \cap S^\circ = (R + S)^\circ.$$

It was essential to the argument that each subspace, such as R, be the subspace orthogonal to a subspace of the dual space; in fact, $R = (R^\circ)^\circ$. The biunique involutorial correspondence $Q \leftrightarrow Q^\circ$ is a fundamental aspect of the "Principle of Duality", by virtue of which certain properties and propositions occur in dual pairs, such as (b) and (c) above, each member of which is said to be dual to the other. Our proof of (c) amounted to showing that it follows from (b) "by duality". Since we shall not appeal to the Principle of Duality as a principle of inference, we forego a precise formulation. It is used extensively in projective geometry.

That Q and Q° determine each other uniquely has this practical consequence: a specification of either implies a specification of the other. If $Q \leq X_n$ and $1 \leq \dim Q = m < n$, then we may specify either a basis $\{q_h\}$ ($h = 1, \ldots, m$) for Q or a basis $\{a_j\}$ ($j = m + 1, \ldots, n$) for Q°. If either is given then the other is determined by the orthogonality conditions

$$a_j q_h = 0 \qquad (h = 1, \ldots, m; j = m + 1, \ldots, n).$$

Now the a_j determine linear forms $a_j x = \sum \alpha_{jk}\xi_k$, and Q consists precisely of those vectors whose components satisfy the equations $a_j x = 0$. We arrive therefore at the following *double description* of Q:

$$\langle q_1, \ldots, q_m\rangle, \qquad \sum \alpha_{jk}\xi_h = 0 \qquad (j = m + 1, \ldots, n).$$

Here is a double description of a line in an X_3:

$$\langle [3, 7, 8]^t\rangle, \qquad \begin{aligned} 3\xi + \eta - 2\zeta &= 0 \\ 2\xi - 2\eta + \zeta &= 0. \end{aligned}$$

For a plane, similarly:

$$\langle [3, 1, -2]^t, [2, -2, 1]^t\rangle, \qquad 3\xi + 7\eta + 8\zeta = 0.$$

EXERCISES

3. In a real X_3 with fixed dual bases $\{p_h\}$ for X and $\{b_k\}$ for X^d, find in each case another description for the subspace with the given description:

(a) the plane $2\xi - 3\eta + \zeta = 0$,

(b) the line $x = \tau[3, 1, 4]^t$,

(c) the plane $x = [2\sigma - \tau, \sigma + 3\tau, 3\sigma + \tau]^t$,

(d) the line orthogonal to the functionals

$$[5, 2, -1] \qquad \text{and} \qquad [1, -3, 2].$$

4. Prove the statements of 1 regarding B. (T)

5. Prove 2(c) by showing, for each equality, that each member is a subspace of the other. (T)

6. Suppose that $f \in X^d$, $f \neq 0$, and $fx_0 = 1$. Use the decomposition $x = (fx)x_0 + (x - (fx)x_0)$ to prove that $X = \langle x_0\rangle \oplus N_f$; hence conclude that $\dim f^\circ = \dim X - 1$. Describe the projections involved (cf. A2 and 6C). (T)

7. Comment in the present context on the fact (cf. 5F17) that if $Y \leq X$ then Y is the intersection of the hyperspaces containing Y.

8. Let $\{b_k\}$ $(k = 1, \ldots, n)$ be a basis for X^d and let β_k be given constants. Prove that there is a unique $x \in X$ such that $b_k x = \beta_k$ $(k = 1, \ldots, n)$. (T)

9. If $X = Y \oplus Z$ then Y^d and Z° are isomorphic, Z^d and Y° are isomorphic, and $X^d = Z^\circ \oplus Y^\circ$. (Each $x = y_x + z_x$ for unique $y_x \in Y$ and $z_x \in Z$. Prove first that if $f \in Z^\circ \cap Y^\circ$ then $f = 0$, whence $Z^\circ \cap Y^\circ = \langle 0\rangle$. Given $f \in X^d$ define f_Y by the equation $f_Y x = f y_x$ and f_Z by the equation $f_Z x = f z_x$. Prove that $f_Y \in Z^\circ$ and $f_Z \in Y^\circ$. Establish an isomorphism between Y^d and the set of all f_Y and between Z^d and the set of all f_Z.) (T)

10. Prove that if $B \leq X^d$ then $B^\circ = \bigcap_{g \in B} N_g$. Just as $f^\circ = N_f$, we may call $x^\circ \leq X^d$ the nullspace of x and write $x^\circ = N_x$. Prove that if $W \leq X$ then $W^\circ = \bigcap_{x \in W} N_x$. (T)

11. Is each subspace of X^d (or of X) the subspace orthogonal to some subspace of X (or of X^d)? (T)

D. The Dual of a Transformation

We are given linear spaces X and Y of positive dimension over the same field. Notation is assigned for this section as follows: w, $x \in X$; y, $z \in Y$; b, $c \in X^d$; f, $g \in Y^d$.

A linear transformation $L : X \to Y$ establishes certain correspondences between subspaces of X and of Y. In view of the biunique relationship between orthogonal subspaces of X and X^d, and of Y and Y^d, L must establish certain correspondences between subspaces of X^d and of Y^d. This fact suggests that L must induce a linear mapping either on X^d into Y^d or on Y^d into X^d. In this section our aim is to define this mapping and to investigate its connection with L and with orthogonal pairs of subspaces.

With $f \in Y^d$ examine the mapping on X into F_1 given by $x \to f(Lx)$. Evidently

$$\alpha w + \beta x \to fL(\alpha w + \beta x) = f(\alpha Lw + \beta Lx) = \alpha fLw + \beta fLx.$$

Hence the resultant fL defines a linear functional on X. With each $f \in Y^d$ we have therefore associated an element $b = fL$ of X^d. We denote this mapping by L^d and call it the *dual* of L. The formal definition is this:

1. $$L^d \text{ on } Y^d \text{ into } X^d : f \to fL^d = b$$

where, for each $x \in X$, $bx = fLx$.

It would be in accord with our previous work, since $bx = fLx$, to write simply $b = fL$; why is the "d" needed? If the "f" were always there, the "d" would indeed be superfluous, but we shall often wish to use an isolated symbol and must therefore distinguish between $L : X \to Y$ and its dual $L^d : Y^d \to X^d$.

We are introducing here a definite convention regarding the relative positions of the symbols for a linear transformation and an element of its domain; if the domain is the "primal" space X or Y then the symbol for the transformation is put to the left, while if the domain is the dual space X^d or Y^d then the symbol for the transformation is put to the right. The presence of the "d" on the symbol for the transformation often implies proper location for parentheses, which may then safely be omitted. For example,

$$(fL^d)x = fL^dx = fLx = f(Lx).$$

That L^d is linear is clear from the following equations:

$$((\alpha f + \beta g)L^d)x = (\alpha f + \beta g)(Lx) = \alpha fLx + \beta gLx = (\alpha fL^d + \beta gL^d)x.$$

For example, let L be defined on a real X_3 with vectors $[\xi, \eta, \zeta]^t$ into a real Y_2 with vectors $[\lambda, \mu]^t$ by the equations (assuming bases in X^d and Y^d dual to those in X and Y)

$$\lambda = 3\xi - 2\eta + \zeta, \qquad \mu = \xi + 2\eta - \zeta.$$

Then to the functional $[\alpha, \beta] \in Y^d$ will correspond the linear form

$$\alpha\lambda + \beta\mu = (3\alpha + \beta)\xi + (-2\alpha + 2\beta)\eta + (\alpha - \beta)\zeta.$$

The dual mapping L^d is therefore

$$[\alpha, \beta] \to [\alpha, \beta]L^d = [3\alpha + \beta, -2\alpha + 2\beta, \alpha - \beta] \in X^d.$$

It is evident that $0^d = 0$, that if L is an endomorphism of X then L^d is an endomorphism of X^d, and that $(I_X)^d = I_{X^d}$. Proofs of the following two results are left as exercises.

2.   If $\alpha \in F$ then $(\alpha L)^d = \alpha L^d$.

3. $$(L + M)^d = L^d + M^d.$$

Given $L : X \to Y$ and $M : Y \to Z$, we have seen how to form the resultant $ML : X \to Z$. Its dual $(ML)^d$ will have domain Z^d and codomain X^d. If $\varphi \in Z^d$ and $x \in X$ then repeated use of 1 yields

$$(\varphi(ML)^d)x = \varphi MLx = (\varphi M^d)Lx = ((\varphi M^d)L^d)x = (\varphi M^d L^d)x.$$

Since this is true for every x and φ, we have

4. $$(ML)^d = M^d L^d.$$

It must be emphasized that this result is a direct consequence of our convention regarding the position of the symbols for the transformation and the element of the domain. Since the domain of M^d is Z^d and $\varphi \in Z^d$, our convention requires that the expression start at the left with φM^d . . . . If our convention had been, on the contrary, the more usual one that puts the transformation always on the left and the element of the domain on the right, then the argument given above, with appropriate changes, yields

4′. $$(ML)^d = L^d M^d.$$

(Some writers put the transformation always on the right and the element of the domain always on the left; with that convention the resultant of L followed by M is LM and the dual relation is $(LM)^d = M^d L^d$, which is equivalent to 4′.)

The transformation $L^{dd} = (L^d)^d$ has domain $X^{dd} = X$ and codomain $Y^{dd} = Y$. By paraphrasing 1 dually we have

$$L^{dd} \text{ on } X \text{ into } Y : x \to L^{dd}x = y$$

where, for each $f \in Y^d$, $fy = fL^d x$. For each $f \in Y^d$, then, it is true for each $x \in X$ that

$$f(L^{dd}x) = (fL^d)x = f(Lx),$$

whence $L^{dd}x = Lx$ and, since x is arbitrary,

5. $$L^{dd} = L.$$

With the mapping L and L^d there are associated the following eight subspaces:

$$N_L \leq X, \qquad N_L^\circ \leq X^d, \qquad R_L \leq Y, \qquad R_L^\circ \leq Y^d,$$
$$R_{L^d}^\circ \leq X, \qquad R_{L^d} \leq X^d, \qquad N_{L^d}^\circ \leq Y, \qquad N_{L^d} \leq Y^d.$$

We shall prove the first and last of the following four remarkable relationships; the others follow immediately by duality.

6.1. $$N_L = R_{L^d}^\circ,$$

6.2. $$N_L^\circ = R_{L^d},$$

6.3. $$R_L = N_{L^d}^\circ,$$

6.4. $$R_L^\circ = N_{L^d}.$$

In infinite-dimensional spaces some of these equalities may be false, but one of the two implied inclusions may still hold.

In proving 6.1 we observe that $x \in N_L$ if and only if $Lx = 0$. But this is true if and only if, for every $f \in Y^d$, $(fL^d)x = f(Lx) = 0$, and this is true, in turn, if and only if $x \in R_{L^d}^\circ$.

To obtain 6.4 we observe, similarly, that $f \in R_L^\circ$ if and only if $fLx = 0$ for each $x \in X$, which is true if and only if $fL^d = 0$ and $f \in N_{L^d}$.

From 6.3 and 6.2 we obtain respectively these new consistency conditions:

7.1. $\qquad Lx = y$ is consistent if and only if $y \in N_{L^d}^\circ$,

7.2. $\qquad fL^d = b$ is consistent if and only if $b \in N_L^\circ$.

These conditions merely say that $y \in R_L$ or $b \in R_{L^d}$. We may spell out 7.1, for example, thus: $fL^d = 0$ implies $fy = 0$, or y annuls every $f \in Y^d$ that is annulled by L^d.

By equating dimensions in 6 and using 6E1 we obtain four relations. The two independent ones are these:

8.1. $$\nu(L) + \rho(L^d) = \dim X,$$

8.2. $$\nu(L^d) + \rho(L) = \dim Y.$$

From either of these it follows, by 6E1, that

8.3. $$\rho(L^d) = \rho(L).$$

From 6.1 and 6.4 (or 8.1 and 8.2) we obtain respectively the following conditions for nonsingularity:

9.1. $\qquad L$ is nonsingular if and only if $R_{L^d} = X^d$,

9.2. $\qquad L^d$ is nonsingular if and only if $R_L = Y$.

These conditions say, of course, that the dual of the respective mapping is *onto its* codomain. We may clarify the meaning of 9.2, for example, by noting that, if R_L is a proper subspace of Y and $f, g \in Y^d, f \neq g$, but $fLx = gLx$ for each $x \in X$ (that is, for each $y \in R_L$), then $(f - g)L^d = 0$ and $f - g \in N_{L^d}$.

If $\dim X > \dim Y$ then L is necessarily singular, and the same is true of L^d if $\dim Y^d > \dim X^d$. But if $\dim Y = \dim X$ then 8.3 implies that $\nu(L^d) = \nu(L)$.

Conversely, if $\nu(L^d) = \nu(L)$ then the left members of 8.1 and 8.2 are the same, implying that dim X = dim Y. The result is this:

10. $\nu(L) = \nu(L^d)$ if and only if dim X = dim Y.

It is now a simple matter to prove the following result.

11. Theorem. Any two of the following three conditions imply the third:

   (a) L is nonsingular,

   (b) L^d is nonsingular,

   (c) dim X = dim Y.

If any two hold then $(L^d)^{-1} = (L^{-1})^d$.

That (a) and (b) imply (c) is a consequence of 10. If (a) and (c) hold then $\nu(L) = 0$ and 10 yields $\nu(L^d) = 0$ and (b) follows. The proof of the other implication is similar. If two of the conditions hold then L is 1-1 on X onto Y and L^d is 1-1 on Y^d onto X^d. We apply 4 to the left of the following pairs of equations to obtain those on the right:

$$L^{-1}L = I_X, \qquad (L^{-1})^d L^d = I_X^d = I_{X^d},$$

$$LL^{-1} = I_Y, \qquad L^d(L^{-1})^d = I_Y^d = I_{Y^d}.$$

Then we appeal to 6D1(h) to conclude that $(L^d)^{-1} = (L^{-1})^d$, completing the proof.

Let us say that L is *regular* if L has any two and hence all three of the properties (a), (b), and (c) of 11.

In examining the equation $fL^d = b$ we are reminded of the important role played in the solution of $Lx = y$ by a pseudo-inverse M of L (cf. 6F1). Since L^d has domain Y^d and codomain X^d we must dualize the definition, so to speak, saying that $J : X^d \to Y^d$ is a pseudo-inverse of L^d if $JL^d = I_{R_{L^d}}$, that is, if $bJL^d = b$ for each $b \in R_{L^d}$.

12. If $M : Y \to X$ is a pseudo-inverse of $L : X \to Y$, then $M^d : X^d \to Y^d$ is a pseudo-inverse of $L^d : Y^d \to X^d$.

We recall from 6E13, to begin with, that $LML = L$ on X. It follows from an evident extension of 4 that $L^d M^d L^d = L^d$ on Y^d. Now let b be given in R_{L^d}. Then $b = fL^d$ for some $f \in Y^d$ and therefore

$$bM^dL^d = fL^dM^dL^d = fL^d = b$$

and it follows, as desired, that $M^dL^d = I_{R_{L^d}}$.

Leaving aside the regular case we have the following dual of 6F1.

13. The equation $fL^d = b$ is consistent if and only if $b \in R_{L^d}$. If L^d is singular and $b \in R_{L^d}$ and $M^d : X^d \to Y^d$ is any pseudo-inverse of L^d then bM^d is a solution, and f is a solution if and only if $f = bM^d + g$ with $g \in N_{L^d}$ or, in other words, if and only if f lies in the flat $bM^d + N_{L^d}$ in Y^d.

That bM^d is a solution, if $b \in R_L d$, follows from 9. If f is any solution then $(f - bM^d)L^d = 0$ and $f - bM^d \in N_{L^d}$.

If we know the matrix and equations of L, as developed in 6G, what can we say about those of L^d? We are given X_n with basis $\{p_k\}$ and Y_μ with basis $\{q_\lambda\}$ and, along with them now, X^d with basis $\{a_k\}$ dual to $\{p_k\}$ and Y^d with basis $\{b_\lambda\}$ dual to $\{q_\lambda\}$. The maps L_{p_k} of the vectors p_k were decisive in 6G. What are the maps $b_\lambda L^d$ of the vectors b_λ under L^d? If $x = \sum \xi_k p_k \in X$, then

$$(b_\lambda L^d)x = b_\lambda L \sum \xi_k p_k = b_\lambda \sum \xi_k L p_k.$$

By 6G2, $L p_k = \sum \alpha_{\theta k} q_\theta$, whence

$$(b_\lambda L^d)x = b_\lambda \sum_k \xi_k \sum_\theta \alpha_{\theta k} q_\theta = \sum_{k\theta} \xi_k \alpha_{\theta k} b_\lambda q_\theta.$$

Since $b_\lambda q_\theta = \delta_{\lambda\theta}$ and $\xi_k = a_k x$, we have

$$(b_\lambda L^d)x = \sum_k \alpha_{\lambda k} \xi_k = \sum_k \alpha_{\lambda k} a_k x.$$

Since x is arbitrary,

$$b_\lambda L^d = \sum \alpha_{\lambda k} a_k.$$

It is an aspect of duality that here we sum over the column index, while in the expression for $L p_k$ the summation was over the row index. With this in mind, we say simply that the matrix of L^d is $[\alpha_{\lambda k}]$, the same as the matrix of L:

13.1.
$$[L^d] = [L].$$

The equations connecting components are easily obtained. If $f = \sum \beta_\lambda b_\lambda$ and $c = \sum \gamma_k a_k$ and $fL^d = c$, then

$$fL^d = \sum \beta_\lambda b_\lambda L^d = \sum \beta_\lambda \sum \alpha_{\lambda k} a_k = \sum \gamma_k a_k,$$

whence

$$\gamma_k = \sum \beta_\lambda \alpha_{\lambda k}.$$

We have therefore the following dual of the Basic Principle (6G2).

14. Theorem. With each mapping $L : X_n \to Y_\mu$ there is associated a unique dual mapping $L^d : Y_\mu^d \to X_n^d$. When a basis $\{a_k\}$ ($k = 1, \ldots, n$) for X_n^d and a basis $\{b_\lambda\}$ ($\lambda = 1, \ldots, \mu$) for Y_μ^d are designated, the mappings L^d are in a biunique correspondence with ordered μ-tuples of vectors in X_n^d, $\mu \times n$ matrices $[\alpha_{\lambda k}]$, and systems of n equations in μ variables, according to the following table:

$$L^d : Y_\mu^d \to X_n^d \qquad\qquad b \to bL^d = a$$
$$\updownarrow \qquad\qquad\qquad\qquad \updownarrow$$
$$\text{ordered } \mu\text{-tuple in } X_n^d \qquad b_\lambda L^d \quad (\lambda = 1, \ldots, \mu)$$
$$\updownarrow \qquad\qquad\qquad\qquad \updownarrow$$
$$\mu \times n \text{ matrix} \qquad\qquad [\alpha_{\lambda k}] \text{ with } b_\lambda L^d = \sum \alpha_{\lambda k} a_k$$
$$\updownarrow \qquad\qquad\qquad\qquad \updownarrow$$
$$n \text{ linear equations} \qquad\qquad \begin{cases} \gamma_k = \sum \beta_\lambda \alpha_{\lambda k} \\ \text{where } (\sum \beta_\lambda b_\lambda)L^d = \sum \gamma_k a \end{cases}$$
$$\text{in } \mu \text{ unknown}$$

It is worth noting that the λth *row* of $[\alpha_{\lambda k}]$ is $b_\lambda L^d \in X^d$, just as the kth column is $Lp_k \in Y$—always referred, of course, to the fixed bases.

In order to illustrate these ideas let us look again at the example displayed in 6D2.1–2. We use coordinates $[\alpha, \beta, \gamma]$ in Y^d and $[\theta, \varphi]$ in X^d dual to those in Y and X. In our present notation we may write L as follows:

$$[\lambda, \mu]^t \rightarrow [3\lambda - 4\mu, \lambda - \mu, 3\lambda - 5\mu]^t.$$

Since L is nonsingular, 6.1 in this instance is $N_L = \langle 0 \rangle = R^\circ_{L^d}$ while 6.2 is $N^\circ_L = R_{L^d} = X^d$. Moreover, (cf. 6.3) $N^\circ_{L^d} = R_L$ is the plane $2\xi - 3\eta - \zeta = 0$, and the space $N_{L^d} = R^\circ_L$ of 6.4 is generated by $[2, -3, -1]$. As a check, we observe that by 14 L^d is

$$[\alpha, \beta, \gamma] \rightarrow [\theta, \varphi] = [3\alpha + \beta + 3\gamma, -4\alpha - \beta - 5\gamma].$$

We see at once that $[2, -3, -1] \in N_{L^d}$, and that $R_{L^d} = X^d$. Since $\nu(L) = 0$, $\nu(L^d) = 1$, and $\rho(L^d) = 2 = \rho(L)$, the dimensional relations 8.1–3 are verified. The dual $J^d : X^d \rightarrow Y^d$ of the mapping J of 6D2.2 is

$$[\theta, \varphi] \rightarrow [-\theta - \varphi, 4\theta + 3\varphi, 0],$$

and we verify readily that, as asserted in 12,

$$[\theta, \varphi]J^dL^d = [\theta, \varphi].$$

The solutions of the equation $[\alpha, \beta, \gamma]L^d = [\theta, \varphi]$ therefore consist of the flat

$$[-\theta - \varphi, 4\theta + 3\varphi, 0] + \tau[2, -3, -1] \qquad (\tau \in F).$$

Let us observe, finally, that the idea of transposition is easily extended to matrices. If $[\alpha_{\lambda k}]$ is a $\mu \times n$ matrix, then its *transpose* $[\alpha_{\lambda k}]^t$ is an $n \times \mu$ matrix $[\beta_{k\lambda}]$ such that $\beta_{k\lambda} = \alpha_{\lambda k}$ ($\lambda = 1, \ldots, \mu; k = 1, \ldots, n$). The kth row vector of the transpose is the transpose of the kth column vector of the original; similarly for columns. For example,

$$\begin{bmatrix} 2 & 3 \\ 0 & -2 \\ -1 & 1 \end{bmatrix}^t = \begin{bmatrix} 2 & 0 & -1 \\ 3 & -2 & 1 \end{bmatrix}, \qquad \begin{bmatrix} \alpha & \beta & \gamma \\ \xi & \eta & \zeta \end{bmatrix}^t = \begin{bmatrix} \alpha & \xi \\ \beta & \eta \\ \gamma & \zeta \end{bmatrix};$$

clearly, $([\alpha_{\lambda k}]^t)^t = [\alpha_{\lambda k}]$.

If $[\alpha_{\lambda k}]$ is being interpreted as the matrix $[L]$ of a transformation $L : X_n \rightarrow Y_\mu$, then the columns of $[L]$ are (the coordinate vectors of) vectors in Y, and the rows of $[L]$ are (the coordinate vectors of) vectors in X^d. The columns of $[L]^t$ are therefore vectors in X and the rows of $[L]^t$ are vectors in Y^d. Let us denote by L^t that mapping on X^d into Y^d whose matrix is $[L]^t$ with respect to bases dual to those of Y and X. We wish to have $[L^t] = [L]^t$ and to have $[x] \rightarrow [y]$ if and only if $[x]^t \rightarrow [y]^t$. We expect, then, that $[x]^t[L]^t = [y]^t$ if and only if $[L][x] = [y]$. A direct calculation based on 8B2 shows that this is indeed so. More generally, if $[K]$ is an $m \times \mu$ matrix, and $[L]$ is a $\mu \times n$ matrix, then $[K][L]$ is an $m \times n$ matrix and

15.
$$([K][L])^t = [L]^t[K]^t.$$

As noted in the context of D4, authors who write both the symbol for the mapping and the symbol for its dual *always* to the left, or *always* to the right, will conclude that $[L^d] = [L]^t$.

EXERCISES

16. We are given a real X_3 with coordinates $[\xi, \eta, \zeta]^t$ and a real Y_2 with coordinates $[\lambda, \mu]^t$, and with coordinates $[\theta, \varphi, \psi]$ in X^d and $[\alpha, \rho]$ in Y^d dual to those in X and Y. Following the numerical illustration given above, discuss the following transformations and their duals:

(a) $K : X \to Y, \lambda = \xi + 3\eta, \mu = 2\xi - \eta + \zeta$;

(b) $L : Y \to X, \xi = \lambda - \mu, \eta = 2\lambda + 3\mu, \zeta = \mu$;

(c) $M : Y \to X, \xi = 3\lambda + \mu, \eta = \lambda - 2\mu, \zeta = 2\lambda + \mu$.

17. Prove 2, 3, 6.2, and 6.3. (T)

18. What is the consistency condition for the equation $b = fL^d$ arising from 6.2? (T)

19. Prove that $L^{ddd} = L^d$.

20. Given $L : X \to Y$ and $M : Y \to X$, prove that $(LML)^d = L^d M^d L^d$.

21. *Dual of a Projection.* Suppose that $X = X_1 \oplus X_2$ and that H projects X onto X_1 along X_2. Prove that H^d projects X^d onto X_2° along X_1°. (T)

22. We are given spaces X and Y and their respective dual spaces X^d and Y^d. With $x \in X$, $y \in Y$, $b \in X^d$, and $f \in Y^d$ all fixed, examine the symbols yb and xf. Interpret yb as a transformation on Y^d into X^d such that $g \to gyb \in X^d$. Is it linear? There are three other transformations here. What is the rank of each? (T)

23. What are the duals of the transformations of 6G9?

24. If $L : X \to y$ is not regular, then dim $X \neq$ dim Y, and either L or L^d must be singular. If dim $Y <$ dim X, which one is necessarily singular? What if dim $X <$ dim Y? (T)

25. Given $M : Y^d \to X^d$, is there necessarily an $L : X \to Y$ such that $M = L^d$?

EIGHT
Some Properties of Matrices

Given linear spaces X_n with basis $\{p_k\}$ and Y_μ with basis $\{q_\lambda\}$, over the same field F, we saw in 6G2 that there is a biunique correspondence $L \leftrightarrow [\alpha_{\lambda k}]$ between the set of linear transformations on X into Y and the set of $\mu \times n$ matrices with elements in F. Since there is an algebra of transformations, it must be possible to set up a corresponding algebra of matrices in such a way that the behavior of the transformations will be in isomorphic correspondence with the behavior of the matrices representing them. Matrices are important objects of study in their own right, however, and we choose therefore to frame our definitions directly in terms of the elements themselves; the connection with transformations will be clarified immediately. The underlying field F is assumed, without further mention, to be the same throughout this chapter.

A. Linear Operations

Since the sum of two transformations is defined only when they have the same domain and the same codomain, we shall define the sum of two matrices only when they have the same number of rows and the same number of columns.

1. The *sum* of two $\mu \times n$ matrices $[\alpha_{\lambda k}]$ and $[\beta_{\lambda k}]$ is the $\mu \times n$ matrix $[\gamma_{\lambda k}]$, where $\gamma_{\lambda k} = \alpha_{\lambda k} + \beta_{\lambda k}$ ($\lambda = 1, \ldots, \mu; k = 1, \ldots, n$); thus

2.
$$[\alpha_{\lambda k}] + [\beta_{\lambda k}] = [\alpha_{\lambda k} + \beta_{\lambda k}].$$

Naturally enough, the row (column) vectors of the sum are the sums of the respective row (column) vectors of the summands; in this sense 2 is simply a generalization to ordered sets of vectors of the familiar rule for adding vectors.

For example,

$$\begin{bmatrix} 1 & 3 & 5 \\ 2 & 4 & 6 \end{bmatrix} + \begin{bmatrix} \alpha & \gamma & \epsilon \\ \beta & \delta & \zeta \end{bmatrix} = \begin{bmatrix} 1+\alpha & 3+\gamma & 5+\epsilon \\ 2+\beta & 4+\delta & 6+\zeta \end{bmatrix}.$$

Let us denote by $\mathfrak{M}_{\mu n}$ the set of all $\mu \times n$ matrices. It is left as an exercise to show that $\{\mathfrak{M}_{\mu n}, +\}$ is an abelian group. The identity of the group is the matrix having each element equal to 0; this matrix will be denoted by the happily ambiguous symbol 0.

3. The *product of a* $\mu \times n$ *matrix* $[\alpha_{\lambda k}]$ *by a scalar* β is the $\mu \times n$ matrix $[\gamma_{\lambda k}]$, where $\gamma_{\lambda k} = \beta \alpha_{\lambda k}$ ($\lambda = 1, \ldots, \mu$; $k = 1, \ldots, n$); thus

4.
$$\beta[\alpha_{\lambda k}] = [\beta \alpha_{\lambda k}].$$

Naturally enough, each row or column vector is multiplied by the scalar β according to the familiar rule for multiplying a vector by a scalar.

For example,

$$\gamma \begin{bmatrix} 1 & 2 & 3 \\ 4 & 5 & 6 \end{bmatrix} = \begin{bmatrix} \gamma & 2\gamma & 3\gamma \\ 4\gamma & 5\gamma & 6\gamma \end{bmatrix}.$$

It is left as an exercise to show that $\{\mathfrak{M}_{\mu n}, +; F, \cdot\}$ is a linear space. This space has a basis $\{E_{\lambda k}\}$, where the matrix $E_{\lambda k}$ has 0 except in the λth row and kth column and has 1 in that position. Hence dim $\mathfrak{M}_{\mu n} = \mu \cdot n$ (cf. 6B3).

It follows too that $[\alpha_{\lambda k}] = \sum_{\lambda, k} \alpha_{\lambda k} E_{\lambda k}$. Thus the λ,k-component of $[\alpha_{\lambda k}]$ is $\alpha_{\lambda k}$. When viewed in this light, the rules 2 and 4 are the familiar rules for component-wise addition of vectors in $\mathfrak{M}_{\mu n}$ and multiplication of a vector in $\mathfrak{M}_{\mu n}$ by a scalar.

A firm connection between transformations and matrices is established in the following theorem.

5. Theorem. Each pair of bases, $\{p_k\}$ for X_n and $\{q_\lambda\}$ for Y_μ, determines an isomorphic correspondence between $\{\mathfrak{M}_{\mu n}, +; F, \cdot\}$ and the space $\{\mathcal{L}, +; F, \cdot\}$ of 6B1 in such a way that $L \leftrightarrow [\alpha_{\lambda k}]$ if and only if $Lp_k = \sum q_\lambda \alpha_{\lambda k}$.

Since we know from 6G2 that the correspondence $L \leftrightarrow [\alpha_{\lambda k}]$ is biunique, we have only to prove that sums and products by scalars correspond. Let us agree to denote by $[L]$ the matrix of a linear mapping $L : X \to Y$ with respect to bases appropriate in the context, here $\{p_k\}$ and $\{q_\lambda\}$. Thus $[L] = [\alpha_{\lambda k}]$, for example, $[x] = [\xi_k]^t$, and $[y] = [\eta_\lambda]^t$. In this notation what we have to prove are these equations:

6.
$$[L] + [M] = [L + M],$$

7.
$$\alpha[L] = [\alpha L].$$

Verification of the first is trivial, and that of the second practically so. The columns of $[\beta L]$ will be

$$(\beta L)p_k = \beta(Lp_k) = \beta \sum \alpha_{\lambda k} q_\lambda = \sum (\beta \alpha_{\lambda k}) q_\lambda,$$

whence $[\beta L] = [\beta \alpha_{\lambda k}] = \beta[L]$, the last equation following from 4.

8. Corollary (cf. 6B1 and 6B3). Dim $\mathcal{L}(X_n, Y_\mu) = \mu n$.

B. Multiplication

When encountered for the first time the rule for multiplying matrices seems rather peculiar, but it stems directly from a requirement that this simple equation shall hold:

1.
$$[K][L] = [KL].$$

We shall calculate the right member of this equation and use the result to define the left member.

Suppose, in fact, that $L : X_n \to Y_\mu$ has matrix $[L] = [\beta_{\lambda k}]$ and that $K : Y_\mu \to Z_\rho$ has matrix $[K] = [\alpha_{\sigma \kappa}]$; the indices have these domains:

$$\sigma = 1, \ldots, \rho; \qquad \kappa, \lambda = 1, \ldots, \mu; \qquad k = 1, \ldots, n.$$

Observe that Y_μ is the domain of K and the codomain of L. This circumstance is reflected in the fact that $[K]$ has μ columns ($\kappa = 1, \ldots, \mu$), while $[L]$ has μ rows ($\lambda = 1, \ldots, \mu$).

In order to calculate $[KL]$, let us suppose that X, Y, and Z have bases $\{p_k\}$, $\{q_\lambda\}$, and $\{r_\sigma\}$. The columns of $[KL]$ are the vectors KLp_k of Z. But $Lp_k = \sum \beta_{\lambda k} q_\lambda$, and therefore

$$KLp_k = \sum_\lambda \beta_{\lambda k} Kq_\lambda = \sum_\lambda \beta_{\lambda k} \sum_\sigma \alpha_{\sigma \lambda} r_\sigma$$

$$= \sum_\sigma r_\sigma (\sum_\lambda \alpha_{\sigma \lambda} \beta_{\lambda k}).$$

Hence $[KL] = [\sum_\lambda \alpha_{\sigma \lambda} \beta_{\lambda k}]$. Accordingly, we adopt the following definition, of which, vice versa, 1 is an obvious consequence.

2. The *product* of a $\rho \times \mu$ matrix $[\alpha_{\sigma \lambda}]$ on the left by a $\mu \times n$ matrix $[\beta_{\lambda k}]$ on the right is the $\rho \times n$ matrix $[\gamma_{\sigma k}]$, where

$$\gamma_{\sigma k} = \sum \alpha_{\sigma \lambda} \beta_{\lambda k} \qquad (\sigma = 1, \ldots, \rho; k = 1, \ldots, n);$$

thus

3.
$$[\alpha_{\sigma \lambda}][\beta_{\lambda k}] = [\sum \alpha_{\sigma \lambda} \beta_{\lambda k}].$$

The product $[K][L]$ is defined if, and only if, the number of columns in the left factor is equal to the number of rows in the right factor.

The element $\gamma_{\sigma k}$ of the product is obtained from the σth *row* of the *left* factor and the kth *column* of the *right* factor. For example, if $\rho \geq 3$ and $n \geq 4$, then

$$\gamma_{34} = \alpha_{31}\beta_{14} + \alpha_{32}\beta_{24} + \ldots + \alpha_{3\lambda}\beta_{\lambda 4} + \ldots + \alpha_{3\mu}\beta_{\mu 4}$$

3.1.
$$= [\alpha_{31} \ldots \alpha_{3\lambda} \ldots \alpha_{3\mu}] \begin{bmatrix} \beta_{14} \\ \cdot \\ \cdot \\ \cdot \\ \beta_{\lambda 4} \\ \cdot \\ \cdot \\ \cdot \\ \beta_{\mu 4} \end{bmatrix} = r_3 c_4,$$

where r_3 is the row vector in the third row of $[K]$ and c_4 is the column vector in the fourth column of $[L]$. The product of a $1 \times \mu$ matrix on the left by a $\mu \times 1$ matrix on the right is a scalar. Here are further examples; in 4, $\rho = \mu = 3$ and $n = 2$.

4.
$$\begin{bmatrix} \beta_{11} & \beta_{12} & \beta_{13} \\ \beta_{21} & \beta_{22} & \beta_{23} \\ \beta_{31} & \beta_{32} & \beta_{33} \end{bmatrix} \begin{bmatrix} \alpha_{11} & \alpha_{12} \\ \alpha_{21} & \alpha_{22} \\ \alpha_{31} & \alpha_{32} \end{bmatrix}$$
$$= \begin{bmatrix} \beta_{11}\alpha_{11} + \beta_{12}\alpha_{21} + \beta_{13}\alpha_{31} & \beta_{11}\alpha_{12} + \beta_{12}\alpha_{22} + \beta_{13}\alpha_{32} \\ \beta_{21}\alpha_{11} + \beta_{22}\alpha_{21} + \beta_{23}\alpha_{31} & \beta_{21}\alpha_{12} + \beta_{22}\alpha_{22} + \beta_{23}\alpha_{32} \\ \beta_{31}\alpha_{11} + \beta_{32}\alpha_{21} + \beta_{33}\alpha_{31} & \beta_{31}\alpha_{12} + \beta_{32}\alpha_{22} + \beta_{33}\alpha_{32} \end{bmatrix}.$$

5.
$$[2 \quad -3]\begin{bmatrix} \alpha \\ \beta \end{bmatrix} = 2\alpha - 3\beta, \qquad \begin{bmatrix} \alpha \\ \beta \end{bmatrix}[2 \quad -3] = \begin{bmatrix} 2\alpha & -3\alpha \\ 2\beta & -3\beta \end{bmatrix}.$$

6.
$$\begin{bmatrix} \xi & \eta & \zeta \\ \theta & \varphi & \psi \end{bmatrix}\begin{bmatrix} 3 \\ 0 \\ -1 \end{bmatrix} = \begin{bmatrix} 3\xi & -\zeta \\ 3\theta & -\psi \end{bmatrix}.$$

7.
$$\begin{bmatrix} 2 & -1 \\ 1 & 2 \\ 3 & -2 \end{bmatrix}\begin{bmatrix} \xi_1 \\ \xi_2 \end{bmatrix} = \begin{bmatrix} 2\xi_1 - \xi_2 \\ \xi_1 + 2\xi_2 \\ 3\xi_1 - 2\xi_2 \end{bmatrix} \text{(cf. 6G3)}.$$

The isomorphism of A5 between $\mathfrak{M}$ and $\mathfrak{L}$, expressed in A6 and A7, is extended by 1 to include multiplication as well. We saw in 6G that L is an endomorphism of X if and only if $[L]$ is square (and of order equal to dim X). In view of the definition of a linear algebra at the end of 6B, and the example $\mathfrak{L}(X, X)$ given there, we are led to suspect that the set of all $n \times n$ matrices with entries in a field F forms a linear algebra with unit I_n. With a fixed basis $\{p_k\}$ in X_n, indeed, the algebra of all $n \times n$ matrices over F is isomorphic with the algebra $\mathfrak{L}(X, X)$ of all endomorphisms of $\{X, +; F, \cdot\}$.

We shall continue to write $[L]$ when we wish to denote the matrix of a transformation L or when we wish to emphasize that we are speaking of a matrix. Having come to appreciate fully the connection between L and $[L]$, along with the essential accompanying provisions, we shall use the capital Latin letters H, I, J, K, L, and M to denote linear mappings or matrices, according to context, when no confusion is possible. It is to be understood that the essential accompanying provisions must be made whenever one passes from L to $[L]$ or vice versa. Our attitude toward x and $[x]$ is the same. We thus arrive at a situation in which the following notations (cf. 6G2) are fully equivalent (agreed bases are implied, of course, in the second and third):

$$Lx = y, \qquad [L][x] = [y], \qquad \sum \alpha_{\lambda k} \xi_k = \eta_\lambda \ (\lambda = 1, \ldots, \mu).$$

Which to use will be a matter of convenience. The dual notations are these:

$$fL^d = c, \qquad [f][L^d] = [c], \qquad \sum \beta_\lambda \alpha_{\lambda k} = \gamma_k \ (k = 1, \ldots, n).$$

In view of the general isomorphism between matrices and transformations, and the known behavior of the latter, it is no surprise to observe in example 6 above that LK may be defined while KL is not, and in example 5 that even if they are both defined it may happen that $LK \neq KL$. Multiplication of matrices is generally not commutative; changing the order of the factors will generally change the result.

Associativity of multiplication and right- and left-distributivity of multiplication with respect to addition follow from 1 and A6 or may be verified directly from 3 and A2. The rules are these:

8. $$K(LM) = (KL)M,$$

9. $$(L + M)K = LK + MK,$$

10. $$K(L + M) = KL + KM.$$

The identity on X_n is denoted (in 6A) by I_n (or by I if the value of n is evident); the corresponding $n \times n$ matrix $[\alpha_{jk}]$ has $\alpha_{jk} = 1$ if $j = k$ and 0 if $j \neq k$. Hence

11. $$[I_n] = [\delta_{jk}] \qquad (j,k = 1, \ldots, n).$$

EXERCISES

12. Endomorphisms of an X_2 have these matrices:

$$L = \begin{bmatrix} 2 & 3 \\ 1 & 2 \end{bmatrix}, \qquad M = \begin{bmatrix} -3 & 2 \\ -6 & 4 \end{bmatrix}.$$

Calculate $3L - 2M$, $L^2 - 4L + I$, $M^2 - M$, LM, and ML (cf. 6B4).

13. Carry out the indicated calculations:

(a) $\begin{bmatrix} 0 & 1 \\ 1 & 0 \end{bmatrix} \begin{bmatrix} \alpha & \beta & \gamma \\ \delta & \epsilon & \zeta \end{bmatrix}$;

(b) $\begin{bmatrix} \alpha & \beta & \gamma \\ \delta & \epsilon & \zeta \end{bmatrix} \begin{bmatrix} 0 & 0 & 3 \\ 0 & 2 & 0 \\ 1 & 0 & 0 \end{bmatrix}$;

(c) $\begin{bmatrix} \alpha & \beta & \gamma \end{bmatrix} \begin{bmatrix} 1 & 3 & -2 \\ 3 & 2 & -1 \\ -2 & -1 & 1 \end{bmatrix} \begin{bmatrix} \xi \\ \eta \\ \zeta \end{bmatrix}$;

(d) $\begin{bmatrix} 1 & 0 & 0 \\ -2 & 1 & 0 \\ -3 & 0 & 1 \end{bmatrix}\begin{bmatrix} 1 & -2 & 3 \\ 2 & -4 & 6 \\ 3 & -6 & 9 \end{bmatrix}$;

(e) $\begin{bmatrix} \alpha \\ \beta \\ \gamma \end{bmatrix}[\delta \quad \epsilon \quad \zeta]$.

14. What is the result in 13(c) if $[\alpha \quad \beta \quad \gamma]$ is replaced by $[\xi \quad \eta \quad \zeta]$? Express $\alpha\xi^2 + 2\beta\xi\eta + \gamma\eta^2$ in the form x^tLx, where x is a column vector $[\xi \quad \eta]^t$ and L a 2×2 matrix.

15. Find all 2×2 matrices that commute with

$$\begin{bmatrix} 0 & 1 \\ -3 & 2 \end{bmatrix}.$$

16. Prove that if the λth row of K is 0 then the λth row of KL is 0. Prove also that if the kth column of L is 0 then the kth column of KL is 0. (T)

17. Prove that $(\alpha L)^t = \alpha L^t$, $(L + M)^t = L^t + M^t$, and $(LK)^t = K^tL^t$. (T)

18. Verify that

$$\begin{bmatrix} 1 & 2 & 0 \\ 1 & 1 & 0 \\ -1 & 4 & 0 \end{bmatrix}\begin{bmatrix} 0 & 0 & 0 \\ 0 & 0 & 0 \\ 1 & 1 & 1 \end{bmatrix} = 0.$$

Hence $KL = 0$ is possible with both $K \neq 0$ and $L \neq 0$. Does $KL = 0$ imply $LK = 0$? If L is the right factor above, find all 3×3 matrices K such that $KL = 0$.

19. With μ fixed let

(a) $H = H(\kappa, \lambda)$ denote I_μ with rows κ and λ interchanged,

(b) $J = J(\kappa, \gamma)$ denote I_μ with row κ multiplied by γ, and

(c) $K = K(\kappa, \gamma; \lambda)$ denote I_μ with row κ multiplied by γ and added to row λ.

With $\mu = 3$, and L a $3 \times n$ matrix, calculate HL, JL, and KL. Prove generally that if L is a $\mu \times n$ matrix then

(a') HL is L with rows κ and λ interchanged,

(b') JL is L with row κ multiplied by γ, and

(c') KL is L with row κ multiplied by γ and added to row λ. (T)

20. Define H, J, and K as in 19 with respect to I_n and its *columns*. With $n = 3$ and L a $\mu \times 3$ matrix, calculate LH, LJ, and LK. Obtain general results similar to 19 (a'), (b'), and (c').

21. Calculate successive powers of J if

$$J = \begin{bmatrix} 0 & 1 & 0 & 0 \\ 0 & 0 & 1 & 0 \\ 0 & 0 & 0 & 1 \\ 0 & 0 & 0 & 0 \end{bmatrix}.$$

Obtain a general result for the $n \times n$ matrix $[\delta_{j+1\,k}]$.

22. Obtain necessary and sufficient conditions that $(L + M)^2 = L^2 + 2LM + M^2$; that $(L + M)(L - M) = L^2 - M^2$. (Prove first that L and M must be square.) Expand $(L - M)^3$.

23. Prove that if $n \geq 2$ then each $n \times n$ matrix L satisfies an equation of the form

$$\alpha_m L^m + \alpha_{m-1} L^{m-1} + \ldots + \alpha_1 L + \alpha_0 I = 0$$

for some value of $m \leq n^2$. (Each $n \times n$ matrix is in the space $\mathfrak{M}$ of $n \times n$ matrices defined in A.) (T)

24. Prove that the set of all matrices $A = \begin{bmatrix} \alpha & 0 \\ 0 & \alpha \end{bmatrix}$ with $\alpha \in R$ a field isomorphic with R, and that the same is true of the set of all matrices $B = \begin{bmatrix} \beta & 0 \\ 0 & 0 \end{bmatrix}$ with $\beta \in R$. Which matrices A and B correspond to the real number 1?

25. Prove that if $L = \begin{bmatrix} \alpha & \beta \\ -\beta & \alpha \end{bmatrix}$ and $M = \begin{bmatrix} \gamma & \delta \\ -\delta & \gamma \end{bmatrix}$ with $\alpha, \beta, \gamma, \delta \in R$ then $LM = ML$. Prove that the set of all matrices $L = \begin{bmatrix} \alpha & \beta \\ -\beta & \alpha \end{bmatrix}$ forms a field which is isomorphic to C under the correspondence $L \leftrightarrow \alpha + \beta i$. (T)

26. In the notation implied by this section the matrices $E_{\lambda k}$ defined in A have the property that

$$E_{\sigma\kappa} E_{\lambda k} = \delta_{\kappa\lambda} E_{\sigma k}.$$

Prove this directly from the definition of multiplication. Then use the expansion $[\beta_{\sigma\kappa}] = \sum_{\sigma,\kappa} \beta_{\sigma\kappa} E_{\sigma\kappa}$, a similar expansion for $[\alpha_{\lambda k}]$, and the distributive law to prove the general formula 3. (T)

27. Given $L : X_n \to Y_{\mu_1}$ and $K : Y_{\mu_2} \to Z_\rho$, with $Y_{\mu_1} \leq Y_{\mu_2}$ (and hence $\mu_2 \geq \mu_1$), it is obvious that the resultant mapping $KL : X_n \to Z_\rho$ is well defined, even if $\mu_2 > \mu_1$. Study possible ways of defining $[K][L]$ if $\mu_2 > \mu_1$.

C. Further Properties of Multiplication; Partitioned Matrices

The operation of multiplication defined by B3 has several properties of both theoretical and practical interest. We begin by displaying the product of two 2×2 matrices in several ways.

1. $\begin{bmatrix} 2 & 3 \\ 4 & 5 \end{bmatrix}\begin{bmatrix} \alpha & \gamma \\ \beta & \delta \end{bmatrix} = \begin{bmatrix} 2\alpha + 3\beta & 2\gamma + 3\delta \\ 4\alpha + 5\delta & 4\gamma + 5\beta \end{bmatrix}$

2. (cols) $= \begin{bmatrix} 2 & 3 \\ 4 & 5 \end{bmatrix}\begin{bmatrix} \alpha & 0 \\ \beta & 0 \end{bmatrix} + \begin{bmatrix} 2 & 3 \\ 4 & 5 \end{bmatrix}\begin{bmatrix} 0 & \gamma \\ 0 & \delta \end{bmatrix}$

3. (rows) $= \begin{bmatrix} 2 & 3 \\ 0 & 0 \end{bmatrix}\begin{bmatrix} \alpha & \gamma \\ \beta & \delta \end{bmatrix} + \begin{bmatrix} 0 & 0 \\ 4 & 5 \end{bmatrix}\begin{bmatrix} \alpha & \gamma \\ \beta & \delta \end{bmatrix}$

4. (rows) $= \begin{bmatrix} 2[\alpha & \gamma] + 3[\beta & \delta] \\ 4[\alpha & \gamma] + 5[\beta & \delta] \end{bmatrix}$

5. (cols) $= \begin{bmatrix} \alpha\begin{bmatrix} 2 \\ 4 \end{bmatrix} + \beta\begin{bmatrix} 3 \\ 5 \end{bmatrix} & \gamma\begin{bmatrix} 2 \\ 4 \end{bmatrix} + \delta\begin{bmatrix} 3 \\ 5 \end{bmatrix} \end{bmatrix}$

6. $= \begin{bmatrix} 2 \\ 4 \end{bmatrix}[\alpha & \gamma] + \begin{bmatrix} 3 \\ 5 \end{bmatrix}[\beta & \delta].$

Corresponding results hold in general; for each of the equations above there is a corresponding equation below, with the designating numeral primed. All can be verified easily.

Notation is assigned as follows, with $\sigma = 1, \ldots, \rho$; $\lambda = 1, \ldots, \mu$; and $k = 1, \ldots, n$:

$$[K] = [\alpha_{\sigma\kappa}] = \begin{bmatrix} r_1 \\ \cdot \\ \cdot \\ \cdot \\ r_\sigma \\ \cdot \\ \cdot \\ \cdot \\ r_\rho \end{bmatrix} = [s_1 \ldots s_\lambda \ldots s_\mu],$$

$$[L] = [\beta_{\lambda k}] = [c_1 \ldots c_k \ldots c_n] = \begin{bmatrix} b_1 \\ \cdot \\ \cdot \\ \cdot \\ b_\lambda \\ \cdot \\ \cdot \\ \cdot \\ b_\mu \end{bmatrix},$$

$$[KL] = [\gamma_{\sigma k}] = \begin{bmatrix} u_1 \\ \cdot \\ \cdot \\ \cdot \\ u_\sigma \\ \cdot \\ \cdot \\ \cdot \\ u_\rho \end{bmatrix} = [v_1 \ldots v_k \ldots v_n] = [K][L].$$

Here the r's, b's, and u's are row vectors and the s's, c's, and v's are column vectors.

1'.
$$[K][L] = [r_\sigma c_k], \qquad \gamma_{\sigma k} = r_\sigma c_k.$$

The element $\gamma_{\sigma k}$ of $[K][L]$ is the product of the σth row of $[K]$ by the kth column of $[L]$.

2'.
$$[K][L] = [Kc_1 \ldots Kc_k \ldots Kc_n], \qquad v_k = Kc_k.$$

The kth column of $[K][L]$ is the result of applying $[K]$ on the left to the kth column of $[L]$.

3'.
$$[K][L] = \begin{bmatrix} r_1L \\ \cdot \\ \cdot \\ r_\sigma L \\ \cdot \\ \cdot \\ r_p L \end{bmatrix}, \qquad u_\sigma = r_\sigma L.$$

The σth row of $[K][L]$ is the result of applying L on the right to the σth row of $[K]$.

4'.
$$[K][L] = [\textstyle\sum \alpha_{\sigma\lambda} b_\lambda], \qquad u_\sigma = \textstyle\sum \alpha_{\sigma\lambda} b_\lambda.$$

The σth row of $[K][L]$ is a linear combination of the rows of $[L]$, and the coefficients are the respective elements of the σth row of $[K]$.

5'.
$$[K][L] = [\textstyle\sum s_\lambda \beta_{\lambda k}], \qquad v_k = \textstyle\sum s_\lambda \beta_{\lambda k}.$$

The kth column of $[K][L]$ is a linear combination of the columns of $[K]$, and the coefficients are the respective elements of the kth column of $[L]$.

Delaying 6', consider an illustration:

$$K = LM = \begin{bmatrix} 1 & 1 & 0 \\ 0 & 1 & 0 \\ 0 & 0 & 2 \end{bmatrix} \begin{bmatrix} 1 & \alpha & 0 \\ 0 & -1 & 0 \\ 0 & 0 & 1 \end{bmatrix}.$$

From 4', the second (third) row of K is equal to the second (twice the third) row of M. From 5', the first (third) column of K is equal to the first (third) column of L. This information yields

$$K = \begin{bmatrix} 1 & \xi & 0 \\ 0 & -1 & 0 \\ 0 & 0 & 2 \end{bmatrix},$$

with only ξ to be evaluated; of course, $\xi = \alpha - 1$.

6'.
$$[K][L] = \textstyle\sum s_\lambda b_\lambda = [s_1 \ldots s_\lambda \ldots s_\mu] \begin{bmatrix} b_1 \\ \cdot \\ \cdot \\ b_\lambda \\ \cdot \\ \cdot \\ b_\mu \end{bmatrix}.$$

For each value of λ, of course, $s_\lambda b_\lambda$ is a $\mu \times n$ matrix. The element in the σth row and kth column of $s_\lambda b_\lambda$ is $\alpha_{\sigma\lambda} \beta_{\lambda k}$ (not summed on λ). Summation over λ yields the element $\gamma_{\sigma k}$ of the product.

193

Equation 6′ says that $[K][L]$ can be calculated as though $[K]$ consisted of a single row of column vectors, and $[L]$ consisted of a single column of row vectors. This suggests a more general procedure.

Suppose, for example, that $\mu \geq 3$ and that we have positive integers μ_1, μ_2, and μ_3 such that $\mu_1 + \mu_2 + \mu_3 = \mu$. Then

$$[\gamma_{\sigma k}] = \left[\sum_{\lambda=1}^{\mu_1} \alpha_{\sigma\lambda}\beta_{\lambda k} + \sum_{\lambda=\mu_1+1}^{\mu_1+\mu_2} \alpha_{\sigma\lambda}\beta_{\lambda k} + \sum_{\lambda=\mu_1+\mu_2+1}^{\mu} \alpha_{\sigma\lambda}\beta_{\lambda k} \right],$$

and therefore

7.
$$[K][L] = [K_1L_1 + K_2L_2 + K_3L_3],$$

where

7.1.
$$[K] = [K_1 \quad K_2 \quad K_3] = [[\alpha_{\sigma\lambda_1}][\alpha_{\sigma\lambda_2}][\alpha_{\sigma\lambda_3}]]$$

with $\lambda_1 = 1, \ldots, \mu_1$, $\lambda_2 = \mu_1 + 1, \ldots, \mu_1 + \mu_2$, $\lambda_3 = \mu_1 + \mu_2 + 1, \ldots, \mu$, and

7.2.
$$[L] = \begin{bmatrix} L_1 \\ L_2 \\ L_3 \end{bmatrix} = \begin{bmatrix} [\beta_{\lambda_1 k}] \\ [\beta_{\lambda_2 k}] \\ [\beta_{\lambda_3 k}] \end{bmatrix}.$$

We may say that $[K]$ and $[L]$ have been partitioned by drawing vertical lines between certain columns of $[K]$ and horizontal lines between certain rows of $[L]$ in such a way that for $j = 1, 2, 3$, K_j has as many columns (μ_j) as L_j has rows. Then the product $[K][L]$ has been calculated as though $[K]$ consisted of a single row with elements K_1, K_2, K_3 and $[L]$ consisted of a single column with elements L_1, L_2, L_3.

A *partition* of a positive integer m is an ordered set $m_1, \ldots, m_p$ of positive integers whose sum is $m : m_1 + m_2 + \ldots + m_p = m$. The essential feature of 7 is that the decompositions 7.1 of $[K]$ and 7.2 of $[L]$ correspond to the *same* partition μ_1, μ_2, μ_3 of μ.

We can go further. We can draw horizontal lines between rows of $[K]$ and vertical lines between columns of $[L]$, each in an entirely arbitrary way, and the product $[K][L]$ may still be calculated as though the elements of $[K]$ and $[L]$ were the resulting submatrices. For example,

7.3.
$$[K][L] = \begin{bmatrix} K_{11} & K_{12} & K_{13} \\ K_{21} & K_{22} & K_{23} \\ K_{31} & K_{32} & K_{33} \end{bmatrix} \begin{bmatrix} L_{11} & L_{12} \\ L_{21} & L_{22} \\ L_{31} & L_{32} \end{bmatrix}$$

$$= \begin{bmatrix} K_{11}L_{11} + K_{12}L_{21} + K_{13}L_{31} & K_{11}L_{12} + K_{12}L_{22} + K_{13}L_{32} \\ K_{21}L_{11} + K_{22}L_{21} + K_{23}L_{31} & K_{21}L_{12} + K_{22}L_{22} + K_{23}L_{32} \\ K_{31}L_{11} + K_{32}L_{21} + K_{33}L_{31} & K_{31}L_{12} + K_{32}L_{22} + K_{33}L_{32} \end{bmatrix}.$$

The idea here is simple enough, and this is one situation in which a precise general statement would require rather fancy notation, and would give more trouble than it is worth. A few definitions and a little comment will suffice.

If from a $\mu \times n$ matrix we choose ν rows ($1 \leq \nu \leq \mu$) and m columns ($1 \leq m \leq n$), and delete the other rows and columns, then the $\nu \times m$ matrix formed by the elements remaining in the chosen ν rows and m columns, displayed in the exact relative order they have in the original matrix, is called a *submatrix* of the original matrix. If the ν rows are consecutive and the m columns are consecutive, then the submatrix is called a *block* submatrix. The matrix

$$\begin{bmatrix} 1 & 2 & 3 \\ \alpha & \beta & \gamma \end{bmatrix}$$

has, in addition to itself and its elements, fourteen submatrices, all of which are block submatrices except these:

$$\begin{bmatrix} 1 & 3 \\ \alpha & \gamma \end{bmatrix}, \quad \begin{bmatrix} 1 & 3 \\ \alpha & \gamma \end{bmatrix}.$$

The result of drawing vertical lines between columns of a matrix and horizontal lines between its rows is to decompose the matrix into block submatrices; the matrix is said to be *partitioned* into block submatrices.

If the product $[K][L]$ exists, let us say that $[K]$ and $[L]$ are *conformably* partitioned if the blocks of columns of $[K]$ are the same blocks as the blocks of rows of $[L]$; this was secured in 1 and 2 by controlling the domains of the indices λ_1, λ_2, and λ_3.

8. If $[K][L]$ exists it may be calculated by introducing any conformable partitions of $[K]$ and $[L]$ and then calculating the product as though the elements of $[K]$ and $[L]$ were the block submatrices resulting from the partitions.

For an illustration let us take $\rho = \mu = 3$ and $n = 2$.

$$[K][L] = \begin{bmatrix} \alpha_{11} & \alpha_{12} & \vdots & \alpha_{13} \\ \alpha_{21} & \alpha_{22} & \vdots & \alpha_{23} \\ \alpha_{31} & \alpha_{32} & \vdots & \alpha_{33} \end{bmatrix} \begin{bmatrix} \beta_{11} & \beta_{12} \\ \beta_{21} & \beta_{22} \\ \beta_{31} & \beta_{32} \end{bmatrix} = \begin{bmatrix} K_{11} & K_{12} \\ K_{21} & K_{22} \end{bmatrix} \begin{bmatrix} L_1 \\ L_2 \end{bmatrix}$$

$$= \begin{bmatrix} K_{11}L_1 + K_{12}L_2 \\ K_{21}L_1 + K_{22}L_2 \end{bmatrix};$$

here, for example,

$$K_{11}L_1 = [\alpha_{11}\beta_{11} + \alpha_{12}\beta_{21} \quad \alpha_{11}\beta_{12} + \alpha_{12}\beta_{22}].$$

Multiplication of partitioned matrices is sometimes called multiplication by blocks. It is particularly useful when a factor has a block submatrix which is 0, or the identity, or has some other advantageous features.

A submatrix of $[L]$ can be interpreted as the matrix of a mapping on a subspace of the domain of L into a subspace of the codomain. When this interpretation is applied to block multiplication the details are intricate without being illuminating; we omit them.

195

An important application will be useful later. Suppose that $X_p = Y_q \oplus Z_r$ and that we are given endomorphisms $M : Y \to Y$ and $N : Z \to Z$. Referred to a basis $\{y_j\}$ for Y, M will have a $q \times q$ matrix $[M]$; referred to a basis $\{z_k\}$ for Z, N will have an $r \times r$ matrix $[N]$. The set

$$B = \{y_1, \ldots, y_q, z_1, \ldots, z_r\}$$

forms a basis for X_p, with $p = q + r$. Now let us define $L : X \to X$ by agreeing that if $x = y + z$ with $y \in Y$ and $z \in Z$ then $x \to Lx = My + Nz$. With B as a basis for X, we see that

9.
$$[L] = \begin{bmatrix} M & 0 \\ 0 & N \end{bmatrix}.$$

If there were a non-zero element in the $r \times q$ box at the lower left, then by $3'$ one of the vectors y would have a map under L not lying in Y, but if $x = y \in Y$ then $Lx = My \in Y$, a contradiction. Similarly, if there were a non-zero element in the $q \times r$ box at the upper right, then by $3'$ one of the vectors z would have an image $Lz \in' Z$, but if $x = z \in Z$ then $Lx = Nz \in Z$.

The essential fact, as the foregoing argument reveals, is that $X = Y \oplus Z$ with both Y and Z invariant under L, i.e., $LY \leq Y$ and $LZ \leq Z$. (See 16.)

It is easy to see, conversely, that if $[L]$ has the form 9 and Y_q is the space spanned by the first q basis vector of X_p and Z_r is the space spanned by the remaining $r (= p - q)$ basis vectors of X, then $X = Y \oplus Z$, $LY \leq Y$, $LZ \leq Z$, and the restrictions of L to Y and Z have the respective matrices $[M]$ and $[N]$.

10. Theorem. A mapping $L : X \to X$ has a matrix of the form 9 if and only if $X = Y \oplus Z$, $LY \leq Y$, $LZ \leq Z$, and the basis for X consists of a basis for Y followed by a basis for Z; the restrictions of L to Y and Z have the respective matrices $[M]$ and $[N]$.

In this situation we may say that L is the *direct sum* of M and N, writing $L = M \oplus N$ and $[L] = [M] \oplus [N]$.

EXERCISES

11. Use multiplication by blocks to calculate HJ, JH, HK, and JK if

$$H = \begin{bmatrix} \alpha & \beta & 0 & 0 \\ \gamma & \delta & 0 & 0 \\ 0 & 0 & \epsilon & 0 \\ 0 & 0 & 0 & \zeta \end{bmatrix}, \quad J = \begin{bmatrix} 1 & 0 & 0 & 0 \\ 0 & 1 & 0 & 0 \\ 2 & -1 & 1 & 0 \\ -3 & 2 & 0 & 1 \end{bmatrix}, \quad K = \begin{bmatrix} 0 & 1 \\ 1 & 0 \\ \theta & 0 \\ 0 & \theta \end{bmatrix}.$$

12. Let $L = [I \quad 0]$ when I is the $m \times m$ identity matrix and 0 is the $m \times n$ zero-matrix. If J is a $\mu \times m$ matrix and K is an $(m + n) \times q$ matrix, what can be said about JL or LK?

13. Let J be square and define $L = \begin{bmatrix} J & I \\ 0 & J \end{bmatrix}$. Calculate L^n $(n = 1, 2, 3, \ldots)$.

14. Let J be $\mu \times n$, K be $\mu \times m$, I be $n \times n$, and define $L = \begin{bmatrix} I & 0 \\ J & K \end{bmatrix}$. Calculate L^n $(n = 1, 2, 3, \ldots)$.

15. Study the possibility of adding matrices "by blocks".

16. Suppose that $X = Y \oplus Z$ and consider $L : X \to X$. What can you say about $[L]$ if Y is invariant under L but Z is not? If Z is invariant under L but Y is not? (Assume that the basis for X is adapted to Y and Z.) (T)

17. Let $J = KLM = [\alpha_{\lambda k}]$ $(\lambda = 1, \ldots, \mu; k = 1, \ldots, n)$. Show that each element $\alpha_{\lambda k}$ of J is a linear combination of the elements of L. (T)

18. Let $j, k = 1, \ldots, n$, and let E_{jk} denote the $n \times n$ matrix having every element zero except the one in position j, k, and having that element equal to 1. (These matrices form a basis for $\{\mathfrak{M}_{nn}, +; F, \cdot\}$.) Show that $E_{jk}L$ has every row zero except the jth, which consists of the kth row of L. What can you say about LE_{jk}? What can you say about L if $E_{jk}L = LE_{jk}$ for all j and k? (T)

D. Column and Row Spaces; Rank and Nullity; Inverses

We deal with a fixed $\mu \times n$ matrix $[L] = [\alpha_{\lambda k}]$, with $\lambda = 1, \ldots, \mu$ and $k = 1, \ldots, n$; the column vectors are $z_k \in F_\mu$, and the row vectors are $a_\lambda \in F_n^d$.

The subspace $\langle z_1, \ldots, z_n \rangle$ of F_μ is the *column space* of $[L]$, and will be denoted by $C[L]$ or simply, since $[L]$ is fixed, by C. The *column rank* of $[L]$ is $\rho_C = \dim C$.

The subspace $\langle a_1, \ldots, a_\mu \rangle$ of F_n^d is the *row space* of $[L]$, and will be denoted by $R[L]$, or by R. The *row rank* of $[L]$ is $\rho_R = \dim R$.

The *column nullspace* of $[L]$ is $R° \leq F_n$ and the *column nullity* ν_C of $[L]$ is $\dim R°$ (cf. 7D6.1 and 4). The *row nullspace* of $[L]$ is $C° \leq F_\mu^d$ and the *row nullity* ν_R of $[L]$ is $\dim C°$ (cf. 7D6.2 and 3).

Now consider a linear mapping $L : X_n \to Y_\mu$, $y = Lx$, whose matrix is $[L]$. The column vectors z_k are the coordinate vectors of the images Lp_k of the vectors p_k of the basis prevailing in X_n (see 8A5 or 6G2).

1. C is isomorphic with the range R_L of L; hence $\rho_C = \rho(L)$.

Similarly, the row vectors a_λ are the coordinate vectors of the images $b_\lambda L^d$ of the vectors b_λ of a basis for Y_μ^d (see 7D14).

2. R is isomorphic with the range R_{L^d} of L^d; hence $\rho_R = \rho(L^d)$.

In 7D8.3 we saw that $\rho(L) = \rho(L^d)$. From 1 and 2 we arrive at the following important result, by virtue of which we may speak simply of the *rank* $\rho[L]$ of $[L]$; in fact, $\rho[L] = \rho(L)$.

3. $\rho_R = \rho_C$; the row rank and column rank of a matrix are equal.

A proof not using duality will be found in 9C17.1.

From 2 and 7D6.1 we conclude that

4. C° is isomorphic with N_{L^d}; hence $\nu_R = \nu(L^d)$.

From 1 and 7D6.4 we conclude that

5. R° is isomorphic with N_L; hence $\nu_C = \nu(L)$.

From 1, 5, and 6E1 we see that

6.
$$\rho_C + \nu_C = n.$$

From 2, 4, and 7D8.2 we see that

7.
$$\rho_R + \nu_R = \mu.$$

Let us say that $[L]$ is *column-singular* or *column-nonsingular* according as its column vectors are dependent or independent, and that $[L]$ is *row-singular* or *row-nonsingular* according as its row vectors are dependent or independent. Let us also say that $[L]$ is:

(a) *regular* if $[L]$ is both row- and column-nonsingular;

(b) *nonsingular* if $[L]$ is either row- or column-nonsingular;

(c) *singular* if $[L]$ is both row- and column-singular.

The terminology differs slightly from that for transformations, reflecting the fact that, although the domain of a transformation is completely specified, the codomain may (depending on context) be any superspace of the range, while a matrix standing alone determines unambiguously the dimension of the codomain of the corresponding transformation. Moreover, a matrix $[L]$ contains specifications for both L and L^d, so to speak, and is entirely neutral as to which is used.

The result corresponding to most of 7D11 is this (see 12):

8. Any two of the following three conditions imply the third:

(a) $[L]$ is column-nonsingular,

(b) $[L]$ is row-nonsingular,

(c) $n = \mu$, i.e., $[L]$ is square.

It follows that $[L]$ is regular if and only if it is square and nonsingular.

Enough has been said to indicate that the results obtained on rank and nullity in 6E and the exercises following it can be taken over almost verbatim for matrices; we mention a few such results in some of the exercises below.

Given now $L : X_n \to Y_\mu$ with $[L] = [\alpha_{\lambda k}]$, we leave it to the reader to prove that: (a) $[L]$ is column-nonsingular if and only if L is nonsingular; (b) $[L]$ is row-nonsingular if and only if L^d is nonsingular; (c) $[L]$ is regular if and only if L is regular. It is also true that $[L]$ is nonsingular if and only if either L or L^d is nonsingular.

If L is regular then $L^{-1} : Y_\mu \to X_n$ exists and $L^{-1}L = I_X$ and $LL^{-1} = I_Y$. By the isomorphism between transformations and matrices,

$$[L^{-1}][L] = I_n = [L][L^{-1}].$$

If $[J]$ and $[K]$ are $q \times q$ matrices such that $[J][K] = [K][J] = I_q$, then we say that $[J]$ and $[K]$ are *inverse* to each other and write, for example, $[J]^{-1} = [K]$. A glance at the displayed equation yields the following result; its converse is also true (see 14).

9. If L is regular then $[L]^{-1} = [L^{-1}]$.

An illustration is afforded by equations 5G2 and 5G3, which are equivalent to these:

$$[\beta_{hj}][\alpha_{jk}] = I_n = [\alpha_{hj}][\beta_{jk}].$$

Thus $[\alpha_{jk}]^{-1} = [\beta_{hj}]$.

Let us say that $[J]$ is a *left-inverse* of $[K]$ and $[K]$ a *right-inverse* of $[J]$ if $[J][K] = I$.

Now assume that $L : X_n \to Y_\mu$ is nonsingular but not regular. Then $\mu = \dim Y > \dim X = n$. We know from 6D1 that $L^{-1} : Y \to X$ exists and that $L^{-1}L = I_X$ and $LL^{-1} = I_{LX}$. From the first of these relations we arrive at the following result.

10. If L is nonsingular but not regular, then $\mu > n$ and the $n \times \mu$ matrix $[L^{-1}]$ has the property that $[L^{-1}][L] = I_n$; in other words, $[L^{-1}]$ is a left-inverse of $[L]$.

At this stage the behavior of matrices becomes less symmetric than that of transformations, for it can happen that $[L][L^{-1}] \neq I_\mu$, so that $[L^{-1}]$ is not a right-inverse of $[L]$. This asymmetry reflects a less obtrusive asymmetry in the behavior of the transformations, for $LL^{-1} = I$ only on LX and LX may be a proper subspace of Y. The situation may be illustrated by multiplying the matrices for the transformations of 6D2.1–2.

$$[J][K] = \begin{bmatrix} -1 & 4 & 0 \\ -1 & 3 & 0 \end{bmatrix} \begin{bmatrix} 3 & -4 \\ 1 & -1 \\ 3 & -5 \end{bmatrix} = \begin{bmatrix} 1 & 0 \\ 0 & 1 \end{bmatrix}.$$

$$[K][J] = \begin{bmatrix} 3 & -4 \\ 1 & -1 \\ 3 & -5 \end{bmatrix} \begin{bmatrix} -1 & 4 & 0 \\ -1 & 3 & 0 \end{bmatrix} = \begin{bmatrix} 1 & 0 & 0 \\ 0 & 1 & 0 \\ 2 & -3 & 0 \end{bmatrix}.$$

Finally, if L^d is nonsingular but not regular, then a similar argument yields a similar result.

11. If L^d is nonsingular but not regular, then $n > \mu$ and the $n \times \mu$ matrix $[(L^d)^{-1}]$ has the property that $[L^d][(L^d)^{-1}] = I_\mu$; in other words, $[(L^d)^{-1}]$ is a right-inverse of $[L^d]$.

Since $[L^d] = [L]$, we are interpreting $[(L^d)^{-1}]$ as the matrix of the inverse of L^d obtained by applying 6D1 to L^d.

Let us say that a matrix is *tall* if it has more rows than columns ($\mu > n$) and *wide* if it has more columns than rows ($\mu < n$). A *tall* matrix is necessarily row-singular; if it is column-nonsingular then it has a *wide left-inverse*. A *wide* matrix is necessarily column-singular; if it is row-nonsingular then it has a *tall right-inverse*.

Little has been said about pseudo-inverses because of complications arising from the fact that $LX = R_L$ may be a proper subspace of the codomain Y. In fact, 9–11 contain no information about singular matrices; such a matrix will have neither a right- nor a left-inverse. We shall return to these questions later; see 9G–H.

EXERCISES

12. Prove 8. (T)

13. Prove that $\rho([L]^t) = \rho([L])$.

14. Prove that if $[L]$ has a (two-sided) inverse $[L]^{-1}$ then $[L]$ is regular.

15. Prove that $[LK]^{-1} = [K]^{-1}[L]^{-1}$ if either side exists.

16. Prove that $[L]$ is regular if and only if $\nu_R[L] = \nu_C[L] = 0$. (T)

17. Prove that the set of all regular $n \times n$ matrices forms a group under the operation of multiplication, and that this group is isomorphic with the group of all non-singular endomorphisms of X_n. This group of matrices is called the *full linear group* on F_n. (T)

18. Prove that $C([L][K]) \leq C[L]$ and that $R([L][K]) \leq R[K]$. Hence show that $\rho([L][K]) \leq \min (\rho[L], \rho[K])$. [Cf. 6D3(a).]

19. Prove that the row nullspace of $[L]$ is a subspace of the row nullspace of $[L][K]$; hence $\nu_R[L] \leq \nu_R([L][K])$. State and prove a similar result regarding column nullspaces.

20. Is 6E3(b) true for matrices? How about 6E6–12?

21. Suppose that $K = \begin{bmatrix} L & 0 \\ 0 & M \end{bmatrix}$ where L and M are given matrices and the zeros indicate zero-matrices of the appropriate order. What can be said about the various row spaces, column spaces, ranks, and nullities? (T)

22. Prove that if $[L]$ is nonsingular then $\rho([L][K]) = \rho[K]$. Is the result true if $[K]$ and $[L]$ are interchanged? (T)

23. Prove that $[\xi_k]^t[\alpha_k]$ has rank 0 or 1. Is it true, conversely, that if a square matrix L has rank 1, then there exist a column vector $[\xi_k]^t$ and a row vector $[\alpha_k]$ such that $L = [\xi_k]^t[\alpha_k]$? (T)

24. Prove that the equations $\sum \alpha_{\lambda k}\xi_k = \eta_\lambda$ are consistent if and only if $\rho([\alpha_{\lambda k}]) = \rho([\alpha_{\lambda k}\eta_\lambda])$. The $\mu \times (n + 1)$ matrix $[\alpha_{\lambda k}\eta_\lambda]$ is called the *augmented matrix* of the system. State and prove a similar consistency condition for the system $\sum \beta_\lambda \alpha_{\lambda k} = \gamma_k$. (T)

25. Let $[K]$ be a regular $q \times q$ submatrix of $[L]$ which is maximal in the sense that every $\mu' \times n'$ submatrix of $[L]$ is singular if either $\mu' > q$ or $n' > q$. Prove that $\rho[K] = \rho[L]$. (T)

26. Use 10 to prove that if $\mu \geq n$ and the equations $\sum \alpha_{\lambda k}\xi_k = 0$ $(\lambda = 1, \ldots, \mu)$ imply that $\xi_k = 0$ $(k = 1, \ldots, n)$, then there exist constants $\beta_{j\lambda}$ such that $\sum_\lambda \beta_{j\lambda}\alpha_{\lambda k} = \delta_{jk}$ $(j, k = 1, \ldots, n)$. State and prove a similar consequence of 11. (T)

E. Square Matrices

Almost all matrices in this section are square. Such a matrix L can have structural features that do not even make sense for nonsquare matrices. For example, it may equal its transpose: $L^t = L$. A matrix with this property is said to be *symmetric*. The corresponding transformation has the property that if $x \in X$ and $f \in Y^d$ and $[x] = [f]^t$, then $[fL^d]^t = [Lx]$.

A matrix L such that $L^t = -L$ is said to be *antisymmetric* or *skew*. Since we assume that F is either R or C (the essential point is that $1 + 1 \neq 0$) we may write

1.
$$L = \tfrac{1}{2}(L + L^t) + \tfrac{1}{2}(L - L^t).$$

Since $L + L^t$ is symmetric and $L - L^t$ is skew, we see that *every square matrix is the sum of a symmetric matrix and a skew matrix*.

If $L = [\alpha_{jk}]$ $(j, k = 1, \ldots, n)$, then the elements α_{kk} are necessarily the same in L and L^t. These n elements lie along the (principal) *diagonal* of L, running from the upper left corner to the lower right corner. The elements $\alpha_{k\,k+1}$ $(k = 1, \ldots, n - 1)$ form the *first upper diagonal*, while the elements $\alpha_{k+1\,k}$ $(k = 1, \ldots, n - 1)$ form the *first lower diagonal*. In

$$\begin{bmatrix} \alpha & \lambda & \nu \\ \xi & \beta & \mu \\ \zeta & \eta & \gamma \end{bmatrix},$$

for example, the diagonal contains α, β, and γ, the first upper diagonal contains λ and μ, and the first lower diagonal contains ξ and η. Passing from L to L^t amounts to reflecting L in its diagonal.

Elements α_{jk} with $j > k$ lie below the diagonal while those with $k > j$ lie above it. If $j > k$ implies $\alpha_{jk} = 0$, then every element below the diagonal is zero and L is said to be *upper-triangular*. Similarly, if $k > j$ implies $\alpha_{jk} = 0$, then every element above the diagonal is zero and L is said to be *lower-triangular*. In each case the adjective *strictly* is used if also every element on the diagonal is zero. A matrix is said to be *triangular* if it is either upper-triangular or lower-triangular.

A matrix that is both upper- and lower-triangular has 0 in every off-diagonal position and is therefore said to be *diagonal*. If L is diagonal and $\alpha_{jj} = \beta_j$ $(j = 1, \ldots, n)$, then we agree to write

2.
$$L = [[\beta_j]].$$
Thus

$$\begin{bmatrix} 1 & 0 \\ 0 & 2 \end{bmatrix} = [[1 \quad 2]].$$

The same usage will be extended later to situations in which the β_j are square submatrices of L.

If $L = [[\beta_j]]$ has $\beta_j = \gamma$ $(j = 1, \ldots, n)$, then $L = \gamma I_n$ and is said to be a *scalar* matrix.

A matrix obtained by permuting the rows (or columns) of I is called a *permutation* matrix. Let e_j denote the jth row of I. If $j \to f_j$ is a permutation f of $1, \ldots, n$ (cf. 4E), then the matrix $[e_{f_i}]$ is the permutation matrix obtained by applying f to the rows of I_n; we call $[e_{f_i}]$ the *row-permutation matrix corresponding to f*. Now let L be an $n \times n$ (or an $n \times q$) matrix and examine $[e_{f_i}]L = [e_{f_i}L] = K$. Since the jth row of this matrix is the f_jth row of L, we see that K is obtained by applying f to the rows of L. *In order to subject the rows of an $n \times q$ matrix L to a permutation $j \to f$, we may form the corresponding $n \times n$ row-permutation matrix $[e_{f_i}]$ and apply it to L from the left* (cf. B19).

If $g : j \to g_j$ is another permutation, then, as a consequence of what we have just proved, $[e_{g_i}][e_{f_i}]$ will arise from I by applying to the rows of I first f and then g. This amounts to applying $g \circ f$, the resultant of f and g. In symbols,

$$[e_{g_i}][e_{f_i}] = [e_{(g \circ f)_i}].$$

What has been said contains the essential steps in a proof of the following result.

3. Theorem. The $n \times n$ row-permutation matrices form a group isomorphic with the group S_n of permutations of n objects.

Similar results hold, of course, for column-permutation matrices. In order to permute the columns of a given $q \times n$ matrix we may form the $n \times n$ *column*-permutation matrix and apply it from the *right* to the given matrix.

We noted in 4G without proof that every finite group is isomorphic with a group of permutations. On the strength of 3 we can now say that every finite group is isomorphic with a group of square matrices. The group of matrices is often said to *represent* the given group. The theory of "group representations" has found notable applications in crystallography and quantum mechanics.

In order to state without proof a similar general theorem we note first that the *order* of a linear algebra (cf. 6B) is its dimension as a linear space. The theorem states that every linear algebra of order n having a multiplicative identity can be represented by (is isomorphic with) an algebra of $n \times n$ matrices.

EXERCISES

4. What is the geometric effect of a transformation whose matrix is $L = [[\beta_j]]$ if $j \neq k$ implies that $\beta_j \neq \beta_k$? Which (necessarily square) matrices commute with L?

5. Which matrices commute with all $n \times n$ matrices?

6. Prove that if L is skew then every diagonal element of L is zero. (T)

7. Prove that if L is skew then $x^tLx = 0$ for every column vector x. (T)

8. A matrix L is *nilpotent* if $L^p = 0$ for some $p \geq 1$. Prove that every strictly triangular matrix is nilpotent (cf. B21). Can a nilpotent matrix be regular? Explain. (T)

9. Prove that the set of all upper-triangular $n \times n$ matrices forms a subspace of the linear space of all $n \times n$ matrices. If J and K are upper-triangular, does it follow that JK is upper-triangular?

10. Does an endomorphism whose matrix is lower-triangular have any invariant subspaces?

11. Let J be an $n \times n$ permutation matrix. Prove that $J^tJ = I_n$.

12. Express each of these matrices as the sum of a symmetric matrix and a skew matrix:

$$\begin{bmatrix} 1 & -2 \\ 3 & -1 \end{bmatrix}, \quad \begin{bmatrix} 2 & -3 & 5 \\ 1 & 4 & -2 \\ 3 & 3 & 2 \end{bmatrix}, \quad \begin{bmatrix} 3 & -2 & 4 \\ -2 & 0 & -3 \\ 4 & -3 & 5 \end{bmatrix}, \quad \begin{bmatrix} 3 & 4 & -5 \\ -4 & -2 & 1 \\ 5 & -1 & 4 \end{bmatrix}.$$

13. Let L be a $\mu \times n$ real matrix of rank ρ. Prove that both L^tL and LL^t have rank ρ. Can either L^tL or LL^t be regular even if L is not? (Consider cases in which L is (a) row-nonsingular, or (b) column-nonsingular.) (T)

F. Change of Basis

We are given X_n with basis $\{p_k\}$ and coordinate vectors $[x] = [\xi_k]^t$, and Y_μ with basis $\{q_\lambda\}$ and coordinate vectors $[y] = [\eta_\lambda]^t$, and $L : X \to Y$ with

1.
$$[\eta_\lambda]^t = [L][\xi_k]^t \quad \text{or} \quad \eta_\lambda = \sum \alpha_{\lambda k}\xi_k.$$

Recalling the formulas developed in 5G for changing bases, we wish to replace $\{p_k\}$ by a new basis $\{p'_k\}$, with respect to which $[x] = [\xi'_k]^t$, in such a way that

203

2.
$$\xi_k = \sum \beta_{kh}\xi'_h \quad \text{or} \quad [\xi_k]^t = [K][\xi'_k]^t.$$

We wish also to replace $\{q_\lambda\}$ by a new basis $\{q'_\lambda\}$, with respect to which $[y] = [\eta'_\lambda]^t$, in such a way that

3.
$$\eta_\lambda = \sum \gamma_{\lambda\kappa}\eta'_\kappa \quad \text{or} \quad [\eta_\lambda]^t = [J][\eta'_\lambda]^t.$$

Our problem is to find equations connecting η'_λ and ξ'_k.

The process is simple. Into the left equation of 1 we substitute from the right equations of 2 and 3, obtaining

4.
$$[J][\eta'_\lambda]^t = [L][K][\xi'_k]^t.$$

Being regular, $[J]$ has an inverse $[J]^{-1}$. This we apply to the left of 4, arriving at

5.
$$[\eta'_\lambda]^t = [J]^{-1}[L][K][\xi'_k]^t$$

and the following theorem.

6. Theorem. If a transformation $L : X \to Y$ has matrix $[L]$ and a new basis is introduced into the domain by means of a matrix $[K]$, as in 2, and a new basis is introduced into the codomain by means of a matrix $[J]$, as in 3, then with respect to the new bases L has the matrix $[J]^{-1}[L][K]$.

If L is an endomorphism of X, and the basis for X as domain is the same as the basis for X as codomain, then there will be only one change of basis involved and the new matrix of L will be $[K]^{-1}[L][K]$. Square matrices $[J]$ and $[L]$ are said to be *similar* if there is a regular matrix $[K]$ such that $[J] = [K]^{-1}[L][K]$; see 10A14 and Chaps. 13 and 14.

After a change of basis having matrix $\begin{bmatrix} 1 & 1 \\ 2 & -1 \end{bmatrix}$, an endomorphism of X_2 having matrix $\begin{bmatrix} -3 & 2 \\ 4 & -1 \end{bmatrix}$ will have the new matrix

$$\tfrac{1}{3}\begin{bmatrix} 1 & 1 \\ 2 & -1 \end{bmatrix}\begin{bmatrix} -3 & 2 \\ 4 & -1 \end{bmatrix}\begin{bmatrix} 1 & 1 \\ 2 & -1 \end{bmatrix} = \begin{bmatrix} 1 & 0 \\ 0 & -5 \end{bmatrix}.$$

The result is a diagonal matrix whose geometric effect can be appreciated immediately.

Can any square matrix be "diagonalized" in this way? Since a diagonal matrix represents an endomorphism (in a peculiarly transparent way) the candidate for diagonalization must represent the same endomorphism referred to another basis and must therefore be square. This by itself is not enough; in particular, a nilpotent matrix (see E8) cannot be diagonalized. We shall learn later on just which matrices can be diagonalized, and that the others can be brought, by a proper choice of basis, to a degree of simplicity short of being diagonal but admitting, nevertheless, a clear geometric interpretation.

We also have, of course, the problem of calculating the inverse of a regular matrix of order > 3. Just as we have done when $n = 2$ or 3, we shall do this in the next chapter by solving linear equations.

EXERCISES

7. Prove 6 by substituting from the left equations of 2 and 3 into the right equations of 1.

8. What is the expression for the endomorphism $\begin{bmatrix} 33 & -17 \\ -17 & 33 \end{bmatrix}$ if new coordinates are introduced by the equations $\xi_1 = (\xi_1' + \xi_2')/\sqrt{2}$, $\xi_2 = (\xi_1' - \xi_2')/\sqrt{2}$?

9. Diagonalize

$$L = \begin{bmatrix} 2 & 1 \\ 4 & 3 \end{bmatrix}.$$

10. The *trace* of an $n \times n$ square matrix $L = [\alpha_{jk}]$ is defined to be the sum of its diagonal elements: $\operatorname{tr} L = \sum \alpha_{kk}$. Prove that $\operatorname{tr} (LM) = \operatorname{tr} (ML)$. Prove also that if L' is similar to L then $\operatorname{tr} L' = \operatorname{tr} L$. (T)

NINE
Systems of Linear Algebraic Equations; Equivalence of Matrices

Systems of linear algebraic equations, such as $\sum \alpha_{\lambda k}\xi_k = \eta_\lambda$ with η_λ given and ξ_k sought, arise in practical situations. Problems in structural statics, electrical networks, and fitting of observational data by "least squares" commonly lead directly to such systems. So do many problems in the vibration of mechanical, electrical, and structural systems. A system of first order linear ordinary differential equations with constant coefficients may be reduced at once to a system of linear algebraic equations containing a parameter. Many methods of approximating solutions of ordinary and partial differential equations lead to a system of difference equations which are or can be transformed easily into systems of linear algebraic equations.

We have already dealt with systems of a few equations in a few unknowns. As the number of equations and unknowns increases, the limitations of pencil-and-paper calculations quickly become apparent. Even with the help of desk computers, a system of a dozen equations in a dozen unknowns with an uncooperative matrix may be quite troublesome.

Along with advances in the theory of numerical calculations, the advent of large, fast digital computers has made it possible to attack systems consisting of many hundreds of equations in a like number of unknowns. Such systems are now being handled successfully in many computing centers throughout the world.

Our aim in this chapter is to develop a theory of systems of linear algebraic equations and the closely related properties of matrices. We venture no detailed comment on the use of mechanical or electronic aids to calculation, nor on the "art" of computing that has burgeoned in recent years. (See, for example, [F3, 4, 5, 6, 10 and 11]). The methods developed here are basic to the more sophisticated techniques in actual use. Although manipulative processes now come to the foreground for the first time, the calculations will have illuminating interpretations in the same context in which the equations themselves may be interpreted.

A. Preliminaries

Let μ and n be fixed positive integers and F a fixed field (R or C). We are interested in the system

1.
$$\sum_{k=1}^{n} \alpha_{\lambda k}\xi_k = \eta_\lambda \qquad (\lambda = 1, \ldots, \mu),$$

in which $\alpha_{\lambda k}, \xi_k, \eta_\lambda \in F$.

The Basic Principle (6G2) states that these equations can be interpreted as the scalar equations of a linear transformation $L : X_n \to Y_\mu, x \to Lx = y$, when bases are given in X and Y. If $[x] = [\xi_k]^t$ and $[y] = [\eta_\lambda]^t$, then the matrix notation is this:

2.
$$[L][x] = [y] \qquad \text{or} \qquad [\alpha_{\lambda k}][\xi_k]^t = [\eta_\lambda]^t.$$

The matrix $[L] = [\alpha_{\lambda k}]$ is called the *matrix of the system*. The equations are *homogeneous* if $y = 0$ and *nonhomogeneous* if $y \neq 0$. If a system $[L][x] = [y]$ is nonhomogeneous, then the system $[L][x] = 0$ is the *corresponding* homogeneous or *reduced* system. We refer briefly to the homogeneous system 1 meaning, of course, the system $\sum \alpha_{\lambda k}\xi_k = 0$.

Another method of interpreting the equations uses the column vectors $z_k = [\alpha_{\lambda k}]$ ($\lambda = 1, \ldots, \mu$). The equations ask whether y is a linear combination $\sum z_k\xi_k$ of the z_k or, in other words, whether y is in the range of L; specifically, whether $[y]$ is in the column space of $[L]$. We know (8D24) that the answer will be affirmative if and only if the $\mu \times n$ matrix $[\alpha_{\lambda k}]$ and the $\mu \times (n + 1)$ matrix $[\alpha_{\lambda k}\eta_\lambda]$ (the "augmented matrix", with $[\eta_\lambda]^t$ as z_{n+1}) have the same rank. The computational force of this *consistency condition* will soon be clear. It is also evident from this interpretation that the solutions of the homogeneous system constitute the column nullspace of the matrix of the system.

An earlier theorem (6F) gives information on the solutions of 1 that is in principle complete and theoretically very satisfying. We must now see how to perform the necessary calculations.

B. Examples

Let us use familiar methods to "solve" the following three systems, in each of which the first two equations are the same:

1.
$$
\begin{array}{lll}
\xi - \eta + 2\zeta = 3 & \xi - \eta + 2\zeta = 3 & \xi - \eta + 2\zeta = 3 \\
2\xi \quad\; + \zeta = 1 & 2\xi \quad\; + \zeta = 1 & 2\xi \quad\; + \zeta = 1 \\
3\xi + 2\eta + \zeta = 4 & 3\xi - \eta + 3\zeta = 4 & 3\xi - \eta + 3\zeta = 5.
\end{array}
$$

On using the first equation to eliminate ξ from the second and third equations, we obtain these systems:

2.
$$\xi - \eta + 2\zeta = 3 \qquad \xi - \eta + 2\zeta = 3 \qquad \xi - \eta + 2\zeta = 3$$
$$2\eta - 3\zeta = -5 \qquad 2\eta - 3\zeta = -5 \qquad 2\eta - 3\zeta = -5$$
$$5\eta - 5\zeta = -5 \qquad 2\eta - 3\zeta = -5 \qquad 2\eta - 3\zeta = -4.$$

Dividing the second equation by 2, and the third equation by 5, and eliminating η in the other equations, we obtain:

3.
$$\xi \quad + \tfrac{1}{2}\zeta = \tfrac{1}{2} \qquad \xi \quad + \tfrac{1}{2}\zeta = \tfrac{1}{2} \qquad \xi \quad + \tfrac{1}{2}\zeta = \tfrac{1}{2}$$
$$\eta - \tfrac{3}{2}\zeta = -\tfrac{5}{2} \qquad \eta - \tfrac{3}{2}\zeta = -\tfrac{5}{2} \qquad \eta - \tfrac{3}{2}\zeta = -\tfrac{5}{2}$$
$$\zeta = 3 \qquad\qquad 0 = 0 \qquad\qquad\quad 0 = 1.$$

Let us examine these systems in turn, bearing in mind that we have been assuming the equations to be true.

In the system on the left we use the third equation to eliminate ζ from the first and second equations, learning that if (ξ, η, ζ) is a solution then $(\xi, \eta, \zeta) = (-1, 2, 3)$, and we verify readily that, conversely, $(-1, 2, 3)$ is a solution. The conclusion is that the system has one and only one solution, namely $(-1, 2, 3)$. Observe next that the solution would still have been unique had the right members all been 0; in other words, the only solution of the corresponding homogeneous system is $(0, 0, 0)$. The matrix of the system is regular. For a calculation of its inverse see F2.7.

From the result above for the middle system we see that a solution must be of the form

4.
$$(\tfrac{1}{2}, -\tfrac{5}{2}, 0) + \zeta(-\tfrac{1}{2}, \tfrac{3}{2}, 1)$$

or, when ζ is replaced by 2θ,

5.
$$(\tfrac{1}{2}, -\tfrac{5}{2}, 0) + \theta(-1, 3, 2).$$

One sees readily, conversely, that these vectors satisfy the original equations for $-\infty < \theta < \infty$. The nullspace N of the matrix of the original system is $\theta(-1, 3, 2)$, and the solutions 5 are seen to constitute the flat $\tfrac{1}{2}(1, -5, 0) + N$ (cf. 6F1).

The rightmost system has led to the contradiction "$0 = 1$"; this system is inconsistent (has no solutions).

The foregoing examples are entirely typical of the general situation, to which we now turn.

C. Elimination; Elementary Operations

We are interested in the equations (cf. 1)

1.
$$_k\!\sum_1^n \alpha_{\lambda k}\xi_k = \eta_\lambda \qquad (\lambda = 1, \ldots, \mu).$$

Our aim is to formulate in general terms the process of elimination (often called Gaussian) used in the preceding section. In order to keep the discussion simple we ignore all questions of computational efficiency. The column vectors of $[\alpha_{\lambda k}]$ will be denoted by z_k ($k = 1, \ldots, n$) and the row vectors by a_λ ($\lambda = 1, \ldots, \mu$).

Step A. Choose the least value of k, say k_1, for which $z_k \neq 0$. (For all lesser values of k all coefficients of ξ_k are 0 and ξ_k is not restricted by the equations.) Then choose the least value of λ, say λ_1, for which $\alpha_{\lambda k_1} \neq 0$. If $\lambda_1 > 1$, *interchange* equation λ_1 with equation 1 and, for convenience, relabel the equations accordingly.

Step B. Divide the first equation by α_{1k_1}; the coefficient of ξ_{k_1} is then unity.

Step C. Use the first equation to *eliminate* ξ_{k_1} from all other equations.

The result of steps A, B, and C is a system of equations with this appearance (after a suitable adjustment of notation):

2.
$$\xi_{k_1} + {}_k\sum_{k_1+1}^{n} \beta_{1k}\xi_k = \theta_1$$

$$_k\sum_{k_1+1}^{n} \beta_{\lambda k}\xi_k = \theta_\lambda \qquad (\lambda = 2, \ldots, \mu).$$

Since equations 2 are consequences of equations 1, every solution of 1 will satisfy 2. Each step (A, B, C), moreover, is reversible by a step of essentially the same kind. It follows that equations 1 are consequences of equations 2, and that every solution of 2 will satisfy 1. Thus 1 and 2 have precisely the same solutions.

Now we apply the same procedure to the $\mu - 1$ residual equations

3.
$$_k\sum_{k_1+1}^{n} \beta_{\lambda k}\xi_k = \theta_\lambda \qquad (\lambda = 2, \ldots, \mu).$$

The result is a system

4.
$$\xi_{k_2} + {}_k\sum_{k_2+1}^{n} \gamma_{2k}\xi_k = \chi_2$$

$$_k\sum_{k_2+1}^{n} \gamma_{\lambda k}\xi_k = \chi_\lambda \qquad (\lambda = 3, \ldots, \mu).$$

This process continues recursively, with one fewer residual equation after each application. The process comes to a halt at a stage, say the ρth, when either $\rho = \mu$, and there are no more equations, or $\rho < \mu$ and Step A cannot be initiated on the residual $\mu - \rho$ equations. In the latter case each row of coefficients in the residual system ($\lambda = \rho + 1, \ldots, \mu$) is zero. Since the first ρ rows are obviously independent, the integer ρ is seen to be the row-rank of the matrix; ρ is also called the *rank* of the system (see 8D3). Clearly $\rho \leq \min(\mu, n)$.

It is convenient to make one final adjustment. The variable with index k_σ *may* appear in earlier equations. We use successively the equations with index σ ($\sigma = 1, \ldots, \rho$) to eliminate the ξ_{k_σ} from each equation with a lesser index. This process was used on equations (B2), *after* η had been eliminated from the third equations, to eliminate η also from the first equations in order to arrive at B3; it was also used in eliminating ζ from the first two equations of the leftmost system of B3 to obtain the result $\xi = -1, \eta = 2, \zeta = 3$.

For the sake of brevity and clarity we now introduce a special index k' whose domain is $1, \ldots, n$ with $k_1, \ldots, k_\rho$ removed:

5.
$$k' = 1, \ldots, n; \qquad k' \neq k_1, \ldots, k_\rho.$$

The equations may now be given this appearance:

6.
$$\xi_{k_\sigma} + \sum_{k'} \tau_{\sigma k'} \xi_{k'} = \zeta_\sigma \qquad (\sigma = 1, \ldots, \rho)$$
$$0 = \zeta_\lambda \qquad (\lambda = \rho + 1, \ldots, \mu).$$

The ζ's on the right are linear combinations of the η's on the right in 1.

Since equations 6 have been obtained from 1 by a finite number of steps, each reversible and each without effect on the solutions of the system, systems 1 and 6 have the same solutions. From 6, however, the whole situation can be read off at a glance. Examples will be found in 12 and 14.

7. Consistency Condition. The equations are consistent if and only if, in 6, either $\rho = \mu$ or $\rho < \mu$ and $\zeta_\lambda = 0$ $(\lambda = \rho + 1, \ldots, \mu)$.

In the examples of B3, the system on the right is inconsistent, while each of the others is consistent.

It is evident in 6 that the column-rank of the matrix of the system is ρ; the condition in 7 says that the equations are consistent if and only if, as we have seen earlier (8D24), the augmented matrix also has rank ρ.

The necessity of the condition stated in 7 is obvious. We assume henceforth that the condition holds, and refer accordingly to the *consistent case*. The condition is met by any homogeneous system, since it always has the trivial solution $x = 0$. We demonstrate the sufficiency of the condition for a nonhomogeneous system by exhibiting a solution.

8. Particular Solution. In the consistent case a solution is (evidently) the column vector x_P with components
$$\xi_{k_\sigma} = \zeta_\sigma \ (\sigma = 1, \ldots, \rho), \qquad \xi_{k'} = 0.$$

9. Uniqueness. In the consistent case the solution given in 8 is unique if and only if $\rho = n$.

Here the sufficiency is obvious, for if $\rho = n$ there are no variables $\xi_{k'}$. We observe that this case arises only if $\mu \geq n$. To prove the necessity of the condition we assume that $\rho < n$ and display nontrivial solutions of the homogeneous system.

10. All Solutions of the Homogeneous System. If $\rho < n$ then the homogeneous system has an $(n - \rho)$-parameter family of solutions in which the $n - \rho$ variables $\xi_{k'}$ are free and the others are determined by the respective homogeneous equations in 6. In the homogeneous system B3, $k' = 3$, the free variable is ζ, and the one-parameter family of solutions is the space $\zeta(-\frac{1}{2}, \frac{3}{2}, 1)$ of B5.

10.1. Basis for the Column Nullspace of $[\alpha_{\lambda k}]$. The column nullspace N of $[\alpha_{\lambda k}]$ is the space of solutions of the homogeneous system. If $\rho < n$ then $[\alpha_{\lambda k}]$ is column-singular and, after an attentive look at equations 6, we define $n - \rho$ column vectors $b_{h'}$ having components $\beta_{kh'}$ as follows:

10.1.1
$$\beta_{k_\sigma h'} = -\tau_{\sigma h'} \qquad (\sigma = 1, \ldots, \rho)$$
$$\beta_{k'h'} = \delta_{k'h'},$$

where $\delta_{k'h'}$ is the Kronecker delta. That these vectors are independent is clear from the form of their components with index k'. The representation of N given in 10 makes it clear that $x = \sum \theta_{h'} b_{h'}$ will satisfy the homogeneous system 6 if and only if

10.1.2
$$\xi_{k_\sigma} = -\sum \tau_{\sigma h'} \theta_{h'} \qquad (\sigma = 1, \ldots, n)$$
$$\xi_{k'} = \theta_{k'}.$$

Since these conditions are satisfied by the definition of x, the vectors $b_{h'}$ are a basis for N.

10.2. Corollary. *Homogeneous System.* The homogeneous system has a non-trivial solution if and only if $\rho < n$.

10.3. Corollary. *Homogeneous System with* $\mu < n$. *Any* homogeneous system with *more* unknowns (n) than equations (μ) has nontrivial solutions.

11. All Solutions of the Nonhomogeneous System. In the consistent case a vector $x \in F_n$ satisfies the system if and only if $x = x_0 + m$, where x_0 satisfies the nonhomogeneous system (for example, $x = x_P$ of 8) and $m \in N$. All solutions therefore constitute the flat $x_0 + N$.

EXAMPLE

12. Suppose that a system of four equations in four unknowns has been reduced to the following form:

12.1.
$$u \quad + 2w + \ x = 1$$
$$v + 3w - 2x = 3.$$

On comparison with 6 we see that here $\zeta_\lambda = 0$ ($\lambda = 3, 4$) and that therefore (cf. 7) the equations are consistent. A particular solution (cf. 8) is obviously given by $x_P = [1 \ \ 3 \ \ 0 \ \ 0]^t$. A basis for the column nullspace (cf. 10.1) is constituted by

$$q_1 = [-2 \ \ -3 \ \ 1 \ \ 0]^t, \qquad q_2 = [-1 \ \ 2 \ \ 0 \ \ 1]^t.$$

211

All solutions (cf. 11) are given by

$$x = x_P + \alpha q_1 + \beta q_2 \qquad -\infty < \alpha, \beta < \infty.$$

Steps A, B, and C were specified above in a quite definite and rigid manner in order that the exact form of the results could be controlled. Greater flexibility is possible and desirable.

Instead of merely interchanging two equations (if necessary), as directed in step A, we could have subjected the equations to any permutation. Instead of merely multiplying the first equation by a non-zero constant (if necessary), as directed in step B, we could have multiplied each equation by a non-zero constant (using 1 when no change is desired). Instead of merely multiplying the first equation by appropriate non-zero constants and adding to the respective equations (in order to eliminate ξ_{k_1}), as in step C, we could have added to any equation any linear combination of all the other equations.

These three operations (permutation of equations, multiplication of an equation by a non-zero constant, and addition to an equation of a linear combination of the other equations) are called *elementary operations*. The effect of an elementary operation can be undone by an elementary operation —indeed, by one of the same kind. If a system S of linear equations is subjected to a finite sequence of elementary operations, resulting in a system S', it therefore follows that S and S' have the same solutions. Two systems having the same solutions are said to be *equivalent*, and we have established the following result.

13. Theorem. In order that two systems of linear equations be equivalent it is sufficient that it be possible to pass from one to the other by a finite sequence of elementary operations.

The necessity of this condition, by no means evident here, will be established later (in the proof of F2).

As a consequence, one will pay close attention, in any specific problem, to the specific character of the equations. Shrewdly chosen elementary operations may be far more effective than the step A, B, C procedure described above; it may be possible, for example, to eliminate more than one variable at a time.

It must be emphasized that, when the solution is not unique, it may be *represented* in many ways. For example (cf. B6) the flats

$$(\tfrac{1}{2}, -\tfrac{5}{2}, 0) + \theta(-1, 3, 2)$$

and

$$(-\tfrac{3}{2}, \tfrac{7}{2}, 4) + \eta(-1, 3, 2)$$

are the same, as one sees by putting $\theta = \eta + 2$. In the light of the representation $x_0 + N$ of 9 this ambiguity is to be expected. The space N can be represented in many ways and the vector x_0, moreover, may be *any* vector terminating in the flat.

EXAMPLE

14. Suppose that a consistent system of four equations in five variables has been reduced, by the step A, B, C process or otherwise, to this system:

15.
$$v + 2w - x - 2y + 3z = 7$$
$$x \qquad + 2z = 5.$$

Here $\mu = 2$, $k_1 = 1$, $k_2 = 3$, and $k' = 2, 4, 5$. By eliminating x from the first equation, we arrive at

16.
$$v + 2w \qquad - 2y + 5z = 12$$
$$x \qquad + 2z = 5.$$

A particular solution is evidently $x_0 = [12, 0, 5, 0, 0]^t$, and a basis for N is furnished by these three vectors:

17.
$$b_2 = [-2, 1, 0, 0, 0]^t$$
$$b_4 = [2, 0, 0, 1, 0]^t$$
$$b_5 = [-5, 0, -2, 0, 1]^t.$$

Thus N may be represented by $\alpha b_2 + \beta b_4 + \gamma b_5$, and the set of all solutions is, of course, the flat $x_0 + N$.

In dealing with a system of equations one may not know, at the outset, whether or not the equations are consistent. In this context, therefore, the word "solve" has come to mean "settle the question of consistency and, if the result is favorable, find *all* solutions". Any system of a finite number of linear equations in a finite number of variables with coefficients in a field can be solved, in principle, by the processes developed above. The calculations, of course, may turn out to be fantastically complicated if the system is "large", even with the advantage of modern computing machinery.

17.1. *Direct Proof that $\rho_R = \rho_C$.* The proof of 8D3 used the fact that $\rho(L) = \rho(L^a)$. Using the notation introduced at the beginning of 8D, we digress here to give a direct proof that $\rho_R = \rho_C$.

The integers ρ_R and ρ_C are equal, respectively, to the numbers of independent rows and columns of $[L]$. There exist ρ_C columns $z_{j'}$ such that every other column $z_{j''}$ is dependent on the $z_{j'}$; here j' runs over a set of ρ_C indices chosen from $1, \ldots, n$, and j'' runs over the complementary set. Thus

(a) $\sum \alpha_{\lambda j'} \zeta_{j'} = 0$ implies that $\zeta_{j'} = 0$, and

(b) there exist scalars $\theta_{j'j''}$ such that $\alpha_{\lambda j''} = \sum_{j'} \alpha_{\lambda j'} \theta_{j'j''}$.

Similarly, there exist ρ_R independent rows $a_{\lambda'}$ such that every other row $a_{\lambda''}$ is dependent on the rows $a_{\lambda'}$. Thus

(c) $\sum \eta_{\lambda'} \alpha_{\lambda' k} = 0$ implies that $\eta_{\lambda'} = 0$, and

(d) there exist scalars $\varphi_{\lambda''\lambda'}$ such that $\alpha_{\lambda'' k} = \sum_{\lambda'} \varphi_{\lambda''\lambda'} \alpha_{\lambda' k}$.

It follows now that

(e) $\sum \alpha_{\lambda'j'}\zeta_{j'} = 0$ implies that $\zeta_{j'} = 0$, for the equations $\sum \alpha_{\lambda''j'}\zeta_{j'} = 0$ follow from (e) by (d).

Similarly

(f) $\sum \eta_{\lambda'}\alpha_{\lambda'j'} = 0$ implies that $\eta_{\lambda'} = 0$, for the equations $\sum \eta_{\lambda'}\alpha_{\lambda'j''} = 0$ follow from (f) by (b).

In (e) we have ρ_R equations in ρ_C unknowns, while in (f) we have ρ_C equations in ρ_R unknowns. If $\rho_R \neq \rho_C$, then one of these systems would have more unknowns than equations and would therefore, by 10.2, have a nontrivial solution. From this contradiction we conclude that $\rho_R = \rho_C$.

EXERCISES

18. Solve each of the following systems by applying steps A, B, and C, as was done in arriving at 6. Solve each system by a more opportunistic method. Verify in each case that the solutions agree. If the system has more than one solution, find a basis for the space N of all solutions of the homogeneous system.

(a)
$$\begin{aligned}
\theta - 3\xi + 2\eta + \zeta &= 2 \\
2\theta - 5\xi + 4\eta + 2\zeta &= 6 \\
2\theta - 3\xi + 4\eta &= 12 \\
3\theta - 12\xi + 6\eta + 13\zeta &= -10
\end{aligned}$$

(b)
$$\begin{aligned}
2\theta - \xi \quad - 2\zeta &= 3 \\
\xi + \eta &= 1 \\
2\theta + \xi + 2\eta - 2\zeta &= 3 \\
4\theta + 2\xi + 4\eta - 4\zeta &= 9
\end{aligned}$$

(c)
$$\begin{aligned}
\theta - 2\xi + 3\eta + \zeta &= 8 \\
3\theta \quad - \eta - \zeta &= 4 \\
2\theta + \xi \quad + 3\zeta &= -9 \\
-2\theta + \xi + 2\eta &= 0
\end{aligned}$$

(d)
$$\begin{aligned}
\theta + 2\xi - \eta + 3\zeta &= 1 \\
\theta + 2\xi \quad + 5\zeta &= 1 \\
4\theta + 8\xi + \eta + 22\zeta &= 4 \\
3\theta + 6\xi + \eta + 17\zeta &= 3
\end{aligned}$$

19. We are given a flat $a + S(a \in' S)$ and a vector b. How can we determine whether or not the endpoint of b belongs to the flat?

20. Subspaces S and T have bases a_λ and b_λ ($\lambda = 1, \ldots, \rho$). Devise a procedure for determining whether or not $S = T$.

21. We have a consistent system of 17 homogeneous equations in 13 variables. The rank of the system is 10. What is the dimension of the space of solutions of the homogeneous system?

22. We have a system of 23 equations in 30 variables. Can the system have a unique solution? What further can be said if the rank of the system is 17?

214

D. Elementary Row Operations on Matrices

The reader will have noted that the variables ξ_k play a minor role in the calculations of the preceding section; only the behavior of the coefficients is important. All the work may be done by dealing with the matrix $L = [\alpha_{\lambda k}]$ of the system, and we propose now to develop details in parallel, so to speak, with the argument of C. The fact that the elementary operations of C were performed on *equations* is reflected now in our use of elementary *row* operations only. We denote by I the $\mu \times \mu$ identity matrix.

1. *Elementary Row Operations.* In step A of C we interchanged two equations of the system. In I let us interchange rows κ and λ, denoting the result by $I_{\kappa,\lambda}$. Then the product $I_{\kappa,\lambda}L$ is obtained from the matrix L of the system by interchanging rows κ and λ, for the 1 in the position $\lambda\kappa$ will pick up the κth row of L and make it the λth row of the product, and the 1 in position $\kappa\lambda$ will bring the λth row of L into the κth row of the product. The first step A of C consisted specifically of passing from L to $I_{1,\lambda_1}L$.

In step B of C we multiplied a row of (the new) L by a non-zero constant. In I let us multiply row κ by $\gamma \neq 0$, denoting the result by $I_{\gamma \cdot \kappa}$. Then $I_{\gamma \cdot \kappa}L$ consists of L with row κ multiplied by γ. The first step B of C consisted specifically of passing from L to $I_{\alpha_{1 k_1}^{-1}\cdot 1}L$.

In step C of Sec. C we multiplied a row of L by respective non-zero constants and added it to respective other rows of L. In I let us multiply row κ by γ and add it to row λ, denoting the result by $I_{\gamma \cdot \kappa+\lambda}$. Then $I_{\gamma \cdot \kappa+\lambda}L$ consists of L with γ times row κ added to row λ. If after step B in C, for example, we had $\alpha_{2k_1} = 3$ then the appropriate portion of step C would have entailed replacing L by $I_{-3\cdot1+2}L$, thus eliminating the variable ξ_{k_1} in the second equation.

By an *elementary matrix* we shall mean a matrix of the form $I_{\kappa,\lambda}$, $I_{\gamma \cdot \kappa}$, or $I_{\gamma \cdot \kappa+\lambda}$. Every elementary matrix is regular: $I_{\kappa,\lambda}^{-1} = I_{\kappa,\lambda}$, $I_{\gamma \cdot \kappa}^{-1} = I_{\gamma^{-1}\cdot\kappa}$, and $I_{\gamma \cdot \kappa+\lambda}^{-1} = I_{-\gamma \cdot \kappa+\lambda}$. It follows at once that *any product of a finite number of elementary matrices of the same order is regular*.

As an example, let us use elementary matrices to imitate the reduction of the left example in B1. We find that we must begin by subtracting twice row 1 from row 2 and then thrice row 1 from row 3, or, on using elementary matrices, we must calculate (cf. the left of B2):

$$I_{-3\cdot1+3}I_{-2\cdot1+2}L = \begin{bmatrix} 1 & 0 & 0 \\ 0 & 1 & 0 \\ -3 & 0 & 1 \end{bmatrix} \begin{bmatrix} 1 & 0 & 0 \\ -2 & 1 & 0 \\ 0 & 0 & 1 \end{bmatrix} \begin{bmatrix} 1 & -1 & 2 \\ 2 & 0 & 1 \\ 3 & 2 & 1 \end{bmatrix}$$

2.
$$= \begin{bmatrix} 1 & -1 & 2 \\ 0 & 2 & -3 \\ 0 & 5 & -5 \end{bmatrix}.$$

Continuing, we must pre-multiply further by

3.
$$I_{2\cdot3}I_{3\cdot3+2}I_{-3+1}I_{-2+3}I_{2+1}I_{\frac{1}{8}\cdot3}I_{\frac{1}{2}\cdot2}.$$

The result is that

4.
$$\frac{1}{5}\begin{bmatrix} -2 & 5 & -1 \\ 1 & -5 & 3 \\ 4 & -5 & 2 \end{bmatrix}\begin{bmatrix} 1 & -1 & 2 \\ 2 & 0 & 1 \\ 3 & 2 & 1 \end{bmatrix} = \begin{bmatrix} 1 & 0 & 0 \\ 0 & 1 & 0 \\ 0 & 0 & 1 \end{bmatrix}.$$

The matrix of the system is therefore regular and its inverse is the left factor of the left member, including the coefficient $\frac{1}{5}$.

EXERCISE

5. Reduce the matrices of the systems in C18 by pre-multiplying by appropriate elementary matrices. By finding the product of these matrices, obtain a single regular pre-factor which will effect the reduction in one step.

E. Arrangement of Calculations

Several practical steps can be taken to generalize and facilitate the calculations of the preceding section.

There we were dealing only with the matrix of the system, as though the system were homogeneous. The nonhomogeneous system can be treated with equal ease simply by using the augmented matrix $[L \quad y]$, in which the column vector on the right side of the equations is adjoined to the matrix of the system as a rightmost column. When the process has terminated, the column then in that position will settle the consistency question and will be essential in finding a particular solution as in C8.

It may happen, moreover, that one will be interested in each of several column vectors on the right. If these vectors are y_j ($j = 1, \ldots, m$) then their components form a $\mu \times m$ matrix $Y = [\eta_{\lambda j}]$. We must allow that each y_j may be the image of a different $x \in X$, and are consequently seeking x_j ($j = 1, \ldots, m$) such that $Lx_j = y_j$ for each value of j. If we write the components of the vectors x_j down in order we arrive at a matrix equation

1.
$$[\alpha_{\lambda k}][\xi_{kj}] = [\eta_{\lambda j}].$$

In this situation it is natural to apply row operations to the $\mu \times (n + m)$ matrix

2.
$$[\alpha_{\lambda k} \quad \eta_{\lambda j}] \qquad (k = 1, \ldots, n; j = 1, \ldots, m).$$

In B1, for example, on the left, the right member was $[3, 1, 4]^t$. Had we also been interested in right members $[2, -1, 3]^t$ and $[1, 1, 2]^t$ we could have applied row operations to the 3×6 matrix

3.
$$\begin{bmatrix} 1 & -1 & 2 & \vdots & 3 & 2 & 1 \\ 2 & 0 & 1 & \vdots & 1 & -1 & 1 \\ 3 & 2 & 1 & \vdots & 4 & 3 & 2 \end{bmatrix}.$$

The vertical dotted line is not necessary, but it helps us to keep in mind the significance of the blocks.

A second helpful step uses the identity matrix. If we are concerned with row operations on a $\mu \times q$ matrix $[M]$, we simply form a $\mu \times (\mu + q)$ matrix $[I \quad M]$ by adjoining the $\mu \times \mu$ identity matrix on the *left* of the given one. The operations performed on $[I \quad M]$ will affect I in the manner indicated in the example in 1. The final result will be a matrix $[J \quad K]$ in which K is the desired reduced form of M and J is a product of elementary matrices with the further property that $JM = K$, for, in fact, $[J][I \quad M] = [J \quad JM] = [J \quad K]$. In particular, if M is regular then J will be its inverse and K will be the identity. Since J^{-1}, like J, is a product of elementary matrices, we reach a conclusion whose converse has already been noted in D1.

4. Every regular matrix can be expressed as a product of elementary matrices.

We mention, finally, a useful check on computations. Suppose that we have set up the matrix $[I \quad M] = [\delta_{\lambda\kappa} \quad \alpha_{\lambda,\mu+k}]$. We adjoin one further column at the far right. The element in the λth row of this column is $-(1 + \sum_k \alpha_{\lambda\mu+k})$, i.e., the negative of the sum of all the elements in the λth row of $[I \quad M]$. It should then be true, after each row operation, that the sum across each row, including the element in the last column, is zero; this check yields strong evidence but not certainty that no error has occurred.

Let us illustrate by applying these methods simultaneously to the middle and right examples from B1. We start with the matrix $[I \quad L \quad z_4 \quad z_5 \quad s]$, where I is the 3×3 identity, L is the matrix of the system, $z_4 = [3 \quad 1 \quad 4]^t$, $z_5 = [3 \quad 1 \quad 5]^t$, and s is the check-sum. Explicitly, the 3×9 matrix is

5.
$$\begin{bmatrix} 1 & 0 & 0 & \vdots & 1 & -1 & 2 & \vdots & 3 & 3 & \vdots & -9 \\ 0 & 1 & 0 & \vdots & 2 & 0 & 1 & \vdots & 1 & 1 & \vdots & -6 \\ 0 & 0 & 1 & \vdots & 3 & -1 & 3 & \vdots & 4 & 5 & \vdots & -15 \end{bmatrix}.$$

The dotted vertical lines, again, merely have the effect of emphasizing the significance of the separate blocks.

The operations $-2 \cdot 1 + 2$ and $-3 \cdot 1 + 3$ yield (cf. B2)

6.
$$\begin{bmatrix} 1 & 0 & 0 & \vdots & 1 & -1 & 2 & \vdots & 3 & 3 & \vdots & -9 \\ -2 & 1 & 0 & \vdots & 0 & 2 & -3 & \vdots & -5 & -5 & \vdots & 12 \\ -3 & 0 & 1 & \vdots & 0 & 2 & -3 & \vdots & -5 & -4 & \vdots & 12 \end{bmatrix}.$$

Since each row-sum is zero, we are encouraged to believe that no error has been made; this check is tacit in what follows.

On performing the operations $-1 \cdot 2 + 3$ and $\frac{1}{2} \cdot 2$ we arrive at

7.
$$\begin{bmatrix} 1 & 0 & 0 & \vdots & 1 & -1 & 2 & \vdots & 3 & 3 & \vdots & -9 \\ -1 & \frac{1}{2} & 0 & \vdots & 0 & 1 & -\frac{3}{2} & \vdots & -\frac{5}{2} & -\frac{5}{2} & \vdots & 6 \\ -1 & -1 & 1 & \vdots & 0 & 0 & 0 & \vdots & 0 & 1 & \vdots & 0 \end{bmatrix}.$$

At this stage we already see (from row 3, columns 4, 5, 6, and 8) that the right member z_5 gives an inconsistent system; also, we have already determined the rank of L.

Now the operation $1 \cdot 2 + 1$ yields (cf. B3)

8.
$$\begin{bmatrix} 0 & \frac{1}{2} & 0 & \vdots & 1 & 0 & \frac{1}{2} & \vdots & \frac{1}{2} & \frac{1}{2} & \vdots & -3 \\ -1 & \frac{1}{2} & 0 & \vdots & 0 & 1 & -\frac{3}{2} & \vdots & -\frac{5}{2} & -\frac{5}{2} & \vdots & 6 \\ -1 & -1 & 1 & \vdots & 0 & 0 & 0 & \vdots & 0 & 1 & \vdots & 0 \end{bmatrix}.$$

We are now in a position to read off the information obtained from B3.

Finally, we verify that the matrix in columns 1–3 in 8, when applied to the matrix in columns 4–8 of 5, does yield the matrix in columns 4–8 of 8; the check-column (9) has been appropriately adjusted.

9.
$$\begin{bmatrix} 0 & \frac{1}{2} & 0 \\ -1 & \frac{1}{2} & 0 \\ -1 & -1 & 1 \end{bmatrix} \begin{bmatrix} 1 & -1 & 2 & \vdots & 3 & 3 & \vdots & -8 \\ 2 & 0 & 1 & \vdots & 1 & 1 & \vdots & -5 \\ 3 & -1 & 3 & \vdots & 4 & 5 & \vdots & -14 \end{bmatrix}$$
$$= \begin{bmatrix} 1 & 0 & \frac{1}{2} & \vdots & \frac{1}{2} & \frac{1}{2} & \vdots & -\frac{5}{2} \\ 0 & 1 & -\frac{3}{2} & \vdots & -\frac{5}{2} & -\frac{5}{2} & \vdots & -\frac{11}{2} \\ 0 & 0 & 0 & \vdots & 0 & 1 & \vdots & -1 \end{bmatrix}.$$

Before presenting a final example of an opportunistic calculation, let us observe that if a 1 can be obtained in *some* row of a column (even where a 0 is desired ultimately), then any chosen element of that column may be made to have the value 1 and then used to eliminate other elements.

We now reduce the matrix L in columns 4 to 7 of the following 3×8 matrix:

$$\begin{bmatrix} 1 & 0 & 0 & \vdots & 2 & -3 & 7 & -11 & \vdots & 4 \\ 0 & 1 & 0 & \vdots & 3 & 1 & 5 & 0 & \vdots & -10 \\ 0 & 0 & 1 & \vdots & -2 & 1 & -5 & 5 & \vdots & 0 \end{bmatrix}.$$

Add the first row to the third and subtract it from the second, getting

$$\begin{bmatrix} 1 & 0 & 0 & \vdots & 2 & -3 & 7 & -11 & \vdots & 4 \\ -1 & 1 & 0 & \vdots & 1 & 4 & -2 & 11 & \vdots & -14 \\ 1 & 0 & 1 & \vdots & 0 & -2 & 2 & -6 & \vdots & 4 \end{bmatrix}.$$

Now subtract the second row from the first, write down the new first row, and use it to eliminate the 1 in row 2 and column 4; the result is

$$\begin{bmatrix} 2 & -1 & 0 & \vdots & 1 & -7 & 9 & -22 & \vdots & 18 \\ -3 & 2 & 0 & \vdots & 0 & 11 & -11 & 33 & \vdots & -32 \\ 1 & 0 & 1 & \vdots & 0 & -2 & 2 & -6 & \vdots & 4 \end{bmatrix}.$$

Now add five times row 3 to row 2, write down the new row 2, and use it to obtain zeros elsewhere in column 5; the result is

$$\begin{bmatrix} 16 & 13 & 35 & \vdots & 1 & 0 & 2 & -1 & \vdots & -66 \\ 2 & 2 & 5 & \vdots & 0 & 1 & -1 & 3 & \vdots & -12 \\ 5 & 4 & 11 & \vdots & 0 & 0 & 0 & 0 & \vdots & -20 \end{bmatrix}.$$

The matrix L is therefore row-equivalent to

$$K = \begin{bmatrix} 1 & 0 & 2 & -1 \\ 0 & 1 & -1 & 3 \\ 0 & 0 & 0 & 0 \end{bmatrix}$$

and the matrix M in the leftmost three columns of the result has the property that $K = ML$.

EXERCISES

10. Use the present methods on the systems in C18. (Save the calculations.)

11. Solve the system

$$\xi + \eta + \alpha\zeta = 1$$
$$\xi + \alpha\eta + \zeta = \alpha$$
$$\alpha\xi + \eta + \zeta = \alpha^2.$$

How does the solution depend on the parameter α?

F. Row-Equivalence of Matrices

We wish now to restate in terms of matrices the general results obtained in C, and a few more as well. A definition will be necessary.

A matrix will be said to be in *row-reduced echelon form*, or to be a *row-reduced echelon matrix* if it has the following four properties:

(a) Every zero row is below every non-zero row;

(b) The leftmost non-zero entry of a non-zero row is 1;

(c) The leftmost non-zero entry of each row (except the first) is to the right of the leftmost non-zero entry of the preceding row;

(d) If a column contains the leftmost non-zero entry (1) of a row, then every other entry in that column is zero.

The concepts "echelon matrix" and "row-reduced matrix" are introduced separately by some writers. Usage is not entirely fixed, however, and we shall need only the amalgamated definition given above. A matrix in row-reduced echelon form is sometimes said to be in *Hermite normal form*.

Properties (b) and (c) imply, as may be verified readily, that the non-zero rows are independent. Since the row-rank cannot exceed the number of non-zero rows, it follows that the row-rank of a matrix is equal to the number of non-zero rows if the matrix has properties (b) and (c).

Let us look, for example, at the matrices in columns 4, 5, and 6 in E6, 7, and 8. The matrices in 6 and 7 are not row-reduced echelon matrices, although the matrix in 7 has properties (a), (b), and (c). The matrix in 8 is a row-reduced echelon matrix. The matrix in columns 4–9 of 8 again has properties (a), (b), and (c); to complete its reduction one would use the 1 in column 8 to replace the entries $\frac{1}{2}$ and $-\frac{5}{2}$ by 0, thus achieving property (d) as well.

The prototype of a $\mu \times n$ row-reduced echelon matrix is the matrix R of the system C6. Rows $\rho + 1, \ldots, \mu$ are zero. For $\sigma = 1, \ldots, \rho$ the σth row has 1 in the k_σth column, $\tau_{\sigma k'}$ in columns k' (cf. C5) and zero elsewhere. Rows $1, \ldots, \rho$ are clearly independent. By reversing the steps leading from C1 to C6 we can express each row of C1 as a linear combination of rows $1, \ldots, \rho$ of C6. Hence R and the matrix $L = [\alpha_{\lambda k}]$ of C1 have the same row space, and rows $1, \ldots, \rho$ of C6 form a basis for that space.

In the matrix R (of C6) furthermore, the columns z_{k_σ} $(\sigma = 1, \ldots, \rho)$ are independent, and the other columns of R are linear combinations of them. In fact,

1.
$$z_{k'} = \sum_\sigma z_{k_\sigma} \tau_{\sigma k'}.$$

Since elementary row operations leave unchanged linear relations between columns, such as 1, it follows that the columns z_{k_σ} $(\sigma = 1, \ldots, \rho)$ of L are independent and the columns k' of L are expressed as linear combinations of them by 6.1. The foregoing remarks yield a new proof that column rank and row rank are equal (cf. C17.1 and 7D8.3).

While L and R have the *same row space*, we have shown only that their *column spaces* have the *same dimension*. That the column spaces themselves may be different is evident from a comparison of L in B1 and R in B3 (right-most systems). The column space of R in B3 has a basis consisting of $[1, 0, 0]^t$ and $[0, 1, 0]^t$; the space they span contains no column of L in 2.1. What is true, however, is that L and R have the same column nullspace; this is evident from the fact that the homogeneous equations $Lx = 0$ and $Rx = 0$ have the same solutions.

Let us now say that two $\mu \times n$ matrices, K and L, are *row-equivalent* if it is possible to pass from one to the other by applying a finite number of elementary row operations. It follows from the results of C, as formulated in D1, that *every $\mu \times n$ matrix is row-equivalent to a $\mu \times n$ matrix in row-reduced echelon form*.

As the terminology implies, the relation of row-equivalence is symmetric, for if a sequence of elementary row operations on L yields K, then the respective inverse operations applied to K in reverse order will yield L. The situation is summarized in the following theorem.

2. Theorem. Let $K = [\alpha_{\lambda k}]$ and $L = [\beta_{\lambda k}]$ be two $\mu \times n$ matrices. The following statements are equivalent:

   (a) K and L are row-equivalent;
   (b) There exists a regular $\mu \times \mu$ matrix M such that $K = ML$;
   (c) K and L are row-equivalent to the same row-reduced echelon matrix R;
   (d) The systems $\sum \alpha_{\lambda k} \xi_k = 0$ and $\sum \beta_{\lambda k} \xi_k = 0$ have the same solutions;
   (e) K and L have the same column nullspace;
   (f) K and L have the same row space.

A product of elementary matrices is regular, and conversely. Consequently, (a) is equivalent to (b).

Suppose now that K is reduced to a row-reduced echelon matrix R by a sequence of elementary row operations whose effect is produced on K by pre-multiplying by a regular matrix J. It then follows from (b) that

2.1
$$JK = JML = R.$$

Since the product JM of the regular matrices J and M is regular, and since each regular matrix is a product of elementary matrices, and (b) implies (a), it follows that L is also row-equivalent to R.

Now the equations $Rx = 0$ are in the form C6, and it follows from 2.1 above that the solutions of $Rx = 0$, of $Kx = J^{-1}Rx = 0$, and of $Lx = M^{-1}J^{-1}Rx = 0$ are identical. Hence (c) implies (d).

That (d) implies (e) follows from the definition of the column nullspace.

With reference to (e) and (f), let us recall 7D6.1, which says that the column nullspace of L is the annihilator of the range of L^d, i.e., of the row space of L. Since identical subspaces have identical annihilators, the equivalence of (e) and (f) is evident. We give, nevertheless, a discussion that involves no explicit appeal to duality.

That (e) implies (f) is of special interest, for the implication is that the set of solutions determines, in an essential way, the system of equations; this is a rephrasing of the idea of "double description" just preceding 7C3. In the context of the present theorem, we may say that if two systems of μ equations in n unknowns have the same solutions, i.e., are equivalent in the sense given just before C13, then their matrices are row-equivalent; this is essentially the converse of C13.

Assuming (e), then, we conclude first that if the common column nullspace N has dimension $n - \rho$ then K and L have rank ρ. If either system had a row r independent of all the rows in the other system, then that other system with the equation $rx = 0$ adjoined would be of rank $\rho + 1$ and still have $n - \rho$ independent solutions belonging to N; this is a contradiction. Hence (e) implies (f).

We now show that (f) implies (b), closing the chain of implications and thus completing the proof of 2. Let s_σ ($\sigma = 1, \ldots, d \leq \mu$) be a basis for the common row space of K and L. Since each row a_λ of K and b_λ of L is a linear combination of the rows s_σ, there exist scalars $\theta_{\lambda\sigma}$ and $\varphi_{\lambda\sigma}$ such that

2.2.
$$a_\lambda = \sum_\sigma \theta_{\lambda\sigma} s_\sigma, \qquad b_\lambda = \sum_\sigma \varphi_{\lambda\sigma} s_\sigma \quad (\lambda = 1, \ldots, \mu).$$

Using the rows s_σ ($\sigma = 1, \ldots, d$) and a $(\mu - d) \times n$ zero-matrix, we define a $\mu \times n$ matrix

2.3.
$$S = \begin{bmatrix} s_\sigma \\ 0 \end{bmatrix}.$$

Then the relations 2.2 may be expressed in terms of matrices as follows:

2.4.
$$K = [a_\lambda] = [\theta_{\lambda\sigma} \ \ 0]S, \qquad L = [b_\lambda] = [\varphi_{\lambda\sigma} \ \ 0]S,$$

where the zeros denote $\mu \times (\mu - d)$ zero-matrices. Now the matrices $[\theta_{\lambda\sigma} \quad 0]$ and $[\varphi_{\lambda\sigma} \quad 0]$ must each have rank d. Otherwise, in fact, either the set $\{a_\lambda\}$ or the set $\{b_\lambda\}$ would have fewer than d independent vectors, and either K or L would have a row space of dimension less than d, which would be a contradiction. We may therefore choose $\mu - d$ columns $\theta_{\lambda\sigma'}$ and $\mu - d$ columns $\varphi_{\lambda\sigma'}$ $(\sigma' = d + 1, \ldots, \mu)$ in such a way that the matrices

2.5.
$$H = [\theta_{\lambda\sigma} \quad \theta_{\lambda\sigma'}], \qquad J = [\varphi_{\lambda\sigma} \quad \varphi_{\lambda\sigma'}]$$

are regular, for this step amounts merely to augmenting the d independent columns $\theta_{\lambda\sigma}$ and $\varphi_{\lambda\sigma}$, respectively, to form a basis for F_μ (cf. 5E1 ff.). It is now evident from 2.4 that

2.6.
$$K = HS, \qquad L = JS,$$

because, on account of the zeros in the last $\mu - d$ rows of S, the columns $\theta_{\lambda\sigma'}$ and $\varphi_{\lambda\sigma'}$ make no contribution, respectively, to K and L. Since H and J are regular $\mu \times \mu$ matrices, it follows that $K = HJ^{-1}L$, establishing (b) and completing the proof of 2.

Suppose now that M is a row-singular $\mu \times n$ matrix and that $JM = K$, where J is regular and K is the row-reduced echelon form of M. The last $\nu_R (= \mu - \rho)$ rows of K vanish. These rows are $r_\lambda M$ $(\lambda = \rho + 1, \ldots, \mu)$, where r_λ is the λth row vector of J. Since J is regular these ν_R rows are independent and therefore form a basis for the row nullspace of M.

2.7. If the $\mu \times n$ matrix M has row-nullity $\nu_R > 0$ and if $JM = K$, where J is regular and K is the row-reduced echelon form of M then the ν_R rows r_λ $(\lambda = \rho + 1, \ldots, \mu)$ of J form a basis for the row nullspace of M. If M is regular $(\mu = n, \nu_R = 0)$ then $K = I$ and $J = M^{-1}$.

Let us notice, finally, the application implied by theorem 2 of the idea of an equivalence relation developed in 4I. Row-equivalence of matrices is an equivalence relation. Reflexiveness is obvious, symmetry has already been observed, and transitivity is an evident consequence of, say, statement (b) of 2. From 4I2 it therefore follows that the set of all $\mu \times n$ matrices with elements in F is partitioned by the relation of row-equivalence into an exhaustive class of mutually exclusive nonvoid equivalence-sets. Statement (c) of 2 states that each equivalence-set contains precisely one row-reduced echelon matrix. Vice versa, given a $\mu \times n$ row-reduced echelon matrix R, a $\mu \times n$ matrix M is row-equivalent to R, i.e., is in the same equivalence-set as R, if and only if there is a regular $\mu \times \mu$ matrix J such that $M = JR$. The other conditions of 2 are also necessary and sufficient in order that K and L belong to the same equivalence-set.

Suppose now that any set S has been partitioned by an equivalence relation r, and that it is possible to specify in some entirely unambiguous (and otherwise useful) way a *unique* element in each equivalence-set. This unique element of an equivalence-set is said to be a *canonical representative* under the relation r, or, in the particular case of matrices, a *canonical form* (or *normal form*) under r for the other elements of the equivalence-set. In this terminology we may say that the canonical form of a $\mu \times n$ matrix L under row-equivalence is a $\mu \times n$ row-reduced echelon matrix R which is row-equivalent to L. The set of such matrices corresponds biuniquely with the class of equivalence-sets under the relation of row-equivalence; each equivalence-set contains precisely one row-reduced echelon matrix, to which every other matrix of the set is row-equivalent.

EXERCISES

3. Here are two row-equivalent matrices:

$$K = \begin{bmatrix} 2 & -3 & 7 & -11 \\ 3 & 1 & 5 & 0 \\ -2 & 1 & -5 & 5 \end{bmatrix}, \quad L = \begin{bmatrix} 4 & 2 & 6 & 2 \\ 2 & -2 & 6 & -8 \\ -3 & 3 & -9 & 12 \end{bmatrix}.$$

Find the equivalent row-reduced echelon matrix R and regular matrices H and J such that $K = HR$ and $L = JR$. Obtain a regular matrix M such that $K = ML$. Find a basis for the row space of K and L and a basis for their common column nullspace.

4. The rows of the matrix

$$H = \begin{bmatrix} 2 & 3 & -1 & 4 & -5 \\ 0 & -2 & 0 & 3 & -1 \end{bmatrix}$$

form a basis for the row space of the matrix

$$M = \begin{bmatrix} 4 & 0 & -2 & 17 & -13 \\ 8 & 14 & -4 & 13 & -19 \\ -4 & -10 & 2 & -2 & 8 \\ -2 & -9 & 1 & 5 & 2 \\ 6 & 19 & -3 & -3 & -10 \\ 2 & 7 & -1 & -2 & -3 \end{bmatrix}.$$

Find a 6×2 matrix J such that $M = JH$. Find also a regular 6×6 matrix K such that $M = KL$, where L is a 6×6 matrix whose first two rows are those of H and whose last four rows are zero.

5. Give a detailed proof of the assertion in the sentence following 1. (T)

G. A Pseudo-Inverse of a Matrix

In our study of singular transformations in 6E we were led to the notion of a pseudo-inverse of $L : X \rightarrow Y$. A $\mu \times n$ matrix L can be interpreted as the matrix of a mapping $L : X_n \rightarrow Y_\mu$. What shall we mean by a pseudo-inverse of a matrix?

It does not seem to be a simple matter to develop as satisfying a theory as that of 6E2 and 6E13–16. The difficulty may be in the fact that it is easy to speak of the restriction to LX of $M : Y \to X$, but if L is a matrix, then LX is not quite so explicitly available as might be desired for calculations with matrices. Nevertheless, useful results can be found.

We deal with a $\mu \times n$ matrix L of rank ρ. If M is to invert L in any way whatever, M must clearly be an $n \times \mu$ matrix. Motivated by 6E13, let us say that an $n \times \mu$ matrix M is a *pseudo-inverse* of a $\mu \times n$ matrix L if $LML = L$.

In order to take advantage of block multiplication (see 8C) we begin by rearranging rows and columns so that the first ρ rows are independent and the first ρ columns are independent. After that adjustment, which may require nontrivial calculations, the $\rho \times \rho$ matrix in the upper left corner is regular. The $\mu \times n$ matrix L may now be written as

1.
$$L = \begin{bmatrix} A_{\rho \times \rho} & B_{\rho \times v_C} \\ C_{v_R \times \rho} & D_{v_R \times v_C} \end{bmatrix}$$

where v_R and v_C are the row- and column-nullities.

The columns of the submatrix

2.
$$\begin{bmatrix} A \\ C \end{bmatrix}$$

generate the column space of L; the corresponding subspace of Y is $R_L = LX$. Similarly, the rows of the submatrix

3.
$$[A \quad B]$$

generate the row space of L; the corresponding subspace of X^d is $R_{L^d} = Y^d L^d$. Here, and in the sequel, we have introduced matrices of designated orders and have then omitted the orders when no confusion can ensue.

Since the last v_R rows of L are linear combinations of the rows of $[A \quad B]$, there exists a $v_R \times \rho$ matrix U such that

$$C = UA, \qquad D = UB.$$

On solving the first equation for U and substituting into the second we obtain the useful relation

4.
$$D = CA^{-1}B.$$

The same result can be obtained, of course, from the fact that the last v_C columns of L are linear combinations of the columns of 2.

Proceeding tentatively, let us consider an $n \times \mu$ matrix

5.
$$M = \begin{bmatrix} Q_{\rho \times \rho} & P_{\rho \times v_R} \\ S_{v_C \times \rho} & T_{v_C \times v_R} \end{bmatrix},$$

where Q, P, S, and T are matrices of the orders respectively indicated. Then we calculate

6.
$$ML = \begin{bmatrix} QA + PC & QB + PD \\ SA + TC & SB + TD \end{bmatrix}.$$

Since L is of rank ρ, ML will be in row-reduced echelon form only if

7. $$QA + PC = I_\rho, \qquad SA + TC = 0, \qquad SB + TD = 0.$$

These equations imply that

8. $$Q = A^{-1} - PCA^{-1}, \qquad S = -TCA^{-1}.$$

The converse is trivial; the verification uses 4.

9. Theorem. With L as in 1 and M as in 5, it is necessary and sufficient, in order that ML be in row-reduced echelon form, that equations 8 hold. If $P_{\rho \times \nu_R}$ and $T_{\nu_C \times \rho_R}$ are arbitrary matrices of the indicated orders and equations 8 hold, then the matrix

9.1. $$ML = \begin{bmatrix} A^{-1} - PCA^{-1} & P \\ -TCA^{-1} & T \end{bmatrix} \begin{bmatrix} A & B \\ C & D \end{bmatrix} = \begin{bmatrix} I_\rho & A^{-1}B \\ 0 & 0 \end{bmatrix}$$

is in row-reduced echelon form. Then, moreover, $LML = L$ and M is a pseudo-inverse of L.

As an example, let us use the matrix L of columns 4, 5, 6 of E5; we know that L has rank 2.

9.2. $$L = \begin{bmatrix} 1 & -1 & \vdots & 2 \\ 2 & 0 & \vdots & 1 \\ \cdots & \cdots & & \cdots \\ 3 & -1 & \vdots & 3 \end{bmatrix}, \qquad A = \begin{bmatrix} 1 & -1 \\ 2 & 0 \end{bmatrix}, \qquad A^{-1} = \tfrac{1}{2} \begin{bmatrix} 0 & 1 \\ -2 & 1 \end{bmatrix}.$$

With $P = [\alpha \quad \beta]^t$ and $T = [\gamma]$, we find

9.3. $$M = \begin{bmatrix} -\alpha & \tfrac{1}{2} - \alpha & \alpha \\ -1 - \beta & \tfrac{1}{2} - \beta & \beta \\ -\gamma & -\gamma & \gamma \end{bmatrix}.$$

It is easy to verify that, for any choices of α, β, and γ,

9.4. $$ML = \begin{bmatrix} 1 & 0 & \tfrac{1}{2} \\ 0 & 1 & -\tfrac{3}{2} \\ 0 & 0 & 0 \end{bmatrix}.$$

One verifies readily (cf. 9.1) that $A^{-1}B = [\tfrac{1}{2} \quad -\tfrac{3}{2}]^t$. We observe that M of 9.3 reduces to the matrix in columns 1, 2, 3 of E8 (or E9) if $\alpha = \beta = 0$ and $\gamma = 1$; then

9.5. $$M = \begin{bmatrix} 0 & \tfrac{1}{2} & 0 \\ -1 & \tfrac{1}{2} & 0 \\ -1 & 1 & 1 \end{bmatrix}.$$

The pseudo-inverse occurring in 9 is

10. $$M = \begin{bmatrix} A^{-1} - PCA^{-1} & P \\ -TCA^{-1} & T \end{bmatrix}.$$

If $\nu_R = 0$ then $\rho = \mu \, (\le n)$ and $L = [A \quad B]$; it follows that $P = T = 0$, and $M = [A^{-1} \quad 0_{\nu_C}]^t$.

If $v_C = 0$ then $\rho = n \leq \mu$ and $L = [A \quad C]^t$; it follows that $T = 0$, $M = [A^{-1} \quad -PCA^{-1} \quad P]$, and $ML = I_n$, so that M is a left-inverse of L (but not a right-inverse unless $\mu = n$).

If $v_R = v_C = 0$ then, of course, $L = A$ is regular, and $M = A^{-1}$.

It is obvious from 10 that, unless $\rho = \mu = n$, M is by no means unique. In the periodical literature, various further conditions are imposed on M in order to make it unique. Without going into this matter, let us observe that M can be made to have rank $\min(n, \mu)$ by choosing $P = 0$ and making T contain as a submatrix the identity of order $\min(v_R, v_C)$.

It would be comforting to know that if $LML = L$ then ML is in row-reduced echelon form. Unfortunately, this is not so; see 8.5.

In C we solved a system of linear equations $Lx = y$ by bringing them into a form (C6) from which a great deal of information could be read off at sight. Most of this information was listed in C7–11. Let us see how to formulate these results in terms of a pseudo-inverse of L. We use here *only* a pseudo-inverse M of the type given by 10; this M has, by 9, the important property that ML is in row-reduced echelon form. We continue to use as numerical examples the L of 9.2 and the (regular) M of 9.5.

The consistency condition of C7 takes here the form that $Lx = y$ is consistent if and only if My has 0 in rows $\rho + 1, \ldots, n$. In our example (cf. columns 7 and 8 of E5 and E8),

11.
$$\begin{bmatrix} 0 & \frac{1}{2} & 0 \\ -1 & \frac{1}{2} & 0 \\ -1 & 1 & 1 \end{bmatrix} \begin{bmatrix} 3 & 3 \\ 1 & 1 \\ 4 & 5 \end{bmatrix} = \begin{bmatrix} \frac{1}{2} & \frac{1}{2} \\ -\frac{5}{2} & -\frac{5}{2} \\ 0 & 1 \end{bmatrix}$$

(cf. columns 7 and 8 of E7); the conclusion is that if $y = [3 \quad 1 \quad 4]^t$, then the equations are consistent and $[\frac{1}{2} \quad -\frac{5}{2} \quad 0]^t$ is a solution, while if $y = [3 \quad 1 \quad 5]^t$, then the equations are inconsistent.

In the consistent case (C8) My is a solution; in 11, if $y = [3 \quad 1 \quad 4]^t$ then $My = [\frac{1}{2} \quad -\frac{5}{2} \quad 0]^t$ has the property that $L(My) = y$.

We can obtain all solutions of the homogeneous system (C10) if we can write down (C10.1) a basis for the column nullspace of L. Observe in 9.1 that $A^{-1}B$ is a $\rho \times v_C$ matrix. Define an $n \times v_C$ matrix

12.
$$N = \begin{bmatrix} -A^{-1}B \\ I_{v_C} \end{bmatrix}.$$

The columns of N are v_C independent vectors and $AN = 0$. It follows that the columns of N are a basis for the column nullspace of L. If $u = [\xi_1, \ldots, \xi_{v_C}]^t$, where the ξ's are scalar parameters, then the column nullspace is represented parametrically by $x = Nu$.

If the nonhomogeneous system $Lx = y$ is consistent, then (cf. C11) all solutions of the system are given by $x = My + Nu$, with N and u as in the preceding paragraph.

EXERCISES

13. Find a pseudo-inverse for the matrices of the systems of equations in C18. (Calculations from E10 may be useful.) Use each pseudo-inverse to investigate the consistency of the respective system and, in the consistent cases, to find a particular solution. Use the row-reduced echelon form of the matrix of the system to obtain a basis for the column nullspace of the matrix of the system. Finally, write down a parametric representation of the flat of all solutions.

14. With $a \in X^d$ and $b \in Y^d$, prove that the equation $a = bL^d$ is consistent if and only if $aN = 0$, with N as in 12. (*Hint:* See 7D6.2.)

15. *Inversion by Blocks.* Let A and D be regular matrices. With B and C of suitable orders, assume that

$$M = \begin{bmatrix} A & B \\ C & D \end{bmatrix}$$

is regular and consider the problem of finding M^{-1}. We try to determine P, Q, R, and S, of suitable orders, in such a way that

$$\begin{bmatrix} A & B \\ C & D \end{bmatrix}\begin{bmatrix} P & Q \\ R & S \end{bmatrix} = I.$$

By carrying out the multiplication on the left and equating blocks on left and right we arrive at four equations. Two of them yield

$$R = -D^{-1}CP, \qquad Q = -A^{-1}BS.$$

By substituting in an obvious way into the others we obtain

$$(A - BD^{-1}C)P = I, \qquad (D - CA^{-1}B)S = I.$$

From these equations we read off two conditions which are jointly necessary for M to be regular. If these conditions are met, conversely, then we are able to calculate P and S, and then R and Q, and hence to find M^{-1}. When would this process be computationally advantageous? (T)

H. Column-Equivalence of Matrices

In D–F we presented a discussion of elementary row operations on matrices and the accompanying idea of row-equivalence of matrices, culminating in theorem 9F2. Our preoccupation with row operations was occasioned by our interest in the equations $[L][x] = [y]$, where x and y were column vectors with n and μ components respectively. It was natural in that situation to investigate the effect of multiplying the matrix of the system of equations on the left by a matrix so constructed as to isolate as many components of x as possible.

Keeping $[L] = [\alpha_{\lambda k}]$ as a $\mu \times n$ matrix, suppose that we are now interested in the equations $[x][L] = [y]$, where x and y are *row* vectors with μ and n components, respectively. The accompanying scalar equations are these:

1. $$\sum \xi_\lambda \alpha_{\lambda k} = \eta_k \qquad (k = 1, \ldots, n).$$

The fully explicit form of these equations would state an equality between n-component row vectors:

2. $$[\textstyle\sum_\lambda \xi_\lambda \alpha_{\lambda 1}, \sum_\lambda \xi_\lambda \alpha_{\lambda 2}, \ldots, \sum_\lambda \xi_\lambda \alpha_{\lambda n}] = [\eta_1, \eta_2, \ldots, \eta_n].$$

For obvious practical reasons, however, we always *think* of equations 1 as written successively, one under the other, in an n-rowed column. We have agreed, at the same time, that in a matrix $[\gamma_{rc}]$ the r shall be the row index and the c the column index. For these two reasons (as well as the inertial reasons of wishing the "variable" (ξ_λ) to *follow* the "coefficient" ($\alpha_{\lambda k}$) and wishing coupled indices of summation to appear in close juxtaposition) we would write F1 as

3. $$\sum \beta_{k\lambda} \xi_\lambda = \eta_k \qquad (k = 1, \ldots, n),$$

where, for $k = 1, \ldots, n$ and $\lambda = 1, \ldots, \mu$, $\beta_{k\lambda} = \alpha_{\lambda k}$. An inspection of these matrices reveals at once, of course, that we have simply formed the transpose $L^t x^t = y^t$ of the original equations $xL = y$.

Now the theory of the *equations* (cf. 3)

4. $$\sum_{\lambda=1} \beta_{k\lambda} \xi_\lambda = \eta_k \ (k = 1, \ldots, n), \qquad [L]^t [x]^t = [y]^t$$

differs from that of C1 only in the interchange of the parameters μ and n; here there are n equations in μ unknowns. With this adjustment the entire theory of elementary row operations on *matrices*, row-equivalence, and canonical (row-reduced echelon) form can be applied to $[\beta_{k\lambda}] = L^t$ precisely as developed in D and F. An elementary row operation can be performed on L^t by multiplying it on the left by an appropriate elementary matrix as defined near the beginning of D; more generally, if M is any regular $n \times n$ matrix then L^t and ML^t are row-equivalent.

Since $(ML^t)^t = LM^t$, and row operations on L^t amount to column operations on L, it comes as no surprise that there is a theory of elementary column operations on matrices, column-equivalence, and column-reduced echelon form similar in every respect to the theory developed in D and F.

There is one difference. There an elementary row operation on L was accomplished by multiplying L on the left (or *pre*-multiplying) by an elementary matrix; we now refer to the elementary matrices of D as elementary row matrices. The elementary column operations (permutation of columns, multiplying a column by a constant, and adding to a column a linear combination of the other columns) can be performed on L by multiplying L on the right (or *post*-multiplying) by a product of elementary column matrices; these we proceed to define.

Let I denote the $k \times k$ identity matrix. Let $J_{i,k}$ denote the result of interchanging columns i and k in I. Let $J_{\gamma \cdot i}$ denote the result of multiplying column i by γ. Let $J_{\gamma \cdot i + k}$ denote the result of multiplying column i by and adding it to column k. Matrices obtained in this way are elementary column matrices.

With this technicality on the record the reader should encounter no difficulty in developing for himself a complete theory analogous to that of D and F. When seeking guidance from systems of equations, he may either look at 4 and take transposes, or look directly at 2 as written (equality between row vectors) and imitate the process of elimination (cf. B and C) as it would be carried out on 2. For later reference we list one result.

4.1. *Two $\mu \times n$ matrices $[L]$ and $[L]'$ are column-equivalent if and only if there exists a regular $n \times n$ matrix $[M]$ such that $[L]' = [L][M]$.*

Column operations can be used, naturally enough, to arrive at a pseudo-inverse of L. An argument analogous to that which yielded G9 and G12 yields the following theorem; we omit details.

5. Theorem. Let the $\mu \times n$ matrix L, of rank ρ, have the form (cf. G1)

$$L = \begin{bmatrix} A_{\rho \times \rho} & B_{\rho \times \nu_C} \\ C_{\nu_R \times \rho} & D_{\nu_R \times \nu_C} \end{bmatrix},$$

where A is regular and ν_R and ν_C are the row-nullity and column-nullity of L. Let $J_{\nu_C \times \rho}$ and $K_{\nu_C \times \nu_R}$ be arbitrary matrices of the indicated orders, and define

$$N = \begin{bmatrix} A^{-1} - A^{-1}BJ & -A^{-1}BK \\ J & K \end{bmatrix},$$

then

$$LN = \begin{bmatrix} I & 0 \\ CA^{-1} & 0 \end{bmatrix}$$

is in column-reduced echelon form, and $LNL = L$. Moreover, the rows of

$$H = [-CA^{-1} \quad I_{\nu_R}]$$

are a basis for the row nullspace of L.

EXERCISES

6. (a) Suppose that $\mu = n$, whence $I_\mu = I_n$. Use the definitions of elementary row matrices given in 4.1 and the definitions of elementary column matrices just given to prove that: (i) $I_{\kappa,\lambda} = J_{\kappa,\lambda}$; (ii) $I_{\gamma \cdot \kappa} = J_{\gamma \cdot \kappa}$; (iii) $I_{\gamma \cdot \kappa + \lambda} = J_{\gamma \cdot \lambda + \kappa}$. Use these results to prove that each elementary column matrix is regular.

(b) Prove directly from its definition that each elementary column matrix is regular.

7. Follow through the reduction by column operations of the transpose of the matrix L of F3. (Note that the first three *rows* now constitute I_3 and that there is a check-*row* at the bottom.)

8. Show that each elementary column operation on a $\mu \times n$ matrix L may be performed by calculating LE where E is the result of performing the operation in question on I_n. (T)

9. Perform an opportunistic column reduction of the matrix

$$J = \begin{bmatrix} 2 & 3 & -2 \\ -3 & 1 & 1 \\ 7 & 5 & -5 \\ -11 & 0 & 5 \end{bmatrix}.$$

10. State and prove a theorem on column-equivalence analogous to F2.

11. Are an elementary column operation and an elementary rwo operation on the same matrix necessarily commutative?

12. What will a matrix look like if it is both a row-reduced echelon matrix and a column-reduced echelon matrix?

13. Let R be in row-reduced echelon form. What further simplifications can be brought about by elementary column operations on R?

14. Let us say that an operation is an *elementary operation* if it is either an elementary row operation or an elementary column operation, and that two matrices are *equivalent* if one can be produced from the other by a finite sequence of elementary operations. Prove that two $\mu \times n$ matrices J and L are equivalent if and only if there are a regular $\mu \times \mu$ matrix K and a regular $n \times n$ matrix M such that $J = KLM$. Show that equivalence between matrices is an equivalence relation. What is the canonical form of a $\mu \times n$ matrix under this relation of equivalence? (T)

15. Interpret column operations on the $\mu \times n$ matrix K in terms of algebraic operations on the system of μ equations in n unknowns for which K is the coefficient matrix. (i.e., as changes of variable).

16. In the context of 5, prove that the equation $Lx = y$ is consistent if and only if $Hy = 0$, with H as in 5. (*Hint:* See 7D6.3.) (T)

I. Equivalence of Matrices

Let us start with a mapping $L : X_n \to Y_\mu$, $x \to Lx = y$, whose equations with respect to given bases in X and Y are (cf. A1 and A2)

1.
$$_k\sum_1^n \alpha_{\lambda k}\xi_k = \eta_\lambda \qquad (\lambda = 1, \dots, \mu)$$

or

1.1.
$$[L][\xi_k]^t = [\eta_\lambda]^t.$$

The effect on $[L]$ of changes of bases in X and Y is described in 8F6. In the present chapter we have regarded 1 as equations with η_λ given and ξ_k sought. Our present aim is to show that the methods developed to solve the equations amount to finding bases in which the equations take on an entirely transparent form.

2. **New Basis in the Domain.** Suppose that the coordinates ξ_k in the domain are replaced by coordinates ξ'_k, where

2.1.
$$[\xi_k]^t = [N][\xi'_k]^t,$$

and $[N]$ is a regular $n \times n$ matrix. Then the equation becomes

2.2.
$$[L][N][\xi_k']^t = [L]'[\xi_k']^t = [\eta_\lambda]^t,$$
where

2.3.
$$[L]' = [L][N].$$

It follows by H4.1 that $[L]$ and $[L]'$ are column-equivalent. Conversely, if 2.3 holds, and ξ_k and ξ_k' are related to each other by 2.1, then it follows from 1.1 that the transformation whose matrix is $[L]$ when the coordinates are ξ_k has the matrix $[L]'$ when the coordinates are ξ_k'. Hence, briefly [cf. 4.1(c) below]:

2.4. *Two distinct $\mu \times n$ matrices are column-equivalent if and only if they express the same transformation with respect to different bases in the domain.*

3. New Basis in the Codomain. In 9F2 we gave the equations 1.1 an advantageous form, namely 9C6, by multiplying on the left by an appropriate regular $\mu \times \mu$ matrix K (called M in 9F2). The result may be expressed as follows:

3.1.
$$[K][L][\xi_k]^t = [L]'[\xi_k]^t$$
$$= [K][\eta_\lambda]^t = [\eta_\lambda']^t,$$
where

3.2.
$$[K][L] = [L]' \quad \text{and} \quad [K][\eta_\lambda]^t = [\eta_\lambda']^t.$$

The latter equations amount to a change of coordinates in the codomain:

3.3.
$$[\eta_\lambda]^t = [K]^{-1}[\eta_\lambda']^t.$$

Conversely, if a transformation L is expressed, using $[L]$, by 1.1 when coordinates η_λ are used in Y, then by virtue of 3.2 and 3.1 L has matrix $[L]'$ when new coordinates η_λ' are introduced into Y by equations 3.3. Briefly [cf. 4.1(c) below]:

3.4. *Two distinct $\mu \times n$ matrices are row-equivalent if and only if they express the same transformation with respect to different bases in the codomain.*

4. New Bases in Both Domain and Codomain. The notion of equivalent matrices was introduced in H14. We present now a theorem analogous to F2.

4.1. Theorem. Let $H = [\alpha_{\lambda k}]$ and $L = [\beta_{\lambda k}]$ be two $\mu \times n$ matrices. The following statements are equivalent:

(a) H and L are equivalent;

(b) There exist a regular $\mu \times \mu$ matrix K and a regular $n \times n$ matrix N such that $H = KLN$;

(c) If coordinates ξ_k and ξ_k' in X are related by the equations $\xi_k = \sum \nu_{kh}\xi_h'$, where $N = [\nu_{kh}]$, and coordinates η_λ and η_λ' in Y are related by the equations $\eta_\lambda = \sum \kappa_{\lambda\sigma}^{-1}\eta_\sigma'$, where $K^{-1} = [\kappa_{\lambda\sigma}^{-1}]$, then the mapping $X \to Y$ given by the equations $\eta_\lambda = \sum \beta_{\lambda k}\xi_k$ is the same as the mapping $X \to Y$ given by the equations $\eta_\lambda' = \sum \alpha_{\lambda k}\xi_k'$;

(d) H and L have the same rank, say ρ;

(e) H and L are both equivalent to the matrix

4.2.
$$J_{\mu,n,\rho} = \begin{bmatrix} I_\rho & 0_{\rho\times(n-\rho)} \\ 0_{(\mu-\rho)\times\rho} & 0_{(\mu-\rho)\times(n-\rho)} \end{bmatrix}.$$

The equivalence of (a) and (b) was established in H14.

Now assume (b) and suppose that $x = [\xi_k]^t \to [\eta_\lambda]^t = Lx$ where $\eta_\lambda = \sum \beta_{\lambda k}\xi_k$. Then, in the new coordinates, $x = [\xi_k']^t$, $\xi_k = \sum \nu_{ki}\xi_i'$, and

$$\xi_k = \sum \nu_{ki}\xi_i' \to \sum \beta_{\lambda k}\nu_{ki}\xi_i' = \eta_\lambda = \sum \kappa_{\lambda\sigma}^{-1}\eta_\sigma'.$$

If $K = [\kappa_{\sigma\lambda}]$ then
$$\eta_\sigma' = \sum \kappa_{\sigma\lambda}\beta_{\lambda k}\nu_{ki}\xi_i'.$$

Since $H = KLN$ we see that

$$x = [\xi_i']^t \to y = [\eta_\sigma']^t = KLNx = Hx,$$

whence, as transformations on X into Y, $H = L$. (We have here a partial converse of 8F6.)

Since the transformations H and L have the same range, the matrices H and L have the same rank ρ. Thus (c) implies (d).

Since both row and column operations are allowable, each of H and L is equivalent to some matrix of the form given in 4.2. Having the same rank ρ, they are both equivalent to $J_{\mu,n,\rho}$.

If now $J_{\mu,n,\rho} = PHQ = RLT$ where P and R are regular $\mu \times \mu$ matrices, and Q and T are regular $n \times n$ matrices, then $H = P^{-1}RLTQ^{-1}$. Thus (e) implies (b) and the proof of 4.1 is complete.

The form $J_{\mu,n,\rho}$ of 4.2 is a canonical form for $\mu \times n$ matrices under the relation of equivalence. It is important to recognize that equivalence, as defined in H14, means row- and column-equivalence, for both row operations and column operations are permitted in arriving at $J_{\mu,n,\rho}$. Equivalent matrices in general, are not row-equivalent and, in general, they are not column-equivalent. The relation of equivalence is weaker, so to speak, than either row-equivalence or column-equivalence separately; there are fewer equivalence-sets under equivalence than under row-equivalence or under column-equivalence, but each equivalence-set is larger. Since the equivalence-sets correspond biuniquely with the canonical forms, and since the distinct canonical forms are $J_{\mu,n,\rho}$ for $\rho = 0, 1, \ldots,$ min (μ, n), we see that *there are* $1 +$ min (μ, n) *equivalence-sets of $\mu \times n$ matrices under equivalence.*

It is clear from 4.1(c) that, as we have often insisted, we must distinguish clearly between a transformation L and its matrix $[L]$ with reference to fixed bases in the domain and codomain. To say that any two *transformations* $X_n \to Y_\mu$ of rank ρ are necessarily the same is patently absurd. If *matrices* H and L have the same rank, however, then there *exist* pairs of bases [by 4.1(c)], referred to which the transformations expressed in those bases by H and L are indeed the same.

232

The connection between equivalence of matrices and solution of equations is evident from an inspection of $J_{\mu,n,\rho}$. If the matrix of 4.1 is equivalent to $J_{\mu,n,\rho}$, and the new coordinates are ξ'_k and η'_λ, then the new equations are (cf. 9C6)

4.3. $$\xi'_\lambda = \eta'_\lambda \ (\lambda = 1, \ldots, \rho), \qquad 0 = \eta'_\lambda \ (\lambda = \rho + 1, \ldots, \mu);$$

in the consistent case the solutions are stated explicitly by these equations.

EXERCISES

5. Reduce each of the following matrices L to the equivalent canonical form $J_{\mu,n,\rho}$, finding in each case matrices K and M such that $KLM = J$.

(a) $L = \begin{bmatrix} 6 & 1 & 2 & 9 \\ 1 & 5 & -2 & 4 \\ 3 & -2 & 4 & 4 \\ 2 & 3 & 2 & 8 \end{bmatrix}$,

(b) $L = \begin{bmatrix} 3-i & 2+i & -4+3i \\ i & 2 & -1-i \\ 2+i & -i & 3 \\ 1-2i & 2+3i & 4i \end{bmatrix}$,

(c) $L = \begin{bmatrix} 2 & -2 & 3 \\ -4 & 1 & -1 \\ 0 & 2 & 5 \\ -3 & -1 & 4 \end{bmatrix}$.

6. Consider equations 4.3 in the consistent case ($\eta'_\lambda = 0$ for $\lambda = \rho + 1, \ldots, \mu$). They appear to have a unique solution. How is this "unique" solution related to the problem of solving 1? Find all other solutions by finding a basis for the null-space of $J_{\mu,n,\rho}$. (T)

7. In R_4 let the subspace U be generated by vectors $[1 \ \ -1 \ \ 2 \ \ 3]^t, [-3 \ \ 2 \ \ 0 \ \ -1]^t$, and $[2 \ \ -3 \ \ 1 \ \ -2]^t$, and let the subspace V be generated by $[4 \ \ 1 \ \ -1 \ \ -2]^t$ and $[-3 \ \ 2 \ \ 3 \ \ -1]^t$. Find bases for U, V, $U \cap V$, and $U + V$.

8. Prove that a $\mu \times n$ matrix L has rank at most 1 if and only if $L = [\alpha_\lambda]^t[\beta_k]$, where $\lambda = 1, \ldots, \mu$ and $k = 1, \ldots, n$. (See 8D23; try to devise a different proof.)

9. Let us say that $\mu \times n$ matrices K and L are in the relation r to each other if they are both row-equivalent and column-equivalent to each other. Is r an equivalence relation? If so, what are the canonical forms under r? (T)

10. We are interested in the equations $Tx = y$, where

$$x = [t \ \ u \ \ v \ \ w]^t, \qquad y = [8\alpha \ \ 4\beta \ \ 8\gamma \ \ 8\delta]^t,$$

where α, β, γ, and δ are scalars, and

$$T = \begin{bmatrix} 1 & 2 & 3 & 4 \\ 5 & 6 & 7 & 8 \\ 7 & 6 & 5 & 4 \\ 3 & 2 & 1 & 0 \end{bmatrix}.$$

(a) Use row operations on the 4×9 matrix $J = [I_4 \quad T \quad y]$ to reduce T to row-reduced echelon form, denoted by U.

(b) Under what conditions are the equations consistent?

(c) Write down a basis for the column nullspace of T.

(d) Assuming that the equations are consistent, write down all solutions.

(e) Find a regular matrix Q such that $U = QT$.

(f) Write down a basis for the rownullspace of T.

(g) Find a regular matrix R such that $UR = T_c$, where T_c is the canonical form of T under equivalence.

TEN

Bilinear and Quadratic Functionals and Forms

In Chap. 7 we discussed linear functionals $f : X \to F_1$, where $\{X, +; F, \cdot\}$ is a linear space over the field F. A linear functional is a scalar-valued linear function of a single variable vector x with domain X.

In geometry, mechanics, statistics, and many other areas we must deal with scalar-valued functions, called functionals, depending on two or more variable vectors. In this chapter we present basic facts regarding functionals of two vectors which develop in a natural way from ideas similar to those of the preceding chapter. Results obtained here will be useful in Chaps. 13 and 14.

A. Bilinear Forms; Congruent Matrices

The domain of a function of two vectors must be the Cartesian product of two linear spaces. Let us suppose that we are working with linear spaces X_n and Y_μ over the same field. We fix notation as follows, with $k = 1, \ldots, n$ and $\lambda = 1, \ldots, \mu$:

	Space	X	X^d	Y	Y^d
0.	Basis	p_k	f_k	q_λ	g_λ
	Coordinates	ξ_k	φ_κ	η_λ	ψ_λ.

The bases $\{p_k\}$ and $\{f_k\}$ are dual; so are $\{q_\lambda\}$ and $\{g_\lambda\}$. Hence

1.
$$f_k p_h = \delta_{kh}, \qquad g_\kappa q_\lambda = \delta_{\kappa\lambda}.$$

For the sake of notational advantages, which will soon become apparent, we choose to define functionals first on $Y^d \times X$. A functional $b : Y^d \times X \to F$ is said to be *bilinear* if, for each $g, g' \in Y^d$, $x, x' \in X$, and $\alpha, \alpha' \in F$, it is true that

2.
$$b(\alpha g + \alpha' g', x) = \alpha b(g, x) + \alpha' b(g', x),$$

3.
$$b(g, \alpha x + \alpha' x') = \alpha b(g, x) + \alpha' b(g, x').$$

In other words, with either of its variables fixed, $b(g, x)$ is a linear functional of the other.

Using coordinates as in 0, and equations 2 and 3, we obtain an expression for $b(h, x)$ when $h = \sum \psi_\lambda g_\lambda$ and $x = \sum \xi_k p_k$.

4.
$$b(h, x) = b(\sum \psi_\lambda g_\lambda, \sum \xi_k p_k) = \sum \psi_\lambda b(g_\lambda, p_k) \xi_k$$
$$= \sum \psi_\lambda \beta_{\lambda k} \xi_k = [\psi_\lambda][\beta_{\lambda k}][\xi_k]^t$$
$$= [h][b][x],$$

where

5.
$$[b] = [\beta_{\lambda k}]$$

is a $\mu \times n$ matrix with

6.
$$\beta_{\lambda k} = b(g_\lambda, p_k) \qquad (\lambda = 1, \ldots, \mu; k = 1, \ldots, n).$$

An expression such as $\sum \psi_\lambda \beta_{\lambda k} \xi_k$ is called a *bilinear form*. The matrix of 5 is the matrix of the form. It is evident that b determines $[b]$ uniquely by 6.

Vice versa, always referred to given bases as in 0, a $\mu \times n$ matrix $[\beta_{\lambda k}]$ determines a form $\sum \psi_\lambda \beta_{\lambda k} \xi_k$ and it is easy to see that, with either the ψ's or the ξ's fixed, the value β of the form depends linearly on the other variables. We have here a means of assigning a number $\beta = \sum \psi_\lambda \beta_{\lambda k} \xi_k$ to each ordered pair (h, x), where $h = \sum \psi_\lambda g_\lambda \in Y^d$ and $x = \sum \xi_k p_k \in X$. If we agree that the same number shall be assigned to (h, x) regardless of the coordinate system (and we shall see very soon how to arrange this) then we have a bilinear functional $b : Y^d \times X$, where $(h, x) \rightarrow b(h, x) = \beta$. These results are a natural extension of the Basic Principle of 6G2.

7. Theorem. In the presence of bases, as in 0, there is a biunique correspondence between bilinear functionals $b : Y_\mu^d \times X_n \rightarrow F$, $\mu \times n$ matrices, and bilinear forms, as follows:

$$b : Y_\mu^d \times X_n \rightarrow F \qquad\qquad (h, x) \rightarrow b(h, x)$$
$$\updownarrow \qquad\qquad\qquad\qquad \updownarrow$$
$$\mu \times n \text{ matrix} \qquad\qquad [\beta_{\lambda k}]$$
$$\updownarrow \qquad\qquad\qquad\qquad \updownarrow$$
$$\text{bilinear form} \qquad\qquad \sum \psi_\lambda \beta_{\lambda k} \xi_k,$$

where $\beta_{\lambda k} = b(g_\lambda, p_k)$.

As a consequence of this theorem, it makes no essential difference whether we speak of a bilinear "functional" or "form". Conventional usage favors "form", and we accept this convention.

Suppose now that new bases are introduced in such a way that

8.
$$[\xi_k]^t = [T][\xi_k']^t, \qquad [\eta_\lambda]^t = [U][\eta_\lambda']^t.$$

We then know from 7B5 that $[\psi_\lambda] = [\psi_\lambda'][U]^{-1}$. It follows that

9.
$$b(h, x) = [\psi_\lambda][b][\xi_k]^t$$
$$= [\psi_\lambda'][U]^{-1}[b][T][\xi_k']^t$$
$$= [\psi_\lambda'][b]'[\xi_k']^t,$$

where

10.
$$[b]' = [U]^{-1}[b][T].$$

11. Theorem. If new (primed) coordinates are introduced as in 8, then the matrix $[b]$ of the bilinear form b is replaced by the matrix $[b]'$ of 10.

Since $[T]$ and $[U]$ are regular, 9I4.1 yields more. We may define the *rank* of a bilinear form to be the rank of its matrix.

12. Corollary. Two $\mu \times n$ matrices are equivalent if and only if they are matrices in their respective coordinate systems of the same bilinear form on some $V_\mu \times W_n$.

13. Corollary. If $b : Y_\mu^d \times X_n \to F$ is of rank ρ then coordinates can be chosen so that its matrix in those coordinates is the matrix $J_{\mu,n,\rho}$ of 9I4.2; in those coordinate systems

13.1
$$b(h, x) = [\psi_\lambda] J [\xi_k]^t = {}_j\sum_1^\rho \psi_j \xi_j.$$

The form 13.1 is therefore the canonical form for a bilinear form of rank ρ on $Y_\mu^d \times X$ under equivalence.

The foregoing discussion can be specialized easily to the case in which $Y = X$. Then $b : X^d \times X \to F$, where $(f, x) \to b(f, x)$, is associated with the form

$$[f][b][x] = [\varphi_k][b][\xi_k]^t = \sum \varphi_j \beta_{jk} \xi_k.$$

When variables are changed as in 8, $[b]$ is replaced (cf. 10) by

14.
$$[b]' = [T]^{-1}[b][T].$$

Square matrices related to each other by 14 are said to be *similar*. See the remark following 8F6 and Chaps. 12 and 14.

Our choice of $Y^d \times X$ as the domain for b led to the harmonious result $b(h, x) = [h][b][x]$; here $[h]$ is a row vector and $[x]$ is a column vector. The scalar product in E_P of Chap. 3, however, is a bilinear form on $E_P \times E_P$ (see 3I), and in Chaps. 13–14 we shall discuss spaces X_n on which a scalar product is defined.

A functional $b : X \times X \to F$ is said to be *bilinear* if for each $x, y \in X$, $b(y, x)$ is linear in x if y is fixed and linear in y if x is fixed; that is, 2 and 3 hold with g and g' replaced by y and y'. Such a form is said, loosely and briefly, to be a "bilinear form on X"; its matrix is obviously square. In 0 we replace Y by X and $\{q_\lambda\}$ by $\{p_k\}$. A calculation like that in 4 then yields

15.
$$b(y, x) = b(\sum \eta_j p_j, \sum \xi_k p_k) = \sum \eta_j b(p_j, p_k) \xi_k$$
$$= \sum \eta_j \beta_{jk} \xi_k = [\eta_j][\beta_{jk}][\xi_k]^t$$
$$= [y]^t[b][x],$$

where

16.
$$[b] = [\beta_{jk}]$$

is an $n \times n$ matrix with

17. $$\beta_{jk} = b(p_j, p_k).$$

Results such as 7 are obtained easily; we forego details. There is a significant difference, however, when coordinates are changed. If (cf. 8)

18. $$[x] = [\xi_k]^t = [T][\xi_k']^t,$$

then

19. $$[y]^t = [\eta_j] = [\eta_j'][T]^t,$$

and, after substitution into 15, we find (cf. 10, 11, and 14) that

20. $$[b]' = [T]^t[b][T].$$

Square matrices related to each other by 20 with T regular are said to be *congruent*. The result corresponding to 12 is that two $n \times n$ matrices are congruent if and only if they are matrices in their respective coordinate systems of the same bilinear form on some X_n.

Congruence of matrices is easily seen to be an equivalence relation. When we seek a canonical form under congruence, however, the situation is by no means as simple as it was for equivalence of matrices ($L' = KLN$, K and N regular) in 9I4.1. The reason is that operating on $[b]$ by $[T]^t[b][T]$ is much more restricted than multiplying $[b]$ on the left and right by unrelated matrices. If, as in 9I2, we interpret the operation $[b] \rightarrow [b][T]$ as a sequence of column operations on $[b]$, then in $[T]^t[b][T]$ we will have to perform on $[b]$ not only the column operations expressed by $[T]$ but, simultaneously, precisely the corresponding row operations. In the 2×2 case, for example, suppose that we are to double the first column and add it to the second. Then $[T] = \begin{bmatrix} 1 & 2 \\ 0 & 1 \end{bmatrix}$ and

$$[T]^t \begin{bmatrix} \alpha & \beta \\ \gamma & \delta \end{bmatrix}[T] = \begin{bmatrix} 1 & 0 \\ 2 & 1 \end{bmatrix}\begin{bmatrix} \alpha & \beta \\ \gamma & \delta \end{bmatrix}\begin{bmatrix} 1 & 2 \\ 0 & 1 \end{bmatrix} = \begin{bmatrix} \alpha & 2\alpha + \beta \\ 2\alpha + \gamma & 4\alpha + 2\beta + 2\gamma + \delta \end{bmatrix};$$

here $[T]^t$ has forced us to double the first row and add it to the second.

It is fortunate that most bilinear forms $b : X \times X \rightarrow F$ of practical importance are either symmetric or antisymmetric (skew). A bilinear form $b : X \times X \rightarrow F$ is said to be *symmetric* if

21. $$b(y, x) = b(x, y),$$

and to be *antisymmetric* (*skew*) if

22. $$b(y, x) = -b(x, y).$$

We verify easily (cf. 8E) that b is symmetric if and only if $[b]$ is symmetric (that is, $[b]^t = [b]$), and that b is skew if and only if $[b]$ is skew (that is, $[b]^t = -[b]$). Also, as in 8E1, every bilinear form is the sum of a symmetric bilinear form and a skew bilinear form. In fact,

23.
$$b(y, x) = \tfrac{1}{2}[b(y, x) + b(x, y)] + \tfrac{1}{2}[b(y, x) - b(x, y)]$$
$$= b_s(y, x) + b_a(y, x),$$

where

24.
$$b_s(y, x) = \tfrac{1}{2}[b(y, x) + b(x, y)] = b_s(x, y)$$

is symmetric, and

25.
$$b_a(y, x) = \tfrac{1}{2}[b(y, x) - b(x, y)] = -b_a(x, y)$$

is antisymmetric. The forms b_s and b_a are called, respectively, the *symmetric part* of b and the *skew part* of b; their uniqueness is easily established.

For the remainder of this section we will be dealing with matrices. Let us write B for $[b]$ and omit the brackets from the matrix of the coordinate transformation. That symmetry and antisymmetry are invariant under congruence (or change of basis) follows from the equations

26.
$$(T^tBT)^t = T^tB^tT = \pm T^tBT,$$

where the upper sign applies to the symmetric case and the lower to the skew case.

The skew case is the simpler. For the time being, let us assume that $B^t = -B \neq 0$. The jth row vector is then the negative of the jth column vector. Moreover, $\beta_{ii} = -\beta_{ii} = 0$; each diagonal element is 0. The cases $n = 1, 2$ being trivial, let us assume that $n \geq 3$.

If the entire first row is zero, then so is the entire first column, and we may deal with a matrix of order $n - 1$ instead of n. Assume, therefore, that the first row has a nonvanishing element β_{1k_0}. Divide the first row and the first column by β_{1k_0}. If $k_0 \neq 2$, interchange the second and k_0th columns and the second and k_0th rows. The result has this appearance:

27.
$$\begin{bmatrix} E & A \\ -A^t & C \end{bmatrix}, \qquad E = \begin{bmatrix} 0 & 1 \\ -1 & 0 \end{bmatrix},$$

where A is a $2 \times (n - 2)$ matrix and C is an $(n - 2) \times (n - 2)$ skew matrix. Now use the $+1$ in E to eliminate the first row of A and the second column of A^t. Then use the -1 in E to eliminate the first column of $-A^t$ and the second row of A. The result is the matrix 27 with A and A^t replaced by zero-matrices. Since the row and column operations are clearly the same, the result is congruent to B. Moreover C is still skew.

If $C = 0$ now, we stop. If $C \neq 0$, then we proceed in the same way with it. Note that if n is odd, $n = 2m + 1$, then $C = 0$ after at most m E's have appeared on the diagonal. Then, in fact, $A = 0$ and C is a single scalar γ; being a diagonal element of a one-element skew matrix, $\gamma = 0$.

28. Theorem. If B is an $n \times n$ skew matrix, then B is congruent to
$$B' = [[E_1, \ldots, E_s, 0]],$$
where for $q = 1, \ldots, s$, $E_q = E$ of 27, and 0 denotes the square zero-matrix of order $n - 2s$; the rank of B is $2s$.

The matrix B' of 28 is a canonical form under congruence for skew matrices of order n and rank $\rho = 2s$. The order and (even) rank determine the canonical form uniquely. Every skew matrix of order n and rank $2s$ is congruent to B' and to every other skew matrix of order n and rank $2s$. It follows that every skew bilinear form of order n and rank $2s$ can be reduced, by a proper choice of coordinates, to the form

29.
$$\eta_1\xi_2 - \eta_2\xi_1 + \eta_3\xi_4 - \eta_4\xi_3 + -\ldots + \eta_{2s-1}\xi_{2s} - \eta_{2s}\xi_{2s-1}.$$

By an appropriate permutation of the columns, followed by the same permutation of the rows, and, therefore, by a further congruence operation, B' can be given the form

30.
$$B'' = \begin{bmatrix} 0 & I_s & 0 \\ -I_s & 0 & 0 \\ 0 & 0 & 0 \end{bmatrix},$$

where the 0's designate zero-matrices of certain obvious orders. The matrix B'' may also be regarded as a canonical form under congruence for a skew matrix of order n and rank $2s$. Whether B' or B'' is "the" canonical form will depend on convenience.

The symmetric case is more complicated. We now assume that $B^t = B \neq 0$, i.e., that $\beta_{ji} = \beta_{ij}$ for $i, j = 1, \ldots, n$.

If $\beta_{11} \neq 0$ then we use column operations to eliminate $\beta_{12}, \ldots, \beta_{1n}$, and the same row operations to eliminate $\beta_{21}, \ldots, \beta_{n1}$. The result is a matrix

31.
$$B_1 = \begin{bmatrix} \beta_1 & 0 \\ 0 & C_1 \end{bmatrix},$$

where $\beta_1 = \beta_{11}$, C_1 is an $(n - 1) \times (n - 1)$ symmetric matrix and the zero-matrices are of the correct order; B_1 is congruent to B.

If $\beta_{11} = 0$ but some diagonal element $\beta_{jj} \neq 0$ then we interchange columns j and 1, and rows j and 1, and arrive at the situation just treated. If $\beta_{jj} = 0$ $(j = 1, \ldots, n)$ but $\beta_{j_0 k_0} \neq 0$, then we add column k_0 to column j_0 and row k_0 to row j_0; the *new* $\beta_{j_0 j_0} \neq 0$, and we move it to the upper left corner and proceed as before. In either case the adjusted matrix is congruent to B.

If $C_1 = 0$ in 31, we stop. Otherwise, we proceed with C, as we did with B. The process terminates with the diagonal matrix

32.
$$B_\rho = [[\beta_1, \ldots, \beta_\rho, 0, \ldots, 0]],$$

where ρ is the rank of B, none of the β's vanishes, and there are $n - \rho$ zeros.

We resisted the temptation at the outset to divide the first row by β_{11} in order to secure a 1 in the upper left corner; congruence would have required us to divide the first column also by β_{11}, resulting in β_{11}^{-1} in the upper left corner. But why not use $\sqrt{\beta_{11}}$? It will not be real unless β_{11} is real and non-negative. The situations in R and C are different.

In C, $\sqrt{\beta_{11}}$ is always available and we may use it to make $\beta_1 = 1$ in 31 and at the upper left corners of succeeding submatrices $C_1, \ldots$. Or, we may obtain the same result by multiplying B_ρ of 32 on the left and right by

$$[[\beta_1^{-1/2}, \beta_2^{-1/2}, \ldots, \beta_\rho^{-1/2}, 1_{\rho+1}, \ldots, 1_n]].$$

33. Theorem. An $n \times n$ symmetric complex matrix of rank ρ is congruent to the diagonal matrix

$$[[1_1, \ldots, 1_\rho, 0_{\rho+1}, \ldots, 0_n]].$$

It follows that a symmetric complex bilinear form can be reduced, by a proper choice of coordinates, to the form

34.
$$_k\sum_1^\rho \eta_k \xi_k.$$

The diagonal matrix of 33 and the form of 34 are canonical forms under congruence of $n \times n$ symmetric complex matrices and forms of rank ρ.

If we are working in R, which is ordered, let us go back to 32 and arrange things, by a permutation of columns and the same permutation of rows, so that (after restoring β_k as the symbols for the diagonal elements)

$$\beta_1 \geq \beta_2 \geq \ldots \geq \beta_\rho.$$

There will be a least positive β (perhaps β_ρ) and a greatest negative β (perhaps β_1); none can vanish, of course. For $j = 1, \ldots, \rho$ let us write $\pi_j = |\beta_j|$; then $\pi_j > 0$. If $p (\leq \rho)$ of the β's are positive, then the rearranged form of B_ρ has this appearance:

$$[[\pi_1, \ldots, \pi_p, -\pi_{p+1}, \ldots, -\pi_\rho, 0_{\rho+1}, \ldots, 0_n]].$$

We now multiply this matrix on the left and right by

$$[[\pi_1^{-1/2}, \ldots, \pi_\rho^{-1/2}, 1_{\rho+1}, \ldots, 1_n]]$$

and arrive at a diagonal matrix with p plus ones, followed by $\rho - p$ minus ones, followed by $n - \rho$ zeros.

The difference $s = p - (\rho - p) = 2p - \rho$ between the number of plus ones and the number of minus ones is called the *signature* (or *inertial index*) of B. It is evident that s and p determine each other uniquely. The integer $s + \rho$ is always even, i.e., s and ρ have the same parity; the possible values for s are clearly

35.
$$\rho, \rho - 2, \ldots, -\rho + 2, -\rho.$$

We can say now that for each $n \times n$ symmetric real matrix S of rank ρ there exists an integer s, belonging to the set 35, such that S is congruent (in R) to the diagonal matrix

36.
$$J_{n,\rho,s} = [[1_1, \ldots, 1_p, -1_{p+1}, \ldots, -1_\rho, 0_{\rho+1}, \ldots, 0_n]],$$

where $p = (s + \rho)/2$. The corresponding bilinear form is

37.
$$b(y, x) = {}_k\sum_1^p \eta_k \xi_k - {}_j\sum_{p+1}^\rho \eta_j \xi_j.$$

Before we can propose 36 and 37 as canonical forms we must show that s (or p) is uniquely determined by S, a result sometimes called "Sylvester's

Law of Inertia". Suppose that S has been reduced, in the coordinates ξ_k, to $J_{n,\rho,s}$ and, in the coordinates ξ'_k, to $J_{n,\rho,s'}$; of course, $J_{n,\rho,s}$ and $J_{n,\rho,s'}$ are congruent. We shall prove that $s = s'$. Let $p = (s + \rho)/2$ and $p' = (s' + \rho)/2$. Assume now that $p > p'$. Define $Y \leq X$ by the equations $\xi_k = 0$ ($k = p + 1$, $\ldots, \rho$) and $Z \leq X$ by the equations $\xi'_k = 0$ ($k = 1, \ldots, p', \rho + 1, \ldots, n$). Since $\rho \geq p > p' \geq 0$, we know that $p > 0$ and $\rho > p'$. Since

$$\dim Y = n - (\rho - p), \qquad \dim Z = \rho - p',$$

neither Y nor X is trivial. It follows from 5F2 that

$$n - (\rho - p) + \rho - p' \leq n + \dim (Y \cap Z),$$

whence

$$\dim (Y \cap Z) \geq p - p' > 0.$$

Now suppose that $x \in Y \cap Z$ with $x \neq 0$. By 37, $x \in Y$ implies that

$$b(x, x) - {}_k\sum_1^p \xi_k^2 \geq 0.$$

By 37 with p replaced by p', $x \in Z$ implies that

$$b(x, x) = -{}_k\sum_{p'+1}^\rho \xi_k'^2 < 0.$$

From this contradiction we conclude that $p \leq p'$. Similarly, $p' \leq p$. Hence $p = p'$ and $s = s'$.

38. An $n \times n$ symmetric real matrix of rank ρ and signature s is congruent (in R) to a unique matrix $J_{n,\rho,s}$ of 36, where $p = (s + \rho)/2$ and there are $n - \rho$ zeros. The corresponding bilinear form is 37.

EXERCISES

39. Let $f \in X^d$ and $g \in Y^d$ and define $b : Y \times X \to F$ so that

$$(y, x) \to b(y, x) = g(y)f(x).$$

Show that b is bilinear. What is the rank of b? Seek a converse of your result. (Cf. 9I8.)

40. Let $M = \begin{bmatrix} 0 & 1 \\ 1 & 1 \end{bmatrix}$. Find T such that $T^t M T$ is the canonical form of M under congruence.

41. Find the canonical form of the bilinear form on $Y_2^d \times X_3$ whose matrix is

$$B = \begin{bmatrix} 2 & 1 & 4 \\ -1 & 3 & -2 \end{bmatrix}.$$

42. Are these bilinear forms equivalent:

$$3\eta_1\xi_1 - 4\eta_2\xi_1 + \eta_3\xi_1 + 5\eta_1\xi_2 - 3\eta_2\xi_2,$$

$$\eta_1\xi_1 - 6\eta_1\xi_2 + 3\eta_2\xi_1 + \eta_2\xi_2 - 4\eta_3\xi_1 + 4\eta_3\xi_2?$$

43. Let b be a bilinear form of rank ρ on X_n and define $Y \leq X$ to consist of those y such that $b(y, x) = 0$ for all $x \in X$. Prove that $\rho + \dim Y = n$. (T)

44. Let b be a bilinear form on X such that $b(x, x) = 0$ for all $x \in X$. Does it follow that $b = 0$? (T)

45. Let b be bilinear on $Y \times X$ and, with y_0 fixed in Y, define $f_{y_0} : X \to F$ so that $x \to f_{y_0} x = b(y_0, x)$. Can y_0 exist such that $f_{y_0} = 0$? (T)

46. Let $\mathfrak{M}$ ($= \mathfrak{M}_{nn}$ of 8A) denote the linear space of all $n \times n$ complex matrices. With tr M as in 8F10, define

$$b(K, L) = n \operatorname{tr}(KL) - (\operatorname{tr} K)(\operatorname{tr} L).$$

Show that B is a symmetric bilinear form on $\mathfrak{M}$. (T)

47. Let L be an arbitrary $\mu \times n$ matrix. Prove that $L^t L$ is symmetric. Is LL^t symmetric? (T)

48. What can be said about KL if K and L are both symmetric? Both skew? Either symmetric and the other skew? Does it make any difference if $KL = LK$?

49. Let S be an $n \times n$ symmetric matrix and suppose that $S(I - S) = 0$. Prove that $\rho(S) + \rho(I - S) = n$. (T)

50. Let A be antisymmetric on a real space X. Prove that, for any $x \in X$, $[\xi_k] A [\xi_k]^t = 0$. (*Hint:* If $\alpha = [\alpha]$ is a scalar then $[\alpha]^t = [\alpha]$; cf. 8E7.)

B. Pre-Hermitian Forms; Conjunctive Matrices

The discussion of the preceding section, up through 32, was valid for both R and C. In this section we confine attention to the case $F = C$ and develop several interesting possibilities not available when $F = R$. We retain the notation of A0, bearing in mind that the spaces X, X^d, Y, and Y^d are now *complex* linear spaces.

Let us first dispose of an appealing but dangerous idea. It is natural to suppose that, in a complex space X, each vector x has an associated conjugate vector $\bar{x}$. In a fixed coordinate system, indeed, the mapping $[x] \leftrightarrow \overline{[x]}$ (i.e., $[\xi_k]^t \leftrightarrow \overline{[\xi_k]}^t = [\bar{\xi}_k]^t$) is an involutorial automorphism. This correspondence, however, is not invariant under a change of basis. If $[\xi_k]^t = [L][\xi'_k]^t$, with $[L]$ regular, then $[\bar{\xi}_k]^t = \overline{[L]}[\bar{\xi}'_k]^t$, *not* $[\bar{\xi}_k]^t = [L][\bar{\xi}'_k]^t$, as it should be if the "automorphism" were to be a genuine linear mapping, independent of the basis. Having put on the record what this symbol $\bar{x}$ does *not* mean, we allow ourselves to use $\bar{x}$ as an abbreviation for $\overline{[x]}$ in contexts in which the presence of the brackets is implied.

Equations A2 and A3 involved both additivity and homogeneity in each variable. We keep the additivity but now allow for conjugation of the scalar coefficients. For functionals defined on $Y \times X$ the possibilities are these:

    (i) $b(\alpha y, x) = \alpha b(y, x)$,   (ii) $b(\alpha y, x) = \bar{\alpha} b(y, x)$,

    (iii) $b(y, \alpha x) = \alpha b(y, x)$,   (iv) $b(y, \alpha x) = \bar{\alpha} b(y, x)$.

In A2 and A3 we used (i) and (iii). A theory similar in every respect can be developed using (ii) and (iv); in a theorem analogous to A7 the form would be $\sum \bar{\eta}_\lambda \beta_{\lambda k} \xi_k$ where $\beta_{\lambda k} = b(q_\lambda, p_k)$. We leave the details of such a theory to the reader, because of the much greater practical interest accorded to situations in which either (i) and (iv) *or* (ii) and (iii) are used. The theories of these two cases are entirely equivalent, and the weights of authority and usage behind each are roughly equal. We choose (ii) and (iii). A functional $b : Y \times X \to C$ is said to be *pre-Hermitian* if, for each $y, y' \in Y$, $x, x' \in X$, and $\alpha, \alpha' \in C$, it is true that

1. $$b(\alpha y + \alpha' y', x) = \alpha b(y, x) + \bar{\alpha}' b(y', x),$$

2. $$b(y, \alpha x + \alpha' x') = \alpha b(y, x) + \alpha' b(y, x').$$

A more revealing but unwieldy adjective would be "(conjugate-linear-)linear".
If $y = \sum \eta_\lambda q_\lambda$ and $x = \sum \xi_k p_k$, then 1 and 2 yield

3. $$b(y, x) = b(\sum \eta_\lambda q_\lambda, \sum \xi_k p_k) = \sum \bar{\eta}_\lambda b(q_\lambda, p_k)\xi_k$$
$$= [\bar{\eta}_\lambda][\beta_{\lambda k}][\xi_k]^t = \overline{[y]}[b][x],$$

where

4. $$[b] = [\beta_{\lambda k}]$$

is a $\mu \times n$ matrix with

5. $$\beta_{\lambda k} = b(q_\lambda, p_k).$$

The form $\sum \bar{\eta}_\lambda \beta_{\lambda k} \xi_k$ is called a *pre-Hermitian* form. For example, if $g \in Y^d$ and $f \in X^d$ and we define b by

$$(y, x) \to b(y, x) = \overline{g(y)}f(x),$$

then b is a pre-Hermitian form.

When bases in X and Y are changed as in A8 then a calculation similar to that of A9 (with ψ's replaced by η's) reveals that $[b]$ is replaced by $[b]'$, where (cf. A10)

6. $$[b]' = \overline{[U]}^t[b][T].$$

Since $[U]$ and $[T]$ are regular, we have here, of course, merely another instance of equivalence. Formulation of results such as A7, 11, 12, and 13 are left to the reader. The canonical form of a pre-Hermitian form of rank ρ on $Y_\mu \times X_n$ is

7. $$\sum_j^\rho \bar{\eta}_j \xi_j.$$

The really interesting situation arises when $Y = X$. Then 6 reduces to (cf. A20)

8. $$[b]' = \overline{[T]}^t[b][T].$$

Square complex matrices so related to each other, with $[T]$ regular, are said to be *conjunctive*. The result corresponding to A12 is that two complex $n \times n$ matrices are conjunctive if and only if they are matrices in their respective coordinate systems of the same pre-Hermitian form on some complex $X_n \times X_n$.

It is fortunate that most pre-Hermitian forms of practical importance are either Hermitian or anti-Hermitian. A pre-Hermitian form $b : X \times X \to C$ is said to be *Hermitian* if

9.
$$b(y, x) = \overline{b(x, y)}$$

and to be *anti-Hermitian* (or *skew-Hermitian*) if

10.
$$b(y, x) = -\overline{b(x, y)}.$$

In the respective cases, of course (cf. 5)

$$\beta_{jk} = b(p_j, p_k) = \pm\overline{b(p_k, p_j)} = \pm\overline{\beta}_{kj}.$$

Thus b is Hermitian if and only if its matrix is *Hermitian* in the sense that

11.
$$[\overline{b}]^t = [b],$$

and anti-Hermitian if and only if its matrix is *anti-Hermitian* in the sense that

12.
$$[\overline{b}]^t = -[b].$$

In the following examples, J is Hermitian and K is anti-Hermitian:

$$J = \begin{bmatrix} 2 & 1+i \\ 1-i & 3 \end{bmatrix}, \qquad K = \begin{bmatrix} 2i & 1+i \\ -1+i & 3i \end{bmatrix}.$$

We may write

13.
$$b(y, x) = \tfrac{1}{2}[b(y, x) + \overline{b(x, y)}] + \tfrac{1}{2}[b(y, x) - \overline{b(x, y)}]$$
$$= b_h(y, x) + b_a(y, x)$$

where

14.
$$b_h(y, x) = \tfrac{1}{2}[b(y, x) + \overline{b(x, y)}]$$

is Hermitian and

15.
$$b_a(y, x) = \tfrac{1}{2}[b(y, x) - \overline{b(x, y)}]$$

is anti-Hermitian. The forms b_h and b_a are called, respectively, the *Hermitian part* of b and the *anti-Hermitian* part of b; their uniqueness is easily established.

For the remainder of this section we will be dealing with matrices. Let us write B for $[b]$ and omit the brackets from the matrix of the coordinate transformation. That a matrix conjunctive with a Hermitian or anti-Hermitian matrix has the same property follows from the equations

16.
$$(\overline{T^t B T})^t = \overline{T}^t \overline{B}^t T = \pm\overline{T}^t BT,$$

with the upper sign in the Hermitian case and the lower in the anti-Hermitian case.

Let us suppose, first of all, that A is anti-Hermitian, that is, $\overline{A}^t = -A$. Consider $H = iA$. We see that

17.
$$\overline{H}^t = -i\overline{A}^t = iA = H;$$

Hence $H = iA$ is Hermitian. Vice versa, if $H = \overline{H}^t$ is Hermitian then $A = iH$

is anti-Hermitian. It is sufficient, therefore, to seek a canonical form for Hermitian matrices under conjunctivity.

It is possible, now, to adjust the argument which led from A31 to A32 in order to obtain the same result. The details are messy, however, and it will be demonstrated later, by more powerful methods (see 14A and B), that an $n \times n$ Hermitian matrix of rank ρ is conjunctive with a diagonal matrix (cf. 32)

18.
$$B_\rho = [[\beta_1, \ldots, \beta_\rho, 0_{\rho+1}, \ldots, 0_n]],$$

where there are $n - \rho$ zeros and $\beta_1, \ldots, \beta_\rho$ are not zero and, above all, are *real*.

From here on the argument leading in R from A32 to A36 and A37 applies verbatim. The idea of signature applies, and Sylvester's Law of Inertia still holds. The result follows.

19. Theorem. An $n \times n$ Hermitian matrix of rank ρ and signature s is conjunctive to a unique matrix

19.1.
$$J_{n,\rho,s} = [[1_1, \ldots, 1_p, -1_{p+1}, \ldots, -1_\rho, 0_{\rho+1}, \ldots, 0_n]]$$

where $p = (s + \rho)/2$. The corresponding Hermitian form is

19.2.
$$h(y, x) = {}_k\sum_1^p \bar{\eta}_k \xi_k - {}_j\sum_{p+1}^\rho \bar{\eta}_j \xi_j.$$

The matrix $J_{n,\rho,s}$, of 19.1 and the form $h(y, x)$ of 19.2 are canonical forms, of course, for Hermitian matrices and forms under conjunctivity.

EXERCISES

20. Prove that if H is Hermitian then, for any $x \in X$, the scalar $\theta = \bar{x}^t H x$ is real. Is the converse true? (T)

21. Prove that if A is anti-Hermitian then, for any $x \in X$, $\bar{x}^t A x$ is purely imaginary. (T)

22. Prove that if H is Hermitian then $A = iH$ is anti-Hermitian. What can you say about iA if A is anti-Hermitian? (T)

23. Show that if S is real and symmetric then $A = iS$ is anti-Hermitian. What can you say about A if S is real and skew? (T)

24. Prove that, for any complex matrix M, both $H = \overline{M^t}M$ and $J = M\overline{M^t}$ are Hermitian. (T)

25. Given $b : X \times X \to C$, write

$$b(y, x) = \frac{1}{2}[b(y, x) + \overline{b(y, x)'}] + \frac{i}{2}\left[\frac{b(y, x) - \overline{b(y, x)}}{i}\right]$$

$$= b_1(y, x) + ib_2(y, x).$$

Show that b_1 and b_2 are both real. Show further that b is Hermitian if and only if b_1 is symmetric and b_2 is skew.

26. Let $H = \begin{bmatrix} 0 & \alpha \\ \bar{\alpha} & 0 \end{bmatrix}$ with $\alpha \neq 0$. Show that H is conjunctive with $[[1 \quad -1]]$.

27. Determine the rank and signature of each of these Hermitian matrices:

$$\begin{bmatrix} 2 & i & 1+2i \\ -i & 0 & -i \\ 1-2i & i & 0 \end{bmatrix} \quad \begin{bmatrix} 5 & 1-i & -2i \\ 1+i & 1 & 1-i \\ 2i & 1+i & 1 \end{bmatrix}.$$

28. Prove that each diagonal element of a Hermitian matrix is real, and that each diagonal element of an anti-Hermitian matrix is purely imaginary. (T)

29. We are given a bilinear form b on a real X_n. Define a mapping f on X into X^d as follows: $x \rightarrow f_x \in X^d$ where for $y \in X$, $f_x y = b(x, y)$. Show that f has the same rank as b. Determine the rank of the mapping $y \rightarrow g_y \in X^d$ when, for $x \in X$, $g_y x = b(x, y)$.

C. Quadratic and Hermitian Forms

Let B be the matrix of a bilinear form b on a *real* space X. We know from A23, 24, and 25 that $B = S + A$ where S is symmetric and A is antisymmetric. From A51 we know that $x^t A x = 0$ for each $x \in X$. The functional $q : X \times X \rightarrow R$ defined by

1.
$$q(x) = b(x, x) = x^t S x = \sum \xi_j \beta_{jk} \xi_k,$$

where $S = [\beta_{jk}]$ with $\beta_{jk} = \beta_{kj}$, is called a *quadratic functional* or a *quadratic form*. The rank and signature of b are said to be the *rank* and *signature* of q. This usage is reasonable because we can recover the symmetric part b_s of b (cf. A23) from q by means of the *polar identity*

2.
$$4b_s(y, x) = q(y + x) - q(y - x).$$

That the right member is symmetric follows easily from the fact that $q(\alpha z) = \alpha^2 q(z)$; also, $q(x) = b_s(x, x)$. It follows from A38 that if S is of order n, rank ρ, and signature s, then a coordinate system can be found in which

3.
$$q(x) = {}_k\sum_1^p \xi_k^2 - {}_k\sum_{p+1}^\rho \xi_k^2,$$

where $p = (s + \rho)/2$; this is the canonical form for a real quadratic form under congruence.

Now let H be the matrix of a *Hermitian* bilinear form b on a *complex* space X. We know that $\bar{H}^t = H$ and (B24) that $H = S + iA$ where S and A are real, S is symmetric, and A is antisymmetric. Moreover, by B19, $\bar{x}^t H x$ is real for each $x \in X$. The functional $h : X \times X \rightarrow C$ defined by

4.
$$h(x) = b(x, x) = \bar{x}^t H x = \sum \bar{\xi}_j \beta_{jk} \xi_k,$$

where $H = [\beta_{jk}]$, with $\beta_{kj} = \bar{\beta}_{jk}$, is called a *Hermitian quadratic functional* or *form* or, more briefly, a *Hermitian form* on X. It is easy to verify that

5.
$$h(\alpha x) = |\alpha|^2 h(x).$$

Conversely, given a Hermitian quadratic form H, we define $b(y, x)$ by

6. $$4b(y, x) = h(y + x) - h(y - x) + ih(iy + x) - ih(iy - x),$$

and verify easily that b is a Hermitian bilinear form on X and that $b(x, x) = h(x)$. The *rank* and *signature* of h are defined to be those of b. It follows from B18 that if H is of order n, rank ρ, and signature s, then a coordinate system can be found in which

7. $$h(x) = {}_k\sum_1^p |\xi_k|^2 - {}_k\sum_{p+1}^\rho |\xi_k|^2,$$

where $p = (s + \rho)/2$; this is the canonical form for a Hermitian form under conjunctivity.

The canonical form can be obtained by completing the square. We give the process for the Hermitian case $h(x) = \sum \bar{\xi}_j \beta_{jk} \xi_k$; in the real symmetric case simply ignore the conjugation.

If $\beta_{11} = 0$ then some $\beta_{1k_0} \neq 0$ or else the form would not contain ξ_1. Put $\xi_1 = \eta_1 + \eta_{k_0}$ and $\xi_{k_0} = \epsilon(\eta_1 - \eta_{k_0})$, where $\epsilon = 1$ or i according as the real part of $\beta_{1k_0} \neq 0$ or $= 0$, and $\xi_j = \eta_j$ $(j = 1, \ldots, n$ with $j \neq 1, k_0)$. In the variables η_k we have (the new) $\beta_{11} \neq 0$.

With $\beta_{11} \neq 0$ we write

8. $$h(x) = \beta_{11}(\bar{\xi}_1 + \beta_{11}^{-1} \sum \beta_{1j'} \bar{\xi}_{j'})(\xi_1 + \beta_{11}^{-1} \sum \bar{\beta}_{1j'} \xi_{j'})$$
$$+ \beta_{11}^{-1} \sum (\beta_{11}\beta_{j'k'} - \beta_{ij'}\bar{\beta}_{1k'})\bar{\xi}_{j'}\xi_{k'}$$
$$= \beta_{11}\bar{\eta}_1\eta_1 + h_1(x),$$

where $j', k' = 2, \ldots, n$, $\eta_1 = \xi_1 + \beta_{11}^{-1} \sum \bar{\beta}_{1k'}\xi_{k'}$, $\eta_{k'} = \xi_{k'}$, and h_1 is a Hermitian form in the variables $\eta_{k'}$. Of course, β_{11} is real. The process may be repeated with the residual form $h_1(x)$. The process terminates naturally, if h is of rank ρ, when the form (in final variables ξ_k)

9. $$h(x) = {}_k\sum_1^\rho \beta_{kk}|\xi_k|^2$$

has been attained. Here the β_{kk} $(k = 1, \ldots, \rho)$ are real. Each may be replaced by ± 1 if desired, by the process used in passing from A32 to A36.

Quadratic and Hermitian forms arise in many problems of practical interest. In mechanics, for example, a particle acted upon by a force which is the gradient of a function $V(\xi_1, \ldots, \xi_n)$ can rest in equilibrium at any point at which V is stationary, at any point, that is, at which $\partial V/\partial \xi_k = 0$ $(k = 1, \ldots, n)$. We can choose the stationary point as the origin and, by adding a constant, if necessary, arrange that $V(0, \ldots, 0) = 0$. A particle in equilibrium at the origin is said to be in *stable* equilibrium if every sufficiently small displacement from the origin subjects the particle to a force directed back toward the origin. It turns out that equilibrium at the origin is stable if and only if V has a strict local minimum there, that is, if and only if $V(\xi_1, \ldots, \xi_n) > 0$ for all sufficiently small values of $\xi_1, \ldots, \xi_n$, not all zero. Now if V is sufficiently smooth, having, for example, third partial derivatives, then for sufficiently small values of $\xi_1, \ldots, \xi_n$ the *sign* of $V(\xi_1, \ldots, \xi_n)$ is the same as that of

10.
$$q(x) = \sum \xi_j \frac{\partial^2 V}{\partial \xi_j \, \partial \xi_k} \xi_k = \sum \xi_j \alpha_{jk} \xi_k,$$

where $\alpha_{jk} = \partial^2 V / \partial \xi_j \, \partial \xi_k = \alpha_{kj}$, the partial derivatives being evaluated at the origin. Since $q(\alpha x) = \alpha^2 q(x)$, we are not restricted, in examining the sign of $q(x)$, to "small" values of the ξ's. The requirement for stable equilibrium, therefore, is that for each $x \in X$

11.
$$q(x) > 0.$$

A quadratic form with this property, and the (symmetric) matrix of the form are said to be *positive* or, in older terminology, *positive definite*.

The question of sign arises also for Hermitian matrices and forms. The terminology is displayed in Table 12.

12. Table. Usage governing sign of $a(x)$, where either $a(x) = q(x) = x^t S x$, with S real and $S^t = S$, or $a(x) = h(x) = \bar{x}^t H x$, with H complex and $\bar{H}^t = H$.

Property of $a(x)$	Adjective	Symbol	Older Terminology
$a(x) > 0$ if $x \neq 0$	positive	$a > 0$	positive definite
$a(x) \geq 0$	nonnegative	$a \geq 0$	positive semi-definite
$a(x) = 0$, all x	zero	$a = 0$	zero
$a(x) \leq 0$	nonpositive	$a \leq 0$	negative semi-definite
$a(x) < 0$ if $x \neq 0$	negative	$a < 0$	negative definite
$a(x_1) > 0$ and $a(x_2) < 0$	indefinite		indefinite
$x_1, x_2 \in X$			

The adjective and the symbol apply also to the matrix of the form. In the context established for 10, we may say that if $A = [\alpha_{jk}]$ is the matrix in 10, then the origin is a point of stable equilibrium if and only if $A > 0$.

The canonical forms 3 and 7 reveal the sign clearly, in nontrivial cases, as follows:

$$p = \rho = n, \quad p = \rho < n, \quad 1 \leq p < \rho, \quad p = 0 < \rho < n, \quad p = 0, \quad \rho = n$$
$$> 0 \qquad\quad \geq 0 \qquad\quad \text{indefinite} \qquad \leq 0 \qquad\qquad < 0$$

Further results on sign will be found in 14A and B.

EXERCISES

13. Determine the signs of the Hermitian matrices of B26 and 27.

14. A positive real symmetric matrix S is congruent to I. Prove that a real symmetric matrix S is positive if and only if there is a real matrix M such that $S = M^t M$ is regular. Prove also that a Hermitian matrix H is positive if and only if there is a complex matrix M such that $H = \bar{M}^t M$ is regular.

15. Let b be a real symmetric bilinear form on X, and set $q(x) = b(x, x)$. Prove that

$$q(x + y) + q(x - y) = 2q(x) + 2q(y).$$

16. Given a real quadratic form q on X, set

$$b(x, y) = \tfrac{1}{2}[q(x + y) - q(x) - q(y)].$$

Show that b is bilinear, that $b(x, y) = b(y, x)$, and that $b(x, x) = q(x)$. (T)

17. Let $G = \begin{bmatrix} 24 & 16 \\ 16 & 29 \end{bmatrix}$ and $H = \begin{bmatrix} 10 & 20 \\ 20 & 29 \end{bmatrix}$. Find canonical forms for G and H under congruence and identify the loci of the equations $x^t G x = 1$ and $x^t H x = 1$ in $\mathcal{E}_2$ with coordinates $[x]$.

18. In C_3, denote the matrix of $(\bar\xi_1 + \bar\xi_2 + \bar\xi_3) \cdot (\xi_1 + \xi_2 + \xi_3)$ by J. Show that J is Hermitian. Is $J > 0$? Explain. What is the canonical form for J under conjunctivity?

19. In a real (or complex) X_n, let $\{q_k\}$ be a basis in which the symmetric (or Hermitian) matrix M has the canonical form $J_{n,\rho,s}$ of B19.1. Let

$$X^+ = \langle q_1, \ldots, q_p \rangle, \qquad X^- = \langle q_{p+1}, \ldots, q_\rho \rangle, \qquad X^0 = \langle q_{\rho+1}, \ldots, q_n \rangle.$$

Prove that $X = X^+ \oplus X^- \oplus X^0$, that $M > 0$ on X^+, $M < 0$ on X^-, and $M = 0$ on X^0.

ELEVEN
Determinants

A. Introduction

Consider the following systems of linear equations, in which all letters represent scalars:

1.
$$ax + by = j \qquad \begin{aligned} ax + dy + gz &= j \\ hx + by + ez &= k \\ fx + iy + cz &= l. \end{aligned}$$
$$cx + dy = k,$$

Solving for y we obtain, respectively,

2.
$$y = \frac{ak - jc}{ad - bc} = \frac{\begin{vmatrix} a & j \\ c & k \end{vmatrix}}{\begin{vmatrix} a & b \\ c & d \end{vmatrix}},$$

3.
$$y = \frac{akc + jef + gli - fkg - lea - cji}{abc + def + ghi - fbg - iea - chd} = \frac{\begin{vmatrix} a & j & g \\ i & k & e \\ f & l & c \end{vmatrix}}{\begin{vmatrix} a & d & g \\ h & b & e \\ f & i & c \end{vmatrix}},$$

provided that the expressions in the denominators do not vanish.

The numerators and denominators in the rightmost members are determinants. They denote the numerators and denominators in the respective solutions. The arrays of scalars inside the vertical bars are square matrices, and each determinant is said to be the determinant of the matrix inside the vertical bars. These determinants are therefore scalar-valued functions (i.e., functionals) of *square* matrices. Our goal in this chapter is to define and discuss determinants of square matrices with elements in a field. The formal definition of the determinant of a matrix is in B.

In 2 and 3 the matrices whose determinants appear in the denominators are the determinants of the matrices of the corresponding systems in 1. Moreover, the determinants in the numerators are obtained from those in the denominators by striking out the column of coefficients of y and replacing it by the column vector on the right in the corresponding system 1. This is an example of Cramer's rule (see H3).

Quite atypical, on the other hand, is the fact that the determinants in 2 and 3 can be evaluated by simple mnemonic devices, as in the adjoining table.

4.
$$\begin{vmatrix} a & b \\ c & d \end{vmatrix} = ad - bc$$

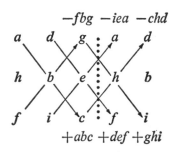

5.
$$\begin{vmatrix} a & d & g \\ h & b & e \\ f & i & c \end{vmatrix} = abc + def + ghi - fbg - iea - chd$$

6. Table. Evaluation of determinants of orders 2 and 3.

In each instance, the determinant is the sum of the products of elements on diagonals that slope downwards minus the sum of the products of elements on diagonals that slope upwards. Any similar device for determinants of matrices of higher order would be hopelessly complicated.

There are several approaches to the theory of determinants. A very elegant approach uses the ideas of multilinear algebra, which are beyond the scope of this book (see, e.g., [A17, 46; C4, 5]). An approach used by Weierstrass is axiomatic; one accepts as axioms the properties (a), (b), and (c) of the next paragraph and proves that a functional with these properties exists (see, e.g., [A12, 16, 19, 26, 35, 47]). Still another approach is recursive, based on the expansion by minors at which we arrive in G (see, e.g., [A48]). We choose the popular combinatorial definition (cf., e.g., [A6, 20, 30, 34, 37, 44]). For this purpose the reader is advised to have the results of 4E well in mind.

All these approaches lead to the same result. Let $L = [r_j] = [c_k]$ be an $n \times n$ square matrix with row vectors r_j and column vectors c_k ($j, k = 1, \ldots, n$), and elements in a field. Then the determinant of L,

$$\det L = |L| = |r_j| = |c_k|,$$

is a functional with these properties:

(a) $|L|$ is linear in the rows r_j and in the columns c_k;
(b) if $p \in S_n$ (cf. 4E) then $|r_{p_j}| = \operatorname{sgn} p |r_j|$ and $|c_{p_k}| = \operatorname{sgn} p |c_k|$; and
(c) $|I| = 1$.

While determinants appeared late in the seventeenth century, matrices were not introduced until about one hundred and fifty years later, occasioning at first a certain amount of confusion between the two ideas. Determinants have been studied in depth for their own sake (see [A23] and Muir's extensive *History of the Theory of Determinants*). They are regarded now as theoretically helpful tools, but of quite modest computational value.

B. Definition

We are given an $n \times n$ matrix $A = [\alpha_{jk}] = [r_j] = [c_k]$; here $\alpha_{jk} \in F$, is the kth component of the jth row vector r_j, and the jth component of the kth column vector c_k. We define the *determinant* of A, det A, and introduce notation for it as follows:

1.
$$\det A = |A| = \det [\alpha_{jk}] = |\alpha_{jk}| = |r_j| = |c_k|$$
$$= \sum_{p \in S_n} \operatorname{sgn} p\, \alpha_{1p_1} \alpha_{2p_2} \ldots \alpha_{np_n} = \sum_{p \in S_n} \operatorname{sgn} p \Pi_h \alpha_{hp_h}$$

The determinant is therefore a sum, with one term for each $p \in S_n$; there are $n!$ terms in the sum. Each term is a product of n factors, having exactly one factor from each row and one from each column of A. The following corollaries are immediate.

2. If a determinant has a row of zeros or a column of zeros then the determinant is zero.

3. If A' is obtained from A by multiplying one row (or column) by a scalar α, then $|A'| = \alpha|A|$. One can factor out, therefore, a common divisor of every element of a row or a column.

The sign preceding the term corresponding to the permutation $p : j \to p_j$ is sgn p. Here are two examples with $n = 5$:

4. The term $a_{13}a_{24}a_{31}a_{45}a_{52}$ has the sign sgn $(34152) = (-1)^5 = -1$, because p has five inversions.

5. The term $a_{14}a_{25}a_{32}a_{41}a_{53}$ has the sign sgn $(45213) = (-1)^7 = -1$, because p has seven inversions.

The following corollaries are immediate, because in each case there is only one nonvanishing term and it is the product of the diagonal elements.

6.
$$|\delta_{jk}| = 1$$

7. If A is a lower-triangular, or an upper-triangular, or a diagonal matrix then det $A = \alpha_{11}\alpha_{22} \ldots \alpha_{nn}$.

It should be observed carefully in 1 and 3, of course, that the vertical bars do not designate absolute value. In 1 the notation $|[\alpha_{jk}]|$ would be more accurate, and may be used in those rare situations when there is danger of confusion with absolute value.

EXERCISES

8. Use 1 to evaluate

$$A = \begin{vmatrix} \alpha_{11} & \alpha_{12} \\ \alpha_{21} & \alpha_{22} \end{vmatrix}, \quad B = \begin{vmatrix} 3 & 2 \\ -1 & 4 \end{vmatrix},$$

$$C = \begin{vmatrix} \alpha_{11} & \alpha_{12} & \alpha_{13} \\ \alpha_{21} & \alpha_{22} & \alpha_{23} \\ \alpha_{31} & \alpha_{32} & \alpha_{33} \end{vmatrix}, \quad D = \begin{vmatrix} 2 & -1 & 0 \\ 1 & 2 & -3 \\ 3 & -2 & 4 \end{vmatrix}.$$

9. In E_P, with coordinates (ξ, η, ζ), the locus of the equation

$$\begin{vmatrix} 2 & \xi + 1 & -1 \\ 1 & \eta - 2 & 0 \\ 3 & \zeta + 5 & -3 \end{vmatrix} = 0$$

is a plane. Prove this, find the form $\alpha\xi + \beta\eta + \gamma\zeta = \delta$ for the equation, and find the coordinates of a point through which it passes.

10. Let A be an $n \times n$ matrix and α a scalar. Prove that $|\alpha A| = \alpha^n |A|$.

11. Suppose that α_{jk} is rational (or an integer) for $j, k = 1, \ldots, n$. Show that then $|\alpha_{jk}|$ is rational (or an integer). Give a 2×2 example to show that $\alpha_{jk} > 0$ ($j, k = 1, \ldots, n$) does not imply $|\alpha_{jk}| > 0$.

C. det A^t = det A

Let $A^t = B = [\beta_{jk}]$. A term of $|A^t|$ is, since $\beta_{jk} = \alpha_{kj}$,

1.
$$\operatorname{sgn} p\beta_{1p_1}\beta_{2p_2} \ldots \beta_{np_n} = \operatorname{sgn} p\alpha_{p_1 1}\alpha_{p_2 2} \ldots \alpha_{p_n n}.$$

Now if $k \to p_k = h$, then $k = p_h^{-1}$ and

2.
$$\alpha_{p_k k} = \alpha_{h p_h^{-1}}.$$

After substituting from 2 into the right member of 1 we may rearrange the factors in $\Pi_h \alpha_{h p_h^{-1}}$ so that $h = 1, \ldots, n$ because multiplication of scalars is commutative. Moreover, $\operatorname{sgn} p^{-1} = \operatorname{sgn} p$. Hence

3.
$$\operatorname{sgn} p\alpha_{p_1 1}\alpha_{p_2 2} \ldots \alpha_{p_n n} = \operatorname{sgn} p^{-1}\alpha_{1 p_1^{-1}}\alpha_{2 p_2^{-1}} \ldots \alpha_{n p_n^{-1}}.$$

Thus each signed term in the expansion of $|A^t|$ has been paired with an equal signed term in the expansion of $|A|$, and this pairing is clearly 1–1. We obtain $|A^t|$ by summing the left number of 3 for $p \in S_n$. On the right we may sum for $p^{-1} \in S_n$, because addition is commutative and the signed terms will occur in some enumeration of $p^{-1} \in S_n$ corresponding to the listing of $p \in S_n$ used on the left; the result on the right is $|A|$.

The rightmost number of B1 is called the *expansion* of $|A|$ *by rows*, while the expansion

4.
$$|A| = \sum_{p \in S_n} \text{sgn } p \, \alpha_{p_1 1} \alpha_{p_2 2} \ldots \alpha_{p_n n}$$

just obtained is called the *expansion* of $|A|$ *by columns*.

EXERCISES

5. Verify that $|A^t| = |A|$ for the determinants in B8.

6. Prove that if n is odd and A is skew then $|A| = 0$. (T)

7. Suppose that each α_{jk} is a real-valued differentiable function of a real variable t, and that $\dot{\alpha}_{jk} \equiv d\alpha_{jk}/dt$. Prove that

$$\frac{d|A|}{dt} = \sum_j \begin{vmatrix} r_1 \\ \cdot \\ \cdot \\ \cdot \\ r_{j-1} \\ \dot{r}_j \\ r_{j+1} \\ \cdot \\ \cdot \\ \cdot \\ r_n \end{vmatrix} = \sum_k |c_1 \ldots c_{k-1} \dot{c}_k c_{k+1} \ldots c_n|.$$

D. Elementary Operations

In dealing with systems of linear equations, and with bilinear and quadratic forms, we used row and column operations on matrices (cf. 9D, 9H) in order to rearrange the matrices so that information contained in them could be indicated more clearly by the appearance of the matrix. The same operations may be used to reduce a determinant to a form in which the expansion B1 will have fewer nonvanishing terms and even those easier to evaluate.

Since the expansions B1 and C4 are equal, we will state our results for rows, leaving to the reader the formulation and proof of similar results for columns.

1. If A' arises from A by interchanging two rows of A, then $|A'| = -|A|$.

In the expansion C4 for $|A'|$, each permutation p used in $|A|$ is replaced by a permutation p' which is the resultant of p and a transposition. Hence $\text{sgn } p' = -\text{sgn } p$ and the result follows.

Now (see 4E) each permutation can be expresed as a product of trans-positions, and if T transpositions are used in expressing a permutation q, then sgn $q = (-1)^T$.

2. If the rows of $|\alpha_{jk}|$ are subjected to a permutation q, then

$$|\alpha_{q_ik}| = |r_{q_i}| = \text{sgn } q|\alpha_{jk}| = \text{sgn } q|r_j|.$$

There is a further immediate corollary of 1.

3. If two rows of A are equal, then $|A| = 0$.

This fact can be used to write down an equation for an $(n - 1)$-flat containing n prescribed points. In the plane, for example, with coordinates (ξ, η), the locus of the equation

$$\begin{vmatrix} \xi & \eta & 1 \\ \alpha & \beta & 1 \\ \gamma & \delta & 1 \end{vmatrix} = 0$$

is a line through (α, β) and (γ, δ).

Now suppose that A has a row, say $r_{j_0} = [\alpha_{j_0k}]$, which is the sum of row vectors s_{j_0} and t_{j_0}:

$$r_{j_0} = [\alpha_{j_0k}] = [\beta_{j_0k} + \gamma_{j_0k}] = [\beta_{j_0k}] + [\gamma_{j_0k}] = s_{j_0} + t_{j_0}.$$

In B1 we replace α_{j_0k} by $\beta_{j_0k} + \gamma_{j_0k}$, apply the distributive law to each term, and arrive at the following result.

4. If A has a row r_{j_0} which is the sum of row vectors s_{j_0} and t_{j_0}, then det $A = $ det $B +$ det C, where B has j_0th row s_{j_0}, C has j_0th row t_{j_0}, and each other row of B and C is the same as the respective row of A.

Here is a 2×2 example:

$$\begin{vmatrix} \alpha + \lambda & \beta + \mu \\ \gamma & \delta \end{vmatrix} = \begin{vmatrix} \alpha & \beta \\ \gamma & \delta \end{vmatrix} + \begin{vmatrix} \lambda & \mu \\ \gamma & \delta \end{vmatrix}.$$

We observe, incidentally, that we have now established properties (a), (b), and (c) mentioned in the introduction. Linearity of A in rows and columns follows from B3 and 4. The combinatorial property (b) is established in 2, and (c) is B6.

By using 4, B3, and 3 we can prove easily the following result:

5. If A' is obtained from A by adding to one row of A any linear combination of the other rows of A, then $|A'| = |A|$.

It is enough, clearly, to establish the effect of adding to one row, say the jth, a scalar multiple of $r_{j'}$ with $j' \neq j$. The result is

$$|A'| = \begin{vmatrix} r_1 \\ \cdot \\ \cdot \\ r_j + \alpha r_{j'} \\ \cdot \\ \cdot \\ r_{j'} \\ \cdot \\ \cdot \\ r_n \end{vmatrix} = \begin{vmatrix} r_1 \\ \cdot \\ \cdot \\ r_j \\ \cdot \\ \cdot \\ r_{j'} \\ \cdot \\ \cdot \\ r_n \end{vmatrix} + \begin{vmatrix} r_1 \\ \cdot \\ \cdot \\ \alpha r_{j'} \\ \cdot \\ \cdot \\ r_{j'} \\ \cdot \\ \cdot \\ r_n \end{vmatrix} = \begin{vmatrix} r_1 \\ \cdot \\ \cdot \\ r_j \\ \cdot \\ \cdot \\ r_{j'} \\ \cdot \\ \cdot \\ r_n \end{vmatrix} + \alpha \begin{vmatrix} r_1 \\ \cdot \\ \cdot \\ r_{j'} \\ \cdot \\ \cdot \\ r_{j'} \\ \cdot \\ \cdot \\ r_n \end{vmatrix} = |A|,$$

because the determinant multiplying α has equal jth and j'th rows and therefore vanishes.

Here are three immediate corollaries (cf. E4, 5 and 6).

6. If the rows (or columns) of A are linearly dependent, i.e., if A is singular, then $|A| = 0$.

7. If $|A| \neq 0$, then the rows (and columns) of A are linearly independent and A is regular.

8. A homogeneous system of n linear equations in n unknowns, $Ax = 0$, has a nontrivial solution only if $|A| = 0$.

We can use 5 and any non-zero element to replace by zero every other element in the same row or column as the non-zero element, without altering the value of the determinant. By this process the evaluation of $|A|$ can be reduced to the evaluation of a determinant of order $n - 1$.

We begin with a special case, using the notation of block matrices.

9.
$$|A| = \begin{vmatrix} \alpha_{11} & 0 \\ R & A_1 \end{vmatrix} = \alpha_{11}|A_1|.$$

Here R is an $(n - 1)$-component column vector. In the expansion B1 for A, in fact, the factor α_{1p_1} vanishes unless $p_1 = 1$, α_{11} can be factored out, and p is then a permutation q of $2, \ldots, n$ having the same sign as p. Hence

$$\sum_{p \in S_n} \text{sgn } p \Pi_k \alpha_{kp_k} = \alpha_{11} \sum_{q \in S_{n-1}} \text{sgn } q \alpha_{2q_2} \ldots \alpha_{nq_n} = \alpha_{11}|A_1|.$$

A similar result for columns follows from C4.

If $\alpha_{jk'} = 0$ for $k' \neq k$, then we can bring the jth row to the first position, leaving all other rows in the same relative order, by $j - 1$ transpositions of adjacent rows, and then bring the kth column to the first position, leaving all other columns in the same relative order, by $k - 1$ transpositions of adjacent columns. The result is $(-1)^{j+k}|A|$, and A has the appearance of the left member of 9, with α_{jk} in place of α_{11}.

10. If $\alpha_{jk'} = 0$ for $k' \neq k$, and if A_1 is obtained from A by striking out the jth row and kth column, then

$$|A| = (-1)^{j+k}\alpha_{jk}|A_1|.$$

There is an entirely similar result, of course, if all elements but one vanish in a column.

EXAMPLES

11.
$$\begin{vmatrix} 0 & 3 & 4 \\ 2 & -1 & 7 \\ 0 & 5 & -3 \end{vmatrix} = (-1)^{2+1}2\begin{vmatrix} 3 & 4 \\ 5 & -3 \end{vmatrix}$$

$$= -2(-9 - 20) = 58.$$

12.
$$\begin{vmatrix} 3 & -1 & 2 & 1 \\ 2 & 1 & -3 & -1 \\ 0 & 0 & 5 & 0 \\ 4 & -2 & 7 & 3 \end{vmatrix} = (-1)^{3+3}5\begin{vmatrix} 3 & -1 & 1 \\ 2 & 1 & -1 \\ 4 & -2 & 3 \end{vmatrix} \overset{*}{=} 5\begin{vmatrix} 3 & -1 & 0 \\ 2 & 1 & 0 \\ 4 & -2 & 1 \end{vmatrix}$$

$$= 5(-1)^{3+3}1\begin{vmatrix} 3 & -1 \\ 2 & 1 \end{vmatrix} = 5\cdot 5 = 25.$$

In equation (*) we added the second column to the third in the left member in in order to get the right member.

13. One becomes sensitive, with experience, to opportunities for quick reduction. Consider the determinant

$$|A| = \begin{vmatrix} 5 & 8 & 5 & 2 \\ 0 & 6 & 8 & 12 \\ -1 & -2 & -1 & 0 \\ 1 & 2 & 1 & -1 \end{vmatrix}.$$

We can factor out a 2 from the second row. We can subtract the first column from the third, or add the third row to the fourth. Choosing the latter, we obtain

$$|A| = 2\begin{vmatrix} 5 & 8 & 5 & 2 \\ 0 & 3 & 4 & 6 \\ -1 & -2 & -1 & 0 \\ 0 & 0 & 0 & -1 \end{vmatrix} = 2(-1)^{4+4}(-1)\begin{vmatrix} 5 & 8 & 5 \\ 0 & 3 & 4 \\ -1 & -2 & -1 \end{vmatrix},$$

where the (-1) is the last element in the diagonal of $|A|$. Now subtract the first column from the third, and factor out -1 from the last row, obtaining

$$|A| = 2\begin{vmatrix} 5 & 8 & 0 \\ 0 & 3 & 4 \\ 1 & 2 & 0 \end{vmatrix} = 2(-1)^{2+3}4\begin{vmatrix} 5 & 8 \\ 1 & 2 \end{vmatrix} = -8(10 - 8) = -16.$$

EXERCISES

14. Evaluate the determinants

$$
\text{(a)} \begin{vmatrix} 2 & -7 & -6 & 5 \\ -3 & 4 & -1 & 0 \\ 1 & -5 & -3 & -4 \\ 4 & 3 & 2 & 3 \end{vmatrix}, \qquad \text{(b)} \begin{vmatrix} 4 & 5 & -2 & -6 \\ -1 & 2 & 6 & 1 \\ 2 & -3 & -1 & -3 \\ 3 & 4 & -5 & 2 \end{vmatrix}.
$$

(*Hints:* For (a), begin by adding thrice the first column to the third. For (b), begin by subtracting twice the third row from the first.)

15. Use D4 to write

$$
|A| = \begin{vmatrix} 2 & \alpha & -1 \\ 1 & \beta & 4 \\ -3 & \gamma & 2 \end{vmatrix} = \begin{vmatrix} 2 & \alpha & -1 \\ 1 & 0 & 4 \\ -3 & 0 & 2 \end{vmatrix} + \begin{vmatrix} 2 & 0 & -1 \\ 1 & \beta & 4 \\ -3 & 0 & 2 \end{vmatrix} + \begin{vmatrix} 2 & 0 & -1 \\ 1 & 0 & 4 \\ -3 & \gamma & 2 \end{vmatrix}.
$$

Now use D10 to evaluate A.

16. For the elementary matrices of 9D and 9H, show that

$$
|I_{\kappa,\lambda}| = |J_{\kappa,\lambda}| = 1, \qquad |I_{\gamma \cdot \kappa}| = |J_{\gamma \cdot \kappa}| = \gamma, \qquad |I_{\gamma \cdot \kappa + \lambda}| = |J_{\gamma \cdot \kappa + \lambda}| = 1.
$$

17. Let $y_1, \ldots, y_n$ be real-valued functions of a real variable t and let $y^{(k)}$ denote the kth derivative of y, with $y^{(0)} \equiv y$. Suppose that $y_j^{(n)}$ is continuous $(j = 1, \ldots, n)$. The Wronskian (determinant) of these functions is defined to be

$$
W(t) = W(t; y_1, \ldots, y_n) = |y_j^{(k-1)}| \ (j, k = 1, \ldots, n);
$$

here $j(k)$ is the column (row) index. Use C7 to find $dW(t)/dt$ by differentiating by rows. Suppose now that each y_j satisfies the linear homogeneous differential equation

$$
y^{(n)} + \alpha_{n-1} y^{(n-1)} + \ldots + \alpha_1 y^{(1)} + \alpha_0 y = 0,
$$

where the α's may depend on t; show that, consequently,

$$
\frac{dW(t)}{dt} = -\alpha_{n-1}(t) \, W(t).
$$

(*Optional:* Deduce that if τ is any fixed value of t, then

$$
W(t) = W(\tau) \exp \left[-\int_\tau^t \alpha_{n-1}(\theta) \, d\theta \right].)
$$

E. det (AB) = (det A)(det B)

We have $n \times n$ matrices $A = [\alpha_{jk}]$ and $B = [\beta_{kl}]$, and we wish to show that the determinant of their product

$$
[\gamma_{jl}] = [\sum \alpha_{jk} \beta_{kl}]
$$

is $|A| \, |B|$. Substitution into B1 and rearrangement yield

$$|AB| = \sum_{p \in S_n} \text{sgn } p \gamma_{1p_1} \cdots \gamma_{np_n}$$

$$= \sum_{p \in S_n} \text{sgn } p(\sum_{k_1} \alpha_{1k_1}\beta_{k_1p_1}) \cdots (\sum_{k_n} \alpha_{nk_n}\beta_{k_np_n})$$

1.
$$= \sum_{k_1, \ldots, k_n} \alpha_{1k_1} \cdots \alpha_{nk_n} \sum_{p \in S_n} \text{sgn } p \beta_{k_1p_1} \cdots \beta_{k_np_n}.$$

Here $j \to k_j$ is a permutation of $1, \ldots, n$. With $k_1, \ldots, k_n$ fixed, the sum for $p \in S_n$ is the expansion by rows of a determinant with rows $r_{k_1}, \ldots, r_{k_n}$ taken from B. This expansion vanishes, by B2, unless $h \to k_h$ is a permutation k of $1, \ldots, n$; in the favorable case the sum for $p \in S_n$ is sgn k det B, by D2. Hence

2.
$$|AB| = |B| \sum_{k \in S_n} \text{sgn } k \alpha_{1k_1} \cdots \alpha_{nk_n} = |A| \, |B|.$$

We know that a regular matrix A has an inverse A^{-1} such that $AA^{-1} = I$. By B6, therefore,

3. If A is regular, then $|A| \, |A^{-1}| = 1$.

4. If A is regular, then $|A| \neq 0$.

5. If $|A| = 0$ then A is singular.

6. The $n \times n$ homogeneous system $Ax = 0$ has nontrivial solutions if and only if $|A| = 0$.

Here 5 is the contrapositive of 4. If $|A| = 0$ then by 5 A is singular and there are non-zero x such that $Ax = 0$; the necessity of the condition is in D8.

EXERCISES

7. Calculate the determinants of the matrices appearing in 9D4. (On the left, observe that the coefficient $\frac{1}{5}$ is, as a *matrix*, $I/5$; this is a general precaution.)

8. Give a 2×2 example to prove that $|A| \, |B| = 1$ does not imply that $AB = I$.

9. Let $A = \begin{bmatrix} 2 & 3 \\ 1 & 4 \end{bmatrix}$. Verify that $|I - A| = |5I - A| = 0$ and find non-zero vectors x and y such that $(I - A)x = 0$ and $(5I - A)y = 0$.

10. Let A be a square matrix and λ a scalar variable. For how many values of λ can $\lambda I - A$ be singular? (*Hint:* det $(\lambda I - A)$ must vanish.)

11. Give a sufficient condition that a sub-diagonal, super-diagonal, or diagonal matrix be singular (cf. B7).

12. Use C to prove that
$$|\alpha_{jk}| \, |\beta_{hl}| = |\sum_k \alpha_{jk}\beta_{hk}| = |\sum_j \alpha_{jk}\beta_{jh}|,$$
i.e., that determinants may be multiplied "by rows" or "by columns".

13. A square matrix A is *orthogonal* if $AA^t = I$. Prove that if A is orthogonal, then $|A| = \pm 1$. Give an example of a 2×2 orthogonal matrix A with $|A| = -1$. (T)

14. A square matrix A with complex elements is *unitary* if $A\overline{A}^t = I$. Prove that if A is unitary then $|A|\,|\overline{A}^t| = 1$ (i.e., the absolute value of det A is 1). (T)

15. We are given vectors u_k and v_k ($k = 1, \ldots, q$) and scalars α_{jk} such that $u_j = \sum \alpha_{jk} v_k$. Prove that if $|\alpha_{jk}| = 0$, then the vectors u_k are dependent. Prove also that if the vectors v_k are independent and the vectors u_k are dependent, then $|\alpha_{jk}| = 0$. (T)

F. Minors and Cofactors

In this section we collect a few necessary definitions.

Let $A = [\alpha_{\lambda k}]$ ($\lambda = 1, \ldots, \mu$; $k = 1, \ldots, n$) be a $\mu \times n$ matrix with elements in a field. If $1 \leq q \leq \min(\mu, n)$ and B is a $q \times q$ submatrix of A (cf. 8C), then $|B| = \det B$ is said to be a *minor* of A of order q. If rows $j_1, \ldots, j_q$ and columns $k_1, \ldots, k_q$ are used, with $j_1 < \ldots < j_q$ and $k_1 < \ldots < k_q$, then the minor is designated by

1.
$$m_{j_1 \ldots j_q, k_1 \ldots k_q};$$

the rows and columns of the minor occur in the exact order in which they occur in A.

If $q = 1$, the comma is omitted:

$$m_{j_1 k_1} = \det[\alpha_{j_1 k_1}] = \alpha_{j_1 k_1}.$$

If A is square, the *principal* minors are those in which the same rows and columns occur; the diagonal of $m_{j_1 \ldots j_q, j_1 \ldots j_q}$ consists of the terms $\alpha_{j_1 j_1}$, $\ldots, \alpha_{j_q j_q}$ of the diagonal of A.

If A is an $n \times n$ matrix and m is a minor of order q, then the minor of order $n - q$ formed from those rows and columns *not* appearing in m, and arranged in the same relative order in which they appear in A, is said to be the minor *complementary* to m. We denote the minor complementary to $m_{j_1 \ldots j_q, k_1 \ldots k_q}$ by $M_{j_1 \ldots j_q, k_1 \ldots k_q}$.

If $q = 1$ we denote by $|A_{jk}|$ the minor complementary to α_{jk}, and call it simply the *minor of* α_{jk}.

The *cofactor* of $m_{j_1 \ldots j_q, k_1 \ldots k_q}$ is

2.
$$C_{j_1 \ldots j_q, k_1 \ldots k_q} = (-1)^{j_1 + \ldots + j_q + k_1 + \ldots + k_q} M_{j_1 \ldots j_q, k_1 \ldots k_q}.$$

If $q = 1$ the cofactor of α_{jk} is $C_{jk} = (-1)^{j+k}|A_{jk}|$. The coefficient $(-1)^{j+k}$ is $+1$ if $j = k$, i.e., if α_{jk} is on the diagonal, is -1 on the first sub-diagonal ($j = k + 1$) and super-diagonal ($k = j + 1$), and is alternately $+1$ and -1 as one proceeds along a row or a column; thus the signs by which the minors are converted to cofactors are arranged like the colors on a chessboard.

Only if A is square do the ideas of principal minor, complementary minor, and cofactor make sense.

EXAMPLE

3. Consider

$$
A = \begin{bmatrix}
\alpha_{11} & \alpha_{12} & \alpha_{13} & \alpha_{14} & \alpha_{15} \\
\alpha_{21} & \alpha_{22} & \alpha_{23} & \alpha_{24} & \alpha_{25} \\
\alpha_{31} & \alpha_{32} & \alpha_{33} & \alpha_{34} & \alpha_{35} \\
\alpha_{41} & \alpha_{42} & \alpha_{43} & \alpha_{44} & \alpha_{45} \\
\alpha_{51} & \alpha_{52} & \alpha_{53} & \alpha_{54} & \alpha_{55}
\end{bmatrix}.
$$

Here

$$
m_{24,35} = \begin{vmatrix} \alpha_{23} & \alpha_{25} \\ \alpha_{43} & \alpha_{45} \end{vmatrix}, \qquad
m_{134,245} = \begin{vmatrix} \alpha_{12} & \alpha_{14} & \alpha_{15} \\ \alpha_{32} & \alpha_{34} & \alpha_{35} \\ \alpha_{42} & \alpha_{44} & \alpha_{45} \end{vmatrix}.
$$

These minors have respective complementary minors

$$
M_{24,35} = \begin{vmatrix} \alpha_{11} & \alpha_{12} & \alpha_{14} \\ \alpha_{31} & \alpha_{32} & \alpha_{34} \\ \alpha_{51} & \alpha_{52} & \alpha_{54} \end{vmatrix}, \qquad
M_{134,245} = \begin{vmatrix} \alpha_{21} & \alpha_{23} \\ \alpha_{51} & \alpha_{53} \end{vmatrix},
$$

and cofactors

$$
C_{24,35} = (-1)^{2+4+3+5} M_{24,35} = M_{24,35},
$$

$$
C_{134,245} = (-1)^{1+3+4+2+4+5} M_{134,245} = -M_{134,245}.
$$

The minor of α_{34} is $|A_{34}| = M_{1245,1235}$, and the cofactor of α_{34} is $(-1)^{3+4}|A_{34}| = -|A_{34}| = C_{34}$.

G. Expansion by Minors of a Row or a Column

The objects defined in F will be used here and in K to derive several useful and illuminating ways of evaluating determinants. The example of D15 is typical of an expansion by minors of the second column given by 5 (below) when $k = 2$.

As a step toward evaluating $|A| = |\alpha_{jk}|$ let us fix $j = j_0$ and denote by $B_{j_0 k}$ $(k = 1, \ldots, n)$ the result of replacing $\alpha_{j_0 k}$ in A by 1 and $\alpha_{j_0 k'}$ by 0 if $k' \neq k$. By applying D4 and B3 we see that, with j_0 fixed,

1. $$|A| = \sum_k \alpha_{j_0 k} |B_{j_0 k}|.$$

By D10, however, $|B_{j_0 k}| = (-1)^{j_0 + k} |A_{j_0 k}| = C_{j_0 k}$, the cofactor of $\alpha_{j_0 k}$. Hence, since j_0 was arbitrary,

2. $$|A| = \sum_k \alpha_{jk} C_{jk} \qquad (j = 1, \ldots, n).$$

For each j, the sum in 2 is called the *expansion* of $|A|$ *by minors of the jth row.* Now consider the sum

3. $$\sum_k \alpha_{hk} C_{jk} \qquad (h \neq j).$$

It is evident that the row r_h of A is one of the rows in B_{jk}, so that 3 is the expansion of a determinant with two equal rows, and therefore vanishes. Both this result and 2 are contained in

4.
$$\sum_k \alpha_{hk} C_{jk} = \delta_{hj} |A|.$$

In the same fashion we can express A in terms of the minors of a column:

5.
$$|A| = \sum_j \alpha_{jk} C_{jk} \qquad (k = 1, \ldots, n).$$

For each fixed k, the sum in 5 is called the *expansion of* $|A|$ *by minors of the kth column*. It is true, as before, that $\sum \alpha_{jk} C_{jh} = 0$ if $h \neq k$. We summarize these results.

6. If $C_{jk} = (-1)^{j+k} |A_{jk}|$ is the cofactor of α_{jk} in $|A| = |\alpha_{jk}|$, then

6.1.
$$\sum_k \alpha_{hk} C_{jk} = \delta_{hj} |A| \qquad (h, j = 1, \ldots, n),$$

6.2.
$$\sum_j \alpha_{jh} C_{jk} = \delta_{hk} |A| \qquad (h, k = 1, \ldots, n).$$

EXAMPLE

7. An expansion by minors of the second column appeared in D15. Here is an expansion by minors of the third row.

$$\begin{vmatrix} 2 & 5 & 3 \\ -3 & 7 & 2 \\ 4 & -2 & 3 \end{vmatrix} = 4(-1)^{3+1} \begin{vmatrix} 5 & 3 \\ 7 & 2 \end{vmatrix} + (-2)(-1)^{3+2} \begin{vmatrix} 2 & 3 \\ -3 & 2 \end{vmatrix} + 3(-1)^{3+3} \begin{vmatrix} 2 & 5 \\ -3 & 7 \end{vmatrix}$$

$$= 4(10 - 21) + 2(4 + 9) + 3(14 + 15) = 69.$$

One cannot prescribe in advance an optimal algorithm for evaluating an arbitrary determinant. One is well-advised to pay close attention to specific features of the determinant. The elementary operations of D can be used to introduce zeros. If all but one element of a row or column can be made to vanish, then D10 can be used; the equation there is, of course, simply $|A| = \alpha_{jk} C_{jk}$, which is the form to which 2 reduces if $\alpha_{jk'} = 0$ if $k' \neq k$. Or, one can use elementary operations to arrive at a sub-diagonal or super-diagonal form and then apply B7. In certain important special cases the Laplace expansion of K (below) may be helpful.

EXERCISES

8. Evaluate the following determinants:

(a) $\begin{vmatrix} 2 & 4 & 3 & 2 \\ 3 & -2 & 5 & -2 \\ -5 & -3 & -4 & 3 \\ 2 & 7 & -6 & 4 \end{vmatrix}$, (b) $\begin{vmatrix} 3 & 7 & -2 & 4 \\ 2 & -6 & 3 & -4 \\ -2 & 5 & -4 & 2 \\ 4 & 3 & 2 & 3 \end{vmatrix}$.

9. Reconsider B9; evaluate the determinant by minors of the second column.

10. The Vandermonde matrix of order n is $V_n = [\alpha_{jk}]$, where $\alpha_{jk} = \xi_j^{k-1}$ $(j, k = 1, \dots, n)$. Show that

$$V_3 = \begin{vmatrix} 1 & \xi_1 & \xi_1^2 \\ 1 & \xi_2 & \xi_2^2 \\ 1 & \xi_3 & \xi_3^2 \end{vmatrix} = (\xi_2 - \xi_1)(\xi_3 - \xi_1)(\xi_3 - \xi_2),$$

and that $|V_n| = \underset{j>k}{\Pi} (\xi_j - \xi_k)$ for $n = 2, 3, \dots$ (*Hint:* The argument can be so arranged that mathematical induction is helpful.)

11. Suppose that in $|A| = |\alpha_{jk}|$ each element is a differentiable function of a scalar variable t. Prove that

$$\frac{d|A|}{dt} = \Sigma_{j,k} \, C_{jk} \frac{d\alpha_{jk}}{dt}$$

and that, consequently,

$$C_{jk} = \frac{\partial|A|}{\partial\alpha_{jk}}.$$

H. Linear Equations

Several important results follow from equations G6.1 and 2.

If A is regular, then $|A| \neq 0$ and we may divide both equations by $|A|$. The results may be written as the following equations between matrices:

1.
$$A \frac{[C_{jk}]^t}{|A|} = I,$$

2.
$$\frac{[C_{jk}]^t}{|A|} A = I.$$

We conclude that *if $|A| \neq 0$, then the inverse of A is*

3.
$$A^{-1} = \frac{1}{|A|} [C_{jk}]^t.$$

The matrix $[C_{jk}]^t$ is sometimes called the (classical) *adjoint* or *adjugate* of A; we shall prefer the latter term.

We can now express by means of determinants the (unique) solution of a regular system of n homogeneous linear equations in n unknowns.

4.
$$Ax = y \quad \text{or} \quad \Sigma \, \alpha_{jk}\xi_k = \eta_j.$$

The solution, of course, is $x = A^{-1}y$ or, by 3,

5.
$$[\xi_k]^t = |A|^{-1}[C_{jk}]^t[\eta_j]^t,$$

or

6.
$$\xi_k = |A|^{-1} \Sigma_j \, \eta_j C_{jk}.$$

Now $\Sigma_j \, \eta_j C_{jk}$ is the expansion by minors of the kth column of the determinant of a matrix obtained from A by replacing its kth column by $[\eta_j]^t$; let us call this matrix A_k. Then our result may be expressed in the following form.

7. **Cramer's Rule.** If $A = [\alpha_{jk}]$ is regular, then the solution of

$$\sum \alpha_{jh}\xi_h = \eta_j \ (j, h = 1, \ldots, n) \quad \text{is} \quad \xi_k = |A_k|/|A| \ (k = 1, \ldots, n).$$

We observe in 6 that the ξ_k are linear combinations of the η_j, the coefficients being the cofactors of the elements in the kth column of A, divided by $|A|$.

EXERCISES

8. Use 7 to solve for η the following systems (cf. 9B1 and 9C18):

(a)
$$\begin{aligned}
\xi - \eta + 2\zeta &= 3 \\
2\xi \quad\ + \zeta &= 1, \\
3\xi + 2\eta + \zeta &= 4
\end{aligned}$$

(b)
$$\begin{aligned}
\theta - 2\xi + 3\eta + \zeta &= 8 \\
3\theta \quad\ - \eta - \zeta &= 4 \\
2\theta + \xi \quad\ + 3\zeta &= -9 \\
-2\theta + \xi + 2\eta \quad\ &= 0
\end{aligned}$$

9. Substitute the right members of 6 into the left members of 4 and verify that the result is $\eta_j \ (j = 1, \ldots, n)$. Do we know without this verification that the ξ_k in 6 actually satisfy 4?

If $|A| = 0$ then the right members of G6.1 and 2 vanish, and those equations yield the following result.

10. **Solutions of a Homogeneous System.** If $A = 0$ then each column vector of the adjugate $[C_{jk}]^t$ of A is a solution of the equations $\sum \alpha_{jk}\xi_k = 0$, while each row of the adjugate is a solution of the dual system $\sum \eta_j\alpha_{jk} = 0$. These solutions are all trivial if and only if $C_{jk} = 0 \ (j, k = 1, \ldots, n)$.

More explicitly, if $|A| = 0$, then a solution x of $Ax = 0$ can be found by choosing any row of A and forming a column vector whose hth component is the cofactor of the hth element of the chosen row.

An important special case arises when we have to solve $n - 1$ homogeneous equations in n unknowns:

11.
$$\sum \alpha_{\lambda k}\xi_k = 0 \quad (\lambda = 1, \ldots, n - 1; k = 1, \ldots, n).$$

To deal with this situation we choose any fixed value of λ, say λ_0, and observe that the $n \times n$ determinant

12.
$$\begin{vmatrix} \alpha_{\lambda k} \\ \alpha_{\lambda_0 k} \end{vmatrix} = 0.$$

On expanding this determinant by minors of the last row, we obtain

$$\sum \alpha_{\lambda_0 k}C_{nk} = 0,$$

where C_{nk} is the cofactor of the element in the nth row and kth column of 12; these numbers do not depend on λ_0. Since λ_0 was arbitrary, the numbers $C_{nk} \ (k = 1, \ldots, n)$ satisfy 11. Moreover,

13.
$$C_{nk} = (-1)^{n+k}|A_{nk}| = (-1)^{n+k}|\alpha_{\lambda k'}|,$$

where $\lambda = 1, \ldots, n-1$, $k' = 1, \ldots, n$, and $k' \neq k$.

14. Solution of $n-1$ Homogeneous Equations in n Unknowns. A solution of 11 is given by the rightmost expressions in 13.

More explicitly, a solution of 11 can be found by forming a column vector whose kth component is the determinant of the submatrix of $[\alpha_{\lambda k}]$ obtained by deleting the kth column, with signs alternating; since the equations are homogeneous, the particular coefficient $(-1)^{n+k}$ in 13 may be ignored, for its effect is merely to make the signs alternate.

For example, the equations

$$\alpha\xi + \beta\eta + \gamma\zeta = 0$$
$$\lambda\xi + \mu\eta + \nu\zeta = 0$$

have the familiar solution

$$\xi = \begin{vmatrix} \beta & \gamma \\ \mu & \nu \end{vmatrix}, \qquad \eta = -\begin{vmatrix} \alpha & \gamma \\ \lambda & \nu \end{vmatrix}, \qquad \zeta = \begin{vmatrix} \alpha & \beta \\ \lambda & \mu \end{vmatrix};$$

these numbers are the components, in a suitable (orthonormal) coordinate system, of the "cross-product" of the row vectors of coefficients (cf. 3J).

EXERCISES

15. Find A^{-1} if $|A| \neq 0$ and

(a) $A = \begin{bmatrix} \alpha & \beta \\ \gamma & \delta \end{bmatrix}$, (b) $A = \begin{bmatrix} 0 & 3 & 4 \\ 2 & -1 & 7 \\ 0 & 5 & -3 \end{bmatrix}$, (c) $A = \begin{bmatrix} 1 & -2 & 3 & 1 \\ 3 & 0 & -1 & -1 \\ 2 & 1 & 0 & 3 \\ -2 & 1 & 2 & 0 \end{bmatrix}$.

16. Prove that $|C_{jk}| = |A|^{n-1}$. If $|A| = 0$ it follows that the rows of $[C_{jk}]$ are dependent; find a linear relation between them. The columns of $[C_{jk}]$ are also dependent if $|A| = 0$; find a linear relation between them. (T)

17. Consider the system

$$2\theta - 3\xi + \eta - \zeta = 0$$
$$\theta + 2\xi - 4\eta + \zeta = 0$$
$$3\theta + \xi + 2\eta - 3\zeta = 0.$$

Does it have a nontrivial solution?

18. If A is symmetric and regular, is A^{-1} symmetric?

I. Determinantal Rank of a Matrix

The minors of a matrix $A = [\alpha_{\lambda k}]$ ($\lambda = 1, \ldots, \mu$; $k = 1, \ldots, n$) were defined in F.

266

If some minor of order r does not vanish, and either $r = \min(\mu, n)$ or every minor of order $r + 1$ vanishes, then A has *determinantal rank r*. Each minor of order $s \geq r + 2$ is a linear combination, by G2, of minors of order $s - 1$, and it follows, by an inductive argument, that every minor of order greater than r vanishes. The integer r is therefore the order of a non-vanishing minor of highest order.

We know (9C17.1) that the column-rank and row-rank of a matrix are equal; their common value is the rank ρ of the matrix. We wish now to prove that $r = \rho$.

1. The determinantal rank of a matrix is equal to its rank.

If the rank of A is ρ, then we can find ρ independent columns $c_{k_1}, \ldots, c_{k_\rho}$ in A. The $\mu \times \rho$ submatrix of A consisting of these ρ columns also has row-rank ρ, so we can find in it ρ independent rows, with indices $j_1, \ldots, j_\rho$. Then, in the notation of F, the minor

$$m_{j_1 \ldots j_\rho, k_1 \ldots k_\rho}$$

of A cannot vanish. Hence $\rho \leq r$.

On the other hand, if

$$m_{j_1 \ldots j_r, k_1 \ldots k_r} \neq 0,$$

then the r-component rows and columns of this minor are independent. Since row-rank and column-rank are equal, each of the submatrices

$$\begin{bmatrix} c_{j_1} \\ \cdot \\ \cdot \\ \cdot \\ c_{j_r} \end{bmatrix} \quad \text{and} \quad [r_{k_1} \ldots r_{k_r}]$$

of A has r independent rows and r independent columns. Hence $r \leq \rho$, completing the proof of 1.

J. Special Result on Rectangular Matrices; Lagrange's Identity

1. Theorem. Let $A = [\alpha_{\lambda k}]$ and $B = [\beta_{\lambda k}]$, with $k = 1, \ldots, n$ and $\lambda = 1, \ldots,$ $\mu \leq n$. Let H denote the set of $\binom{n}{\mu}$ combinations of μ indices chosen from $1, \ldots, n$. For $h \in H$ let $|A_h|$ and $|B_h|$ denote the $\mu \times \mu$ minors of A and B whose columns appear in h. Then

$$|AB^t| = \sum_{h \in H} |A_h| \, |B_h|.$$

In order to prove this theorem, which will be useful in 13G, let $S_\mu(h)$ denote the group of permutations of the indices in h. Then

$$|AB^t| = \sum_{p \in S_\mu} \operatorname{sgn} p \left(\sum_{j_1=1}^{n} \alpha_{1j_1} \beta_{p_1 j_1} \right) \cdots \left(\sum_{j_\mu=1}^{n} \alpha_{\mu j_\mu} \beta_{p_\mu j_\mu} \right)$$

$$= \sum_{h \in H} \sum_{k \in S_\mu(h)} \alpha_{1k_1} \cdots \alpha_{\mu k_\mu} \sum_{p \in S_\mu} \operatorname{sgn} p \beta_{p_1 k_1} \cdots \beta_{p_\mu k_\mu}$$

$$= \sum_{h \in H} \sum_{k \in S_\mu(h)} \alpha_{1k_1} \cdots \alpha_{\mu k_\mu} \operatorname{sgn} k |B_h|$$

$$= \sum_{h \in H} |A_h| \, |B_h|.$$

If $A = B$ the result, often called Lagrange's identity, is $|AA^t| = \sum |A_h|^2$ for $h \in H$. It follows that $|AA^t| \geq 0$.

In $\mathcal{E}_3$, with $\mu = 2$ and $n = 3$,

$$A = \begin{bmatrix} \alpha & \beta & \gamma \\ \xi & \eta & \zeta \end{bmatrix} = \begin{bmatrix} r_1 \\ r_2 \end{bmatrix},$$

$$|AA^t| = \begin{vmatrix} r_1 \cdot r_1 & r_1 \cdot r_2 \\ r_2 \cdot r_1 & r_2 \cdot r_2 \end{vmatrix} = ||r_1||^2 ||r_2||^2 - (r_1 \cdot r_2)^2$$

$$= ||r_1 \times r_2||^2$$

$$= ||r_1||^2 ||r_2||^2 \sin^2 \theta_{12} = \begin{vmatrix} \beta & \gamma \\ \eta & \zeta \end{vmatrix}^2 + \begin{vmatrix} \gamma & \alpha \\ \zeta & \xi \end{vmatrix}^2 + \begin{vmatrix} \alpha & \beta \\ \xi & \eta \end{vmatrix}^2.$$

K. Laplace Expansions

1. Theorem. Let $A = [\alpha_{jk}]$ with $j, k = 1, \ldots, n$. Choose any q rows of A, with indices $j_1 < j_2 < \ldots < j_q$. Let H denote the set of $\binom{n}{q}$ combinations h of q indices $h_1 < h_2 < \ldots < h_q$ chosen from $1, \ldots, n$. Then

$$|A| = \sum_{h \in H} m_{j_1 \ldots j_q, h_1 \ldots h_q} C_{j_1 \ldots j_q, h_1 \ldots h_q},$$

where the m's are given by F1 and the C's by F2. There is a precisely similar expansion using any chosen q columns of A.

Any expansion of the form occurring in 1 is called a *Laplace expansion*. If $q = 1$, of course, the expansion of 1 reduces to the expansion G2 by minors of the j_1th row. One expansion of the determinant of the 5×5 matrix A of F3 would be, with $j_1 = 2$ and $j_2 = 4$,

$$\sum_{h \in H} m_{24, h_1 h_2} C_{24, h_1 h_2},$$

where H consists of the ten pairs 12, 13, 14, 15, 23, 24, 25, 34, 35, and 45.

A Laplace expansion is particularly helpful in evaluating a determinant in which a block of zeros appears. Given, for example, $A_{n \times n}$, $B_{m \times m}$, and $C_{m \times n}$, we see at once from a Laplace expansion using the first n rows that

2.

$$\begin{vmatrix} A & 0 \\ C & B \end{vmatrix} = |A| \, |B|.$$

In order to establish the expansion of 1 we observe first that each term of the expansion is the product of two complementary determinants, one of order q and the other of order $n - q$. Each such product is a sum of $q!(n - q)!$ terms, each of which is a product of n factors, one from each row and one from each column of A, and there are, naturally,

$$\binom{n}{q} q!(n - q)! = n!$$

terms altogether. Each term is a product of a signed term from m, and a signed term from the complementary minor M, and the factor $(-1)^{j_1+\cdots+j_q+h_1+\cdots+h_q}$ which converts the minor M to the cofactor C. We must verify that the sign of the result agrees in all cases with "sgn p" in the expansion of B1.

We begin with the special case in which $j_1 = 1, \ldots, j_q = q$. Our aim is to show that

3.
$$|A| = \sum_{h \in H} m_{1\ldots q, h_1 \ldots h_q} C_{1\ldots q, h_1 \ldots h_q}.$$

Let h' denote the set of indices complementary to $h = (h_1 \ldots h_q)$, also arranged in natural order: $h_{q+1} < \ldots < h_n$. Then

4.
$$k = (h, h') = (h_1, \ldots, h_q, h_{q+1}, \ldots, h_n) \in S_n,$$

and we shall show that

5.
$$\text{sgn } k = (-1)^{h_1+\cdots+h_q - (q(q+1))/2}.$$

We start with $1, \ldots, n$ in their natural order. Bring h_1 into place 1; this requires $h_1 - 1$ (adjacent) transpositions and, because $h_1 < h_2 < \ldots < h_q$, the integers $h_2 \ldots h_q$ are left fixed. Next, bring h_2 into place 2; this requires $h_2 - 2$ transpositions. And so on. After the qth step the arrangement k has been reached and we have used $\sum_1^q (h_j - j) = \sum h_j - (q(q + 1))/2$ transpositions; 5 follows.

Now let $p = (p_1, \ldots, p_q, p_{q+1}, \ldots, p_n)$ be an arbitrary permutation in S_n. We shall express p as the product of a certain permutation having the properties of k in 4 and two other permutations which will have the effect of adjusting the arrangement of k to arrive at p. To this end, with q fixed, let $h = (h_1, \ldots, h_q)$ denote $p_1, \ldots, p_q$ in their *natural* order, and let r denote that element of the group $S_q(h)$ which arranges $h_1, \ldots, h_q$ in the order $p_1, \ldots, p_q$; i.e.,

$$r_{h_j} = p_j \quad (j = 1, \ldots, q).$$

Similarly, let $h' = (h_{q+1}, \ldots, h_n)$ denote $p_{q+1}, \ldots, p_n$ in their *natural* order, and let r' denote that element of the group $S_{n-q}(h')$ which arranges $h_{q+1}, \ldots, h_n$ in the order $p_{q+1}, \ldots, p_n$; i.e.,

$$r'_{h_j} = p_j \quad (j = q + 1, \ldots, n).$$

Then, from 4,

$$r'rk = (r_{h_1}, \ldots, r_{h_q}, r'_{h_{q+1}}, \ldots, r'_{h_n})$$

6.
$$= (p_1, \ldots, p_q, p_{q+1}, \ldots, p_n) = p.$$

It follows by 5 that

7.
$$\operatorname{sgn} p = (-1)^{h_1+\cdots+h_q-(q(q+1))/2} \operatorname{sgn} r \operatorname{sgn} r'.$$

As an example, with $n = 7$ and $q = 3$, consider

$$p = (6, 3, 4, 5, 7, 1, 2).$$

Here

$$h = (3, 4, 6), \qquad r_3 = 6, \qquad r_4 = 3, \qquad \text{and } r_6 = 4,$$

while

$$h' = (1, 2, 5, 7), \qquad r_1' = 5, \qquad r_2' = 7, \qquad r_5' = 1, \qquad \text{and } r_7' = 2;$$

of course,

$$k = (3, 4, 6, 1, 2, 5, 7).$$

We are now ready to prove 3. Let H denote the set of $\binom{h}{q}$ combinations h of q indices, with $h_1 < \ldots < h_q$, chosen from $1, \ldots, n$. Then

8.
$$|A| = \sum_{p \in S_n} \operatorname{sgn} p \alpha_{1p_1} \cdots \alpha_{qp_q} \alpha_{q+1p_{q+1}} \cdots \alpha_{np_n}$$

$$= \sum_{h \in H} \sum_{\substack{r \in S_q(h) \\ r' \in S_{n-q}(h')}} (-1)^R \operatorname{sgn} r \operatorname{sgn} r' \alpha_{1r_{h_1}} \cdots \alpha_{qr_{h_q}} \alpha_{q+1r'_{h_{q+1}}} \cdots \alpha_{nr'_{h_n}}$$

$$= \sum_{h \in H} m_{1\ldots q, h_1 \ldots h_q} (-1)^R M_{1 \ldots q, h_1 \ldots h_q}$$

$$= \sum_{h \in H} m_{1\ldots q, h_1 \ldots h_q} C_{1 \ldots q, h_1 \ldots h_q},$$

where $R = h_1 + \ldots + h_q - q(q+1)/2$ and the last equation follows because, in the exponent in F2, $1 + \ldots + q = q(q+1)/2$. The proof of 3 is complete.

The general expansion of 1 may be reduced to the special expansion of 3 by bringing rows $j_1, \ldots, j_q$ into positions $1, \ldots, q$, requiring (cf. 5) $j_1 + \ldots + j_q - q(q+1)/2$ transpositions. The exponent of -1 in the third line of 8 will be

$$j_1 + \ldots + j_q + h_1 + \ldots + h_q - q(q+1).$$

Since $q(q+1)$ is even, this reduces to the exponent required by F2.

EXERCISES

9. Use the third and fifth rows to develop a Laplace expansion of

$$\delta = \begin{vmatrix} 2 & -1 & -4 & 3 & 5 \\ -3 & 0 & 2 & 1 & 4 \\ 4 & 0 & 0 & 3 & -1 \\ 5 & 2 & 3 & -2 & 2 \\ -2 & 0 & 0 & 1 & -1 \end{vmatrix}.$$

10. Expand the determinant in 9 using the second and third columns.

11. Prove 2 directly from the definition in B1. (T)

12. Prove that

$$
\begin{vmatrix}
\alpha_{11} & 0 & \alpha_{12} & 0 & \alpha_{13} & 0 & \alpha_{14} & 0 \\
0 & \beta_{11} & 0 & \beta_{12} & 0 & \beta_{13} & 0 & \beta_{14} \\
\alpha_{21} & 0 & \alpha_{22} & 0 & \alpha_{23} & 0 & \alpha_{24} & 0 \\
0 & \beta_{21} & 0 & \beta_{22} & 0 & \beta_{23} & 0 & \beta_{24} \\
\alpha_{31} & 0 & \alpha_{32} & 0 & \alpha_{33} & 0 & \alpha_{34} & 0 \\
0 & \beta_{31} & 0 & \beta_{32} & 0 & \beta_{33} & 0 & \beta_{34} \\
\alpha_{41} & 0 & \alpha_{42} & 0 & \alpha_{43} & 0 & \alpha_{44} & 0 \\
0 & \beta_{41} & 0 & \beta_{42} & 0 & \beta_{43} & 0 & \beta_{44}
\end{vmatrix}
= |\alpha_{jk}| \, |\beta_{jk}| \; (j, k = 1, \ldots, 4).
$$

13. Prove that

$$
\begin{vmatrix}
\alpha & \beta & \eta_1 & \eta_2 & \eta_3 \\
\gamma & \delta & \zeta_1 & \zeta_2 & \zeta_3 \\
\lambda_1 & \mu_1 & 0 & 0 & 0 \\
\lambda_2 & \mu_2 & 0 & 0 & 0 \\
\lambda_3 & \mu_3 & 0 & 0 & 0
\end{vmatrix}
= 0
$$

no matter how the λ's, μ's, η's, and ζ's may be chosen.

L. Determinants of Bordered Matrices

Let $A = [\alpha_{jk}]$ be an $n \times n$ matrix, $[\xi_j]^t$ a column vector, $[\eta_k]$ a row vector, and ζ a scalar. The $(n + 1) \times (n + 1)$ matrix,

1.
$$
B = \begin{bmatrix} \alpha_{jk} & \xi_j \\ \eta_k & \zeta \end{bmatrix},
$$

is said to arise by *bordering* A. Of course, any matrix of order $n > 1$ arises in this way by bordering its upper left principal submatrix of order $n - 1$. It so happens, however, that matrices of the form B occur naturally in certain problems in geometry, sometimes in situations in which $\zeta = 0$.

On expanding $|B|$ by minors of the last row, we obtain

$$
|B| = \zeta|A| + \textstyle\sum_k \eta_k (-1)^{n+1+k} |[\alpha_{jk'} \xi_j]| \qquad (k' \neq k).
$$

Then, on expanding the rightmost determinant by minors of its last column, we obtain

2.
$$
|B| = \zeta|A| + \textstyle\sum_k \eta_k (-1)^{n+1+k} \sum_j \xi_j (-1)^{n+j} M_{jk} = \zeta|A| - \sum_{j,k} C_{jk} \xi_j \eta_k,
$$

where C_{jk} is the cofactor of α_{jk} in A. Thus an expansion of $|B|$ from 1 is given by 2.

If $\zeta = 0$, then 2 is simply a bilinear form in the ξ's and η's.

EXERCISES

3. Use 2 to evaluate

$$
|B| = \begin{vmatrix}
2 & -3 & 1 & \lambda \\
-2 & 4 & 3 & \mu \\
5 & -1 & 2 & \nu \\
\alpha & \beta & \gamma & \zeta
\end{vmatrix}.
$$

4. Given a bilinear form $b = \sum \xi_i \beta_{jk} \eta_k$, does there exist a matrix $[\alpha_{jk}]$ such that, when bordered as in 1 to yield B, with $\zeta = 0$, $|B| = -b$ (cf. 2 with $\zeta = 0$)?

5. In plane projective geometry, with homogeneous coordinates, a conic has an equation $\sum \alpha_{jk} \xi_j \xi_k = 0$; here $j, k = 1, 2, 3$, and $[\alpha_{jk}]$ is symmetric. It can be shown that a line with the equation $\sum \lambda_j \xi_j = 0$ is tangent to the conic if and only if the equations $\sum \alpha_{jk} \xi_k - \rho \lambda_j = 0$, $\sum \lambda_j \xi_j = 0$ have a nontrivial solution for the four scalars ξ_k, ρ. Show that this will be true if and only if $\sum C_{jk} \lambda_j \lambda_k = 0$.

TWELVE
Similar Operators

We deal with a complex linear space X of dimension n. An endomorphism of X is a linear mapping L on X into X; we shall say henceforth that L is an *operator on* X. To each $x \in X$ there corresponds a unique $y = Lx \in X$, and y depends linearly on x.

When a basis is assigned for X there is associated with L a well-determined $n \times n$ matrix $[L] = [\alpha_{jk}] = [c_k]$, where the kth column vector c_k of $[L]$ is the coordinate vector of the image under L of the kth basis vector.

All these facts were brought out in Chap. 6, and it was shown there that if new coordinates are introduced in such a way that $[x] = [T][x]'$, where $[T]$ is a regular $n \times n$ matrix, then the matrix representing L in the new coordinates is

$$[L]' = [T]^{-1}[L][T];$$

thus $[L]'$ is similar to $[L]$.

Given L, or $[L]$, we wish to choose new coordinates in such a way that $[L]'$ will reveal the effect of L in as clear a way as possible. For example, if $[L]'$ is diagonal, i.e., if $[L]$ is similar to a diagonal matrix $[[\beta_1, \ldots, \beta_n]]$, then $x = [\xi_k']^t \rightarrow y = Lx = [\eta_k']^t$, where $\eta_k' = \beta_k \xi_k' (k = 1, \ldots, n)$; the effect of L is obvious.

Even if $[L]$ cannot be diagonalized, we shall see that coordinates can be found in which $[L]'$ consists of blocks along the diagonal of the general form

$$\begin{bmatrix} \beta & 1 & 0 & 0 & 0 \\ 0 & \beta & 1 & 0 & 0 \\ 0 & 0 & \beta & 0 & 0 \\ 0 & 0 & 0 & \beta & 0 \\ 0 & 0 & 0 & 0 & \beta \end{bmatrix}.$$

Then $[L]'$ is said to be in Jordan normal (or canonical) form. It is not hard to see that the β's must be the eigenvalues of L (defined in A), but the number and arrangement of the 1's on the first super-diagonal is a more delicate matter.

The process has myriad applications, for example, in geometry, differential equations, electrical networks, and both classical and quantum mechanics.

A. Characteristic Polynomial; Eigenvalues, and Eigenvectors

If $[L]$ can be diagonalized, then, as we saw above, with a basis $\{q_k\}$ with respect to which $[L] = [[\beta_1, \ldots, \beta_n]]$, the effect of L is simply to map q_k onto $\beta_k q_k$; $q_k \to L q_k = \beta_k q_k$ ($k = 1, \ldots, n$). It follows that $L\langle q_k \rangle = \langle q_k \rangle$ unless $\beta_k = 0$, when $L\langle q_k \rangle = \langle 0 \rangle$. In either case, $L\langle q_k \rangle \leq \langle q_k \rangle$ and the one-dimensional space $\langle q_k \rangle$ is invariant under L. This fact suggests that we might help ourselves, even if $[L]$ cannot be diagonalized, by seeking subspaces invariant under L.

If $x \neq 0$ then $L\langle x \rangle \leq \langle x \rangle$ if and only if there is a scalar λ such that $Lx = \lambda x$. If a scalar λ and a vector $x \neq 0$ have the property that $Lx = \lambda x$ then we say that λ is a *characteristic value*, or *proper value*, or *eigenvalue* of L, and that x is a *characteristic vector*, or *proper vector*, or *eigenvector corresponding to* λ. We shall use the linguistically inelegant hybrids "eigenvalue" and "eigenvector" (from the German "Eigenwert" and "Eigenvektor") because of their wide acceptance in the literature of the sciences and engineering. It may also be noted that the definitions are valid for an operator on a linear space of any dimension. Whenever one has a linear space X and an operator L on X, and seeks a scalar λ and a vector $x \neq 0$ such that $Lx = \lambda x$, one refers to the problem as an *eigenvalue problem*.

As an example, let us suppose that we have a linear space X and, in it, a fixed operator L and a vector $x(\tau)$ depending differentiably on a scalar τ. Let us consider the differential equation $Lx = dx/d\tau$. We seek a scalar λ and a constant non-zero vector y such that $x - e^{\lambda \tau} y$ will satisfy the differential equation. On substituting into the differential equation and cancelling the non-vanishing factor $e^{\lambda \tau}$, we obtain $Ly = \lambda y$ or $(\lambda - L)y = 0$ (here, as frequently, we have abbreviated λI to λ); this is an eigenvalue problem.

Another example, chosen from geometry, concerns *quadric surfaces*, which are defined to be the level surfaces of quadratic forms (see 10.3). If the form is $q(x) = \frac{1}{2} \sum \alpha_{jk} \xi_j \xi_k$, then it can be shown that the normal to a level surface at a point $[\xi_k]^t$ on the surface has components $\sum \alpha_{jk} \xi_k$ ($j = 1, \ldots, n$); this vector is in fact the gradient of q at $[\xi_k]^t$. The direction (from the origin) determined by a vector $[\xi_k]^t \neq 0$ is said to be *self-conjugate* (with respect to q) if and only if $[\xi_k]^t$ and the normal to the level surface at $[\xi_k]^t$ are parallel, i.e., if and only if there is a scalar λ such that $\sum \alpha_{jk} \xi_k = \lambda \xi_j$ ($j = 1, \ldots, n$). This is an eigenvalue problem expressed in terms of coordinates. The diagram (1) illustrates the idea when $n = 2$. The vectors from 0 to A and C determine self-conjugate directions because they are parallel to the normals at A and C, while those to B and D do not have this property and do not determine self-conjugate directions.

Of course, if λ is an eigenvalue of L, and $x \neq 0$ is a corresponding eigenvector ($Lx = \lambda x$), and μ is any scalar other than 0, then μx is also an eigenvector corresponding to λ. An eigenvector is thus determined only up to a factor of proportionality; it is the space $\langle x \rangle$ that counts. We shall see in Chap. 14, however, that if λ is an eigenvalue, then its particular numerical value is related to L in a quite intimate way.

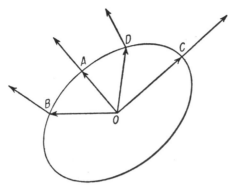

1. Diagram of ellipse ($n = 2$).

If λ is an eigenvalue of L, then $\lambda - L$ is singular. The nullspace of $\lambda - L$ is called the *eigenspace* corresponding to λ, and its dimension, the nullity of $\lambda - L$, is called the *geometric multiplicity* of λ.

Now $\lambda - L$ is singular if and only if λ is chosen in such a way that

2.
$$f(\lambda) \equiv f(L; \lambda) \equiv |[\lambda - L]| = (-1)^n |[L - \lambda]| = 0.$$

The polynomial $f(\lambda)$ is called the *characteristic polynomial* of L, and 2 is called its *characteristic equation*. It follows that a *scalar λ is an eigenvalue of L if and only if λ is a root of the characteristic equation of L.*

An example is given in 11E9. As a further example, let us consider an operator L on X_2 having the matrix

$$[L] = \begin{bmatrix} 0 & 6 \\ 1 & 1 \end{bmatrix}.$$

The characteristic equation is

$$\begin{vmatrix} \lambda & -6 \\ -1 & \lambda - 1 \end{vmatrix} = \lambda^2 - \lambda - 6 = (\lambda + 2)(\lambda - 3).$$

The eigenvalues are 3 and -2. A nontrivial solution of $[3 - L][x] = 0$ is $[x] = [2 \ 1]^t$, while a nontrivial solution of $[-2 - L][y] = 0$ is $[y] = [3 \ -1]^t$. Equations introducing x and y as basis vectors are

$$\xi = 2\xi' + 3\eta'$$
$$\eta = \xi' - \eta',$$

and the matrix of L in the coordinates ξ', η' is

3.
$$[L]' = \tfrac{1}{5}\begin{bmatrix} 1 & 3 \\ 1 & -2 \end{bmatrix}\begin{bmatrix} 0 & 6 \\ 1 & 1 \end{bmatrix}\begin{bmatrix} 2 & 3 \\ 1 & -1 \end{bmatrix} = \begin{bmatrix} 3 & 0 \\ 0 & -2 \end{bmatrix}.$$

With the eigenvectors x and y as basis vectors, the matrix of L is $[[3, -2]]$;

275

the eigenvalues associated with the respective basis vectors are on the diagonal. In general, unfortunately, the situation is more complicated.

Returning now to 2 we use the fact (cf. 4H18) that $\mathcal{C}$ is algebraically closed. There exist r distinct complex numbers $\lambda_1, \ldots, \lambda_r$, and positive integers $a_1, \ldots, a_r$ such that $\sum a_k = n$ and

4.
$$f(\lambda) = |[\lambda - L]| = {}_k\Pi_1^r (\lambda - \lambda_k)^{a_k};$$

the integer a_k is called the *algebraic multiplicity* of the eigenvalue λ_k. From the considerations following 4H18 we see that if $[L]$ is real, then the eigenvalues of L occur in conjugate complex pairs, each root of a pair having the same algebraic multiplicity. The set of eigenvalues of L, each counted with its algebraic multiplicity, is called the *spectrum* of L.

An eigenvalue was defined for an operator L, and was then seen to be obtainable from the matrix $[L]$ of L. Since $[L]$ depends on the coordinate system, we must assure ourselves that the eigenvalues do not.

5. If matrices L and L' are similar, then (cf. 2) $f(L; \lambda) \equiv f(L'; \lambda)$.

Indeed, if $L' = T^{-1}LT$, then
$$\lambda I - L' = T^{-1}\lambda IT - T^{-1}LT$$
and
$$f(L'; \lambda) = |\lambda - L'| = |T^{-1}(\lambda - L)T| = |T|^{-1}|T| \, |\lambda - L|$$
$$= |\lambda - L| = f(L; \lambda).$$

It follows that L and L' have identical characteristic polynomials and, therefore, identical spectra. It makes no difference, consequently, whether we speak of the characteristic polynomial or spectrum of an operator L or of the matrix $[L]$ of L with respect to some basis for X. The omission of brackets in 5 and its proof anticipated this freedom, of which we shall avail ourselves when convenient.

We close these preliminary remarks by showing that if α is an eigenvalue of L with algebraic multiplicity a and geometric multiplicity g, then $g \leq a$. Let p_k ($k = 1, \ldots, g$) be a basis for the eigenspace W corresponding to α, and let $p_{k'}$ ($k' = g + 1, \ldots, n$) be a basis for a complement of W. In the basis $\{p_k, p_{k'}\}$ for X, the first g columns of $[L]$ have $\alpha I_{g \times g}$ in the top g rows and zeros in rows $g + 1, \ldots, n$. Hence $|\lambda - L|$ has $\lambda - \alpha$ as a factor at least g times, and $a \geq g$.

In order to see that a may in fact exceed g, consider the space P of real polynomials $p(\tau)$ of degree $\leq n$, and define an operator L on P so that $p \to Lp$, where $Lp(\tau) = dp(\tau)/d\tau$. Here the only eigenvalue of L is 0. The corresponding eigenspace is the subspace $\langle 1 \rangle$, whence $g = 1$. With respect to the basis $1, \tau, \tau^2, \ldots, \tau^n$ the matrix $[L]$, of order $n + 1$, has zeros except on the first super-diagonal, where the entries in the respective rows are $1, 2, \ldots, n$; it follows that $f(L; \lambda) = \lambda^{n+1}$ and $a = n + 1$.

EXERCISES

6. (a) Find the eigenvalues λ, μ and corresponding eigenvectors z_λ, z_μ of $[L] = \begin{bmatrix} 0 & 2 \\ 1 & 1 \end{bmatrix}$.

Introduce z_λ and z_μ as a basis and obtain the new expression $[L]'$ for the matrix of L.

(b) Proceed similarly with $[M] = \begin{bmatrix} 2 & -3 \\ -1 & 4 \end{bmatrix}$.

7. Find the eigenvalues and corresponding eigenvectors of

(a) $\begin{bmatrix} 1 & 1 \\ -1 & 1 \end{bmatrix}$, (b) $\begin{bmatrix} 0 & 1 \\ -1 & 0 \end{bmatrix}$, (c) $\begin{bmatrix} 1 & 1 & 0 \\ 0 & 1 & 0 \\ 0 & 0 & 2 \end{bmatrix}$.

Determine the algebraic and geometric multiplicity of each eigenvalue.

8. Suppose that we have L, λ, and $x \neq 0$ such that $Lx = \lambda x$. Prove (by induction) that $L^m x = \lambda^m x$ for $m = 1, 2, 3, \ldots$. It follows that if p is any polynomial, then $p(L)x = p(\lambda)x$ and, therefore, that if λ is an eigenvalue of L, then $p(\lambda)$ is an eigenvalue of $p(L)$. (T)

9. Let λ_k ($k = 1, \ldots, r$) be distinct eigenvalues of L, with corresponding eigenvectors v_k. Prove that the vectors v_k are independent. (*Hint:* Apply L repeatedly to the equation $\sum \alpha_k v_k = 0$; the results of 11G10 are pertinent.) (T)

10. Suppose that, in 4, $r = n$; it follows that each $a_k = 1$. Introduce eigenvectors v_k ($k = 1, \ldots, n$) corresponding respectively to λ_k as a basis (cf. 9), obtaining $[L]' = [[\lambda_1, \ldots, \lambda_n]]^k$. *An $n \times n$ matrix with n distinct eigenvalues λ_k is similar to the matrix $[[\lambda_1, \ldots, \lambda_n]]$; the corresponding basis consists of eigenvectors v_k corresponding to the respective λ_k.* (T)

11. Prove that λ is an eigenvalue of L if and only if it is an eigenvalue of L^d.

12. Let λ be an eigenvalue of L. Prove that $\lambda + \mu$ is an eigenvalue of $L + \mu I$.

13. Let

$$L = \begin{bmatrix} 0 & 0 & \ldots & 0 & -\alpha_0 \\ 1 & 0 & \ldots & 0 & -\alpha_1 \\ 0 & 1 & \ldots & 0 & -\alpha_2 \\ \cdot & \cdot & \ldots & \cdot & \cdot \\ \cdot & \cdot & \ldots & \cdot & \cdot \\ \cdot & \cdot & \ldots & \cdot & \cdot \\ 0 & 0 & \ldots & 0 & -\alpha_{n-2} \\ 0 & 0 & \ldots & 1 & -\alpha_{n-1} \end{bmatrix},$$

that is, L has 1's on the first sub-diagonal, the last column is $-\alpha_0, \ldots, -\alpha_{n-1}$, and each other entry is 0. Expand $|\lambda - L|$ by minors of the last column to show that $f(L; \lambda) = {}_k\sum_0^n \alpha_k \lambda^k$, with $\alpha_n = 1$. It follows that any polynomial $g(\lambda) = \sum_0^n \beta_k \lambda^k$ of positive degree n, if it is *monic* ($\beta_n = 1$), is the characteristic polynomial of a well-determined $n \times n$ matrix. Note how simply L can be constructed from f; L is called the *companion matrix* of f. (See F.) (T)

14. In 4, observe that
$$f(0) = (-1)^n |L| = (-1)^n \, \Pi_1^n \, \lambda_k^{\alpha k};$$
that is, $|L|$ is the product of the eigenvalues of L, each raised to a power equal to its algebraic multiplicity. Try to find a similar result for tr L (see 8F10).

15. In the context of 6C, what can you say about the eigenvalues of a projection? Of a reflection?

16. Give an example of a real matrix having no real eigenvalue.

17. How are the eigenvalues of αL related to those of L?

B. Super-Diagonal Form

Consider the system of linear differential equations with constant coefficients:

1.
$$\dot{\xi} = \alpha \xi + \beta \eta + \gamma \zeta, \qquad \dot{\eta} = \lambda \eta + \mu \zeta, \qquad \dot{\zeta} = \nu \zeta.$$

The third equation can be solved at once for ζ. With ζ known, the second equation is a nonhomogeneous linear equation which can be solved for η explicitly. With η and ζ known, finally, the first equation can be solved explicitly for ξ. This process works because the matrix of the three linear forms on the right, namely,

$$\begin{bmatrix} \alpha & \beta & \gamma \\ 0 & \lambda & \mu \\ 0 & 0 & \nu \end{bmatrix},$$

is a super-diagonal matrix. Had the equations come to us in the form $\dot{\theta}_j = \sum \alpha_{jk} \theta_k$ $(j, k = 1, 2, 3)$, with $[\alpha_{jk}]$ not super-diagonal (nor sub-diagonal), it would clearly be advantageous to find a coordinate system in which they would have the form 1. We shall show in this section that for any operator L there is always a coordinate system in which $[L]$ is super-diagonal, with its eigenvalues along the diagonal. In following sections the process will be refined so that the part above the diagonal will be simplified still further; the final result is E1.

Let $\{p_k\}$ $(k = 1, \ldots, n)$ be a basis in which $[L]$ is super-diagonal. The diagonal elements are necessarily the eigenvalues of L. It is evident, on a moment's reflection, that, for $k = 1, \ldots, n$, the subspace $S_k = \langle p_1, \ldots, p_k \rangle$ is invariant under L, has dimension k, and is a subspace of S_{k+1}. A vector x in S_k will have, in fact, components $\xi_{k+1} = \ldots = \xi_n = 0$, and its product Lx with the super-diagonal matrix L will have the same property and, therefore, will belong to S_k.

Let us say, for the moment, that a set of n subspaces S_k $(k = 1, \ldots, n)$ is a *special* set (with respect to L) if dim $S_k = k$, $S_k \leq S_{k+1}$, and $LS_k \leq S_k$. We observe now that if S_k $(k = 1, \ldots, n)$ is a special set of subspaces, then we can introduce a basis $\{p_k\}$ for X which is adapted to S_k in the sense that

$S_k = \langle p_1, \ldots, p_k \rangle$ $(k = 1, \ldots, n)$, and that, with respect to this basis, $[L]$ is super-diagonal. If, in fact, $[L]$ were to have an element $\alpha_{hj} \neq 0$ with $h > j$, then the image of p_j would have hth component differing from 0, violating the facts that, because dim $S_k = k$, S_j is a proper subspace of S_h if $h > j$, and that $LS_j \leq S_j$. (Cf. 8C16.)

It remains only to show that a special set of subspaces always exists.

2. For any operator L on a complex linear space X_n there exist subspaces S_k $(k = 1, \ldots, n)$ such that dim $S_k = k$, $LS_k \leq S_k$, and $S_1 \leq S_2 \leq \ldots \leq S_n = X_n$.

The result is trivial if $n = 1$. Assume it true if $n = p$ and study X_{p+1}. The dual operator L^d on X^d has (cf. 1.4) an eigenvalue γ and a corresponding eigenvector e. Then $\langle e \rangle^0 \leq X$, dim $\langle e \rangle^0 = p$, and $L\langle e \rangle^0 \leq \langle e \rangle^0$. In fact, if $eL^d = \gamma e$ and $ex = 0$, then

$$e(Lx) = (eL)^d x = \gamma ex = 0.$$

By the inductive hypothesis, a special set of subspaces S_k $(k = 1, \ldots, p)$ exists for $\langle e \rangle^0$, with $S_p = \langle e \rangle^0$. The proof is complete if we choose $S_{p+1} = X_{p+1}$.

By choosing a basis adapted to the subspaces in 2 we obtain the following theorem.

3. **Theorem.** For any operator L on a complex linear space X_n, any $[L]$ is similar to a super-diagonal $[L]$; more precisely, there exists a basis in which $[L]$ is in super-diagonal form with the eigenvalues of L on the diagonal.

EXERCISES

4. The sum of two nth-order super-diagonal matrices is obviously super-diagonal. How about the product?

5. Find super-diagonal matrices similar to:

(a) $\begin{bmatrix} 0 & 1 \\ -1 & 0 \end{bmatrix}$, (b) $\begin{bmatrix} 1 & 4 & 5 \\ 2 & 5 & 7 \\ 3 & 6 & 9 \end{bmatrix}$;

give also the respective bases.

6. Suppose that, with a basis $\{p_k\}$ for X_3,

$$[L] = \begin{bmatrix} 0 & 1 & 2 \\ 0 & 0 & 1 \\ 0 & 0 & 0 \end{bmatrix}.$$

Let $S_k = \langle p_1, \ldots, p_k \rangle$ $(k = 1, 2, 3)$. Determine Lp_k and LS_k.

7. Suppose that all the eigenvalues of L are zero. Show that $L^q = 0$ for some positive integer q. (Such an operator is said to be *nilpotent*.) (T)

C. Decomposition of the Domain of a Singular Operator

In some situations it is enough to have the matrix of an operator L in super-diagonal form. It is often necessary, and fortunately possible, to analyze an operator in much greater detail. In this section we display a decomposition of the domain of a singular operator and then apply this decomposition for the singular operators $L_k = L - \lambda_k$, where λ_k is an eigenvalue of L (see A4). The result is a decomposition of X into the direct sum of certain subspaces, the root-spaces N_k (defined presently) of the eigenvalues λ_k.

The nullspaces of successive powers of L are important. For $p = 1, 2,$ $\ldots$, let $N^p = \{x : L^p x = 0\}$; that is, N^p is the nullspace of L^p. Clearly,

$$N^1 \leq N^2 \leq \ldots \leq N^p \leq N^{p+1} \leq \ldots,$$

but only a finite number of these spaces can be distinct because $\dim N^p \leq n$ for all p. The least integer $q \geq 1$, such that $N^{q+1} = N^q$, is called the *index* of L. If L is regular, of course, then $N^p = \langle 0 \rangle$ for all p and the index as just defined does not exist; it is harmless and convenient to define the index of a regular L to be zero. If L is of index q and nilpotent, then $L^q = 0$, but $L^{q-1} \neq 0$.

The definition will be justified by showing that if $N^{q+1} = N^q$, then $N^{q+r} = N^q$ for $r = 1, 2, 3, \ldots$. If $x \in N^{q+r}$, then $0 = L^{q+r}x = L^{q+1}(L^{r-1}x)$, whence $L^{r-1}x \in N^{q+1}$. But then $L^{r-1}x \in N^q$, $L^{q+r-1}x = 0$, and $x \in N^{q+r-1}$. By repeating this process $r - 1$ times, we see that $x \in N^{q+1} = N^q$. Hence $N^{q+r} \leq N^q$; since $N^q \leq N^{q+r}$ obviously, $N^q = N^{q+r}$.

If L is a singular operator on X, then the index q of L is positive, and a first step in analyzing the effect of L is to split X into the direct sum of the nullspace of L^q and the range of L^q. If L is regular the same decomposition is effective, but trivial.

1. Theorem. If an operator L on X has index q, and N^q denotes the nullspace of L^q, and R^q denotes the range of L^q, then $X = N^q \oplus R^q$, L is nonsingular on R^q and nilpotent of index q on N^q, and N^q and R^q are invariant under L.

That $N^q \cap R^q = \langle 0 \rangle$ follows obviously from the fact that L is nonsingular on R^q. Suppose, then, that $y = L^q x \in R^q$ and that also $Ly = L^{q+1}x = 0$. But then $L^q x = y = 0$ and L is nonsingular on R^q. Moreover, $\dim N^q + \dim R^q = \dim X$ (by 6E1), whence $X = N^q \oplus R^q$. On N^q, L is clearly nilpotent of index q, and both N^q and R^q are evidently invariant under L.

By choosing for X a basis adapted to N^q and R^q, we obtain, by 8C10, the following result.

2. Corollary. If an operator L on X has index q, then, in a coordinate system adapted to N^q and R^q,

$$[L] = [H] \oplus [K],$$

where $[H]$ is of order dim N^q and is nilpotent of index q, and $[K]$ is of order dim R^q and regular.

3. **Example.** Consider

$$L = \begin{bmatrix} 1 & 2 & 4 & -1 \\ -1 & 0 & -2 & -1 \\ 0 & -1 & -1 & 1 \\ 2 & 1 & 5 & 1 \end{bmatrix} \quad \text{and} \quad L^2 = \begin{bmatrix} -3 & -3 & -9 & 0 \\ -3 & -1 & -7 & 2 \\ 3 & 2 & 8 & 1 \\ 3 & 0 & 6 & 3 \end{bmatrix}.$$

Both L and L^2 have rank 2; L has index 1. A basis for the common null-space N^1 is

$$\begin{bmatrix} 2 & 1 & -1 & 0 \end{bmatrix}^t \quad \text{and} \quad \begin{bmatrix} 1 & -1 & 0 & -1 \end{bmatrix}^t.$$

Using, further, two independent columns of L (a basis for R^1) to construct T we find

$T^{-1}LT$

$$= \tfrac{1}{3} \begin{bmatrix} 3 & 3 & 6 & 0 \\ 1 & -1 & 1 & -1 \\ -1 & -2 & -4 & 1 \\ 3 & 3 & 9 & 0 \end{bmatrix} \begin{bmatrix} 1 & 2 & 4 & -1 \\ -1 & 0 & -2 & -1 \\ 0 & -1 & -1 & 1 \\ 2 & 1 & 5 & 1 \end{bmatrix} \begin{bmatrix} 2 & 1 & 1 & -1 \\ 1 & -1 & -1 & -1 \\ -1 & 0 & 0 & 1 \\ 0 & -1 & 2 & 1 \end{bmatrix}$$

$$= \begin{bmatrix} 0 & 0 & 0 & 0 \\ 0 & 0 & 0 & 0 \\ 0 & 0 & -6 & 1 \\ 0 & 0 & 3 & 1 \end{bmatrix} = L',$$

where L' denotes the matrix in the new coordinates of the operator whose matrix in the old coordinates is L.

The effect of theorem 1 is to reduce the study of a singular operator M of index q to the study of the restriction of M^q to R^q, which is regular, and of the restriction of M^q to N^q, which is nilpotent of index q. If λ is an eigenvalue of L, then $L - \lambda$ is singular and the theorem may be applied to it. The ultimate result is a decomposition of X into a direct sum of subspaces N_k, one for each eigenvalue λ_k, such that the restriction of $L - \lambda_k$ to N_k is nilpotent. Nilpotent operators will be studied in the next section. We turn to details.

Let the characteristic polynomial of L be

$$f(L; \lambda) = |\lambda - L| = {}_k\Pi_1^r (\lambda - \lambda_k)^{a_k}.$$

For the remainder of this section assign k the range $1, \ldots, r$. Set $L_k = L - \lambda_k$ and denote the index of L_k by q_k. Now let N_k denote the nullspace of $L_k^{q_k}$ and R_k its range. The space N_k is called the *root-space* of, or associated with, λ_k.

Let us define $M_k = \underset{j \neq k}{+} N_j$, and prove that $N_k \cap M_k = \langle 0 \rangle$ or, in other words, that the spaces N_k are independent (see 5F). It will suffice to show that L_k is regular on M_k. Suppose, on the contrary, that $y \in M_k$ and $L_k y = 0$. Then $Ly = \lambda_k y$. If $j \neq k$, moreover, then

$$L_j y = Ly - \lambda_j y = (\lambda_k - \lambda_j)y.$$

Now $y = \sum x_j$ with $x_j \in N_j$. Since L_j is nilpotent of index q_j on N_j,

$$0 = \prod_{j \neq k} L_j^{q_i} y = \prod_{j \neq k} (\lambda_k - \lambda_j)_y^{q_i}.$$

The numerical coefficient of y is not zero, whence $y = 0$ and the spaces N_k are independent. Our next aim is to show that $X = {}_k\bigoplus_1^r N_k$.

By theorem 1, $X = N_1 \oplus R_1$, with L_1 regular on R_1 and nilpotent of index q_1 on N_1. By the corollary 2, with a basis adapted to N_1 and R_1,

$$[L_1] = [H_1] \oplus [K_1],$$

where $[H_1]$ is of order $\dim N_1$ and nilpotent, while $[K_1]$ is of order $\dim R_1 = n - \dim N_1$ and regular. Now $|\lambda - L| = |\lambda - H| |\lambda - K|$, where $H = H_1 + \lambda_1$ and $K = K_1 + \lambda_1$. We know that $|\lambda_1 - H| = 0$ and, since K_1 is regular, that $|\lambda_1 - K| \neq 0$. In other words, $\lambda - \lambda_1$ cannot be a factor of $|\lambda - K|$. It follows that $\dim N_1 = a_1$ and $\dim R_1 = n - a_1$. With the basis now in use, therefore,

$$[L] = \begin{bmatrix} \lambda_1 + H_1 & 0 \\ 0 & \lambda_1 + K_1 \end{bmatrix}$$

where $\lambda_1 + H_1$ is of order a_1 and $\lambda_1 + K_1$, of order $n - a_1$, is the matrix of the restriction of L to R_1.

The eigenvalues and the characteristic polynomial are unchanged. The characteristic polynomial of $\lambda_1 + H_1$ is $(\lambda - \lambda_1)^{a_1}$, whence that of $\lambda_1 + K_1$ is

$$_h\Pi_2^r (\lambda - \lambda_h)^{a_h}.$$

It follows that the restriction M_2 of L_2 to R_1 is of index q_2, and the theorem yields $R_1 = N_2 \oplus R_{21}$ where R_{21} is the range of $M_2^{q_2}$. In a basis adapted to N_1, N_2, and R_{21},

$$[L] = [\lambda_1 + H_1] \oplus [\lambda_2 + H_2] \oplus [\lambda_2 + K_2],$$

where H_2 is of order a_2 and nilpotent of index q_2 on N_2. We now use L_3 to obtain $R_{21} = N_3 \oplus R_{32}$ and, in a suitable basis,

$$[L] = [\lambda_1 + H_1] \oplus [\lambda_2 + H_2] \oplus [\lambda_3 + H_3] \oplus [\lambda_3 + K_3].$$

The process terminates with

$$X = {}_k\bigoplus_1^r N_k \qquad \text{and} \qquad [L] = {}_k\bigoplus_1^r [\lambda_k + H_k].$$

We summarize our results.

4. **Theorem.** Let $|\lambda - L| = {}_k\Pi_1^r (\lambda - \lambda_k)^{a_k}$, set $L_k = L - \lambda_k$ ($k = 1, \ldots, r$), let L_k have index q_k, and denote by N_k the nullspace of $L_k^{q_k}$. Then $\dim N_k = a_k$, the spaces N_k are independent, and $X = {}_k\bigoplus_1^r N_k$. In a basis adapted to the

spaces N_k, $[L] = {}_k\bigoplus^r [\lambda_k + H_k]$, where $\lambda_k + H_k$ is of order a_k and H_k is nilpotent of index q_k on N_k.

5. Example. Consider the matrix

$$L = \tfrac{1}{4} \begin{bmatrix} 7 & 3 & -3 & 5 \\ 3 & 3 & 1 & -3 \\ -5 & 3 & 5 & 1 \\ 3 & -1 & 5 & 5 \end{bmatrix}.$$

Here $|\lambda - L| = (\lambda - 2)^3(\lambda + 1)$ and the eigenvalues are $\lambda_1 = 2$ and $\lambda_2 = -1$.

$$L_1 = L - 2 = \tfrac{1}{4} \begin{bmatrix} -1 & 3 & -3 & 5 \\ 3 & -5 & 1 & -3 \\ -5 & 3 & -3 & 1 \\ 3 & -1 & 5 & -3 \end{bmatrix}$$

has rank 3, L_1^2 has rank 2, and

$$L_1^3 = \tfrac{27}{4} \begin{bmatrix} -1 & 1 & -1 & 1 \\ 1 & -1 & 1 & -1 \\ -1 & 1 & -1 & 1 \\ 1 & -1 & 1 & -1 \end{bmatrix}$$

and L_1^4 both have rank 1; hence the index of L_1 is 3. By inspection, one basis for N_1, the nullspace of L_1^3, is

$$[1 \quad 1 \quad 0 \quad 0]^t, \qquad [0 \quad 1 \quad 1 \quad 0]^t, \qquad \text{and} \qquad [0 \quad 0 \quad 1 \quad 1]^t,$$

while a basis for R_1 is $[-1 \quad 1 \quad -1 \quad 1]^t$. With these vectors, in this order, as a basis, and as columns of a matrix T, we find that

$$T^{-1}LT = \tfrac{1}{16} \begin{bmatrix} 3 & 1 & -1 & 1 \\ -2 & 2 & 2 & -2 \\ 1 & -1 & 1 & 3 \\ -1 & 1 & -1 & 1 \end{bmatrix} \begin{bmatrix} 7 & 3 & -3 & 5 \\ 3 & 3 & 1 & -3 \\ -5 & 3 & 5 & 1 \\ 3 & 1 & 5 & 5 \end{bmatrix} \begin{bmatrix} 1 & 0 & 0 & -1 \\ 1 & 1 & 0 & 1 \\ 0 & 1 & 1 & -1 \\ 0 & 0 & 1 & 1 \end{bmatrix}$$

$$= \tfrac{1}{16} \begin{bmatrix} 40 & 0 & 8 & 0 \\ -16 & 16 & -16 & 0 \\ 8 & 16 & 40 & 0 \\ 0 & 0 & 0 & -16 \end{bmatrix}.$$

The matrix of order 1 in the lower right corner has, of course, the eigenvalue $\lambda_2 = -1$ with $a_2 = 1$; here H_2 is a zero-matrix of order 1. The matrix of order 3 in the upper left corner is $H_1 + 2$. We find readily that

$$2H_1 = \begin{bmatrix} 1 & 0 & 1 \\ -2 & -2 & -2 \\ 1 & 2 & 1 \end{bmatrix},$$

and verify that, as expected, $H_1^2 \ne 0$ but $H_1^3 = 0$.

EXERCISES

6. An operator L on X_n has n distinct eigenvalues. Prove that each has index 1 and show again (cf. A10) that there is a coordinate system in which $[L] = [[\lambda_1, \lambda_2, \ldots, \lambda_n]]$. (T)

7. The matrix

$$M = \tfrac{1}{4} \begin{bmatrix} 9 & 7 & 1 & 3 \\ 1 & 7 & 1 & -1 \\ -4 & -4 & 4 & 6 \\ 0 & 0 & 0 & 4 \end{bmatrix}$$

has the characteristic polynomial $(\lambda - 2)^2(\lambda - 1)^2$. Perform the reduction supplied by 4.

D. Nilpotent Operators

We begin by experimenting with an operator which will turn out to be broadly typical. Consider an operator L on X_n and a basis $\{p_k\}$ for X_n such that, in the matrix $[L] = [\alpha_{jk}]$ of L with respect to the basis $\{p_k\}$, $\alpha_{jk} = 0$ *except* that

1.
$$\alpha_{12} = \alpha_{23} = \ldots = \alpha_{j\,j+1} = \ldots = \alpha_{n-1\,n} = 1.$$

That is,

2.
$$[L] = \begin{bmatrix} 0 & 1 & 0 & \ldots & 0 & 0 \\ 0 & 0 & 1 & \ldots & 0 & 0 \\ 0 & 0 & 0 & \ldots & 0 & 0 \\ \cdot & \cdot & \cdot & \ldots & \cdot & \cdot \\ \cdot & \cdot & \cdot & \ldots & 1 & 0 \\ 0 & 0 & 0 & \ldots & 0 & 1 \\ 0 & 0 & 0 & \ldots & 0 & 0 \end{bmatrix}.$$

$[L]$ has 1's on the first super-diagonal and 0's elsewhere. One sees readily that

3.
$$Lp_1 = 0, \qquad Lp_2 = p_1, \ldots, \qquad Lp_{k+1} = p_k, \ldots, \qquad Lp_n = p_{n-1}.$$

It follows that $L^{n-1}X = \langle p_1 \rangle \neq \langle 0 \rangle$ while $L^n = 0$; thus L is nilpotent of index n.

What happens if some of the 1's on the first super-diagonal are replaced by 0's? If for example $\alpha_{q\,q+1} = 0$, then $Lp_{q+1} = 0$, $L^2p_{q+2} = 0$, and so on. Experimentation using multiplication by blocks convinces one that the length of the *longest* string of consecutive 1's is decisive. If there is a string of $p - 1$ consecutive 1's on the super-diagonal, but no longer string, then $L^{p-1} \neq 0$ but $L^p = 0$, and L has index p.

284

It may be shown easily (see 14) that if operators K and L are similar, and either is nilpotent of index p, then so is the other. Our aim is to show that if L is nilpotent of index p (≥ 2) then a basis can be found in which $[L]$ has 0's except on the first super-diagonal, and each element on the first super-diagonal is either 0 or 1, and the longest string of consecutive 1's is of length $p - 1$. In fact, $[L]$ will consist of boxes along the diagonal of the form

4.
$$J_h = \begin{bmatrix} 0 & 1 & 0 & \cdots & 0 & 0 \\ 0 & 0 & 1 & \cdots & 0 & 0 \\ 0 & 0 & 0 & \cdots & 0 & 0 \\ \cdot & \cdot & \cdot & \cdots & \cdot & \cdot \\ \cdot & \cdot & \cdot & \cdots & 1 & 0 \\ 0 & 0 & 0 & \cdots & 0 & 1 \\ 0 & 0 & 0 & \cdots & 0 & 0 \end{bmatrix},$$

where J_h is an $h \times h$ matrix with $\alpha_{12} = \alpha_{23} = \ldots = \alpha_{h-1\,h} = 1$ and zeros elsewhere.

Let the operator L on X_n be nilpotent of index p. Assign g the domain $1, 2, \ldots, p$. Let N_g denote the nullspace of L^g and let $n_g = \dim N_g$; of course $N_p = X$ and $n_p = n$. Let $W_1 = N_1$ and, for $g = 2, \ldots, n$, let W_g denote a complement of N_{g-1} in N_g; thus

5.
$$N_g = N_{g-1} \oplus W_g = W_1 \oplus \ldots \oplus W_{g-1} \oplus W_g \qquad (g = 2, \ldots, p).$$

Define

6.
$$d_g = \dim W_g = n_g - n_{g-1};$$

here we agree, conventionally, that $n_0 = 0$. It follows that $\sum d_g = n_p = n$.

Now $d_p > 0$ because $L^{p-1} \neq 0$ while $L^p = 0$. It will follow from an argument to which we now turn that

7.
$$0 < d_p \leq d_{p-1} \leq \ldots \leq d_2 \leq d_1 = n_1.$$

Let us consider a typical W_g with $g \geq 2$. Let v_{ghg} ($h_g = 1, \ldots, d_k$) be a basis for W_g. These vectors are independent and belong to N_g but, since $N_{g-1} \cap W_g = \langle 0 \rangle$, they do not belong to N_{g-1}. Let us examine the vectors

8.
$$Lv_{g1}, \ldots, Lv_{ghg}$$

and the subspace

$$Z = \langle Lv_{g1}, \ldots, Lv_{ghg} \rangle.$$

Since L^{g-1} annihilates each of the vectors in 8, $Z \leq N_{g-1}$.

We wish to show that $Z \cap N_{g-2} = \langle 0 \rangle$. If $L^{g-2}z = 0$, where

$$z = \sum \alpha_{h_g} Lv_{ghg} = L \sum \alpha_{h_g} v_{ghg},$$

then $L^{g-1} \sum \alpha_{h_g} v_{ghg} = 0$ and a linear combination of v_{ghg} belongs to N_{g-1}. This vector, however, is also in W_g and therefore vanishes. Hence $z = 0$ and $Z \cap N_{g-2} = \langle 0 \rangle$.

Since $g \geq 2$, in fact, no combination of the v_{gh_g} can belong to N_1. In other words, the vectors of 8 are independent. Thus W_{g-1} contains at least the d_g independent vectors 8, and

9.
$$d_{g-1} = \dim W_{g-1} \geq \dim Z = d_g.$$

The foregoing facts justify a process for obtaining the results displayed in the accompanying Table 10. First we choose a basis $w_{p1}, \ldots, w_{pd_p}$ for W_p. Proceeding recursively, suppose that a basis $v_1, \ldots, v_{d_{g+1}}$ is available for W_{g+1}. Form the vectors

$$Lv_1, \ldots, Lv_{d_{g+1}}.$$

If $d_g = d_{g+1}$ these vectors form a basis for W_g. If $d_g > d_{g+1}$, we choose $d_g - d_{g+1}$ further vectors $w_{g\,d_{g+1}+1}, \ldots, w_{gd_g}$ in such a way that the vectors

$$Lv_1, \ldots, Lv_{d_{g+1}}, w_{g\,d_{g+1}+1}, \ldots, w_{gd_g}$$

are independent and the subspace W_g they generate is a complement of N_{g-1} in N_g : $N_g = N_{g-1} \oplus W_g$. The vectors on row g of 10 constitute a basis for W_g.

From the construction of the table, and the argument concerning the vectors 8, it follows that the vectors in 10 are independent. Moreover, there are d_p columns with p elements, $d_{p-1} - d_p$ columns with $p - 1$ elements, ..., and $d_1 - d_2$ columns with one element; and

$$pd_p + (p - 1)(d_{p-1} - d_p) + \ldots + g(d_g - d_{g+1}) + \ldots$$
$$+ 1(d_1 - d_2) = \sum d_g = n.$$

The vectors in 10, therefore, span the space X.

In order to arrive at a basis for X we have merely to assign an order to the vectors in 10. The effect of L is to annul each vector in $W_1 = N_1$, those on the bottom row in 10, and to map each vector not in N_1 onto the one immediately below it. The vectors in each of the n_1 *columns* of 10 generate a subspace S_j ($j = 1, \ldots, n_1$) which is invariant under L, and X is the direct sum of these subspaces: $X = \oplus_j S_j$. Moreover, no vector in S_j is the image under L of any vector in S_h if $h \neq j$. If we choose bases in each S_j separately, then, by an obvious extension of 10, $[L]$ will consist of n_1 blocks along the diagonal, one for each S_j, and zeros elsewhere.

As for the order of the vectors *within* a column (i.e., as a basis for S_j), we recall 3, and its relation to 2, and decide to order the vectors from bottom to top. The basis for S_1 is then

$$q_1 = L^{p-1}w_{p1}, \; q_2 = L^{p-2}w_{p1}, \; \ldots, \; q_{p-1} = Lw_{p1}, \; q_p = w_{p1}.$$

The corresponding contribution to $[L]$ will be a $p \times p$ block of the form J_p in 4. The basis for S_j will consist of the vectors in the jth column of 10, in order from bottom to top. The corresponding contribution to $[L]$ will be a block on the diagonal of the form $J_{\dim S_j}$ in 4. See the example in 11. The subspaces S_j are often called *cyclic* subspaces.

Space	Dimension	Basis					On and below row of first occurrence
W_p	$d_p = n - n_{p-1}$	w_{pj_p}					$j_p = 1, \ldots, d_p$
W_{p-1}	$d_{p-1} = n_{p-1} - n_{p-2}$	Lw_{pj_p}	$w_{p-1,j_{p-1}}$				$j_{p-1} = d_p + 1, \ldots, d_{p-1}$
$\vdots$	$\vdots$						$\vdots$
W_g	$d_g = n_g - n_{g-1}$	$L^{p-g}w_{pj_p}$	$L^{p-g-1}w_{p-1,j_{p-1}}$	w_{gj_g}			$j_g = d_g + 1, \ldots, d_{g-1}$
$\vdots$	$\vdots$						$\vdots$
W_2	$d_2 = n_2 - n_1$	$L^{p-2}w_{pj_p}$	$L^{p-3}w_{p-1,j_{p-1}}$	$L^{p-g-1}w_{gj_g}$	w_{2j_2}		$j_2 = d_3 + 1, \ldots, d_2$
W_1	$d_1 = n_1$	$L^{p-1}w_{pj_p}$	$L^{p-2}w_{p-1,j_{p-1}}$	$L^{p-g}w_{gj_g}$	Lw_{2j_2}	w_{1j_1}	$j_1 = d_2 + 1, \ldots, d_1$
		S_{j_p}	$S_{j_{p-}}$	S_{j_g}	S_{j}	S_{j_1}	

10. Bases for spaces W_k and S_{j_g}.

Space	Dimension	Basis		
W_4	$d_4 = 1$	$w_{41} = q_4$		
W_3	$d_3 = 1$	$Lw_{41} = q_3$		
W_2	$d_2 = 2$	$L^2w_{41} = q_2$	$w_{22} = q_6$	
W_1	$d_1 = 3$	$L^3w_{41} = q_1$	$Lw_{22} = q_5$	$w_{13} = q_7$
		S_1	S_2	S_3

$$
\begin{bmatrix}
0 & 1 & 0 & 0 \cdot 0 & & & \\
0 & 0 & 1 & 0 \cdot 0 & 0 & & \\
0 & 0 & 0 & 1 \cdot 0 & & & \\
0 & 0 & 0 & 0 \cdot 0 & 0 & 0 & \\
\multicolumn{7}{c}{\cdots\cdots\cdots\cdots\cdots} \\
& & & 0 \cdot 0 & 1 \cdot 0 & & \\
& 0 & & 0 \cdot 0 & 0 \cdot 0 & & \\
\multicolumn{7}{c}{\cdots\cdots\cdots} \\
& & & 0 \cdot 0 & 0 \cdot 0 & &
\end{bmatrix} = [L] \text{ in basis } \{q_h\} = J_4 \oplus J_2 \oplus J_1.
$$

11. Example with $n = 7$, $p = 4$, $n_1 = 3$, $n_2 = 5$, $n_3 = 6$, $n_4 = 7$; for J_h see 4.

Our results may be summarized in the following theorem; the form of a nilpotent $[L]$ occurring here is its *classical* or *Jordan* canonical form under similarity.

12. Theorem. Let the operator L be nilpotent of index p on X_n. With $g = 1, \ldots, p$, let N_g denote the nullspace of L^g, let $n_g = \dim N_g$, and define $d_g = n_g - n_{g-1}$ (with $n_0 = 0$).
Then
$$0 < d_p \leq d_{p-1} \leq \ldots \leq d_2 \leq d_1 = n_1$$
and there exists a basis for X in which $[L]$ has all entries zero except for boxes of the form J_h on the diagonal; there will be d_p boxes J_p, $d_{p-1} - d_p$ boxes $J_{p-1}, \ldots, d_{g-1} - d_g$ boxes $J_g, \ldots, d_2 - d_3$ boxes J_2, and $d_1 - d_2$ boxes J_1. A basis with this property is given by the vectors in 10, in which those in column j precede those in column $j + 1$, and, in column j, the vectors are ordered from bottom to top.

EXAMPLE

13. The matrix $L = \begin{vmatrix} 1 & 1 & 3 \\ 5 & 2 & 6 \\ -2 & -1 & -3 \end{vmatrix}$ has $L^2 = \begin{vmatrix} 0 & 0 & 0 \\ 3 & 3 & 9 \\ -1 & -1 & -3 \end{vmatrix}$ and $L^3 = 0$; L is of

index 3. Here $n_3 = 3$, $n_2 = 2$, and $n_1 = 1$; $d_3 = d_2 = d_1 = 1$. The vector
$$w_{31} = [1 \quad 1 \quad 3]^t$$
is not annulled by L^2. If we introduce w_{31},
$$Lw_{31} = [11 \quad 25 \quad -12]^t, \quad \text{and} \quad L^2w_{31} = [0 \quad 3 \quad -1]^t$$

as a basis, we find that

$$-\tfrac{1}{121}\begin{bmatrix} 87 & -45 & 14 \\ -10 & 1 & 3 \\ -11 & -11 & 33 \end{bmatrix} L \begin{bmatrix} 0 & 11 & 1 \\ 3 & 25 & 1 \\ -1 & -12 & 3 \end{bmatrix} = \begin{bmatrix} 0 & 1 & 0 \\ 0 & 0 & 1 \\ 0 & 0 & 0 \end{bmatrix}.$$

EXERCISES

14. Let L be nilpotent on X_n with index $p < n$. What is the characteristic equation of L? Does L satisfy the equation? Can you find an equation of lower degree which L satisfies? (T)

15. Suppose that L is nilpotent of index p and that K is similar to L. Prove that K is nilpotent of index p.

16. Give a direct proof that the n vectors of 10 are independent.

17. Let L be nilpotent of index p on X_n, and let the numbers d_g have the meaning assigned to them in the text. Let $g = p, p-1, \ldots, 1$, let $\beta_g = d_{g+1} + 1, \ldots, d_g$ (with $d_{p+1} = 0$), and $\gamma_g = g - 1, \ldots, 0$ (and agree that $L^0 = I$). Verify that the vectors of 10 are given by

$$L^{\gamma_g} w_{g\beta_g}$$

and that they are enumerated in the order which yields the canonical form for L by the following rule, as g takes on the values $p, p-1, \ldots, 1$:

With g and β_g fixed, let $\gamma_g = g - 1, \ldots, 0$.
If $\beta_g < d_g$, increase β_g by 1 and let γ_g run again.
If $\beta_g = d_g$, decrease g by 1, replace β_g by $d_g + 1$ and start over.

E. The Jordan Canonical Form

Our goal is now within reach. We return to the decomposition of C4. In each space N_k choose a basis so that H_k is in the canonical form delivered by D12. The diagonal terms λ_k are unaffected by a similarity transformation. The resulting block $[\lambda_k + H_k]$ has λ_k in every position on the diagonal, and strings of 1's down the first super-diagonal, the strings of 1's not increasing in length from top to bottom, and 0's elsewhere.

1. Jordan Canonical Form. Let L be a linear operator on a complex space X_n and suppose that

$$|\lambda - L| = {}_k\Pi_1^r (\lambda - \lambda_k)^a k$$

with λ_k ($k = 1, \ldots, r$) distinct. Let $L_k = L - \lambda_k I$ have index q_k and define N_k to be the nullspace of $L_k^{q_k}$. Then dim $N_k = a_k$ and $X = {}_k\bigoplus_1^r N_k$. In a basis adapted to the spaces N_k, $[L]$ has r boxes on the diagonal, the kth box being of order a_k, and zeros elsewhere. The kth box is of the form $\lambda_k I_{a_k} + H_k$, where H_k is in the normal form, given by D12, of the matrix of the restriction to N_k of the nilpotent operator L_k, of index q_k.

2. Example. Reconsider (cf. C5) the matrix

$$L = \tfrac{1}{4}\begin{bmatrix} 7 & 3 & -3 & 5 \\ 3 & 3 & 1 & -3 \\ -5 & 3 & 5 & 1 \\ 3 & -1 & 5 & 5 \end{bmatrix}.$$

Since $|\lambda I - L| = (\lambda - 2)^3(\lambda + 1)$, the eigenvalues are 2 and -1. We deal first with

$$L_1 = M - 2I = \tfrac{1}{4}\begin{bmatrix} -1 & 3 & -3 & 5 \\ 3 & -5 & 1 & -3 \\ -5 & 3 & -3 & 1 \\ 3 & -1 & 5 & -3 \end{bmatrix}.$$

L_1 has rank 3 and N_{L_1} is generated by $[1 \quad 1 \quad -1 \quad -1]^t$.

$$L_1^2 = \tfrac{1}{2}\begin{bmatrix} 5 & -4 & 5 & -4 \\ -4 & 5 & -4 & 5 \\ 4 & -5 & 4 & -5 \\ -5 & 4 & 5 & 4 \end{bmatrix}.$$

L_1^2 has rank 2 and $N_{L_1^2}$ is generated by

$$[1 \quad 0 \quad -1 \quad 0]^t \quad \text{and} \quad [0 \quad 1 \quad 0 \quad -1]^t.$$

$$L_1^3 = \tfrac{27}{4}\begin{bmatrix} -1 & 1 & -1 & 1 \\ 1 & -1 & 1 & -1 \\ -1 & 1 & -1 & 1 \\ 1 & -1 & 1 & -1 \end{bmatrix}.$$

L_1^3 has rank 1 and so does L_1^4. Hence L_1 is of index 3.

We apply the process developed in D12 for obtaining a basis for $N_{L_1^3}$. The vector $w_{31} = \tfrac{1}{2}[1 \quad 1 \quad 1 \quad 1]^t$ is in $N_{L_1^3}$ but not in $N_{L_1^2}$. We form the vectors

$$L_1 w_{31} = \tfrac{1}{2}[1 \quad -1 \quad -1 \quad 1]^t$$

and

$$L_1^2 w_{31} = 2[1 \quad 1 \quad -1 \quad -1]^t.$$

The vectors $L_1^2 w_{31}$, $L_1 w_{31}$, and w_{31} form a basis for $N_{L_1^3}$.

As for $L_2 = L + I$, corresponding to the eigenvalue -1, its rank is 3 and a corresponding eigenvector is $v = [-1 \quad 1 \quad -1 \quad 1]^t$.

We now introduce as basis, by a transformation T, the vectors $L_1^2 w_{31}$, $L_1 w_{31}$, w_{31}, and v, normalizing them. We verify that

$T^{-1}LT$

$$= \tfrac{1}{16} \begin{bmatrix} 1 & 1 & -1 & -1 \\ 1 & -1 & -1 & 1 \\ 1 & 1 & 1 & 1 \\ -1 & 1 & -1 & 1 \end{bmatrix} \begin{bmatrix} 7 & 3 & -3 & 5 \\ 3 & 3 & 1 & -3 \\ -5 & 3 & 5 & 1 \\ 3 & -1 & 5 & 5 \end{bmatrix} \begin{bmatrix} 1 & 1 & 1 & -1 \\ 1 & -1 & 1 & 1 \\ -1 & -1 & 1 & -1 \\ -1 & 1 & 1 & 1 \end{bmatrix}$$

$$= \begin{bmatrix} 2 & 1 & 0 & 0 \\ 0 & 2 & 1 & 0 \\ 0 & 0 & 2 & 0 \\ 0 & 0 & 0 & -1 \end{bmatrix};$$

this is the Jordan normal form for L.

As an application, consider the differential equations $\dot{x} = Lx$. Put $x = Ty$, obtaining $\dot{y} = T^{-1}LTy$. If $y = [\xi \ \ \eta \ \ \zeta \ \ \theta]^t$, then the equations are

$$\dot{\xi} = 2\xi + \eta, \qquad \dot{\eta} = 2\eta + \zeta, \qquad \dot{\zeta} = 2\zeta, \qquad \dot{\theta} = -\theta.$$

The homogeneous equations for θ and ζ can be solved immediately. With ζ known the nonhomogeneous equation for η can be solved, and then ξ can be found from the first equation. Observe that the final calculations will usually be simpler than they will with L merely in super-diagonal form (cf. B1).

We now exploit the detailed form of the H_k given by D12. Suppose that there are n_k strings of 1's on the first super-diagonal in H_k, and that the lengths of the successive strings are

$$q_{k1} - 1, q_{k2} - 1, \ldots, q_{kn_k} - 1,$$

occurring in sub-boxes of orders $q_{k1}, \ldots, q_{kn_k}$, so that $_j\sum_1^{n_k} q_{kj} = a_k$. Here $q_{kj} \geq q_{kj+1}$, and $q_{kj} = 1$ if and only if the string is vacuous. In the following example $a_k = 4$, $n_k = 2$, $q_{k1} = 3$, and $q_{k2} = 1$:

$$\begin{bmatrix} \lambda_k & 1 & 0 & 0 \\ 0 & \lambda_k & 1 & 0 \\ 0 & 0 & \lambda_k & 0 \\ 0 & 0 & 0 & \lambda_k \end{bmatrix}.$$

The polynomials $(\lambda - \lambda_k)^{q_{kj}}$ $(j = 1, \ldots, n_k)$ are called the *elementary divisors* of L, associated with the eigenvalue λ_k; the integer q_{kj} is the *multiplicity* of the elementary divisor. Since similar operators have the same Jordan form, they have identical elementary divisors. There is an elaborate algebraic theory of elementary divisors, into which we cannot go here.

It is evident that $[L]$ in 1 will be diagonal if and only if $H_k = 0$ $(k = 1, \ldots, r)$. This will be true, in turn, if and only if each string of 1's is vacuous, $n_k = a_k$ $(k = 1, \ldots, r)$, and $q_{kj} = 1$ $(j = 1, \ldots, n_k)$. For each eigenvalue λ_k, in this situation, there are a_k independent eigenvectors, and the geometric multiplicity g_k is equal to the algebraic multiplicity a_k. To λ_k there correspond a_k elementary divisors $(\lambda - \lambda_k)^{q_{kj}}$; an elementary divisor for which $q_{kj} = 1$ is said to be *simple*. It follows that *a matrix is similar to a diagonal matrix if and only if each of its elementary divisors is simple.*

Consider now the operator

3.
$$_k\Pi_1^r L_k^{q_{k1}}.$$

Since $q_{k1} - 1$ is the length of a longest string of consecutive 1's in H_k, $q_{k1} = q_k$, the index of L_k. It follows that $L_k^{q_{k1}} X_k = 0$, while $L_k^p X_k \neq 0$ if $p < q_{k1}$. Since the operators L_k commute, we see that the operator 3 annuls X; in other words the operator is zero. If any one of the exponents were decreased, moreover, the operator 3 would not be zero.

The polynomial

4.
$$g(L; \lambda) = {}_k\Pi_1^r (\lambda - \lambda_k)^{q_{k1}}$$

is called the *minimal polynomial* of L, and the equation

5.
$$g(L; \lambda) = 0$$

is the *minimal equation* of L. The remarks following 4 show that if we form the polynomial $g(L; \lambda)$, and then substitute L for the scalar variable λ, then $g(L; L)$ is the operator 4 and, therefore, vanishes. We express this by saying that L satisfies its minimal equation: $g(L; L) = 0$.

6. Every operator on a complex linear space satisfies its minimal equation, but satisfies no algebraic equation of lower degree.

We observe now that $q_{k1} \leq a_k$ $(k = 1, \ldots, r)$. It follows that the minimal polynomial $g(L; \lambda)$ of 4 divides the characteristic polynomial $f(L; \lambda)$ of A2. We arrive, by 6, at the celebrated Hamilton-Cayley Theorem.

7. Every operator on a complex linear space satisfies its own characteristic equation; $f(L; L) = 0$.

It is evident that we know all there is to know about an operator L, and every operator similar to L, if we can write down the Jordan form for $[L]$. What does it take to do this? First of all, we need the eigenvalues λ_k and their algebraic multiplicities a_k $(k = 1, \ldots, r)$; these we can get from the factored form of the characteristic polynomial. The integer a_k gives the size of the box having λ_k on the diagonal. We also need the numbers n_k of strings of consecutive 1's on the first super-diagonal of the kth box, and the numbers q_{kj} $(j = 1, \ldots, n_k)$ determining the lengths of the strings of 1's. The n_k's and the q_{kj}'s come from the analysis, as in D12, of L_k, which is nilpotent of index q_k $(= q_{k1})$ on the space N_k of C2.

8. The numbers λ_k, a_k, n_k $(k = 1, \ldots, r)$ and q_{kj} $(j = 1, \ldots, n_k)$ form a complete set of invariants under similarity for operators L on a complex linear space.

The *Segre characteristic* of L results from writing down in parentheses in non-increasing order, all q_{kj} corresponding to each λ_k $(k = 1, \ldots, r)$, thus:

$$(q_{11}q_{12} \ldots q_{1n_1}) \ldots (q_{k1} \ldots q_{kn_k}) \ldots (q_{r1} \ldots q_{rn_r}).$$

Since $_j\sum_1^{n_k} q_{kj} = a_k$ $(k = 1, \ldots, r)$, the Segre characteristic enables us to infer the values of a_k and, consequently, of $n = \sum a_k$. We can write down the Jordan form, therefore, if we have the Segre characteristic and the corresponding eigenvalues. For example, if $\lambda_1 = \alpha$ and $\lambda_2 = \beta$ and the Segre characteristic is (3 1)(2 1), then the canonical form is

$$\begin{bmatrix} \alpha & 1 & 0 & 0 & 0 & 0 & 0 \\ 0 & \alpha & 1 & 0 & 0 & 0 & 0 \\ 0 & 0 & \alpha & 0 & 0 & 0 & 0 \\ 0 & 0 & 0 & \alpha & 0 & 0 & 0 \\ 0 & 0 & 0 & 0 & \beta & 1 & 0 \\ 0 & 0 & 0 & 0 & 0 & \beta & 0 \\ 0 & 0 & 0 & 0 & 0 & 0 & \beta \end{bmatrix}.$$

There is a related pattern of numbers called the Weyr characteristic; see [A48].

EXERCISES

9. Prove that if L is regular on X_n, then L^{-1} can be expressed as a polynomial in L of degree at most $n - 1$. (T)

10. Assuming that $\lambda \neq 0$, find the inverses of

$$J = \begin{bmatrix} \lambda & 1 \\ 0 & \lambda \end{bmatrix}, \qquad K = \begin{bmatrix} \lambda & 1 & 0 \\ 0 & \lambda & 1 \\ 0 & 0 & \lambda \end{bmatrix}.$$

Find also the Jordan normal forms for J^{-1} and K^{-1}.

11. A 5×5 matrix L has characteristic polynomial $f(\lambda) = (\lambda - 2)^3(\lambda + 3)^2$. Write down all possible Jordan canonical forms for L.

12. A 6×6 matrix L has characteristic polynomial $f(\lambda) = (\lambda - 2)^4(\lambda + 1)^2$ and minimal polynomial $(\lambda - 2)^2(\lambda + 1)$. What are the possible elementary divisors of L? What can you say about its Jordan canonical form?

13. An operator L has eigenvalues α, β, γ, and Segre characteristic (3 3 1)(2 2) (1 1). What is the order of L? Write down the boxes L_α, L_β, and L_γ corresponding to α, β, and γ in the Jordan normal form for L.

14. Prove that each eigenvalue of L is a linear combination of the elements of L. (Cf. 8C17.) (T)

F. Companion Matrices

We have seen in A13 that a monic polynomial $f(\lambda) = \sum_0^n \alpha_k \lambda^k$, having $\alpha_n = 1$, is the characteristic polynomial of its companion matrix

1.

$$L = \begin{bmatrix} 0 & 0 & \ldots & 0 & -\alpha_0 \\ 1 & 0 & \ldots & 0 & -\alpha_1 \\ 0 & 1 & \ldots & 0 & -\alpha_2 \\ \cdot & \cdot & \ldots & \cdot & \cdot \\ \cdot & \cdot & \ldots & \cdot & \cdot \\ \cdot & \cdot & \ldots & \cdot & \cdot \\ 0 & 0 & \ldots & 0 & -\alpha_{n-2} \\ 0 & 0 & \ldots & 1 & -\alpha_{n-1} \end{bmatrix},$$

which has every entry 0 except for 1's on the sub-diagonal and the last column, where the kth entry is $-\alpha_{k-1}$ $(k = 1, \ldots, n)$, the coefficient of λ^{k-1} in $f(\lambda)$.

The effect of L on the basis vectors is easily seen:

2.
$$L p_k = p_{k+1} \qquad (k = 1, \ldots, n - 1),$$
$$L p_n = -\alpha_0 p_1 - \alpha_1 p_2 - \ldots - \alpha_{n-1} p_n,$$
$$L^n p_1 = -(\alpha_0 + \alpha_1 L + \ldots + \alpha_{n-1} L^{n-1}) p_1,$$

whence
3.
$$f(L) p_1 = 0.$$

As a consequence, the n vectors $L^h p_1 = p_{h+1}$ $(h = 0, \ldots, n - 1)$ form a basis.
For any $x \in X$, therefore,

4.
$$x = \sum \xi_k p_k = \sum \xi_k L^{k-1} p_1 = g(x; L) p_1$$

where $g(x; L)$ is a polynomial of degree $n - 1$ whose respective coefficients are the components of x with respect to the basis p_k. Now suppose that $h(\lambda) = \sum_0^{n-1} \xi_{j+1} \lambda^j$ is any polynomial in λ of degree at most $n - 1$. We use its coefficients to form a vector x_h, necessarily not zero, and we see from 4 that

$$x_h = g(x_h; L) p_1 = h(L) p_1 \neq 0.$$

It follows that, while $f(L) = 0$, L can satisfy no algebraic equation of degree less than n and, consequently, $f(\lambda)$ *is the minimal polynomial for L.*

An interesting brief article on "The Companion Matrix and its Properties," by Louis Brand, appears in the *Am. Math. Monthly*, **71** (1964) No. 6. Like many authors, he uses the transpose of our L. His discussion of column eigenvectors can be imitated for row eigenvectors of our L.

Our reason for introducing companion matrices is that the Jordan canonical form is necessarily valid only in an algebraically closed field, while if the elements of L lie in a field F, then we can find, by operations that stay in F, a basis in which L is the direct sum of certain companion matrices.

One factors the characteristic polynomial $f(L; \lambda)$ into factors which are irreducible in F and knows that $L = T^{-1}L'T$, where L' is a direct sum of companion matrices, one for each irreducible factor of f, and T has entries in F. We say that L' is the *rational* (or *F-*) *canonical* form for L because L' can be obtained from L by rational operations in F.

To develop all details would require a considerable excursion into algebra. We are content, therefore, to illustrate with the polynomial $f(\lambda) = (\lambda^4 + 1)^2 = \lambda^8 + 2\lambda^4 + 1$. Its companion matrix L has zeros except for seven 1's on the sub-diagonal and the eighth column, which is

5.
$$[-1 \quad 0 \quad 0 \quad 0 \quad -2 \quad 0 \quad 0 \quad 0]^t.$$

The polynomial is reducible. The elementary divisors of the corresponding matrix L in certain fields are as follows:

6. complex $\qquad (\lambda - \theta_k)^2, \; \theta_k = e^{k\pi i/4} \; (k = 1, 3, 5, 7);$

7. real $\qquad (\lambda^2 + \lambda\sqrt{2} + 1)^2, (\lambda^2 - \lambda\sqrt{2} + 1)^2;$

8. rational $\qquad (\lambda^4 + 1)^2.$

The rational canonical form for the rational field was given above. The rational canonical form for the real field is the direct sum

9.
$$\begin{bmatrix} 0 & 0 & 0 & -1 \\ 1 & 0 & 0 & -2\sqrt{2} \\ 0 & 1 & 0 & -4 \\ 0 & 0 & 1 & -2\sqrt{2} \end{bmatrix} \quad \text{and} \quad \begin{bmatrix} 0 & 0 & 0 & -1 \\ 1 & 0 & 0 & +2\sqrt{2} \\ 0 & 1 & 0 & -4 \\ 0 & 0 & 1 & +2\sqrt{2} \end{bmatrix}.$$

The rational canonical form for the complex field is the direct sum of four boxes:

10.
$$\begin{bmatrix} 0 & -i \\ 1 & 2\theta_1 \end{bmatrix}, \quad \begin{bmatrix} 0 & i \\ 1 & 2\theta_3 \end{bmatrix}, \quad \begin{bmatrix} 0 & -i \\ 1 & 2\theta_5 \end{bmatrix}, \quad \begin{bmatrix} 0 & i \\ 1 & 2\theta_7 \end{bmatrix}.$$

The Jordan canonical form is the direct sum of

11.
$$\begin{bmatrix} \theta_k & 1 \\ 0 & \theta_k \end{bmatrix}$$

for $k = 1, 3, 5, 7$.

It is worth noting that, for example,

12.
$$\begin{bmatrix} 0 & 1 \\ 1 & \theta_1 \end{bmatrix}\begin{bmatrix} 0 & -i \\ 1 & 2\theta_1 \end{bmatrix}\begin{bmatrix} -\theta_1 & 1 \\ 1 & 0 \end{bmatrix} = \begin{bmatrix} \theta_1 & 1 \\ 0 & \theta_1 \end{bmatrix};$$

the similarity transformation leading from the rational to the Jordan form is not unitary.

EXERCISES

13. Write down the companion matrix L for the polynomial $f(\lambda) = \lambda^4 - 1$. What are the eigenvalues of L? The eigenvectors? The Jordan normal form?

14. What is the companion matrix for a nilpotent operator?

15. It is evident from 1 that L is regular if and only if $|L| = (-1)^n \alpha_0 \neq 0$. Verify that if $\alpha_0 \neq 0$, then the inverse of L is given by

$$
L^{-1} = \begin{bmatrix}
-\dfrac{\alpha_1}{\alpha_0} & 1 & 0 & \cdots & 0 & 0 \\[2ex]
-\dfrac{\alpha_2}{\alpha_0} & 0 & 1 & \cdots & 0 & 0 \\[1ex]
\cdot & \cdot & \cdot & \cdots & \cdot & \cdot \\
\cdot & \cdot & \cdot & \cdots & \cdot & \cdot \\
\cdot & \cdot & \cdot & \cdots & \cdot & \cdot \\[1ex]
-\dfrac{\alpha_{n-1}}{\alpha_0} & 0 & 0 & \cdots & 0 & 1 \\[2ex]
-\dfrac{1}{\alpha_0} & 0 & 0 & \cdots & 0 & 0
\end{bmatrix}.
$$

THIRTEEN
Unitary and Euclidean Spaces

The ideas of length, distance, and angle were prominent in our study (Chap. 3) of vectors in three-dimensional Euclidean space, but these metric ideas have not appeared since then. Having seen what can be done without measurement, in the strict sense of the word, we turn now to the rich properties of spaces in which measurement is possible. Spaces having an inner (or scalar) product (x, y), in which a vector x has length $\sqrt{(x, x)}$, are of particular importance, both theoretical and practical. A complex (real) space with an inner product is said to be a unitary (Euclidean) space. Such a space is self-dual, in a sense that will be clarified below (F). An operator $L : X \to X$ on such a space has an adjoint $L^a : X \to X$ related in a very intimate way to its dual $L^d : X^d \to X^d$. Of special interest, naturally enough, are those operators which preserve lengths and distances.

A. Norm and Distance

We recall the great utility of the length, or norm, of a vector in E_p. Let us say that a real-valued function on a linear space X, with the value of the function at x designated by $||x||$, is a *norm* on X if:

1.
$$||0|| = 0; \text{ if } x \neq 0 \text{ then } ||x|| > 0;$$

2.
$$||\alpha x|| = |\alpha| \, ||x||;$$

and

3.
$$||x + y|| \leq ||x|| + ||y||.$$

A linear space on which a norm is defined is called a *normed* linear space. On C_n (or R_n), for example, with $p \geq 1$, define

4.
$$||x||_p = [\sum |\xi_k|^p]^{1/p}.$$

Properties 1 and 2 are obvious. That $||x||_p$ satisfies 3 (often called the "triangle inequality") is known in the literature as "Minkowski's Inequality"; we omit its derivation (cf. 3K24 for $p = 2$). It is enlightening to take $n = 2$

and draw the unit circles $||x||_p = 1$ for various values of p. One can show that as $p \to \infty$

5.
$$||x||_p \to \max_k |\xi_k|,$$

and the latter, often denoted by $||x||_\infty$, is also a norm in C_n with its natural basis.

As another example, consider the space of those real-valued functions $\alpha \to f(\alpha)$ defined for $0 \le \alpha \le 1$ in such a way that f^2 is integrable; take $||f||^2 = \int_0^1 f^2(\alpha)\,d\alpha$.

We are thinking of $||x||$ and $||y||$ as the lengths of the vectors x and y. The distance between their endpoints is

6.
$$d(x, y) = ||x - y||,$$

which is simply the length of $x - y$. The real-valued function d has these properties:

6.1. $\qquad\qquad d(x, x) = 0$; if $x \ne y$ then $d(x, y) > 0$;

6.2. $\qquad\qquad d(x, y) = d(y, x)$;

and

6.3. $\qquad\qquad d(x, z) \le d(x, y) + d(y, z)$.

The first two properties are obvious and the third follows from the triangle inequality applied to

$$||x - z|| = ||(x - y) + (y - z)||.$$

A set S and a function $d : S \times S \to R$ having properties 6.1–3 is called a *metric space*, and d is called the *distance function* or the *metric*. Since it follows from the properties of the norm (1–3) that the function d of 6 is a distance function on X, we may say that *every normed linear space is a metric* (linear) *space*.

It is often possible to define several distance functions on a given set S. On R_1, for example, both

7.
$$d(\xi, \eta) = |\xi - \eta|, \qquad d'(\xi, \eta) = \frac{|\xi - \eta|}{1 + |\xi - \eta|}$$

are distance functions. The study of different metrics for a given underlying set S is an important part of the topological theory of metric spaces.

Given now a metric linear space X with metric d, it is an appealing idea to try to use $d(x, 0)$ as a norm. Our suspicions are aroused, however, by the fact that no use is made of the linear structure of the space in the requirements for d in 6.1–3. It will not be possible, in general, to prove that $d(\alpha x, 0) = |\alpha|$ $d(x, 0)$, which is requirement 2 for $||x||$. In a normed linear space, if $x \ne 0$, $||\alpha x||$ takes on every positive real value as α varies. In 7, however, $d'(\xi, 0) < 1$; it follows that d' cannot be derived by 6 from a norm for $\mathcal{R}_1$. The function d of 7 comes, of course, from $||\xi|| = |\xi|$.

Now let X_n be a normed linear space. It may be possible to introduce a norm into X^d, the space dual to X (see 7B), in a variety of ways, but there is a special norm in X^d which is induced, so to speak, by the norm in X, and will be used in X^d unless the contrary is explicitly stated. For $a \in X^d$ define

8.
$$||a|| = \max \{|ax| : ||x|| = 1\}.$$

It is a theorem of elementary analysis that the number on the right exists if dim X is finite, for then the set $||x|| = 1$ is "compact" and ax is continuous on that set. If dim X is infinite, then, on the right in 8, "max" must be replaced by "sup" (or "lub").

For example, the space dual to C_n with $||x||_p$ given by 4 is C_n with $||x||_q$ given by 4, with $p^{-1} + q^{-1} = 1$ (and $q = \infty$ (cf. 5) if $p = 1$).

Many details have been omitted because we shall be interested henceforth only in normed spaces in which the norm comes from an inner product, as explained in the next section.

EXERCISES

9. Prove (cf. 3D8) the "strong" triangle inequality:
$$|\ ||x|| - ||y||\ | \le ||x \pm y|| \le ||x|| + ||y||. \text{ (T)}$$

10. Prove that $||_i\sum_1^k \alpha_i x_i|| \le {}_i\sum_1^k |\alpha_i|\ ||x_i||.$ (T)

11. With $a \in X^d$ prove that $||a|| = \max \{|ax|/||x|| : x \in X, x \ne 0\}.$ (T)

12. Suppose that $x \in X$ and $a \in X^d$. Prove that $|ax| \le ||a||\ ||x||.$ (T)

13. In a linear space X_n, let a real-valued function $||x||$ have properties 2 and 3, and property 1' : $||x|| \ge 0$. Prove that the set X_0 of those $x \in X$ for which $||x|| = 0$ form a subspace; it follows incidentally that $||0|| = 0$. Prove also that if $X = X_0 \oplus Y$, then the restriction of $||x||$ to Y is a norm on Y. (T)

B. Inner Product

An *inner product* on a complex (real) space is a positive Hermitian (symmetric) functional. These functionals, or forms, were studied in Chap. 10. Being positive, an inner product has rank = signature = dim X.

The properties of an inner product are so important that we list them here for easy reference. As is usual in this context, we omit the symbol for the functional, writing merely (x, y).

Complex   Real

1.
$$\begin{cases} (x + y, z) = (x, z) + (y, z) \\ (x, y + z) = (x, y) + (x, z) \end{cases}$$

2.
$$\begin{cases} (\alpha x, y) = \bar{\alpha}(x, y), \qquad (\alpha x, y) = \alpha(x, y) \\ (x, \alpha y) = \alpha(x, y), \qquad (x, \alpha y) = \alpha(x, y) \end{cases}$$

3. $(y, x) = \overline{(x, y)},$ $(y, x) = (x, y)$

4. $(0,0) = 0;$ if $x \neq 0$ then $(x, x) > 0.$

Let p_k $(k = 1, \ldots, n)$ be a basis for X_n. In the complex case, 10B3 and 10C4 apply, and we see that

5. $(x, y) = \bar{x}^t H y = \sum \bar{\xi}_j \beta_{jk} \eta_k$

where

6. $\beta_{jk} = (p_j, p_k) = \bar{\beta}_{kj}.$

In the real case, similarly,

7. $(x, y) = x^t S y = \sum \xi_j \beta_{jk} \eta_k$

where

8. $\beta_{jk} = (p_j, p_k) = \beta_{kj}.$

When coordinates are changed, the matrix H transforms by conjunctivity (cf. 10B), while S transforms by congruence (cf. 10A). We know (10B19 and 10A38) that coordinates can be found in which $\beta_{jk} = \delta_{jk}$ $(k = 1, \ldots, n)$; such a coordinate system is said (see C) to be *orthonormal*. In any case, the matrix $[\beta_{jk}]$ is called the *metric* (more properly, the metric tensor).

A complex (real) linear space with an inner product is called a *unitary* (*Euclidean*) space. We deal henceforth only with such spaces. In what follows we shall speak usually of unitary spaces, leaving to the reader any trivial simplifications in the real case; nontrivial simplifications will be noted. A Hilbert space is an infinite-dimensional unitary space with certain convenient topological properties.

We begin with a fundamental inequality which obviously (from the proof) holds in any linear space with an inner product. Although there are good historical reasons for associating other names with it (Cauchy, Bouniakowski), we use only the name by which it is most frequently cited.

9. Schwarz' Inequality.

$$|(x, y)|^2 \leq (x, x)(y, y),$$

equality holding if and only if $(y, y)x = (y, x)y$.

Evidently

$$0 \leq (\alpha x + \beta y, \alpha x + \beta y) = |\alpha|^2(x, x) + \bar{\alpha}\beta(x, y) + \alpha\bar{\beta}\overline{(x, y)} + |\beta|^2(y, y).$$

On choosing $\alpha = (y, y)$ and $\beta = -\overline{(x, y)}$, we obtain

$$0 \leq ((y, y)x - \overline{(x, y)}y, (y, y)x - \overline{(x, y)}y)$$

$$= (y, y)[(x, x)(y, y) - |(x, y)|^2].$$

The result being trivial if $(y, y) = 0$, we assume $y \neq 0$ and obtain both the inequality and the condition for equality.

10. If (x, y) is an inner product on a complex space X_n, then $||x|| = \sqrt{(x, x)}$ is a norm on X.

Properties A1 and A2 are obvious from 4 and 3. To obtain A3 we start with

$$||x + y||^2 = (x + y, x + y) = (x, x) + (x, y) + (y, x) + (y, y)$$
$$\leq ||x||^2 + 2||x||\,||y|| + ||y||^2 = (||x|| + ||y||)^2$$

and take non-negative square roots; the *in*equality follows from 9 in the form

11. $$|(x, y)| \leq ||x||\,||y||.$$

If X is real, one may define an angle θ_{xy} by agreeing that

12. $$\cos \theta_{xy} = (x, y)/||x||\,||y||,$$

but we shall rarely use this idea.

It is worth noting that

$$||\alpha x||^2 = (\alpha x, \alpha x) = |\alpha|^2(x, x) = |\alpha|^2||x||^2.$$

For this reason, a norm arising from an inner product (cf. 10) is often called a "quadratic" norm; the value of $||x||^2$ is a Hermitian or quadratic form in the components of x.

Our present situation should be contrasted with that in Chap. 3. There the ideas of distance and angle were intuitive *data*, in terms of which norm and inner (scalar or dot) product were *defined*. Here the *datum* is an inner product, and norm and distance are *defined* in terms of the inner product. Our position is now entirely axiomatic; we are studying a linear space on which an inner product is defined a priori.

As foundations for the development of further consequences, however, the situations are conceptually equivalent. Many arguments in following sections will simply imitate those of 3I and 3K. In particular, the results regarding lines and *hyper*planes may be taken over almost verbatim.

We digress, for the sake of completeness, to comment on a question similar to that noticed in A. There we saw that not every metric linear space is normed (in the sense that there exists a norm from which the metric comes by definition A6). The question now is whether every norm comes from an inner product, as in 10. Given a normed linear space, is it always possible to define on it an inner product (x, y), having properties 1–4, such that $||x||^2 = (x, x)$?

A necessary condition consists in the fact that (cf. 10C6) if $||x||$ is a norm arising from an inner product (x, y), then

13. $$4(x, y) = ||x + y||^2 - ||x - y||^2 + i||ix + y||^2 - i||ix - y||^2$$

or, in the real case (cf. 10C2),

14.
$$4(x, y) = ||x + y||^2 - ||x - y||^2.$$

These relations are called *polarization identities*.

Given, now, merely a norm $x \to ||x||$, we observe that *if* there is an inner product (x, y) such that $||x||^2 = (x, x)$, then it can be calculated from the right member of 13 (or 14). Our only hope, then, is to use 13 (or 14) to *define* (x, y) and try to verify properties 1–4. This turns out to be possible if and only if the norm obeys the familiar "parallelogram law": if $x, y \in X$, then

15.
$$||x + y||^2 + ||x - y||^2 = 2(||x||^2 + ||y||^2).$$

Many equivalent conditions can be found in the literature. It is a consequence, for example, that the norm $||x||_p$ of A4 comes from an inner product if and only if $p = 2$.

Fortunately enough, many of the spaces that occur in analysis and in the applications have more or less natural inner products. In the study of Fourier series, for example, one may be interested in the space of complex-valued functions $\alpha \to x(\alpha)$ defined for $-\pi < \alpha < \pi$ in such a way that x^2 is integrable; in this space a very natural inner product is

16.
$$(x, y) = \int_{-\pi}^{\pi} \overline{x(\alpha)}y(\alpha) \, d\alpha.$$

Vectors x and y in a unitary space are said to be *orthogonal* (or perpendicular) if and only if $(x, y) = 0$. By 13, $(x, y) = 0$ if and only if both

$$||x + y||^2 = ||x - y||^2 \quad \text{and} \quad ||ix + y|| = ||ix - y||;$$

in a real space, by 14, the first condition is necessary and sufficient for orthogonality.

A vector x is said to be *normalized* or to be a *unit* vector if $||x|| = 1$. If $x \neq 0$, then (cf. 3C) $\hat{x} = x/||x||$ is a unit vector; x and $\hat{x}$ will be said to have the same *direction*.

EXERCISES

17. Let x have the property that $y \in X$ implies $(x, y) = 0$; prove that $x = 0$.

18. Prove that in a Euclidean space, $(x, y) = 0$ if and only if (Pythagoras) $||x + y||^2 = ||x||^2 + ||y||^2$. (Cf. 3I10(c).)

19. Let z be a fixed vector. For which vectors x is it true that $||x - z|| = 1, \leq 16, > -4, \geq 100$?

20. Let $z \neq 0$ be a fixed vector and write

$$x = (x, \hat{z})\hat{z} + (x - (x, \hat{z})\hat{z}).$$

The first vector on the right is called the (orthogonal) *projection* of x on z. The vector in parentheses on the right is in the plane of x and z (unless $x = 0$ or $x = \pm\hat{z}$) and is perpendicular to z. Thus the equation analyzes x into a part along z and a part perpendicular to z (cf. 3I6). (T)

21. Let S be any subset of X and define $S^\perp$ (read "S perp") by

$$S^\perp = \{x : y \in S \text{ implies } (y, x) = 0\}.$$

Prove that $S^\perp$ is a subspace of X and that $\langle S \rangle^\perp = S^\perp$. Prove also that if $Y \leq X$, then $Y \cap Y^\perp = \langle 0 \rangle$, and that $Z \leq Y$ implies $Y^\perp \leq Z^\perp$. (T)

22. In a unitary X_n, let $\{p_k\}$ $(k = 1, \ldots, n)$ be a basis. Prove that there exist vectors q_j $(j = 1, \ldots, n)$ such that $(q_j, p_k) = \delta_{jk}$ $(j, k = 1, \ldots, n)$. Prove also that the vectors q_j are independent. The basis $\{q_j\}$ is said to be *reciprocal* to the basis $\{p_k\}$; cf. 3J19. (T)

C. Orthonormal Sets

A set Q of non-zero vectors in a unitary space X is said to be an *orthogonal* set if $x, y \in Q$ and $x \neq y$ imply that $(x, y) = 0$. The basis P_k $(k = 1, 2, 3)$ of 3K5 is an example. In the space of complex-valued functions $x(\xi)$ on $0 \leq \xi \leq 1$, with $(x, y) = \int_0^1 \overline{x(\xi)} y(\xi) \, d\xi$, the functions $x_n(\xi) = e^{2\pi i n \xi}$ $(n = 0, \pm 1, \pm 2, \ldots)$ form an orthogonal set. In the space of real-valued functions $x(\xi)$ on $-\pi \leq \xi \leq \pi$, with $(x, y) = \int_{-\pi}^{\pi} x(\xi) y(\xi) \, d\xi$, the functions 1, $\cos n\xi$, $\sin n\xi$ $(n = 1, 2, 3, \ldots)$ form an orthogonal set.

An orthogonal set Q is an *orthonormal* set if $x \in Q$ implies that $\|x\| = 1$, that is, if each element of Q is normalized. Normalization is always possible, of course; each vector x is replaced by $\hat{x} = x/\|x\|$. The first two examples above are orthonormal sets. The third set, after normalization, is

$$\frac{1}{\sqrt{2\pi}}, \quad \frac{\cos n\xi}{\sqrt{\pi}}, \quad \frac{\sin n\xi}{\sqrt{\pi}} \quad (n = 1, 2, 3, \ldots).$$

If $Q = \{q_1, q_2, \ldots\}$ is an orthogonal set, then every finite subset of Q is independent. Indeed, if $x = \sum \alpha_k q_k = 0$, we form (x, q_j); only the term for which $k = j$ survives, and that term is $\bar{\alpha}_j = 0$. It follows that $\dim \langle Q \rangle \leq \dim X$.

Now let $Q = \{q_1, \ldots, q_m\}$, with $m \leq n = \dim X$, be an orthonormal set. Thus $(q_j, q_k) = \delta_{jk}$ $(j, k = 1, \ldots, m)$.

The *Fourier coefficients* of a vector x with respect to the set q_k are defined to be the scalars $\alpha_k = (x, q_k)$. Given now an arbitrary $x \in X$, we seek a point $x_Q \in \langle Q \rangle$ closest to x, that is, for which $\|x - x_Q\|$ is least. We try to choose the coefficients β_k so that $\|x - x_Q\|$ shall be least when $x_Q = \sum \beta_k q_k$. On calculating

$$\begin{aligned}
\|x - x_Q\|^2 &= \|x\|^2 + \|x_Q\|^2 - (x, x_Q) - \overline{(x, x_Q)} \\
&= \|x\|^2 + \sum |\beta_k|^2 - \sum \beta_k \bar{\alpha}_k - \sum \bar{\beta}_k \alpha_k \\
&= \|x\|^2 + \sum |\beta_k - \alpha_k|^2 - \sum |\alpha_k|^2,
\end{aligned}$$

where the α_k are the Fourier coefficients, we draw two important conclusions. The best choice for the β's is $\beta_k = \alpha_k$ $(k = 1, \ldots, m)$. Even with that choice, moreover, $\|x - x_Q\|^2 \geq 0$, and we arrive at *Bessel's inequality*.

1. If q_k $(k = 1, \ldots, m)$ is an orthonormal set then, for each $x \in X$,

$$\sum |(x, q_k)|^2 \le ||x||^2.$$

Now write $x_Q = \sum (x, \overline{q_k})q_k$ and consider the identity

2.
$$x = x_Q + (x - x_Q).$$

Of course, $x_Q \in \langle Q \rangle$, and if $x \in \langle Q \rangle$ then $x = x_Q$. We assert now that in any case $x - x_Q \in \langle Q \rangle^{\perp}$. In fact (note the disappearance of the bar, as a result of B2),

$$
\begin{aligned}
(x - x_Q, q_j) &= (x - \sum (\overline{x, q_k})q_k, q_j) \\
&= (x, q_j) - (\sum (x, q_k)q_k, q_j) \\
&= (x, q_j) - \sum (x, q_k)(q_k, q_j) \\
&= (x, q_j) - (x, q_j) = 0.
\end{aligned}
$$

3. Let $Q = \{q_k\}$ $(k = 1, \ldots, m)$ be an orthonormal set in a unitary space. Each vector x is the sum of a unique vector $x_Q = \sum (\overline{x, q_k})q_k \in \langle Q \rangle$ and the vector $x - x_Q \in \langle Q \rangle^{\perp}$. The endpoint of x_Q is the point of $\langle Q \rangle$ closest to the endpoint of x.

The last statement can be made more precise, as we see from the calculation preceding 1. If $y = \sum \beta_k q_k$ is any vector of $\langle Q \rangle$ other than x_Q, then $||x - y||^2$ exceeds $||x - x_Q||^2$ by an amount

$$\sum |\beta_k - (\overline{x, q_k})|^2.$$

The vector x_Q of 3 is the (orthogonal) *projection of x onto* $\langle Q \rangle$, and the vector $x - x_Q$ is the (orthogonal) *projection of x perpendicular* (or orthogonal) *to* $\langle Q \rangle$.

D. Complete Orthonormal Sets; Orthogonal Projections

An orthonormal set in a unitary space X is *complete* if it is not a proper subset of an orthonormal set.

1. An orthonormal set $\{p_k\}$ $(k = 1, 2, \ldots)$ in a unitary space X is complete if and only if any one of the following equivalent conditions holds:

1.1. $(x, p_k) = 0$ $(k = 1, 2, \ldots)$ implies that $x = 0$;

1.2. for each $x \in X$ there exist scalars $\alpha_k = (\overline{x, p_k})$ such that $x = \sum \alpha_k p_k$;

1.3. $(x, y) = (\sum (\overline{x, p_k})p_k, \sum (\overline{y, p_j})p_j) = \sum (x, p_k)(\overline{y, p_k})$;

1.4. $||x||^2 = \sum |(x, p_k)|^2$;

1.5. if dim $X = n$ is finite, then $k = 1, \ldots, n$ and the set $\{p_k\}$ forms a basis for X.

Our proof is formal in that we ignore questions of convergence when the set $\{p_k\}$ is infinite.

Assume that the orthonormal set $\{p_k\}$ is complete. If 1.1 were false, then there would exist $y \in X$ with $\|y\| = 1$ such that $(y, p_k) = 0$ $(k = 1, 2, \ldots)$, and $\{p_k\}$ would be a proper subset of the orthonormal set $\{y, p_k\}$ $(k = 1, 2, \ldots)$.

The vector $y = x - \sum \overline{(x, p_k)} p_k$ is orthogonal to each p_j and therefore vanishes by 1.1. The equation 1.3 follows from 1.2 by formal expansion. From 1.3 we obtain 1.4 by setting $y = x$. From 1.4 we see that if $\{p_k\}$ were not complete then there would exist a y with $\|y\| \neq 0$, while $\|y\|^2 = \sum |(y, p_k)|^2 = 0$, contradicting 1.1.

We show now that 1.5 is equivalent to 1.2. If dim X is finite, then 1.2 implies that X is spanned by the set $\{p_k\}$; since they are independent, they form a basis for X and $k = 1, \ldots, n = \dim X$. Conversely, if $k = 1, \ldots, n = \dim X$ and the orthonormal set $\{p_k\}$ is a basis for X, then 1.2 follows.

Either 1.3 or 1.4 may be cited as the *Parseval relation* or the *completeness relation*.

If dim $X = n$ is finite, and $\{p_k\}$ $(k = 1, \ldots, n)$ is an orthonormal basis for X, and $x = \sum \xi_k p_k$ and $y = \sum \eta_k p_k$, then $(x, y) = \sum \bar{\xi}_k \eta_k$. If this is true, conversely, for every pair $x, y \in X$, then it is true, in particular, for the basis vectors, and the set $\{p_k\}$ is an orthonormal basis for X.

We have already observed that, because of 10B18 and 10A38, every finite-dimensional unitary space has an orthonormal basis, and we shall see later that any unitary (or in the real case, orthogonal) change of basis replaces one orthonormal basis by another. We wish now to establish the following result.

2. Let X_n be a unitary space and let $\{q_k\}$ $(k = 1, \ldots, n)$ be *any* basis for X. Then there exists an orthonormal basis $\{p_k\}$ $(k = 1, \ldots, n)$ for X such that, for $k = 1, \ldots, n$,

$$\langle q_1, \ldots, q_k \rangle = \langle p_1, \ldots, p_k \rangle.$$

The vectors p_k are constructed from the q's by a recursive process known as the *Gram-Schmidt* (orthogonalization) *process* (cf. 3114). Put $p_1 = q_1 / \|q_1\|$. If $k \geq 2$, $p_1, \ldots, p_{k-1}$ have been defined, and they form an orthonormal set, and $\langle q_1, \ldots, q_{k-1} \rangle = \langle p_1, \ldots, p_{k-1} \rangle$, then set

3.
$$p_k = \frac{q_k - \sum_{j=1}^{k-1} \overline{(q_k, p_j)} p_j}{\left\| q_k - \sum_{j=1}^{k-1} \overline{(q_k, p_j)} p_j \right\|}.$$

Since $q_k \in' \langle p_1, \ldots, p_{k-1} \rangle$, the numerator (and therefore the denominator) cannot vanish and p_k is well defined. It is also clear that $\langle p_1, \ldots, p_k \rangle =$

$\langle q_1, \ldots, q_k \rangle$, and that $(p_k, p_j) = 0$ $(j = 1, \ldots, k - 1)$. The process terminates with the construction of p_n.

From 2 we obtain the following result (cf. B21).

4. If X_n is a unitary space and $Y \le X$, then $X = Y \oplus Y^{\perp}$.

Let dim $Y = m$. If $m = 0$ or $m = n$ there is nothing to prove, so assume that $0 < m < n$. Let $\{q_k\}$ $(k = 1, \ldots, n)$ be a basis for X which is adapted to Y; that is, $Y = \langle q_1, \ldots, q_m \rangle$. Then 2 yields an orthonormal basis $\{p_k\}$ for X such that $Y = \langle p_1, \ldots, p_m \rangle$. Now consider the space $Z = \langle p_{m+1}, \ldots, p_n \rangle$. Clearly $Z \le Y^{\perp}$. Since $Y \cap Y^{\perp} = \langle 0 \rangle$ by B21, dim $Y^{\perp} \le n - $ dim $Y = $ dim Z. Hence $Y^{\perp} = Z$ and 4 is established.

We know from 5F that any nontrivial subspace Y of a linear space X has many complements Z, that is, subspaces Z of X such that $X = Y \oplus Z$. We have just learned in 4 that every subspace of Y of a *unitary* space X has a *unique orthogonal* complement $Y^{\perp}$. The importance of this fact can scarcely be exaggerated. For example, without appealing to the construction given in C3, we can state the following result.

5. Orthogonal Projection Theorem. If X_n is a unitary space, $Y \le X$, and $x \in X$, then there exist unique vectors $x_Y \in Y$ and $x_{Y^{\perp}} \in Y^{\perp}$, whence $(x_Y, x_{Y^{\perp}}) = 0$, such that

$$x = x_Y + x_{Y^{\perp}}.$$

The vectors x_Y and $x_{Y^{\perp}}$ are called the *orthogonal projections* of x on Y and on $Y^{\perp}$ respectively.

Examples of orthonormal sets were given at the beginning of C. Here we give several examples of a rather special kind which are important in the applications. We deal with spaces of real-valued functions x of a real variable ξ defined and integrable on some interval. An inner product is defined in the space, often by means of an integral over the interval. The polynomials $1, \xi, \xi^2, \ldots$ are linearly independent. Applied to them, the Gram-Schmidt process yields an orthonormal set of polynomials $p_n(\xi)$. In Table 6 we give five examples. In the formulas for $p_n(\xi)$ the superscript (n) means nth derivative with respect to ξ. It must be verified in each case, of course, that the stated inner product actually has the required properties (B1–4).

Interval	Inner product (x, y)	$p_n(\xi)$	Name
$-1 \le \xi \le 1$	$\displaystyle\int_{-1}^{1} x(\xi)y(\xi)\,d\xi$	$\dfrac{\sqrt{(n+1)/2}}{2^n n!}[(\xi^2 - 1)^n]^{(n)}$	Legendre
$-1 \le \xi \le 1$	$\displaystyle\int_{-1}^{1} \dfrac{x(\xi)y(\xi)}{\sqrt{1 - \xi^2}}\,d\xi$	$\sqrt{\dfrac{2}{\pi}}\cos(n \arccos \xi)$	Tchebychef
$-1 \le \xi \le 1$	$\displaystyle\int_{-1}^{1} x(\xi)y(\xi)(1 - \xi)^p(1 + \xi)^q\,d\xi$ $(p, q > -1)$	$\dfrac{(-1)^n(1 - \xi)^{-p}(1 - \xi)^{-q}[(1 - \xi)^{n+p}(1 + \xi)^{n+q}]^{(n)}}{2^{p+q+1}}\sqrt{p + q + 2n + 1}\,\dfrac{\Gamma(p + n + 1)\Gamma(q + n + 1)}{n!\Gamma(p + q + n + 1)}$	Jacobi
$0 < \xi < \infty$	$\displaystyle\int_{0}^{\infty} x(\xi)y(\xi)e^{-\xi}\,d\xi$	$\dfrac{(-1)^n e^{\xi}(\xi^n e^{-\xi})^{(n)}}{n!}$	Laguerre
$-\infty < \xi < \infty$	$\displaystyle\int_{-\infty}^{\infty} x(\xi)y(\xi)e^{-\xi^2/2}\,d\xi$	$\dfrac{(-1)^n e^{\xi^2/2}(e^{-\xi^2/2})^{(n)}}{\sqrt{n!}\,\sqrt{2\pi}}$	Hermite

6. Certain systems of orthonormal polynomials; $n = 1, 2, 3, \ldots$, with $p_0(\xi) = 1/\sqrt{(1, 1)}$.

EXERCISES

7. Show that $\begin{bmatrix} 1 & 1 \\ 1 & 2 \end{bmatrix}$ is a metric in R_2. Are the vectors $p = [1 \; 0]^t$ and $q = [0 \; 1]^t$ orthogonal with respect to this metric? Are they normalized? Find orthonormal vectors p' and q' such that $\langle p' \rangle = \langle p \rangle$. What is the metric if p' and q' are introduced as basis vectors?

8. In R_3, with an orthonormal basis, let $p = [2 \; -1 \; 2]^t$ and $q = [2 \; 2 \; -1]^t$. Show that p and q are orthogonal. Normalize them. Determine r so that p, q, and r shall be an orthonormal basis.

9. In general, are the vectors $p_k = [0 \ldots 0 \quad 1_k \quad 0 \ldots 0]$ orthogonal? Normalized? Explain. (T)

10. Show that the vector x_Y of 5 is the same as the vector x_Q of C3 if Q is an orthonormal basis for Y.

11. In a Euclidean X_n, with a fixed $u \in X$, we know that $(u, x) = 0$ defines a hyperplane. For which x is it true that $(u, x) \geq 0, > 0, = 1, \geq 4, \leq -3$?

12. In a Euclidean X_n, let Y be a hyperplane. How can one choose $y \in X$, with $||y|| = 1$, such that the equation of Y is $(y, x) = 0$. What is the equation of the $(n-1)$-flat parallel to Y and at a distance five units from Y, counted positively in the direction of y?

13. If $\{x, y\}$ is an orthonormal set, calculate $||x - y||$.

14. In a Euclidean X_n, suppose that $||x|| = ||y||$. Prove that $(x - y, x + y) = 0$. What can you prove if X_n is unitary and $||x|| = ||y||$?

15. In a unitary X_n, prove that $(Y + Z)^\perp = Y^\perp \cap Z^\perp$ and that $(Y \cap Z)^\perp = Y^\perp + Z^\perp$. (T)

16. Let a unitary X_n have inner product (x, y), and let L be a nonsingular (regular) operator on X. Define $(x, y)_L = (Lx, Ly)$. Show that it is also an inner product on X.

17. Let a unitary X_n have an orthonormal basis $\{p_k\}$ adapted to $Y_m \leq X_n$, with $0 < m < n$. Observe that $x \in Y^\perp$ if and only if $(x, p_k) = 0$ $(k = 1, \ldots, m)$. Let $x = [\xi_k]^t$ and write down the scalar equations. How many independent solutions are there? What is dim $Y^\perp$? (T)

18. Verify that the formulas for (x, y) in 6 actually have the properties B1–4 required of an inner product in a real space.

19. Use the Gram-Schmidt process to calculate the Legendre polynomials $p_n(\xi)$ (cf. 6) for $n = 1, 2, 3, 4$. Verify that your results agree with the formula in 6.

20. Let $\{p_k\}$ $(k = 1, \ldots, n)$ be an orthonormal basis for a unitary X_n. Prove that if $Lp_k = \sum \alpha_{jk} p_j$, then $(p_h, Lp_k) = \alpha_{hk}$.

21. Let X and Y be unitary spaces with respective inner products (x, x') and (y, y'). Show that on $Z = X \oplus Y$, with $z = [x, y]$, the functional

$$(z, z') = ([x, y], [x', y']) = (x, x') + (y, y')$$

is an inner product.

E. Linear Functionals; Riesz' Theorem

Let $y \neq 0$ be a fixed vector in a unitary space X. Then (y, x) depends linearly on x, and is therefore an element of X^d, the space of linear functionals on X. Let us define a mapping $S : X \to X^d$, with $y \to Sy = g$ where, for $x \in X$,

1.
$$gx = (y, x).$$

It follows from B1 that if $Sy = g$ and $Sz = h$, then $S(y + z) = g + h$; S is additive. When we seek $S(\alpha y)$, however, B2 yields $(\alpha y, x) = \bar{\alpha}(y, x) = (\bar{\alpha} Sy)(z)$. The mapping S is therefore conjugate-linear.

We show now that S is *isometric*, in the sense that the norm of each image equals the norm of its original; $||Sy|| = ||y||$. From B9, in fact,

2.
$$|gx| = |(y, x)| \leq ||y|| \, ||x||,$$

and it follows from A8 that $||g|| \leq ||y||$. On taking $x = y$, moreover, we see from A8 that $||y|| \leq ||g||$. It follows, as desired, that $||Sy|| = ||y||$. Being isometric, S is nonsingular.

The question now is, whether or not X^d is covered. Does there exist, for each $f \in X^d$, a vector $w \in X$ such that if $x \in X$ then $fx = (w, x)$?

Given $f \in X^d$ and an orthonormal basis $\{p_k\}$ for X_n, we set $w = \sum \overline{fp_k} \, p_k$ and observe that

3.
$$(w, x) = (\sum \overline{fp_k} \, p_k, \sum \xi_j p_j) = \sum \xi_k fp_k = fx.$$

Having obtained an affirmative answer, let us develop a basis-free argument, valid in any unitary space. If $f = 0$ we may take $w = 0$, so assume that $f \neq 0$. The nullspace N_f of f is a hyperplane. Choose $v \neq 0$, $v \in N_f^\perp$. Now consider αv as a candidate for w. In order that $fx = (w, x)$ it is necessary, as we see on putting $x = v$, to have

$$fv = (\alpha v, v),$$

whence $\alpha = \overline{fv}/||v||^2$. Our candidate for w, therefore, is $w = \overline{fv} \, v/||v||^2$.

We are now ready to define a mapping $S' : X^d \to X$. Given $f \in X^d$, choose $v \in N_f^\perp$, $v \neq 0$, and let $f \to S'f = w$, where

4.
$$w = \frac{\overline{fv}}{||v||^2} \, v.$$

It is clear that any non-zero $v \in N_f$ will yield the same result. We must verify that w has the desired properties.

First of all,

5.
$$||w||^2 = \frac{|fv|^2}{||v||^2} = fw.$$

Then the equation

6.
$$x = \left(x - \frac{fx}{fw} w\right) + \frac{fx}{fw} w$$

expresses x as the sum of a vector in N_f and a multiple of $w \in N_f^\perp$. Using 5, we obtain, as desired,

7.
$$0 = \left(w, x - \frac{fx}{fw} w\right) = (w, x) - fx.$$

If also $(w', x) = fx$ for all $x \in X$, then $(w - w', x) = 0$ for all $x \in X$. On taking $x = w - w'$ we see that $w = w'$ and w is uniquely determined by f.

Suppose now that, for all $x \in X$, both $fx = (w, x)$ and $gx = (y, x)$. Then, for all $x \in X$, $(f + g)x = (w + y, x)$. Hence S' is additive; this is by no means evident from the construction. Obviously, $S'(\alpha f) = \bar{\alpha} S' f$, so S', like S, is conjugate-linear. Finally, S' is isometric.

$$|fx| = |(w, x)| \le \|w\| \|x\|,$$

whence $\|f\| \le \|w\|$. From 5 and A12, at the same time,

$$\|w\|^2 = fw \le \|f\| \|w\|,$$

whence $\|w\| \le \|f\|$ and hence $\|w\| = \|f\|$.

Now 1 says that if $g = Sy$ then $y = S'g$. Similarly, from 7, if $w = S'f$, then $f = Sw$. Thus the mappings S and S' are inverse to each other. We summarize.

8. Theorem. If X is any unitary space then there is a conjugate-linear isometric isomorphism between X and X^d. The mapping $S : X \to X^d$ is given by 1 and its inverse $S' : X^d \to X$ by 4.

This result justifies the statement that a unitary (or Euclidean) space is *self-dual*.

That any linear functional f on a unitary space can be represented as (w, x) for a unique $w \in X$ is often cited as Riesz' theorem; variants of it occur in diverse branches of analysis. As indicated by 3 (cf. 9) examples in a finite-dimensional space with an orthonormal basis are almost trivial. For an intuitive example see 7A15; recall that the level surfaces of f form a family of parallel planes.

EXERCISES

9. In a real X_3, with an orthonormal basis, suppose that $fx = \alpha\xi + \beta\eta + \gamma\zeta$. Construct $S'f = w$ according to the prescription of 4 and verify that $(w, x) = fx$ for all x.

10. Given X_n with an inner product (x, y), and the mapping $f \to S'f$ of 4, prove that $(f, g) = (S'f, S'g)$ defines an inner product on X^d and (cf. A11) that $\|f\|^2 = (f, f)$.

11. Let X_n be unitary and suppose that $W \le X$. Show that the isomorphism of 8 mates $W^\circ \le X^d$ (cf. 7C) with $W^\perp \le X$. What can you say about subspaces $V \le X^d$? (T)

12. Let P_4 denote the space of all real polynomials of degree ≤ 3 with $0 \le \xi \le 1$ and with

$$(f, g) = \int_0^1 f(\xi)g(\xi)\, d\xi.$$

Observe that, with η fixed, $f(\eta)$ is a linear functional on P. Determine $f_\eta \in P$ so that, for each $g \in P$, $(f_\eta, g) = g(\eta)$.

F. Adjoint L^a of an Operator L

Let L be an operator on a unitary space X. We saw in 7D that L has a dual $L^d : X^d \to X^d$ such that if $x \in X$ and $f \in X^d$ then $(fL^d)x = f(Lx)$.

The self-duality of X brought out in E8 suggests that the operator $L^d : X^d \to X^d$ may be associated with an operator on X. Indeed, since (y, Lx) depends linearly on x, it is an element Sy of L^d (cf. E1). Then $(Sy)L^d \in X^d$ has, by E8, a mate $S'((Sy)L^d) \in X$. We define an operator L^a on X by agreeing that

1.
$$y \to L^a y = S'((Sy)L^d).$$

This operator L^a is called the adjoint of L.

The situation is illustrated in 2.

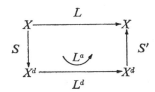

The diagram should not suggest that $L^a = L$. If L does have the property that $L^a = L$ then L is said to be *self-adjoint*; such operators have many important applications.

Being the resultant of the conjugate-linear mapping S, the linear mapping L^d, and the conjugate-linear mapping S', L^a is linear (and the name "operator" is justified).

The essential property of L^a is that, for all $x, y \in X$,

3.
$$(y, Lx) = (L^a y, x).$$

To see this we merely calculate

$$(y, Lx) = Sy(Lx) = ((Sy)L^d)x = (S'((Sy)L^d), x)$$
$$= (L^a y, x).$$

Some authors use 3 as a definition of L^a, its existence being, in some instances, left open to question. In any event, 3 determines L^a uniquely, for if also $(y, Lx) = (My, x)$, then $((L^a - M)y, x) = 0$ for all x and y; take $x = (L^a - M)y$ to see that $(L^a - M)y = 0$ for all y, whence $M = L^a$. Moreover, the properties of L^a follow from 3.

The algebraic properties of L^a are simple:

(a) $0^a = 0$ (b) $I^a = I$ (c) $(K + L)^a = K^a + L^a$

4.   (d) $(\alpha L)^a = \bar{\alpha} L^a$ (e) $(KL)^a = L^a K^a$.

The last equation follows because $(y, KLx) = ((KL)^a y, x)$, while, at the same time,

$$(y, KLx) = (K^a y, Lx) = (L^a K^a y, x).$$

How is $[L^a]$ related to $[L]$? Let us use an orthonormal basis, in which $(y, x) = \overline{[y]}^t [x]$. Then

$$(y, Lx) = \overline{[y]}^t [L][x] = (\overline{[L]}^t [y])^t [x] = (L^a y, x),$$

and we reach the following result.

5. Let L be an operator on a unitary (or Euclidean) space X. If the basis for X is orthonormal then:

if X is unitary then $[L^a] = \overline{[L]}^t$;

if X is Euclidean then $[L^a] = [L]^t$.

It is customary to write $[L]^*$ to denote $\overline{[L]}^t$ in the complex case and $[L]^t$ in the real case. With this understanding, $[L^a] = [L]^*$.

EXERCISES

6. Let X be a unitary (Euclidean) space with an orthonormal basis. Prove that if $L^a = L$ then $[L]$ is Hermitian (symmetric). Are the converse statements valid? (T)

7. What will $[L^a]$ look like (cf. D1.3) if the basis is not orthonormal?

8. Prove that $(L^a)^a = L$.

9. Prove that if L is regular, then L^a is regular and $(L^a)^{-1} = (L^{-1})^a$. (T)

10. Suppose that $K^a = K$ and $L^a = L$. Does it follow that $(KL)^a = KL$?

11. In C_2 with an orthonormal basis $\{p_1, p_2\}$, suppose that $Lp_1 = [i \quad 2]^t$ and $Lp_2 = [-1 \quad 4i]^t$. Determine L^a.

12. Given an operator L on a unitary X_n, define

$$J = \tfrac{1}{2}(L + L^a), \qquad K = \frac{1}{2i}(L - L^a).$$

Prove that $J = J^a$, $K = K^a$, and $L = J + iK$.

13. If $L^a = L$ then, for any K, $(K^a L K)^a = K^a L K$. If K is regular and $(K^a L K)^a = K^a L K$, then $L^a = L$.

14. Suppose that $L^a = L$. Prove that if $||x|| = 1$ then $||Lx||^2 \leq ||L^2 x||$, and that the equality holds if and only if $\lambda = ||Lx||^2$ is an eigenvalue of L^a and x is an eigenvector of L^2 corresponding to λ.

15. Given a unitary $X, L : X \rightarrow X$, and $Z \leq X$ such that $LZ \leq Z$, prove that $L^a Z^\perp \leq Z^\perp$. (T)

G. Gram Matrices and Determinants; Hadamard's Inequality

We deal with a unitary space X_n with an orthonormal basis

$$\{p_k\} \qquad (k = 1, \ldots, n).$$

Suppose that we have m vectors $x_j = \sum \xi_{kj} p_k \, (j = 1, \ldots, m \leq n)$. The *Gram matrix* of the vectors x_j is the $m \times m$ matrix

1.
$$G = [(x_j, x_h)] = [\sum \bar{\xi}_{kj} \xi_{kh}] = [[x_j]^*[x_h]].$$

Now G^t will have $(x_h, x_j) = \overline{(x_j, x_h)}$ in row j and column h; hence G is Hermitian. We observe further that $G = I_m$ if and only if the vectors $x_j \, (j = 1, \ldots, m)$ form an orthonormal set.

The *Gram determinant* of the vectors x_j is

2.
$$G(x_1, \ldots, x_m) = |G| = |(x_j, x_h)| = |\sum \bar{\xi}_{kj} \xi_{kh}| = |[x_j]^*[x_h]|.$$

By Lagrange's Identity (11J), with obvious modifications,

3.
$$G(x_1, \ldots, x_m) = \sum \overline{|A_q|} \, |A_q| \geq 0,$$

where q runs over the set of $\binom{n}{m}$ combinations of m indices chosen from $1, \ldots, n$, and $|A_q|$ denotes the minor of order m of $[\xi_{kj}]$ corresponding to q. It follows that the vectors x_j are dependent or independent according as $G(x_1, \ldots, x_m) = 0$ or > 0, i.e., according as the determinantal rank of $[\xi_{kj}]$ is $< m$ or $= m$ (cf. 11I).

We now establish an important connection between the Gram determinant and the orthogonal projections of D5.

4. If the vectors $x_j \, (j = 1, \ldots, m < n)$ are independent, and $W = \langle x_1, \ldots, x_m \rangle$, and $y \in X$, then

$$G(y, x_1, \ldots, x_m) = ||y_{W^\perp}||^2 G(x_1, \ldots, x_m).$$

We seek scalars β_j such that

$$(y - \sum \beta_j x_j, x_h) = 0 \qquad (h = 1, \ldots, m);$$

that is, we seek to solve the equations

$$\sum (x_j, x_h) \bar{\beta}_j = (y, x_h) \qquad (h = 1, \ldots, m).$$

Since $[(x_j, x_h)]$ is regular, we let $[H_{jh}] = [(x_j, x_h)]^{-1}$; that is

$$H_{jh} = \frac{(-1)^{j+h} \cdot \text{minor of } (x_h, x_j) \text{ in } \lfloor (x_j, x_h) \rfloor}{G(x_1, \ldots, x_m)}.$$

Then, by 11H7 (Cramer's Rule)

$$\bar{\beta}_j = \sum (y, x_h) H_{hj},$$

and

$$y_{W\perp} = y - \sum (\overline{y, x_h}) \bar{H}_{hj} x_j.$$

It follows that

$$\| y_{W\perp} \|^2 = (y_{W\perp}, y) = \| y \|^2 - \sum (y, x_h) H_{hj}(x_j, y).$$

The right member of this equation, however, when multiplied by $G(x_1, \ldots, x_m)$ is the expansion, by 11L, of $G(y, x_1, \ldots, x_m)$ considered as $G(x_1, \ldots, x_m)$ bordered by (y, x_h) and $\| y \|^2$; 4 is established.

An important corollary follows by induction.

5.
$$0 \le G(x_1, \ldots, x_m) \le {}_a\Pi_1^m \| x_a \|^2.$$

In particular, if $m = n$, then

6.
$$|\det [\xi_{jk}]| \le {}_k\Pi_1^n \| x_k \| = {}_k\Pi_1^n (\sum_j |\xi_{jk}|^2)^{1/2}.$$

Suppose now that we have an upper bound for the absolute values of the elements: $|\xi_{jk}| \le M \ (j, k = 1, \ldots, n)$. Then (Hadamard) from 6 we see that the absolute value of the determinant cannot exceed

7.
$$M^n n^{n/2}.$$

This estimate is considerably better than the estimate $n! \ M^n$ obtained by arguing that there are $n!$ terms, none greater than M^n. With a small *relative* error, in fact (Stirling's Formula),

$$n! \cong \sqrt{2\pi n} \ e^{-n} n^n;$$

to get from 7 to $n! \ M^n$, one must multiply by

$$\sqrt{2\pi} \ e^{-n} n^{(n+1)/2},$$

and this factor increases rapidly with n.

In a real X_n it is possible to use 4 to develop a theory of volume for parallelepipeds. For details see [A40], [A43], or [A6]. This theory explains the occurrence and behavior of Jacobians when variables are changed in multiple integrals.

EXERCISES

In these exercises it is always assumed that an orthonormal basis is in use.

8. Calculate the Gram matrices and determinants for the following sets of vectors:

(a) $\begin{bmatrix} 2 \\ 1 \\ -3 \end{bmatrix}, \begin{bmatrix} 3 \\ 0 \\ -1 \end{bmatrix}$;

(b) $\begin{bmatrix} 1 - i \\ 2 \\ 3 - 4i \end{bmatrix}, \begin{bmatrix} i \\ -3 \\ 2 - i \end{bmatrix};$

(c) $\begin{bmatrix} -1 \\ 2i \\ 3 + i \\ -i \end{bmatrix}, \begin{bmatrix} i \\ 2 + i \\ 3 \\ 0 \end{bmatrix}, \begin{bmatrix} -4 - 3i \\ 1 \\ 4 - i \\ 1 + 2i \end{bmatrix}.$

9. Let G be the Gram matrix of vectors x_a $(a = 1, \ldots, m)$. Show that the principal minors $m_{j_1 \ldots j_q, j_1 \ldots j_q}$ of G (cf. 11F) are Gram determinants and that they are (therefore) ≥ 0.

10. Let the vectors x_a $(a = 1, \ldots, m \leq n)$ be the columns of an $n \times m$ matrix M, and let G be the Gram matrix of the vectors x_a. Show that M and G have the same rank.

11. Use the fact that $\sum \|\alpha_a x_a\|^2 = \sum \bar{\alpha}_a (x_a, x_b) \alpha_b$ to show that the matrix $[(x_a, x_b)]$ is ≥ 0. (T)

12. In experimental work one sometimes encounters a system of equations

$$\sum \alpha_{\lambda k} \xi_k = \eta_\lambda \qquad (k = 1, \ldots, n; \lambda = 1, \ldots, \mu > n),$$

which is inconsistent. There being no exact solutions, one asks for values of the ξ's for which

$$\sum_\lambda \left(\sum_k \alpha_{\lambda k} \xi_k - \eta_\lambda \right)^2$$

is least (a "least squares" solution). Writing the equations in the form $Lx = y$, with $L = [\alpha_{\lambda k}]$, and putting $z = Lx - y$, we wish to minimize $(z, z) = z^t z$. On setting the gradient equal to zero, we find it necessary to have $L^t L x = L^t y$. If $L^t L$ is regular, then there is a unique solution $x = (L^t L)^{-1} L^t y$. Of course, $L^t L$ is the Gram matrix of the columns of L, and is regular if and only if L has n independent rows. (T)

H. Unitary and Orthogonal Operators and Matrices

An operator L on a unitary (or Euclidean) space X_n is *isometric* or an *isometry* if $x, y \in X$ imply that

1. $$(x, y) = (Lx, Ly).$$

By virtue of the polarization identity B13 (or B14) it is an equivalent requirement that, for each x,

2. $$\|Lx\| = \|x\|.$$

From 1 we see at once that

3. $$(x, y) = (L^a Lx, y)$$

and, since this is to hold for each y and for each x,

4. $$L^a L = I.$$

It was obvious from 2 that L is regular, and 4 tells us that $L^{-1} = L^a$. The converse is trivial. An operator L such that $L^{-1} = L^a$ is said to be *unitary* (or *orthogonal*).

5. An operator L on a unitary (or Euclidean) X_n is isometric if and only if it is unitary (or orthogonal), i.e., $L^{-1} = L^a$.

In terms of matrices the condition that L be unitary (or orthogonal) is evidently this:

6.
$$[L]^{-1} = \overline{[L]}^t \quad \text{(or } [L]^{-1} = [L]^t\text{)}.$$

If the columns of L are vectors p_k $(k = 1, \ldots, n)$ then, in an orthonormal basis for X, the equation $[L]^t[L] = I$ tells us that the vectors p_k form an orthonormal basis; we observe that $\overline{[L]}^t[L]$ is the Gram matrix of the vectors p_k.

By taking determinants, we see that if L is unitary (or orthogonal), then

7.
$$|\det [L]| = 1 \quad \text{and} \quad \det [L] = e^{i\theta} \quad \text{(or } \det [L] = \pm 1\text{)}.$$

The resultant of two unitary operators is easily seen to be unitary, and the set of all unitary operators on a given unitary X_n therefore forms a group. The subset of those L for which $\det [L] = 1$ forms a subgroup. This subgroup is important in certain branches of physics; the unitary matrices $[L]$ with $\det [L] = 1$ are sometimes called "special unitary matrices". In the real case those orthogonal L for which $\det [L] = 1$ are sometimes called *proper* orthogonal operators, or *rotations*, while those for which $\det [L] = -1$ are said to be *improper* orthogonal operators. A rotation preserves orientation, while an improper orthogonal operator is the resultant of a rotation and a reflection.

Canonical forms for unitary and orthogonal matrices will be obtained in the next chapter.

EXERCISES

8. If L is an operator on a finite-dimensional unitary space then it can be shown (cf. the remark following A8) that
$$\nu_1 = \max \{\|Lx\| : \|x\| = 1\}$$
exists and, moreover, (cf. A11) that if
$$\nu_2 = \max \{\|Lx\|/\|x\| : x \neq 0\},$$
then $\nu_1 = \nu_2$. Prove that if $x \in X$ then $\|Lx\| \leq \|L\| \|x\|$. (*Optional:* Prove that there exists an x_L with $\|x_L\| = 1$ such that $\|Lx_L\| = \|L\|$.) Prove further that if K and L are operators, then $\|KL\| \leq \|K\| \|L\|$.

9. Prove that $\|L^a\| = \|L\|$ and that if L is unitary then $\|L\| = 1$. Give an example of a non-unitary L for which $\|L\| = 1$.

10. Can any projection other than the identity be unitary?

11. Suppose that $W \leq X$ and, if $x = x_W + x_{W^\perp}$ (cf. D5), define $L : X \to X$ by $x \to Lx = x_W - x_{W^\perp}$. Prove that $L^a = L = L^{-1}$. (Cf. 6C.)

12. Prove that if $[\alpha_{jk}]$ is real and orthogonal and $\eta_j = \sum \alpha_{jk}\xi_k$, then $\sum \eta_j^2 = \sum \xi_j^2$. If, conversely, $\sum \eta_j^2 = \sum \xi_j^2$ for all real vectors $[\eta_j]^t$ and $[\xi_j]^t$, does it follow that $[\alpha_{jk}]$ is orthogonal? What is the analogous result in the complex case? (T)

13. Let L be unitary (or orthogonal) and suppose that λ is an eigenvalue of L. Show that $1/\bar{\lambda}$ (or $1/\lambda$) is also an eigenvalue of L.

14. Let S be a real skew operator. Show that the operators $I \pm S$ are regular and that the operator $L = (I - S)^{-1}(I + S)$ is orthogonal and does not have -1 as an eigenvalue. Show conversely that, if L is an orthogonal operator not having -1 as an eigenvalue, then the operator $S = (L - I)(L + I)^{-1}$ is skew. (T)

15. Let H be an Hermitian operator. Show that the operators $I \pm iH$ are regular and that the operator $U = (I - iH)^{-1}(I + iH)$ is unitary and does not have the eigenvalue -1. Conversely, if U is a unitary operator not having the eigenvalue -1, then $H = i(I - U)(I + U)^{-1}$ is Hermitian. (T)

16. (*Optional.*) If t is a real variable then $w = (1 + it)(1 - it)^{-1} = e^{i\alpha}$ with $t = \tan(\alpha/2)$. As t runs from $-\infty$ to $+\infty$, α runs from $-\pi$ to π (exclusive); w does not take on the value -1. Vice versa, if $w = e^{i\beta}$ then $t = i(1 - w)(1 + w)^{-1} = \tan(\beta/2)$ runs from $-\infty$ to ∞ as β runs from $-\pi$ to π (exclusive). In the light of these results there is an analogy between Hermitian (or symmetric) operators and real numbers, and between unitary (or orthogonal) operators and unimodular complex numbers. In 14, S and L are said to be *Cayley transforms* of each other; so are H and U in 15.

FOURTEEN
Similar Operators on a Unitary Space

In a unitary space each operator L has an adjoint L^a (see 13F), and it makes sense to ask whether or not L and L^a commute. If $LL^a = L^aL$, then we say that L is *normal*. Fortunately, many operators of practical interest are normal; these include the Hermitian and the anti-Hermitian, the symmetric and the skew, and the unitary and the orthogonal.

The argument used to obtain 12A10 and 12B3 can be recast here in a much stronger form to show (see A6 and 7 below) that a normal matrix is unitarily similar to a diagonal matrix with the eigenvalues on the diagonal.

In Chap. 10 we found canonical forms for certain normal matrices under congruence and conjunctivity. Those canonical forms, where diagonal, had each diagonal entry equal to 0, 1, or -1. We are now insisting on unitary conjunctivity (or similarity) and orthogonal congruence (or similarity). It is somewhat remarkable that with these more restricted transformations the diagonal form turns out to have just the eigenvalues on the diagonal. It could not be otherwise. For one thing, eigenvalues are preserved under similarity. If, moreover, a matrix is in diagonal form $D = [[\alpha_1, \ldots, \alpha_n]]$ with respect to a basis p_k $(k = 1, \ldots, n)$, then $Dp_k = \alpha_k p_k$ $(k = 1, \ldots, n)$; the kth entry α_k of D is an eigenvalue of D and p_k is the corresponding eigenvector.

A. Normal Operators in a Unitary Space; Spectral Representation

An operator L on a unitary space X is said to be *normal* if $LL^a = L^aL$. In terms of matrices, with an orthonormal basis and $[L]^*$ meaning $\overline{[L]}^t$, the condition (cf. 13E3) is

1.
$$[L][L]^* = [L]^*[L]$$

or, in the real case,

2.
$$[L][L]^t = [L]^t[L],$$

and a complex (real) matrix satisfying 1 (2) is said to be *normal*. It is easy to verify that a matrix which is unitarily similar to a normal matrix is itself normal.

318

3. L is normal if and only if, for each $x, y \in X$, $(Lx, Ly) = (L^a x, L^a y)$.

If L is normal, then

$$(Lx, Ly) = (L^a Lx, y) = (LL^a x, y) = (L^a x, L^a y).$$

If the condition holds, conversely, then

$$(L^a Lx, y) = (LL^a x, y)$$

or

$$((L^a L - LL^a)x, y) = 0.$$

We now choose $y = (L^a L - LL^a)x$. Then $y = 0$ for every x and $L^a L = LL^a$.

4. Corollary. If L is normal then $\|Lx\| = \|L^a x\|$ for each x.

5. If L is normal then $Lx = \lambda x$ if and only if $L^a x = \bar{\lambda} x$.

In fact, $(L - \lambda)^a = L^a - \bar{\lambda}$, whence, by 4,

$$\|(L - \lambda)x\| = \|(L^a - \bar{\lambda})x\|$$

and 5 follows.

We are now prepared to prove a first basic result for normal operators; comparison with 12A10 and 12B3 is instructive.

6. Theorem. If L is a normal operator on a unitary space X, then X has an orthonormal basis consisting of eigenvectors of L.

If $n = 1$ there is nothing to prove, so assume the theorem true for $n = q$ and let L be normal on X_{q+1}. It has an eigenvalue μ and a corresponding eigenvector y, and we may arrange to have $\|y\| = 1$. By 13D4, $X_{q+1} = \langle y \rangle \oplus Z_q$, where $Z_q = \langle y \rangle^\perp$. Now Z is invariant under L. If, in fact, $(x, y) = 0$ then, by 5,

$$(Lx, y) = (x, L^a y) = (x, \bar{\mu} y) = \mu(x, y) = 0$$

and $Lx \in Z$.

An entirely similar argument shows that Z is invariant also under L^a.

Now let M denote the restriction of L to Z. We wish to show that the operator M^a on Z is equal to the restriction to Z of L^a. Let $u, v \in Z$. Then

$$(u, Lv) = (u, Mv) = (M^a u, v)$$

and

$$(u, Lv) = (L^a u, v),$$

whence $((L^a - M^a)u, v) = 0$. By choosing $v = (L^a - M^a)u$ we see that $L^a = M^a$ on Z.

Since $LL^a = L^a L$ on Z, $MM^a = M^a M$ on Z and M is normal on Z.

The inductive hypothesis now delivers an orthonormal basis $z_2, \ldots, z_{q+1}$ for Z, where each z_j is an eigenvector of M. Now if $Mz = \lambda z$ with $z \neq 0$ in Z, then $Lz = Mz = \lambda z$ in X. Put $p_1 = y$ and, for $j = 2, \ldots, q + 1, p_j = z_j$. The

319

orthonormal set $\{p_k\}$ is a basis for X_{q+1} consisting of eigenvectors of L, and 7 is proved.

The transformation introducing the orthonormal basis p_k is a unitary transformation. In that basis, moreover, $[L]$ is diagonal, with the kth diagonal entry being the eigenvalue λ_k corresponding to the basis vector p_k. We draw the following conclusion.

7. **Corollary.** A normal matrix is unitarily similar to a diagonal matrix in which the elements on the diagonal are the eigenvalues.

From this corollary we can obtain a pseudo-inverse (9G) of a normal matrix M. If M has rank $\rho \leq n$, then we may arrange the order of its eigenvalues so that all zeros are last. There is a unitary matrix U such that $U^*MU = D = [[\lambda_1, \ldots, \lambda_\rho, 0, \ldots, 0]]$, with $\lambda_k \neq 0$ for $k = 1, \ldots, \rho$. Now consider

$$D' = [[\lambda_1^{-1}, \ldots, \lambda_\rho^{-1}, 0, \ldots, 0]].$$

It is obvious that $DD'D = D$, whence D' is a pseudo-inverse of D. One verifies readily that if $M' = UD'U^*$ then $MM'M = M$ and M' is a pseudo-inverse of M.

We turn now to the spectral representation of a normal operator. If L is normal, then, by 7 and 12E1, the Jordan normal form of L is diagonal. This is equivalent to saying that if λ is an eigenvalue of L then the index of $L - \lambda$ is one (see 12C). Thus the minimal polynomial of L is $\Pi(\lambda - \lambda_k)$, where λ_k $(k = 1, \ldots, r)$ are the *distinct* eigenvalues of L.

Now let the characteristic polynomial of the normal operator L be

8.
$$f(L; \lambda) = |\lambda - L| = \prod_{k=1}^{r} (\lambda - \lambda_k)^{a_k};$$

here $\sum a_k = n$. The diagonal matrix of 7 can be rearranged by a permutation (hence unitary) similarity so that equal eigenvalues are adjacent to each other. This amounts to enumerating the vectors of the orthonormal basis in such a way that all those corresponding to the same eigenvalue occur consecutively. Let us define an $a_k \times a_k$ matrix

9.
$$H_{a_k} = \lambda_k I_{a_k} \qquad (k = 1, \ldots, r).$$

Then the diagonal form of L consists of blocks H_{a_k} $(k = 1, \ldots, r)$ down the diagonal, and zeros elsewhere. The diagonal matrix $L - \lambda_k$ will have zeros where L has λ_k and non-zero elements $\lambda_j - \lambda_k$ $(j \neq k)$ elsewhere on the diagonal. Thus the nullspace of $L - \lambda_k$ is precisely the subspace X_k generated by the a_k eigenvectors of the basis corresponding to λ_k; hence dim $X_k = a_k$. Since $X = {}_j\bigoplus_1^n \langle p_j \rangle$, $X = {}_k\bigoplus_1^r X_k$. The orthogonal projection P_k of X onto X_k will have a matrix with entries zero everywhere except in the kth box, where I_{a_k} appears. These considerations enable us to prove the following theorem.

320

10. Spectral Representation of Normal Operators. Let L be a normal operator on a unitary space X_n, let $|\lambda - L| = {}_k\Pi_1^r (\lambda - \lambda_k)^{a_k}$ with the λ_k distinct and $\sum a_k = n$, and for $k = 1, \ldots, r$ let P_k be the orthogonal projection of X onto the nullspace X_k of $L - \lambda_k$. Then $P_j P_k = 0$ if $j \neq k$, $\sum P_k = I$, $LP_k = P_k L = \lambda_k P_k$, and $L = \sum \lambda_k P_k$.

Since the spaces X_k are mutually orthogonal, it is evident that $P_j P_k = 0$ if $j \neq k$; one says that P_j and P_k themselves are *orthogonal*.

As we saw above, $X = \oplus X_k$, whence $\sum P_k = I$.

Now $P_k X = X_k = P_k X_k$. Let us denote by x_k the projection $P_k x$ of x onto X_k. Then $Lx_k = \lambda_k x_k$ and $LP_k x = Lx_k = \lambda_k x_k$, and $P_k Lx = P_k L(\sum x_j) = P_k(\sum \lambda_j x_j) = \lambda_k x_k$, whence $LP_k = P_k L = \lambda_k P_k$.

Again, $Lx = L \sum x_k = \sum \lambda_k x_k = \sum \lambda_k P_k x$, whence $L = \sum \lambda_k P_k$. The same result may be obtained by adding the equations $LP_k = \lambda_k P_k$ and observing on the left that $\sum P_k = I$.

Here L is displayed as a linear combination of mutually orthogonal projections P_k, with $\sum P_k = I$, and the coefficients are the eigenvalues of L. Since these coefficients, with their multiplicities, constitute the spectrum of L (defined following 12A4), the representation $L = \sum \lambda_k P_k$ is called the *spectral representation* of L. It is a tremendously helpful expression. We give two applications.

11. If $L = {}_k\sum_1^r \lambda_k P_k$ is a normal operator in its spectral representation, then an operator K commutes with L if and only if K commutes with P_k ($k = 1, \ldots, r$).

The sufficiency of the condition being obvious, we have only to establish its necessity. It is clear that if $KL = LK$, then K commutes with any polynomial in L. Our problem is to express P_k as a polynomial in L. We observe that if p is a polynomial, then, from the spectral representation of L, $p(L) = \sum p(\lambda_k) P_k$. With k_0 fixed ($1 \leq k_0 \leq r$), choose

12.
$$p_{k_0}(\lambda) = \Pi_{k \neq k_0} \frac{\lambda - \lambda_k}{\lambda_{k_0} - \lambda_k}.$$

It follows that $Kp_{k_0}(L) = p_{k_0}(L)K$. But $p_{k_0}(\lambda_j) = \delta_{k_0 j}$. Hence

$$p_{k_0}(L) = \sum p_{k_0}(\lambda_k) P_k = P_{k_0}$$

and, finally, as desired, $Kp_{k_0}(L) = KP_{k_0} = P_{k_0}K$.

The necessity of the conditions stated in the following theorem are obvious from the spectral representation of L.

13. If L is a normal operator then L has the property stated in the left column below if and only if all the eigenvalues of L have the property stated in the right column:

321

1. Hermitian	1'. Real
2. ≥ 0	2'. ≥ 0
3. > 0	3'. > 0
4. Anti-Hermitian	4'. Purely imaginary
5. Unitary	5'. Of absolute value 1
6. Regular	6'. $\neq 0$
7. Idempotent	7'. 0 or 1

To prove the sufficiency of these conditions we observe first that the spectral representation of L^a is $\sum \bar{\lambda}_k P_k$. Hence 1' implies 1. From the equations

$$(x, Lx) = \sum (x, \lambda_k P_k x) = \sum \lambda_k(x, x_k) = \sum \lambda_k ||x_k||^2$$

it follows that 2' and 3' imply 2 and 3 respectively. Condition 4' implies that $L^a = -L$, which is 4. Condition 5' implies that $L^a L = LL^a = \sum |\lambda_k|^2 P_k = \sum P_k = I$, and 5 follows. From 6' we are able to form $K = \sum \lambda_k^{-1} P_k$ and show that $KL = LK = I$. From 7' it follows that $L^2 = \sum \lambda_k^2 P_k = \sum \lambda_k P_k = L$, which is 7.

We underscore once again that the conditions in the right column are significant because the spectrum is invariant under similarity. For a discussion of normal transformations on a real space, using real numbers only, see [A47, pp. 240–248].

EXERCISES

14. Prove that if L is Hermitian, skew-Hermitian, symmetric, skew, unitary, or orthogonal, then L is normal. (T)

15. Suppose that L is normal, that $Lx = \lambda x$, $Ly = \mu y$, $x \neq 0$, $y \neq 0$, and $\lambda \neq \mu$. It is obvious from the text that $(x, y) = 0$. Give a direct proof of this fact.

16. Given a normal operator L, define

$$J = \tfrac{1}{2}(L + L^a) \qquad \text{and} \qquad K = \frac{1}{2i}(L - L^a).$$

Clearly $L = J + iK$. Prove that J and K are Hermitian and that $JK = KJ$. The operators J and K are called, respectively, the *real* and *imaginary* parts of L. Suppose, conversely, that $L = G + iH$ where G and H are Hermitian and $GH = HG$. Prove that L is normal.

17. Suppose that J and K are normal. Can any conclusion be reached regarding $J + K$, JK, or KJ?

18. In our proof of 6 it turned out that if L is normal, $y \neq 0$, and $L\langle y \rangle \leq \langle y \rangle$, then $L\langle y \rangle^{\perp} \leq \langle y \rangle^{\perp}$. Show that the same is true of any $Y \leq X$ and that, conversely, if $Y \leq X$ and $LY \leq Y$ imply that $LY^{\perp} \leq Y^{\perp}$, then L is normal. (T)

19. Give a complete set of invariants for a normal operator under unitary (or orthogonal) similarity. (T)

20. Express the matrix $[L]$ of an operator L as $[L] = [x_k] = [y_k]$, where for $k = 1, \ldots, n$ the x_k are *column* vectors and the y_k are *row* vectors. Then (cf. 1) $[L^aL] = [\bar{x}_j^t x_k]$ and $[LL^a] = [y_j \bar{y}_k^t]$. Hence L will be normal if and only if, for $j, k = 1, \ldots, n$,

20.1.
$$y_j \bar{y}_k^t = \bar{x}_j^t x_k.$$

It follows, in particular, that $\|x_k\| = \|y_k\|$. Now suppose that we know, further, that $[L] = [\alpha_{jk}]$ is super-diagonal. Then

$$|\alpha_{11}|^2 = \|x_1\|^2 = \|y_1\|^2 = \sum |\alpha_{1k}|^2,$$

whence $\alpha_{1k} = 0$ for $k = 2, \ldots, n$. Knowing that $\alpha_{12} = 0$, we can say that

$$|\alpha_{22}|^2 = \sum_2^n |\alpha_{2k}|^2,$$

whence $\alpha_{2k} = 0$ for $k = 3, \ldots, n$. Continuing, we conclude that $[L] = [[\alpha_{11}, \ldots, \alpha_{nn}]]$; *if a normal matrix is super-diagonal, then it is diagonal.* (T)

21. Can a nilpotent operator be normal?

22. In a unitary space X with inner product (x, y), let H be a positive Hermitian operator. Show that the functional $f(x, y) = (x, Hy)$ is also an inner product on X.

B. Hermitian and Skew-Hermitian Matrices

If a Euclidean 2-space is rotated through 90° about the origin by an operator L then $(x, Lx) = 0$ for each x. The situation in a complex space is entirely different.

1. If L is an operator on a unitary space such that $(x, Lx) = 0$ for each vector x, then $L = 0$.

For each x and y it is true, by hypothesis, that

$$(x + y, L(x + y)) = 0 \qquad \text{and} \qquad (x + iy, L(x + iy)) = 0.$$

On expanding these identities, observing that $(x, Lx) = (y, Ly) = 0$, and manipulating the results, we learn that $(y, Lx) = 0$. Now put $y = Lx$ to obtain $\|Lx\| = 0$, whence $L = 0$.

We know already (cf. A13(1)) that a normal operator L on a unitary space is Hermitian if and only if (x, Lx) is real for every x. It is essential to recognize that this property is invariant under conjunctivity $(L' = T^*LT)$ but not necessarily under similarity $(L' = T^{-1}LT)$ unless T is unitary $(T^{-1} = T^*)$, and in this case L' is also, of course, conjunctive to L.

Since L is skew-Hermitian if and only if $H = iL$ is Hermitian, it will suffice to study the Hermitian case.

Being normal, a Hermitian operator H is unitarily similar to $[[\lambda_1, \ldots, \lambda_n]]$, where the λ's are the eigenvalues of H and hence real. This representation is unique up to the order in which the λ's appear. The corresponding Hermitian quadratic form is $x^*Hx = \sum_1^r \lambda_k |\xi_k|^2$, where r is the rank of H.

The eigenvalues determine the sign of H (10C12). It is indefinite if and only if at least one eigenvalue is positive and at least one is negative. Otherwise $H > 0, \geq 0, = 0, \leq 0, < 0$ according as all the eigenvalues are, respectively, $> 0, \geq 0, = 0, \leq 0, < 0$.

Since the rank r of H is equal to the number of its non-zero eigenvalues, we see that if $H \geq 0$ and $r = n$ then $H > 0$; the converse is obvious. We present three conditions, each of which guarantees that $H \geq 0$.

2. $H \geq 0$ if and only if $H = J^2$, where J is Hermitian, of the same rank as H, and unique if $J \geq 0$.

If H has rank r and is ≥ 0, then its canonical form is

2.1.
$$[[\lambda_1, \ldots, \lambda_r, 0, \ldots, 0]],$$

where each λ is positive. Simply take
$$J = [[\lambda_1^{1/2}, \ldots, \lambda_r^{1/2}, 0, \ldots, 0]].$$
The converse is obvious. Note that uniqueness of J is lost if the condition $J \geq 0$ is dropped, for then some $-\lambda_k^{1/2}$ could be used.

The equation $H = J^2$ permits us to call J a square root of H, and the substance of 2 is that if $H \geq 0$, then H has a square root $J \geq 0$.

3. $H \geq 0$ if and only if $H = K^*K$, where K is of the same rank as H.

The sufficiency of the stated condition is obvious, for $x^*K^*Kx = \|Kx\|^2 \geq 0$. We saw in 10C that if $H \geq 0$ and has rank r, then H is conjunctive with
$$[[1, \ldots, 1_r, 0, \ldots, 0]] = [[I_r \quad 0]] = J_r \quad ;$$
J_r is an abbreviation. There exists, therefore, a regular operator L such that
$$H = L^*J_rL = (J_rL)^*J_rL.$$
We may take $K = J_rL$, which consists of L with its last $n - r$ rows replaced by zeros. Since the rows of L are independent, K has rank r.

The matrix $H = K^*K$ is the Gram matrix (see 13G) of the column vectors of J_rL. If these vectors are denoted by x_k ($k = 1, \ldots, n$), then $H = [(x_j, x_k)]$.

From this fact it can be seen that if $H \geq 0$ (or > 0) then every principal minor of $H \geq 0$ (or > 0). In fact, a principal minor M of H or order p will be of the form $|(x_{j'}, x_{k'})|$, where j' and k' run over the *same* subset of p indices chosen from $1, \ldots, n$. These minors are necessarily ≥ 0 and, if $H > 0$ then they must all be > 0, for otherwise the vectors $x_{k'}$ occurring in M would be dependent, a contradiction.

4. If $H \geq 0$ (or > 0) then all principal minors of H are ≥ 0 (or > 0), and conversely.

Our proof of the converse uses the characteristic polynomial, which we write as

5. $$f(\lambda) = |\lambda I - H| = \lambda^n + {}_k\sum_1^n(-1)^k\alpha_k\lambda^{n-k}.$$

Now if $H = [\beta_{jk}]$, then

6. $$f(\lambda) = \sum \text{sgn } \sigma(\lambda\delta_{1\sigma_1} - \beta_{1\sigma_1}) \ldots (\lambda\delta_{n\sigma_n} - \beta_{n\sigma_n}).$$

In order for λ to appear to the power $n - k$ we must have $\sigma_j = j$ for exactly $n - k$ values of j. Each time this happens the coefficient is a principal minor formed from those k rows and columns for which $\sigma_j \neq j$. Thus α_k is the sum of all principal minors of order k. Now $f(-\lambda) = (-1)^n [\lambda^n + {}_k\sum_1^n \alpha_k\lambda^{n-kt}]$. If each α_k is ≥ 0 (or > 0) then $f(-\lambda)$ can have no root ≥ 0 (or > 0), whence every root of $f(\lambda)$ (and they are known to be real) must be ≥ 0 (or > 0).

EXERCISES

7. If L is an operator on a real space then (x, Ly) is always real. What must be true of L if $(x, Ly) = (Lx, y)$ for all x and y? (T)

8. Let

$$H = \begin{bmatrix} 14 & 6 - 10i & 0 \\ 6 + 10i & 9 & 0 \\ 0 & 0 & 9 \end{bmatrix}.$$

Prove that all principal minors of H are > 0. Find a Hermitian $J > 0$ such that $H = J^2$. Find also K such that $H = K^*K$.

9. Prove that if $H = [\beta_{jk}]$ then for $H \geq 0$ (or > 0) it is sufficient that all the n particular principal minors $|\beta_{j'k'}|$ be ≥ 0 (or > 0) where $j', k' = 1, \ldots, p \leq n$. (T)

10. If $x, y \neq 0$ then $(x, y) > 0$ if and only if there is an operator $H > 0$ such that $y = Hx$.

11. Let L be a Hermitian operator and suppose that all the eigenvalues of L lie in the interval $\alpha < \lambda < \beta$. How can one choose μ so as to guarantee that $L^3 + \mu I > 0$?

12. Let us say that $K < L$ (or $K \leq L$) if $L - K > 0$ (or ≥ 0). Is "$\leq$" a partial order on the set of operators in the sense of 4J?

13. Suppose that H is Hermitian, $H \geq 0$, and that a vector x has the property that $(x, Hx) = 0$. Prove that then $Hx = 0$. [*Hint:* For all α and y, $0 \leq (x + \alpha y, H(x + \alpha y)).$]

14. Prove that the relation $H = J^2$ is preserved under a similarity but not necessarily under a conjunctivity.

15. We outline a proof by induction that $h_n(x) = \sum_1^n \xi_j\beta_{jk}\xi_k$, with $[\beta_{jk}]$ real and symmetric, is > 0 if and only if the particular minors $m_p = |\beta_{j'k'}|$ ($j', k' = 1, \ldots, p \leq n$) are > 0. The assertion is obvious if $n = 1$, so assume it true for $n = q$ and consider

$$h_{q+1}(\eta; x) = \alpha\eta^2 + 2 \sum_1^n \beta_k\xi_k\eta + h_q(x).$$

In order that $h_{q+1} > 0$ it is necessary and sufficient that $h_q > 0$, $\alpha > 0$ and that $h_{q+1}(\eta; x)$, considered as a quadratic in η, shall have no real roots. The latter condition is that

$$\alpha h_q(x) - (\sum \beta_{ik} \xi_k)^2 > 0$$

or that

$$g_q(x) = \sum \xi_i (\alpha \beta_{jk} - \beta_j \beta_k) \xi_k > 0$$

for all x. This will be true, by the inductive hypothesis, if and only if the determinants

$$d_p = |\alpha \beta_{j'k'} - \beta_{j'} \beta_{k'}| \qquad (j', k' = 1, \ldots, p \leq m)$$

are all positive. A short calculation reveals that the minor m_{p+1} of the matrix of h_{q+1} is equal to a power of α times d_p, and the result follows. (T)

C. Extremal Properties of Eigenvalues of Hermitian Operators

If H is a Hermitian operator on a unitary space and $Hx = \lambda x$ with $x \neq 0$, then $(x, Hx) = \lambda(x, x)$ and

1.
$$\lambda = \frac{(x, Hx)}{(x, x)} = r(x),$$

where $r(x)$, an abbreviation for the middle expression, is the *Rayleigh ratio* (or quotient) for H and x. Since $r(\alpha x) = r(x)$ if $\alpha \neq 0$ it is obvious that $r(x) = r(\hat{x})$ if we agree, for the time being, that the circumflex on $\hat{x}$ shall mean that $||\hat{x}|| = 1$.

The substance of the foregoing remark is that each eigenvalue of H is to be found among the values of $r(x)$ as x varies, indeed (see 13), among the values of $r(\hat{x})$ as $\hat{x}$ varies over the unit sphere $||x|| = 1$. We appeal again (cf. 13A8) to the theorem that a function, such as $r(x)$, continuous on a "compact" set (such as $||x|| = 1$ when dim X is finite), has a maximum. If this maximum is μ and is attained when $\hat{x} = \hat{y}$ then

2.
$$\mu = \max r(\hat{x}) = (\hat{y}, H\hat{y}).$$

Now consider the operator $\mu - H$. Observe that if $x \neq 0$, then

$$(x, (\mu - H)x) = \mu(x, x) - (x, Hx)$$
$$= ||x||^2 (\mu - r(x)) \geq 0.$$

Hence $\mu - H \geq 0$. But, if $x = \hat{y}$,

$$(\hat{y}, (\mu - H)\hat{y}) = \mu - r(\hat{y}) = 0.$$

It follows by B13 that $(\mu - H)\hat{y} = 0$, or $H\hat{y} = \mu\hat{y}$; that is, μ is an eigenvalue of H and $\hat{y}$ is a corresponding eigenvector. We now designate μ by λ_1 and $\hat{y}$ by y_1. Since every eigenvalue is to be found among the values of $r(\hat{x})$, λ_1 is a greatest eigenvalue of H.

The reader will find it enlightening to consider the problem of finding stationary values (in the real case) of $\alpha \xi^2 + 2\beta \xi \eta + \gamma \eta^2$ subject to the constraint $\xi^2 + \eta^2 = 1$. He will seek stationary points of the function

3.
$$\alpha \xi^2 + 2\beta \xi \eta + \gamma \eta^2 - \lambda(\xi^2 + \eta^2 - 1);$$

here the parameter λ is a "Lagrange multiplier". The resulting equations

$$(\alpha - \lambda)\xi + \beta\eta = 0$$

$$\beta\xi + (\gamma - \lambda)\eta = 0$$

constitute an eigenvalue problem, for λ is being sought such that the equations have a nontrivial solution. A diagram is instructive.

Now augment y_1 to an orthonormal basis y_k ($k = 1, \ldots, n$) and introduce new coordinates by the equation (in an obvious notation) $x = [y_k]y$. Then

4.
$$\begin{aligned}
h(x) = x^*Hx &= y^*[y_k]^*H[y_k]y \\
&= y^*[y_k]^*[\lambda_1 y_1 \, Hy_2 \ldots Hy_n]y \\
&= y^*[[\lambda_1 \, [y_{j'}^*Hy_{k'}]]]y \\
&= \lambda_1|\eta_1|^2 + h_{n-1}(y),
\end{aligned}$$

where j', $k' = 2, \ldots, n$ and $h_{n-1}(y) = y^*[y_{j'}^*Hy_{k'}]y$, in which only the components $\eta_2, \ldots, \eta_n$ of y appear. Since the basis is orthonormal, in fact, $(y_{k'}, y_1) = 0$ and it follows that

$$(y_1, Hy_{k'}) = (Hy_1, y_{k'}) = \bar{\lambda}_1(y_1, y_{k'}) = 0.$$

It is easy to verify that $H_{n-1} = [y_{j'}^*Hy_{k'}]$ is Hermitian, and we may proceed to reduce $h_{n-1}(y) = y^*H_{n-1}y$ by a unitary change of the variables $\eta_2, \ldots, \eta_n$ to the form $\lambda_2|\xi_2|^2 + h_{n-2}(z)$. Here λ_2 is the greatest eigenvalue of H_{n-1}, the ζ's are new variables (with $\zeta_1 = \eta_1$), and $h_{n-2}(z)$ is a Hermitian form in $\zeta_3, \ldots, \zeta_n$.

It is essential to observe that if $w = [0, \eta_2, \ldots, \eta_n]^t$ is an eigenvector of H_{n-1} corresponding to λ_2, then

$$\begin{bmatrix} \lambda_1 & 0 \\ 0 & H_{n-1} \end{bmatrix} w = \lambda_2 w.$$

Since eigenvalues (and eigenvectors) are invariant under unitary similarity, λ_2 is an eigenvalue of H and w is a corresponding eigenvector. Of course, $\lambda_2 \leq \lambda_1$.

Continuing, we arrive finally at a coordinate system in which $H = [[\lambda_1, \ldots, \lambda_n]]$ and

$$h(x) = x^*Hx = \sum \lambda_k|\xi_k|^2,$$

with $\lambda_1 \geq \lambda_2 \geq \ldots \geq \lambda_n$.

5. For each Hermitian form x^*Hx there exists an orthonormal coordinate system in which $x^*Hx = \sum \lambda_k|\xi_k|^2$, where the λ's are eigenvalues of H and $\lambda_1 \geq \lambda_2 \geq \ldots \geq \lambda_n$.

This form may differ, of course, from that of B2.1, where all r non-zero eigenvalues are put first and all $n - r$ zeros follow.

The foregoing stepwise process delivers the eigenvalues in non-increasing succession, along with a corresponding eigenvector for each eigenvalue. In many problems of practical interest it suffices to know the eigenvalues regardless of the eigenvectors and, indeed, to know something of the kth eigenvalue (in non-increasing succession) regardless of the others. We know that $\lambda_1 = \max h(\hat{x})$. A general procedure is suggested by a more relaxed approach to the evaluation of λ_2. Choose $y \in X$ arbitrarily and consider

6.
$$\mu(y) = \max_{(y,\,\hat{x})=0} h(\hat{x})$$

Since $\max h(\hat{x})$ for $(y_1, \hat{x}) = 0$ is λ_2, clearly $\lambda_2 \le \mu(y)$. Moreover, when $y = y_1$, $\max h(\hat{x}) = \lambda_2$ if $(y_1, x) = 0$. Hence λ_2 is the minimum of $\mu(y)$ if y is allowed to vary; that is,

7.
$$\lambda_2 = \min_{y} \max_{(y,\,\hat{x})=0} h(\hat{x}).$$

8. Mini-max Property of Eigenvalues of a Hermitian Matrix. Let a Hermitian matrix H have eigenvalues $\lambda_1 \ge \ldots \ge \lambda_n$. Let $h(\hat{x}) = x^*Hx$ with $\|\hat{x}\| = 1$. Then $\lambda_1 = \max h(\hat{x})$ and, for $k = 2, \ldots, n$,

$$\lambda_k = \min_{\substack{y_j \\ j=1,\ldots,k-1}} \max_{(y_j,\,\hat{x})=0} h(\hat{x}).$$

That is, with $k \ge 2$ fixed, and $k - 1$ chosen vectors y_j, we form the intersection Y of the $k - 1$ hyperplanes $(y_j, x) = 0$, maximize $h(\hat{x})$ on the intersection of Y with the unit sphere, and then let the vectors y_j vary so as to minimize $\max h(\hat{x})$.

The proof is straightforward. Even if $\hat{x}$ satisfies the further equations $\xi^{k+1} = \ldots = \xi^n = 0$, the $k - 1$ equations $(y_j, x) = 0$ $(j = 1, \ldots, k - 1)$ still involve k free variables and therefore have a solution $\hat{x}$. For such an $\hat{x}$,

$$h(\hat{x}) = \sum_{m=1}^{k} \lambda_m |\xi_m|^2 \ge \lambda_k \sum_{m=1}^{k} |\xi_m|^2 = \lambda_k.$$

Hence the minimum of $\max h(\hat{x})$ is not less than λ_k. At the same time, if we impose only the $k - 1$ constraints $\xi^1 = \ldots = \xi^{k-1} = 0$ then $h(\hat{x}) = \sum_{m=k}^{n} \lambda_m |\xi_m|^2 \le \lambda_k$, so that the minimum is actually attained when $\hat{x}$ is the kth basis vector.

The Rayleigh ratio is tremendously useful in numerical work involving eigenvalues and eigenvectors. Although we cannot go into details (see F in the bibliography), we can indicate one important result.

Suppose (cf. 2 and 1) that

9.
$$\mu = (\hat{y}, H\hat{y}) = \max r(\hat{x}).$$

If $0 < |\epsilon| < 1$ and $(\hat{z}, \hat{y}) = 0$, then the endpoint of the vector

10.
$$\hat{x} = \sqrt{1 - \epsilon^2}\hat{y} + \epsilon\hat{z}$$

is on the surface of the unit sphere, the closer to the endpoint of $\hat{y}$ the closer $|\epsilon|$ is to zero. In fact,

$$\|\hat{y} - \hat{x}\|^2 = \|(1 - \sqrt{1 - \epsilon^2})\hat{y} - \epsilon\hat{z}\|^2$$

$$= (1 - \sqrt{1 - \epsilon^2})^2 + \epsilon^2$$

11.
$$= 2(1 - \sqrt{1 - \epsilon^2}) = \epsilon^2 + 0_4,$$

where we have used O_q to indicate terms of order q or more in ϵ.

Of course, $r(\hat{x}) \le \mu = r(\hat{y})$. Let us calculate the error in using $r(\hat{x})$ as an estimate for μ.

$$r(\hat{y}) - r(\hat{x}) = \mu - (\hat{x}, H\hat{x})$$

$$= -\epsilon\sqrt{1 - \epsilon^2} \operatorname{Re}(\hat{z}, H\hat{y}) + \epsilon^2[\mu - r(\hat{z})],$$

where $\operatorname{Re} \zeta$ denotes the real part of ζ. If, in addition to the requirement $(\hat{z}, \hat{y}) = 0$, we impose the further requirement that $(\hat{z}, H\hat{y}) = 0$, then

12.
$$\mu - r(\hat{x}) = \epsilon^2[\mu - r(\hat{z})].$$

We note that if $n \ge 3$ then there is certainly a $z \ne 0$ such that both $(\hat{z}, \hat{y}) = 0$ and $(\hat{z}, H\hat{y}) = 0$.

The upshot is that if $\hat{z}$ meets these two conditions, and if $\hat{x}$ is defined by 10, then it follows from 11 and 12 that an error of order ϵ in $\hat{x}$ (as measured by $\|\hat{y} - \hat{x}\|$) entails an error $\mu - r(\hat{x})$ in $r(\hat{x})$ of the order ϵ^2. In other words, if x is within ϵ of $\hat{y}$ then $r(\hat{x})$ is within ϵ^2 of μ. A good estimate $\hat{x}$ of $\hat{y}$ will yield a *very* good estimate $r(\hat{x})$ of $\mu = r(\hat{y})$.

EXERCISES

13. Prove that $\max_{\hat{x}} r(\hat{x}) = \max_{x \ne 0} r(x)$.

14. Prove directly that $\lambda_n = \min r(\hat{x})$.

15. Prove that if H is Hermitian then (cf. 13H8) $\|H\|^2 = \lambda_1$, where λ_1 is the largest eigenvalue of H^2.

16. *Imposition of linear constraints.* Suppose that $1 \le p < n$, that v_j ($j = 1, \ldots, p$) are p independent vectors, and that x is required to satisfy the p linear constraints $(v_j, x) = 0$ ($j = 1, \ldots, p$). A Hermitian form $h(x) = (x, Hx)$ reduces to a Hermitian form $g(z) = (z, Gz)$ on an $n - p$ dimensional subspace Z. The form $g(z)$ will have $n - p$ eigenvalues $\mu_1 \ge \mu_2 \ge \ldots \ge \mu_{n-p}$. Fortunately, we can get information relating the μ's and the λ's without actually getting down into Z or finding the matrix $[G]$. In order to find μ_k we shall have to impose $k - 1$ linear constraints on $g(z)$; but the numbers in competition are then simply the values of $h(x)$ subject to $p + k - 1$ constraints. Since p of these constraints are not arbitrary, the least maximum μ_k cannot be less than the least maximum λ_{p+k}, obtained with $p + k - 1$ arbitrary constraints; that is, $\mu_k \ge \lambda_{p+k}$. At the same time, a maximum subject to $p + k - 1$ constraints cannot exceed a maximum subject to a subset consisting of $k - 1$ of those constraints. Hence

$$\lambda_k \geq \mu_k \geq \lambda_{k+p}. \text{ (T)}$$

17. Let $j, k = 1, \ldots, n$ and consider $h(x) = \sum \bar{\xi}_j \beta_{jk} \xi_k$, with $\bar{\beta}_{kj} = \beta_{jk}$. Let q be a fixed integer, $1 \leq q < n$, and choose a subset Q of q integers from $1, \ldots, n$. Let j' and k' have domain Q and consider $g(x) = \sum \bar{\xi}_{j'} \beta_{j'k'} \xi_{k'}$. Obtain inequalities similar to those of 16 relating the eigenvalues of g and those of h.

18. Let H and P be Hermitian forms, with $P > 0$. What can you say about the eigenvalues of $H + P$ compared with those of H? (T)

D. Real Symmetric Matrices; Central Quadrics

A real symmetric operator L is normal, and has the property that $[L^a] = [L]^t$. The results of A–C carry over almost verbatim to the present case, in which, of course, $[L]^* = [L]^t$. That all the eigenvalues of a real symmetric operator are real follows from C1 and can easily be proved directly. A real symmetric matrix of rank r is orthogonally similar (hence congruent) to $[[\lambda_1, \ldots, \lambda_r, 0, \ldots, 0]]$. A reduction analogous in every particular to that in C5 yields the following result.

1. For each real quadratic form $x^t S x$ there exists an orthonormal coordinate system in which $x^t S x = \sum \lambda_k \xi_k^2$, with $\lambda_1 \geq \ldots \geq \lambda_n$. The mini-max property (C8) also holds.

In Euclidean 3-space it is customary to use an orthonormal basis and coordinate vectors $[x \quad y \quad z]^t$. As an example, let

2.
$$q(x, y, z) = 2x^2 + 11y^2 + 5z^2 - 4xy - 16yz - 20xz$$

$$= [x \quad y \quad z] \begin{bmatrix} 2 & -2 & -10 \\ -2 & 11 & -8 \\ -10 & -8 & 5 \end{bmatrix} \begin{bmatrix} x \\ y \\ z \end{bmatrix} = X^t S X,$$

where $X = [x \quad y \quad z]^t$ and S is the (symmetric) matrix of q. Here $|\lambda - S| = (\lambda^2 - 81)(\lambda - 18)$. We obtain the following eigenvalues and corresponding (orthonormal) eigenvectors:

Eigenvalue	Eigenvector
$\lambda_1 = \quad 9$	$p_1 = \frac{1}{3}[-2 \quad 2 \quad 1]^t$
$\lambda_2 = -9$	$p_2 = \frac{1}{3}[\ 2 \quad 1 \quad 2]^t$
$\lambda_3 = \quad 18$	$p_3 = \frac{1}{3}[\ 1 \quad 2 \quad -2]^t.$

If $X = x'p_1 + y'p_2 + z'p_3$, then

$$3x = -2x' + 2y' + \ z'$$
$$3y = \ \ 2x' + \ y' + 2z'$$
$$3z = \ \ \ x' + 2y' - 2z';$$

in the new coordinates

3.
$$X^t S X = 9x'^2 - 9y'^2 + 18z'^2.$$

We continue with the notation of the preceding paragraph and assume, for simplicity, that S has rank 3. It is customary to replace

4.
$$\lambda_1 x^2 + \lambda_2 y^2 + \lambda_3 z^2$$
by

5.
$$\pm \frac{x^2}{a^2} \pm \frac{y^2}{b^2} \pm \frac{z^2}{c^2},$$

where the sign is that of the respective λ and $a^2 = |\lambda_1|^{-1}$, $b^2 = |\lambda_2|^{-1}$, and $c^2 = |\lambda_3|^{-1}$. The loci obtained by setting 5 equal to 1 (or zero) are called (central) quadric surfaces (or cones). The accompanying table (7) refers to three representative cases in which the respective signatures are 3, 1, and -1. In the instance of 3, the equation would be (if the primes were dropped)

6.
$$\frac{x^2}{(\frac{1}{3})^2} - \frac{y^2}{(\frac{1}{3})^2} + \frac{z^2}{(1/3\sqrt{2})^2} = 1.$$

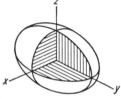

$$\frac{x^2}{a^2} + \frac{y^2}{b^2} + \frac{z^2}{c^2} = \begin{cases} 1 & \text{Ellipsoid} \\ 0 & \text{Point locus; origin} \end{cases}$$

Ellipsoid

$$\frac{x^2}{a^2} + \frac{y^2}{b^2} - \frac{z^2}{c^2} = \begin{cases} 1 & \text{One-sheeted hyperboloid} \\ 0 & \text{Cone, axis along } z\text{-axis} \end{cases}$$

One-sheeted hyperboloid

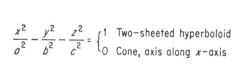

$$\frac{x^2}{a^2} - \frac{y^2}{b^2} - \frac{z^2}{c^2} = \begin{cases} 1 & \text{Two-sheeted hyperboloid} \\ 0 & \text{Cone, axis along } x\text{-axis} \end{cases}$$

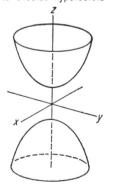

Two-sheeted hyperboloid

7. Certain quadric surfaces.

This is the equation of a one-sheeted hyperboloid which does not cut the y-axis (in real points). The respective semi-axes are $\frac{1}{3}$, $\frac{1}{3}$, and $1/3\sqrt{2}$.

We have here a geometric interpretation of the absolute value of an eigenvalue. In the coordinate system of 1, the coordinate axes are the principal axes of the quadric in the geometric sense, as explained in an example in 12A. The number $|\lambda_k|^{-1}$, moreover, is the squared length of the corresponding "semi-axis"; if $\lambda_k > 0$, the semi-axis is the intercept on the corresponding coordinate axis. The reduction of 2 to 4 is often called a *principal-axis transformation*, and the same terminology is applied, quite generally, in the context of 4.1 and C5. One speaks loosely of reducing a quadratic (or Hermitian) form to "a sum of squares" without implying that all the coefficients are positive.

EXERCISES

8. Justify the diagrams in 7 by considering sections of the locus by planes perpendicular to various coordinate axes.

9. Use the method of 8 to form an idea of the locus of $z = x^2 + y^2/4$.

10. Ditto for $z = x^2 - y^2/4$.

11. Observe from 2 that

$$q(\xi, \eta, \zeta) = 2(\xi - \eta - 5\zeta)^2 + 9(\eta - 2\zeta)^2 - 81\zeta^2$$

11.1.
$$= 2\alpha^2 + 9\beta^2 - 81\gamma^2.$$

Give equations connecting (ξ, η, ζ) with (α, β, γ). With S as in 2, find a matrix Q such that $Q^t S Q = [[2, 9, -81]]$. Show also that S is congruent to $[[1, 1, -1]]$. It was shown above that 2 is orthogonally similar to $[[9, -9, 18]]$; can 2 be orthogonally similar to any other diagonal form (apart from the order in which the diagonal terms occur)?

12. Prove directly that every eigenvalue of a real symmetric matrix is real.

13. Reduce to a sum of squares:

   (a) $2\xi\eta$,

   (b) $2\xi\eta + 2\xi\zeta + 2\eta\zeta$,

   (c) $\xi^2 + 2\eta^2 + 3\zeta^2 - 4\xi\eta - 4\xi\zeta$,

   (d) $2\xi^2 - \eta^2 + \zeta^2 - \xi\eta + 3\eta\zeta$.

14. In a Euclidean X_n let u be a fixed vector and consider $f(x) = x^t S x + u^t x + \gamma$, where S is symmetric and γ is a scalar. If S has rank r, then in 4.1 $n - r$ of the λ's will be zero. By a permutation of coordinates (which is orthogonal per se) these $n - r$ λ's can be made to follow all non-zero eigenvalues, with the non-increasing order of the latter maintained. Let P be an orthogonal matrix such that $P^{-1}SP = D = [[\lambda_1, \ldots, \lambda_r, 0, \ldots, 0]]$ with $\lambda_1 \geq \ldots \geq \lambda_r$, and put $x = Py$. Then

$$f(x) = f(Py) = g(y) = y^t D y + u^t P y + \gamma.$$

If $y = [\eta_1 \ldots \eta_r]^t$ then $\eta_1, \ldots, \eta_r$ may be combined respectively with $\lambda_1 \eta_1^2, \ldots, \lambda_r \eta_r^2$ by completing the square to form $\lambda_k (\eta_k + \alpha_k)^2$ ($k = 1, \ldots, r$), and the compensating scalars can be absorbed into a new γ. If $\zeta_k = \eta_k + \alpha_k$ ($k = 1, \ldots, r$) and $\zeta_k = \eta_k$ ($k = r + 1, \ldots, n$), and $z = [\zeta_k]^t$ (a translation by $[\alpha_1 \ldots \alpha_r 0 \ldots 0]^t$), then

14.1. $$g(y) = h(z) = {}_k\sum_1^r \lambda_k \zeta_k^2 + {}_k\sum_{r+1}^n \beta_k \zeta_k + \gamma.$$

It is easy, using this expression, to study the level surfaces of h. The resultant of the rotation P followed by the translation is a rigid motion (of the level surfaces if we are thinking of mappings, or of an orthonormal basis (to a new origin $[-\alpha_1 \ldots -\alpha_r 0 \ldots 0]^t$) if we are thinking of a change of variable). The result is that $f(x)$ may be brought by a rigid motion to the form 14.1. For a complete discussion for $n = 3$ see [D3, Chap. IX]. (T)

E. Pairs of Hermitian or Quadratic Forms

Problems involving pairs of forms arise quite naturally in mechanics. Consider a conservative dynamical system with n degrees of freedom, with coordinates $x = [\xi_k]^t$ ($k = 1, \ldots, n$) near a position of equilibrium, which we take to be $x = 0$. It is shown in books on mechanics that such a system satisfies certain differential equations of the form $Ax'' + Bx = 0$, or

1. $$\sum \alpha_{jk} \xi_k'' + \sum \beta_{jk} \xi_k = 0 \qquad (j = 1, \ldots, n),$$

where $[A] = [\alpha_{jk}]$ is symmetric and positive, $[B] = [\beta_{jk}]$ is symmetric, and each prime denotes a derivative with respect to time. Actually, $x'^t A x'$ is twice the kinetic energy of the system and $x^t B x$ is twice the term of order two in the Taylor series at $x = 0$ of the potential energy (cf. 10C10).

In principle, any or all of the ξ's may appear in each of the equations 1; if this happens, then the behavior of each ξ depends, apparently, on that of all the others and the variables (or the equations) are said to be "coupled". It turns out, fortunately enough, that we can find coordinates η_k (often called *normal* coordinates) in which $[A] = I$ and $[B]$ is diagonal. Then the equations 1 take the form

2. $$\eta_k'' + \beta_k \eta_k = 0 \qquad (k = 1, \ldots, n).$$

Each of these equations can be solved explicitly and independently of all the others. The variables η_k (or the equations 2) are said to be "uncoupled". The motion of the system is the "sum", or "superposition", of the motions taking place separately and independently in the subspaces of each coordinate.

Whenever $\beta_k > 0$ in 2, the motion in η_k is oscillatory and is said to be a "normal mode" of vibration. If $\beta_k \leq 0$, however, η_k increases with t (unless $\eta_k = \eta_k' = 0$ when $t = 0$, in which case $\eta_k = 0$). If $\beta_k > 0$ ($k = 1, \ldots, n$), then the equilibrium at $x = 0$ is said to be stable. If $\beta_k \leq 0$ ($k = 1, \ldots, n$) the equilibrium is said to be totally unstable. If $\beta_k > 0$ for some values of k while $\beta_k \leq 0$ for other values of k, then the equilibrium is said to be conditionally stable, meaning stable for small displacements in those coordinates for which $\beta_k > 0$.

Let us start with a trial solution $x = ze^{i\mu t}$, where $z = [\zeta_k]^t$ is a fixed vector. We obtain $(-\mu^2 A + B)z = 0$ or

3.
$$\sum (-\mu^2 \alpha_{jk} + \beta_{jk})\zeta_k = 0.$$

There will be a solution $z \neq 0$ if and only if

4.
$$|-\mu^2 \alpha_{jk} + \beta_{jk}| = 0;$$

this equation is often called the *secular* equation.

Given operators P and S let us consider quite generally the problem of finding a vector $x \neq 0$ and a scalar λ such that

5.
$$(\lambda P - S)x = 0.$$

We agree in this context to follow the usage, already adopted when $P = I$, of calling a scalar λ and a corresponding vector $x \neq 0$ which satisfy 5 an *eigenvalue* and an *eigenvector of the pair P and S*.

It is an appealing idea, if P is regular, to reduce 5 to $(\lambda - P^{-1}S)x = 0$. Unfortunately, however, even if P and S are normal, $P^{-1}S$ may fail to be normal unless P and S commute. (For conditions under which operators commute see [A18, Sec. 23].) We can show by an example, moreover, with P and S real and symmetric, and $n = 2$, that $|\lambda P - S|$ may vanish identically or may have two, one, or no zeros (roots of $|\lambda P - S| = 0$).

Let us assume that P and S are Hermitian, with $P > 0$; then our results will apply to 1. In

6.
$$g(\lambda) = |\lambda P - S|$$

the coefficient of λ^n is $|P| > 0$ and the constant term is $(-1)^n |S|$. Now suppose that $g(\lambda) = 0$ and that $\lambda Px = Sx$. Then $\lambda(x, Px) = (x, Sx)$, and we obtain the following conclusion.

7. If P and S are Hermitian, with $P > 0$, then the eigenvalues of the pair P, S are real; they are all positive (negative) if and only if $S > 0 (< 0)$.

It follows, incidentally, that equilibrium is stable if $S > 0$, totally unstable if $S < 0$, and conditionally stable otherwise. (See the paragraph containing 10C10.)

It follows from 10C7 that there exists a regular operator T such that $T^a PT = I$. The equation $g(\lambda) = 0$ can then be made to read

8.
$$|\lambda - S'| = 0$$

where $S' = T^a ST$ is again Hermitian. By C5, a further unitary operator U will replace S' by

9.
$$D = U^a S'U = [[\lambda_1, \ldots, \lambda_n]],$$

where the λ's are the eigenvalues of S' and $\lambda_1 \geq \ldots \geq \lambda_n$; since T is regular, the λ's are eigenvalues of the pair P and S, for

10.
$$|T^a||\lambda P - S||T| = |\lambda - T^a ST|.$$

11. If P and S are Hermitian operators in a unitary X_n, and $P > 0$, then there is a coordinate system in which both $[P] = [I]$ and $[S] = [[\lambda_1, \ldots, \lambda_n]]$, where the λ's satisfy the equation $|\lambda P - S| = 0$.

In the application to 1, $A = P$ and $B = S$. The effect of T followed by U is to replace A by I and B by D; if the final coordinates are η_k $(k = 1, \ldots, n)$ then the equations in the η's are (cf. 2)

12.
$$\eta_k'' + \lambda_k \eta_k = 0.$$

The equation

13.
$$U^a T^a (\lambda P - S) T U = \lambda I - D$$

suggests that the basis in 11 may be orthogonal; since we do not know the metric, however, this conclusion would be unfounded. What we can say is that the columns of $[TU]$ are P-orthonormal in the sense that

14.
$$[U^a T^a P T U] = [\delta_{jk}].$$

A direct proof will be given as a foundation for a process, to which we now turn, for using the eigenvalues and eigenvectors of P and S to find the basis in which $P = I$ and $S = D$; the process may be compared with that which led to C5.

Let λ_k $(k = 1, \ldots, t)$ be the *distinct* roots of the equation $g(\lambda) = 0$ (cf. 6). Assign k the domain $1, \ldots, t$ and m the domain $t + 1, \ldots, n$. Let p_k be an eigenvector corresponding to λ_k and adjust $\|p_k\|$ so that $(p_k, Pp_k) = 1$. Let q_m be a basis for $\langle p_1, \ldots, p_t \rangle^{\perp}$.

From the equations

15.
$$\lambda_k Pp_k = Sp_k, \qquad \lambda_{k'} Pp_{k'} = Sp_{k'} \qquad (k \neq k'),$$

we obtain

16.
$$(p_{k'}, \lambda_k Pp_k) = (p_{k'}, Sp_k),$$

17.
$$(p_k, \lambda_{k'} Pp_{k'}) = (p_k, Sp_{k'}) = (Sp_k, p_{k'}) = \overline{(p_{k'}, Sp_k)}.$$

The left member of 16 is $\lambda_k(p_{k'}, Pp_k)$. We may write 17 as $\lambda_{k'} \overline{(p_{k'}, Pp_k)} = \overline{(p_{k'}, Sp_k)}$. Recalling that the λ's are real, we take conjugates and subtract from 16 obtaining

18.
$$(\lambda_k - \lambda_{k'})(p_{k'}, Pp_k) = 0.$$

Since $\lambda_k \neq \lambda_{k'}$, $(p_{k'}, Pp_k) = 0$ whence, by 16, $(p_{k'}, Sp_k) = 0$ also.

Referred to the basis formed by the p's and q's,

335

19.
$$[P] = \begin{bmatrix} I_t & 0 \\ 0 & P_{n-t} \end{bmatrix}, \qquad [S] = \begin{bmatrix} D_t & 0 \\ 0 & S_{n-t} \end{bmatrix},$$

where $D_t = [[\lambda_1, \ldots, \lambda_t]]$, P_{n-t} and S_{n-t} are Hermitian, and $P_{n-t} > 0$.

Now proceed similarly with P_{n-t}, S_{n-t}, and $h(\lambda) = |\lambda P_{n-t} - S_{n-t}|$; the roots of $h(\lambda) = 0$ are those roots of $g(\lambda) = 0$ having multiplicity at least two.

The process terminates with $[P]$ and $[S]$ in the form given in 11. One says that P and S have been reduced simultaneously to sums of squares, or referred simultaneously to principal axes.

EXERCISES

20. The matrix $T^a U^a P T U$ is clearly conjunctive with P. Under what circumstances will it be similar to P?

21. Show that the form $2\xi^2 + 3\eta^2 + 2\zeta^2 + 2\xi\zeta$ is positive. Reduce it and the form

$$2\xi^2 - 2\eta^2 - 3\zeta^2 + 2\xi\zeta - 10\eta\zeta$$

simultaneously to sums of squares. (*Optional.* Use your results to "uncouple" and hence to solve explicitly the following system of differential equations:

$$\begin{cases} 2\xi'' & + \zeta'' + 2\xi & + \zeta = 0 \\ 3\eta'' & - 2\eta - 5\zeta = 0 \\ \xi'' & + 2\zeta'' + \xi - 5\eta - 3\zeta = 0. \end{cases}$$

[*Hint:* If the final variables are α, β, and γ, the differential equations may be brought to the form $\alpha'' + \alpha = 0$, $\beta'' + \beta = 0$, $\gamma'' - 4\gamma = 0$.])

22. The mini-max property of C8 can be extended to pairs of Hermitian operators P and S with $P > 0$. Let the eigenvalues of the pair P, S be $\lambda_1 \geq \ldots \geq \lambda_n$. Define $g(\hat{x}) = (x, Sx)/(x, Px)$, where we may assume that $\|\hat{x}\| = 1$. Prove that $\lambda_1 = \max g(\hat{x})$ and, for $k = 2, \ldots, n$

$$\lambda_k = \min_{\substack{y_i \\ i=1,\ldots,k-1}} \quad \max_{(y_i,\hat{x})=0} \quad g(\hat{x}).$$

Prove directly that $\lambda_n = \min g(\hat{x})$. (T)

23. Prove that $\xi^2 - 2\xi\eta + 3\zeta^2$ is positive and reduce it and the form $\xi^2 + \xi\eta - \zeta^2$ simultaneously to diagonal form.

24. The form $9\xi^2 + 36\eta^2 + 81\zeta^2$ is clearly positive. Find coordinates α, β, γ in which this form has the expression $\alpha^2 + \beta^2 + \gamma^2$ and in which the matrix of the form

$$61\xi^2 + 64\eta^2 + 46\zeta^2 + 44\xi\eta - 28\xi\zeta - 16\eta\zeta$$

is diagonal.

25. Let H and K be Hermitian matrices and U a unitary matrix such that both U^*HU and U^*KU are diagonal. Prove that $HK = KH$. Prove conversely that if $HK = KH$ then there exists a unitary matrix U such that both U^*HU and U^*KU are diagonal. (T)

F. Real Skew Matrices

In 10A28 we obtained a canonical form for skew matrices under congruence. That form consisted of blocks $\begin{bmatrix} 0 & 1 \\ -1 & 0 \end{bmatrix}$ down the diagonal. The methods of this chapter yield an orthogonally similar diagonal matrix with the eigenvalues on the diagonal. We shall elucidate the relation between these canonical forms. One canonical form under orthogonal similarity will have blocks $\begin{bmatrix} 0 & \lambda \\ -\lambda & 0 \end{bmatrix}$ down the diagonal, with—and this is no longer a surprise—λ an eigenvalue.

Quick insight results from the fact that if L is skew ($L^t = -L$), then $H = -iL$ is Hermitian. By A7, therefore, H is unitarily similar to

$$[[\lambda_1, \ldots, \lambda_n]],$$

where the λ's are the (real) eigenvalues of H. The same unitary similarity will reduce L to

$$[[i\lambda_1, \ldots, i\lambda_n]].$$

The eigenvalues of L are seen to be purely imaginary. Since L is real the coefficients of $|\lambda - L|$ are real and the eigenvalues occur in conjugate pairs. Only an even number do not vanish and the rank of L is even. We may arrange matters by a permutation, if necessary, so that each λ with an odd subscript is non-negative, and so that all non-zero eigenvalues precede all zero eigenvalues. Here is the conclusion:

1. If L is a real skew matrix of rank $r = 2s$, then L is unitarily similar to $D = [[i\lambda_1, -i\lambda_1, \ldots, i\lambda_s, -i\lambda_s, 0, \ldots, 0]]$, where $\lambda_h > 0$ ($h = 1, \ldots, s$).

If U is a unitary matrix such that $U^*LU = D$, then the columns of U are an orthonormal set of eigenvectors of L. Each column vector p_k of U can be expressed, with respect to whatever basis was originally in use, in the form $p_k = q_k + ir_k$, where the components of q_k and r_k are real. Since L is real, the vectors p_k ($k = 2s + 1, \ldots, n$) corresponding to the eigenvalue 0 may be taken to be real ($r_k = 0$). The following lemma gives useful information.

2. If L is a real skew matrix and $i\lambda$, with λ real, is a non-zero eigenvalue of L, and $Lx = i\lambda x$, with $x \neq 0$, and $x = y + iz$, with the components of y and z real, then $||y|| = ||z||$ and $(y, z) = 0$.

From $L(y + iz) = \lambda(-z + iy)$ it follows that

3.
$$Ly = -\lambda z, \qquad Lz = \lambda y.$$

337

Hence

$$(\lambda y, y) = (Lz, y) = (z, L^a y) = (z, -Ly) = (z, \lambda z)$$

and since $\lambda \neq 0$, $||y|| = ||z||$. We may take $||y|| = ||z|| = 1$. Moreover,

$$(\lambda y, z) = (Lz, z) = (z, L^a z) = -(z, Lz) = -(Lz, z),$$

whence $(Lz, z) = 0$ and, since $\lambda \neq 0$, $(y, z) = 0$.

Now we introduce a new basis m_k $(k = 1, \ldots, n)$ as follows:

$$m_{2h-1} = q_h, m_{2h} = r_h \ (h = 1, \ldots, s); \qquad m_k = p_k = q_k \ (k = 2s + 1, \ldots, n).$$

By 3, then,

$$
\begin{aligned}
Lm_{2h-1} &= Lq_h = -\lambda_h r_h = -\lambda_h m_{2h} & (h = 1, \ldots, s) \\
Lm_{2h} &= Lr_h = \lambda_h q_h = \lambda_h m_{2h-1} & (h = 1, \ldots, s)
\end{aligned}
$$

and $Lm_k = 0$ $(k = 2s + 1, \ldots, n)$.

The new basis is a real orthonormal basis, and we have the following result.

4. If L is a real skew matrix of rank $2s$ with non-zero eigenvalues $i\lambda_h$ $(h = 1, \ldots, s)$, with each λ_h real, then L is orthogonally similar to

$$[[E_1, \ldots, E_s, 0, \ldots, 0]],$$

where, for $h = 1, \ldots, s, \lambda_h > 0$ and

$$E_h = \begin{bmatrix} 0 & \lambda_h \\ -\lambda_h & 0 \end{bmatrix}.$$

5. **Corollary.** Two skew matrices of the same order are orthogonally similar if and only if they have the same eigenvalues with the same respective multiplicities.

As an example, let us consider the skew matrix

6.
$$L = \begin{bmatrix} 0 & -1 & 2 \\ 1 & 0 & -2 \\ -2 & 2 & 0 \end{bmatrix}.$$

Its eigenvalues are $\pm 3i$ and 0. Respective eigenvectors are

$$[2 + 6i, 2 - 6i, -8]^t, \qquad [2 - 6i, 2 + 6i, -8]^t,$$

and

$$[2 \quad 2 \quad 1]^t.$$

We pick off the orthogonal real vectors $[2 \quad 2 \quad -8]^t$ $[6 \quad -6 \quad 0]^t$ and $[2 \quad 2 \quad 1]^t$. Normalizing them, we obtain the orthogonal matrix

$$Q = \begin{bmatrix} \dfrac{1}{3\sqrt{2}} & -\dfrac{1}{\sqrt{2}} & \dfrac{2}{3} \\[2ex] \dfrac{1}{3\sqrt{2}} & \dfrac{1}{\sqrt{2}} & \dfrac{2}{3} \\[2ex] -\dfrac{4}{3\sqrt{2}} & 0 & \dfrac{1}{3} \end{bmatrix},$$

where the sign of the second vector has been adjusted to make $|Q| = +1$, and verify that

$$Q'LQ = \begin{bmatrix} 0 & 3 & 0 \\ -3 & 0 & 0 \\ 0 & 0 & 0 \end{bmatrix}.$$

EXERCISES

7. What is the analogue in the present context of 10A29? Of B'' in 10A30?

8. Reconsider the process which led to 10A28. If we refrain from dividing by $\beta_{1k_0} (= \beta)$ then the first result will be of the form 10A27 with $E = \begin{bmatrix} 0 & \beta \\ -\beta & 0 \end{bmatrix}$ and $A = 0$. Does it follow, or not, that β is an eigenvalue of B?

9. Let $D = [[i\lambda, -i\lambda]]$. Find a unitary matrix U such that $U^a DU = E$ of F4 (without the "h").

10. Let

$$L = \begin{bmatrix} 0 & -3 & 6 \\ 3 & 0 & -2 \\ -6 & 2 & 0 \end{bmatrix}.$$

Find the eigenvalues and eigenvectors of L. Find also an orthogonal matrix Q such that $Q'LQ$ has the form given in 4.

11. Let L be skew and define $f(\lambda) = |\lambda - L|$. Show that $f(\lambda)$ is even or odd (i.e., $f(-\lambda) = \pm f(\lambda)$) according as n is even or odd. (*Hint:* We know something about the coefficients of $f(\lambda)$; see the proof of B4.) (T)

12. Let P be a positive symmetric operator and L a skew operator. Prove (cf. E11) that there is a coordinate system in which $[P] = I$ and $[L]$ has the form given in 4. (T)

13. If L is real, skew, of rank $2s$ and order $2s$, then, by 4, $\det L = (\lambda_1\lambda_2 \ldots \lambda_s)^2$; use 12E14 to show that $\det L$ is the square of a product of linear combinations of elements of L. (T)

G. Unitary and Orthogonal Matrices

We know from A13(5) that a normal operator U is unitary if and only if each of its eigenvalues has absolute value 1, and is therefore of the form $e^{i\theta}$ where θ is a real angle. From A1 we read off the following result.

1. A unitary matrix U is unitarily similar to

$$[[e^{i\theta_1}, \ldots, e^{i\theta_n}]]$$

where, for $k = 1, \ldots, n$, θ_k is real and $e^{i\theta_k}$ is an eigenvalue of U.

Of course, the numbers $1, i, -1, -i$ will occur as eigenvalues if the respective θ's are 0 (or 2π), $\pi/2$, π, or $3\pi/2$.

There is not much more to be said about unitary matrices without drawing upon the theory of groups and group representations; see, however, H1 and 13H15–16.

The limitations of the system of real numbers make it necessary to say a little more about (real) orthogonal matrices. We recall from 13H that a real matrix Q is orthogonal if and only if $Q^t Q = I$. This property is invariant under orthogonal similarity, but not under congruence unless the transforming matrix is orthogonal and, in that case, congruence means orthogonal similarity.

The approach now is similar in some respects to that of F. If Q is real and orthogonal then $R = -iQ$ is unitary. Since R is unitarily similar to the matrix in 1, Q is unitarily similar to the matrix of 1 multiplied by i. At the same time, Q is real; its eigenvalues therefore occur in conjugate pairs, and we have the following result, in which θ_h is the θ_h of 1 plus $\pi/2$ (reduced mod 2π).

2. An orthogonal matrix Q is unitarily similar to a diagonal matrix

$$[[e^{i\theta_1}, e^{-i\theta_1}, \ldots, e^{i\theta_s}, e^{-i\theta_s}, 1, \ldots, 1, -1, \ldots, -1]]$$

where the diagonal elements are eigenvalues of Q and, for $h = 1, \ldots, s$, $\theta_h \neq 0, \pm\pi$, or 2π.

We observe that if n is odd, then either a 1, with $\theta = 0$ or 2π, or a -1, with $\theta = \pm\pi$ (or both), must actually occur. Vectors corresponding to an eigenvalue 1 are fixed, while those corresponding to an eigenvalue -1 are reflected in the origin. If $|Q| = 1$ then Q is called a *proper* orthogonal operator, while if $|Q| = -1$ then Q is called an *improper* orthogonal operator. The number of -1's in the diagonal matrix in 2 is even if and only if Q is proper. If there are no -1's at all, then Q is said to be a *rotation*.

Now, as in F, write the basis yielding 2 in the form $p_k = q_k + ir_k$ ($k = 1, \ldots, n$), where q_k and r_k have real components. We know that

$$Q(q_k + ir_k) = e^{i\theta_k}(q_k + ir_k) \qquad (k = 1, 3, \ldots, 2s - 1).$$

Since Q is real,

$$Q(q_k - ir_k) = e^{-i\theta_k}(q_k - ir_k) \qquad (k = 2, 4, \ldots, 2s).$$

In other words, $p_{2h} = \bar{p}_{2h-1}$ $(h = 1, \ldots, s)$. Now introduce a new basis m_k $(k = 1, \ldots, n)$ as follows:

$$m_{2h-1} = \frac{p_{2h-1} + p_{2h}}{\sqrt{2}} = \sqrt{2}q_{2h-1} \qquad (h = 1, \ldots, s)$$

$$m_{2h} = \frac{p_{2h-1} - p_{2h}}{i\sqrt{2}} = \sqrt{2}r_{2h-1} \qquad (h = 1, \ldots, s)$$

$$m_k = p_k \, (= q_k) \qquad (k = 2s + 1, \ldots, n).$$

The effect of Q on m_k $(k = 2s + 1, \ldots, n)$ is obvious. For $h = 1, \ldots, s$ we have

$$Qm_{2h-1} = \frac{e^{i\theta_h}p_{2h-1} + e^{-i\theta_h}p_{2h}}{\sqrt{2}}$$

$$= \sqrt{2}(\cos\theta_h q_{2h-1} - \sin\theta_h r_{2h-1})$$

$$= \cos\theta_h m_{2h-1} - \sin\theta_h m_{2h},$$

$$Qm_{2h} = \sin\theta_h m_{2h-1} + \cos\theta_h m_{2h}.$$

From the fact that the basis p_k $(k = 1, \ldots, n)$ is orthonormal it can be shown (see 12) that the real vectors m_k $(k = 1, \ldots, n)$ form an orthonormal basis, and we have arrived at the following canonical form for the matrix of an orthogonal operator.

3. If Q is an orthogonal operator on a real space, then there exists an orthonormal basis with respect to which

$$[Q] = [[R_1, \ldots, R_s, 1, \ldots, 1, -1, \ldots, -1]],$$

where, for $h = 1, \ldots, s$,

$$R_h = \begin{bmatrix} \cos\theta_h & -\sin\theta_h \\ \sin\theta_h & \cos\theta_h \end{bmatrix},$$

with real angles $\theta_h \neq 0, \pm\pi, 2\pi$.

As an illustration, consider the orthogonal matrix

4.

$$Q = \tfrac{1}{3}\begin{bmatrix} 2 & 1 & 2 \\ 2 & -2 & -1 \\ 1 & 2 & -2 \end{bmatrix}.$$

The characteristic equation of the unitary matrix iQ is

5.

$$\lambda^3 - \frac{2i}{3}\lambda^2 + \tfrac{2}{3}\lambda - i = 0.$$

Since $n = 3$, Q must have an eigenvalue ± 1, whence iQ must have an eigenvalue $\pm i$; we verify that $-i$ is an eigenvalue with corresponding eigenvector $[3 \quad 1 \quad 1]^t$. With $\lambda + i$ factored out, 5 becomes

6.
$$\lambda^2 - \tfrac{5}{3}i\lambda - 1 = 0.$$

A trial solution $e^{i\alpha}$ yields

7.
$$\frac{e^{i\alpha} - e^{-i\alpha}}{2i} = \sin \alpha = \tfrac{5}{6},$$

whence $\cos \alpha = \pm\sqrt{11}/6$. Each of $(\pm \sqrt{11} + 5i)/6$ satisfies 6 and is therefore an eigenvalue of iQ. A complex eigenvector of either will yield real orthonormal eigenvectors for Q.

Using $(\sqrt{11} + 5i)/6$ we find an eigenvector

$$[4 - 2\sqrt{11}i \quad -17 + \sqrt{11}i \quad 5 + 5\sqrt{11}i]^t.$$

Picking off the orthogonal real vectors

$$[4 \ -17 \ 5]^t \quad \text{and} \quad [-2 \ 1 \ 5]^t,$$

we form the orthogonal matrix

8.
$$P = \begin{bmatrix} \dfrac{4}{\sqrt{330}} & \dfrac{-2}{\sqrt{30}} & \dfrac{3}{\sqrt{11}} \\[2mm] \dfrac{-17}{\sqrt{330}} & \dfrac{1}{\sqrt{30}} & \dfrac{1}{\sqrt{11}} \\[2mm] \dfrac{5}{\sqrt{330}} & \dfrac{5}{\sqrt{30}} & \dfrac{1}{\sqrt{11}} \end{bmatrix}$$

and verify that

9.
$$P^t Q P = \begin{bmatrix} -\dfrac{5}{6} & \dfrac{\sqrt{11}}{6} & 0 \\[2mm] -\dfrac{\sqrt{11}}{6} & -\dfrac{5}{6} & 0 \\[2mm] 0 & 0 & 1 \end{bmatrix}.$$

Since $n = 3$, we could have found first the real eigenvalue 1 of Q and a corresponding eigenvector $v = [3 \ 1 \ 1]^t$. We can complete the basis by choosing any mutually orthogonal pair in $\langle v \rangle^\perp$, for example, $[-1 \ 3 \ 0]^t$ and $[-3 \ -1 \ 10]^t$. With these vectors we form the orthogonal matrix

10.
$$R = \begin{bmatrix} \dfrac{-1}{\sqrt{10}} & \dfrac{-3}{\sqrt{110}} & \dfrac{3}{\sqrt{11}} \\[2mm] \dfrac{3}{\sqrt{10}} & \dfrac{-1}{\sqrt{110}} & \dfrac{1}{\sqrt{11}} \\[2mm] 0 & \dfrac{10}{\sqrt{110}} & \dfrac{1}{\sqrt{11}} \end{bmatrix}$$

and verify that

11.
$$R^tQR = \begin{bmatrix} -\dfrac{5}{6} & -\dfrac{\sqrt{11}}{6} & 0 \\[2mm] \dfrac{\sqrt{11}}{6} & -\dfrac{5}{6} & 0 \\[2mm] 0 & 0 & 1 \end{bmatrix}.$$

That the signs of the entry $\sqrt{11}/6$ are opposite in 9 and 11 does not disturb us, for if with u, v as basis a matrix has the form $\begin{bmatrix} \alpha & -\beta \\ \beta & \alpha \end{bmatrix}$, then with v, u as basis it has the form $\begin{bmatrix} \alpha & \beta \\ -\beta & \alpha \end{bmatrix}$; we made no effort to match P and R, and it appears that, in the plane $\langle [3 \quad 1 \quad 1]^t \rangle^{\perp}$, the first two columns of P and those of R are oppositely oriented.

EXERCISES

12. Show that if $q + ir$ and $q - ir$ are an orthonormal pair, with q and r real, then $||q||^2 = ||r||^2 = \frac{1}{2}$ and $(q, r) = 0$.

13. Prove directly that if an operator U on a unitary space has the property that $||Ux|| = ||x||$ for every vector x, and if λ is an eigenvalue of U, then $|\lambda| = 1$.

14. We know that Q of 4 has an eigenvalue 1. What are its other eigenvalues? How are they related to 9 and 11?

15. Prove that if a 2×2 orthogonal operator M has an eigenvalue $\alpha + i\beta$, with α and β real and $\alpha^2 + \beta^2 = 1$, then a basis can be found in which $[M] = \begin{bmatrix} \alpha & -\beta \\ \beta & \alpha \end{bmatrix}$.

16. Prove that if L is an operator on a unitary space such that $||L|| \le 1$, and λ is an eigenvalue of L, then $|\lambda| \le 1$.

17. List the possible canonical forms for an orthogonal matrix for $n = 3$, 4, and 5. Which are rotations?

18. Find the canonical form for the orthogonal matrix

$$Q = \begin{bmatrix} 0 & 1 & 0 \\ 0 & 0 & 1 \\ 1 & 0 & 0 \end{bmatrix},$$

and find an orthogonal matrix R such that R^tQR is the canonical form.

19. Prove that if a real symmetric matrix S commutes with every real orthogonal matrix, then there is a scalar α such that $S = \alpha I$ (i.e., S is a scalar matrix). (T)

H. Polar Representation of an Operator on a Unitary Space

The polar representation of a complex number is $\rho e^{i\theta}$, where ρ and θ are real and $\rho \geq 0$. Now there is a weak analogy between real numbers and Hermitian operators, and between unimodular complex numbers and unitary operators. However weak, the analogy suggests the *polar representation* $L = HU$ of the following theorem.

1. Any operator L on a unitary space X can be expressed in the form $L = HU$ where U is unitary and H is Hermitian, ≥ 0, unique, and of the same rank as L; U is unique if and only if L is regular.

By B3, LL^a is Hermitian and ≥ 0. There exists, therefore, by B2, a unitary operator V such that $VLL^aV^a = D^2$, where

$$[D] = [[\pi_1^{1/2}, \ldots, \pi_r^{1/2}, 0, \ldots, 0]],$$

with r the rank of L and $\pi_k > 0$ for $k = 1, \ldots, r$. We observe now that $H = V^aDV$ is Hermitian, ≥ 0, and of rank r. It follows that $H^2 = V^aD^2V = LL^a$.

Suppose first that L is regular. Then so is H and

$$I = H^{-1}LL^aH^{-1} = H^{-1}L(H^{-1}L)^a,$$

whence $H^{-1}L = U$ is unitary and $L = HU$. If also $L = KT$ with T unitary and K Hermitian, ≥ 0, and regular, then $HU = KT$. It follows that

$$H^2 = HUU^aH = KTT^aK = K^2.$$

Since both $H \geq 0$ and $K \geq 0$, we see from B2 that $H = K$ and, consequently, that $U = T$.

In order to deal with the case in which L and, therefore, H is singular, we note first that, in any case,

1.1. $\qquad \|Hx\|^2 = (Hx, Hx) = (H^2x, x) = (LL^ax, x) = \|L^ax\|^2.$

If $y = Hx$ (i.e., $y \in HX$) then we define $U^ay = L^ax$. First of all, U^a is well-defined, for if $Hx = Hx'$ then, by 1.1, $L^ax = L^ax'$. Moreover, U^a is unitary on HX, for, if $y \in HX$, then

$$(U^ay, U^ay) = (L^ax, L^ax) = (Hx, Hx) = (y, y).$$

Now extend U^a to all of X by making U^a the identity on $(HX)^\perp$. Then U^a is unitary on X, $U^aHx = L^ax$ for all $x \in X$, $U^aH = L^a$, and $L = HU$.

EXERCISES

2. Suppose that we have applied 1 to L^a, getting $L^a = KV$. What expression will we then have for L?

3. Find a polar representation for

$$\text{(a)} \begin{bmatrix} 0 & 0 & 1+i \\ 0 & 2-i & 0 \\ 3 & 0 & 0 \end{bmatrix}, \qquad \text{(b)} \begin{bmatrix} 1 & i & 1+i \\ 2 & -i & 2-i \\ 1 & -1 & 0 \end{bmatrix}.$$

4. Imitate the proof of 1 to show that if L is an operator on a Euclidean space, then L can be expressed in the form SQ, where Q is orthogonal and S is symmetric, ≥ 0, unique, and of the same rank as L. Can the form RP be obtained, with P symmetric and ≥ 0 and R orthogonal (cf. 2)? The result shows that any operator can be expressed as the resultant of a rotation (the effect of Q or R) and a dilatation (the effect of P or S). (T)

5. Let $L = HU$ be a polar representation of L as in 1. Prove that L is normal if and only if $UH = HU$.

6. Prove that a matrix M is similar to a diagonal matrix D if and only if there exists a positive Hermitian matrix such that $N = H^{-1}MH$ is normal. (For this and other criteria for normality see a paper by B. E. Mitchell in the *Am. Math. Monthly*, **60** (1953) 94–96.) (T)

7. Suppose that the operators K and L on a unitary space X have the property that, for each $x \in X$, $\|Kx\| = \|Lx\|$. Prove that there exists a unitary operator U such that $UK = L$. (T)

BIBLIOGRAPHY

In view of the vast literature on linear algebra and geometry, an exhaustive bibliography is out of the question. Much helpful material may often be found in sources not listed here; for example, in books on the theory of equations, higher algebra, analytic (especially projective) geometry, vector analysis, and tensor analysis, in handbooks and compendia, and so on.

Current research will be found in the periodical literature, which is reviewed in *Mathematical Reviews*.

Reference to the periodical literature is of special importance in connection with headings F and G below. Interest in linear calculations has been greatly increased by the advent of large, fast computers, and systematic work on linear inequalities is primarily a postwar development. These matters have received, quite naturally, less systematic expository attention than older, more fully developed theories, and the student is therefore more likely to find it necessary to go directly to original sources.

Many of the items listed below have extensive bibliographical indications. Most of the texts have problems.

A. Texts, Treatises, and Surveys on Linear Spaces, Transformations, and Matrices (see also C)

1. Aitken, A. C., *Determinants and Matrices*, Interscience, New York, 1954.
2. Albert, A. A., *Modern Higher Algebra*, University of Chicago Press, Chicago, 1937.
3. Ayres, Frank, Jr., *Theory and Problems of Matrices*, Schaum Publishing Co., New York, 1962.
4. Beaumont, R. A., and R. W. Ball, *Introduction to Modern Algebra and Matrix Theory*, Rinehart and Co., New York, 1954.
5. Bellman, Richard, *Introduction to Matrix Analysis*, McGraw-Hill, New York, 1960.
6. Birkhoff, G., and S. MacLane, *A Survey of Modern Algebra* (3rd Ed.), Macmillan Co., New York, 1965.
7. Bôcher, M., *Introduction to Higher Algebra*, Macmillan Co., New York, 1930.
8. Browne, E. T., *Introduction to the Theory of Determinants and Matrices*, University of North Carolina Press, Chapel Hill, N. C., 1958.

9. Cherubino, S., *Calcolo delle Matrice*, Edizione Cremonese, Rome, 1957.

10. Curtis, Charles W., *Linear Algebra*, Allyn & Bacon, Boston, 1963.

11. Ferrar, W. L., *Finite Matrices*, Oxford University Press, Oxford, 1941.

12. Finkbeiner, D. T., II, *Introduction to Matrices and Linear Transformations*, W. H. Freeman, San Francisco, 1960.

13. Frazer, R. A., W. J. Duncan, and A. R. Collar, *Elementary Matrices*, Cambridge University Press, Cambridge, 1938.

14. Fuller, Leonard E., *Basic Matrix Theory*, Prentice-Hall, Englewood Cliffs, N. J., 1962.

15. Gantmacher, F. R., *The Theory of Matrices* (2 vols., translated from the Russian), Chelsea, New York, 1959; extensive bibliography.

16. Graeub, W., *Lineare Algebra*, Springer, Berlin, 1958.

17. Halmos, P. R., *Finite Dimensional Vector Spaces*, Princeton University Press, Princeton, 1942. (2nd ed., 1958.)

18. Hamburger, H. L., and M. E. Grimshaw, *Linear Transformations*, Cambridge University Press, Cambridge, 1951.

19. Hoffman, K., and R. Kunze, *Linear Algebra*, Prentice-Hall, Englewood Cliffs, N. J., 1961.

20. Hohn, F. E., *Elementary Matrix Algebra* (2nd ed.), Macmillan Co., New York, 1964.

21. Jaeger, A., *Introduction to Analytic Geometry and Linear Algebra*, Holt, Rinehart, and Winston, New York, 1960.

22. Julia, G., *Introduction Mathématique aux Théories Quantiques, Première Partie* (Cahiers Scientifiques, Fasc. 16), Gauthier-Villars, Paris, 1949.

23. Kowalewski, G., *Determinantentheorie*, Chelsea, New York, 1948.

24. Lichnerowicz, A., *Algèbre et Analyse Linéaires*, Masson, Paris, 1947.

25. MacDuffee, C. C., *The Theory of Matrices*, Springer, Berlin, 1933 (Chelsea, New York, 1946).

26. MacDuffee, C. C., *Vectors and Matrices*, Mathematical Association of America (Carus Monograph No. 7), 1943.

27. Malcev, A. I., *Foundations of Linear Algebra*, W. H. Freeman, San Francisco, 1963.

28. Marcus, M., *Basic Theorems in Matrix Theory*, National Bureau of Standards, Applied Mathematics Series, No. 57 (1960); definitions and results only.

29. Marcus, M., and H. Minc, *A Survey of Matrix Theory and Matrix Inequalities*, Allyn & Bacon, Boston, 1964.

30. Mirsky, L., *An Introduction to Linear Algebra*, Clarendon Press, Oxford, 1955.

31. Murdoch, D. C., *Linear Algebra for Undergraduates*, Wiley, New York, 1957.

32. Narayan, S., *Matrices*, S. Chand and Co., Delhi, 1953.

33. Neiss, F., *Determinanten und Matrizen* (5th ed.), Springer, Berlin, 1959.

34. Nering, E. D., *Linear Algebra and Matrix Theory*, Wiley, New York, 1963.

35. Paige, L. J., and J. D. Swift, *Elements of Linear Algebra*, Ginn and Co., Boston, 1961.

36. Parker, W. V., and J. C. Eaves, *Matrices*, Ronald Press, New York, 1960.

37. Pedoe, Daniel, *A Geometric Introduction to Linear Algebra*, Wiley, New York, 1963.

38. Perlis, S., *Theory of Matrices*, Addison-Wesley, Cambridge, Mass., 1952.

39. Pipes, Louis A., *Matrix Methods for Engineering*, Prentice-Hall, Englewood Cliffs, N. J., 1963.

40. Schreier, O., and E. Sperner, *Introduction to Modern Algebra and Matrix Theory* (2 vols.), Chelsea, New York, 1951.

41. Schwerdtfeger, H., *Introduction to Linear Algebra and the Theory of Matrices*, Noordhoff, Groningen, 1950.

42. Shields, Paul C., *Linear Algebra*, Addison-Wesley, Reading, Mass., 1964.

43. Shilov, Georgi F., *Introduction to the Theory of Linear Spaces*, edited by R. A. Silverman, Prentice-Hall, Englewood Cliffs, N. J., 1961.

44. Silverman, R. A., (ed.), *Academician V. I. Smirnov's Linear Algebra and Group Theory*, McGraw-Hill, New York, 1961.

45. Souriau, J. M., *Calcul Linéaire*, Presses Univ. de France, Paris, 1959.

46. Stewart, Frank M., *Introduction to Linear Algebra*, Van Nostrand, Princeton, 1963.

47. Stoll, R. R., *Linear Algebra and Matrix Theory*, McGraw-Hill, New York, 1952.

48. Thrall, R. M., and L. Tornheim, *Vector Spaces and Matrices*, Wiley, New York, 1957.

49. Turnbull, H. W., and A. C. Aitken, *An Introduction to the Theory of Canonical Matrices*, Blackie, Glasgow, 1948. (Reprint, Dover, New York, 1961.)

50. Wade, T. L., *The Algebra of Vectors and Matrices*, Addison-Wesley, Cambridge, Mass., 1951.

51. Wedderburn, J. H. M., *Lectures on Matrices*, American Mathematical Society (Colloquium Publications, vol. 17), 1934.

52. Zurmühl, R., *Matrizen* (2nd ed.), Springer, Berlin, 1958.

B. Groups of Linear Transformations (see also A41, A44)

1. Cartan, E., *Leçons sur la théorie des spineurs* (2 vols.), Hermann, Paris, 1938.

2. Chevalley, C. C., *The Algebraic Theory of Spinors*, Columbia University Press, New York, 1954.

3. Dieudonné, J., *La Géométrie des groupes classiques*, Ergebnisse der Math., Neue Folge, Heft 5, Springer, Berlin, 1955.

4. Murnaghan, F. D., *The Theory of Group Representations*, Johns Hopkins Press, Baltimore, 1938.

5. van der Waerden, B. L., *Die Gruppentheoretische Methode in der Quantenmechanic*, Springer, Berlin, 1932.

6. van der Waerden, B. L., *Gruppen von Linearen Transformationen*, Springer, Berlin, 1935. (Reprint, Chelsea, New York, 1948.)

7. Weyl, H., *The Classical Groups*, Princeton University Press, Princeton, 1939.

C. Linear Spaces over Division Rings (Non-Commutative Fields)

1. Artin, E., *Geometric Algebra*, Interscience, New York, 1957.

2. Baer, R., *Linear Algebra and Projective Geometry*, Academic Press, New York, 1952.

3. Bourbaki, N., *Algèbre* (Ch. II, "Algèbre Linéaire"), (Actualités Scientifiques et Industrielles, No. 1032), Hermann, Paris, 1947.

4. Bourbaki, N., *Algèbre* (Ch. III, "Algèbre Multilinéaire"), (Actualités Scientifiques et Industrielles, No. 1044), Hermann, Paris, 1948.

5. Jacobson, N., *Lectures in Abstract Algebra* (vol. II, "Linear Algebra"), Van Nostrand, New York, 1953.

D. Tensor Algebra (and Analysis) (see also A24, also C)

1. Brillouin, L., *Les Tenseurs en Mécanique et en Elasticité*, Masson, Paris, 1938 (Dover, New York, 1946).

2. Coburn, N., *Vector and Tensor Analysis*, Macmillan Co., New York, 1955.

3. McConnell, A. J., *Applications of the Absolute Differential Calculus*, Blackie, London, 1936.

4. Nickerson, H. K., D. C. Spencer, and N. E. Steenrod, *Advanced Calculus*, Van Nostrand, Princeton, 1959.

5. Veblen, O., *Invariants of Quadratic Differential Forms*, Cambridge University Press, Cambridge, 1933.

6. Weyl, H., *Mathematische Analyse des Raumproblems*, Springer, Berlin, 1923.

E. Functional Analysis (Including Integral Equations) (see also A24)

1. Courant, R., and D. Hilbert, *Methods of Mathematical Physics*, Interscience, New York, 1953.

2. Day, Mahlon M., *Normed Linear Spaces*, Springer, Berlin, 1958.

3. Friedman, B., *Principles and Techniques of Applied Mathematics*, Wiley, New York, 1956.

4. Goffman, C., and G. Pedrick, *First Course in Functional Analysis*, Prentice-Hall, Englewood Cliffs, N.J., 1965.

5. Hellinger, E., and O. Toeplitz, *Integralgleichungen und Gleichungen mit Unendlichvielen Unbekannten* (from Ency. Math. Wiss.), Chelsea, New York, 1953.

6. Kelley, J. L., I. Namioka, *et al.*, *Linear Topological Spaces*, Van Nostrand, Princeton, 1963.

7. Kolmogorov, A. N., and S. V. Fomin, *Functional Analysis* (vol. II, translated from the Russian), Graylock Press, Albany, New York, 1961.

8. Lorch, E. R., *Spectral Theory*, Oxford University Press, New York, 1962.

9. Riesz, F., and B. Sz.-Nagy, *Leçons d'Analyse Fonctionnelle*, Akadémiai Kiadó, Budapest, 1953.

10. Stone, M. H., *Linear Transformations in Hilbert Space*, American Mathematical Society (Colloquium Publications, vol. 15), 1932.

11. Taylor, A. E., *Introduction to Functional Analysis*, Wiley, New York, 1958.

12. von Neumann, J., *Mathematische Grundlagen der Quantenmechanik*, Springer, Berlin, 1932 (Dover, New York, 1943).

13. Wilansky, A., *Functional Analysis*, Blaisdell, New York, 1964.

14. Zaanen, A. C., *Linear Analysis*, Noordhoff, Groningen, 1953.

F. Linear Calculations (see also A13, A39, A52)

1. Bodewig, E., *Matrix Calculus*, Interscience, New York, 1956.

2. Dwyer, P. S., *Linear Computations*, Wiley, New York, 1951.

3. Faddeeva, D. K., and V. N. Faddeeva, *Computational Methods of Linear Algebra* (translated from the Russian), W. H. Freeman, San Francisco, 1963; extensive bibliography.

4. Forsythe, G. E., "Solving Linear Equations Can Be Interesting," *Bull. Am. Math. Soc.* **59** (1955) 299–329; extensive bibliography.

5. Hamming, R. W., *Numerical Methods for Scientists and Engineers*, McGraw-Hill, New York, 1962 (Chaps. 29, 30).

6. Householder, A. S., *Principles of Numerical Analysis*, McGraw-Hill, New York, 1953.

7. Householder, A. S., *Theory of Matrices in Numerical Analysis*, Blaisdell, New York, 1964.

8. Macon, N., *Numerical Analysis*, Wiley, New York, 1963.

9. Milne, W. E., *Numerical Calculus*, Princeton University Press, Princeton, 1949.

10. Milne, W. E., *Numerical Solution of Differential Equations*, Wiley, New York, 1953.

11. Ralston, A., and H. S. Wilf (eds.), *Mathematical Methods for Digital Computers* (Part II), Wiley, New York, 1960.

12. Todd, John (ed.), *Survey of Numerical Analysis*, McGraw-Hill, New York, 1962 (Chaps. 6, 8).

G. Linear Inequalities and Linear Programming (see also A48)

1. Charnes, A., W. W. Cooper, and A. Henderson, *An Introduction to Linear Programming*, Wiley, New York, 1953.

2. Churchman, C. W., R. L. Ackoff, and E. L. Arnoff, "Linear Programming," chapter in *Introduction to Operations Research*, Wiley, New York, 1957.

3. Dantzig, G. B., *Linear Programming and Extensions*, Princeton University Press, Princeton, 1963.

4. Dorfman, R., P. A. Samuelson, and R. M. Solow, *Linear Programming and Economic Analysis*, McGraw-Hill, New York, 1957.

5. Eisemann, Kurt, "Linear Programming," *Quart. Appl. Math.*, **13** (1955) 209–232.

6. Ficken, F. A., *The Simplex Method of Linear Programming*, Holt, Rinehart, and Winston, New York, 1961. (Theory only.)

7. Gale, David, *The Theory of Linear Economic Models*, McGraw-Hill, New York, 1960.

8. Gass, S. I., *Linear Programming*, McGraw-Hill, New York, 1958.

9. Harrison, J. O., Jr., "Linear Programming and Operations Research," chapter in *Operations Research for Management*, J. F. McCloskey and F. N. Trefethen, eds., Johns Hopkins Press, Baltimore, 1954.

10. Henderson, A., and R. Schlaifer, "Mathematical Programming," *Harvard Business Review*, **32** (1954) 73–100.

11. Karlin, S., *Mathematical Methods and Theory in Games, Programming, and Economics*, Addison-Wesley, Reading, Mass., 1959.

12. Koopmans, T. C., *et al.*, *Activity Analysis of Production and Allocation*, Wiley, New York, 1951.

13. Kuhn, H. W., and A. W. Tucker, eds., *Linear Inequalities and Related Systems*, Princeton University Press, Princeton, 1956.

14. Tucker, A. W., *Game Theory and Programming*, Oklahoma State University, Stillwater, 1955.

15. Vajda, S., *The Theory of Games and Linear Programming*, Wiley, New York, 1956.

16. Vazsonyi, A., *Scientific Programming in Business and Industry*, Wiley, New York, 1958.

H. Auxiliary References

1. Allendoerfer, C. B., and C. O. Oakley, *Principles of Mathematics* (rev. ed.), McGraw-Hill, New York, 1963.

2. Courant, R., and H. Robbins, *What is Mathematics?*, Oxford University Press, New York, 1941.

3. Freund, John E., *A Modern Introduction to Mathematics*, Prentice-Hall, Englewood Cliffs, N. J., 1956.

4. Hardy, G. H., *Pure Mathematics* (5th ed.), Cambridge University Press, Cambridge, 1928.

5. Kelley, J. L., *General Topology*, Van Nostrand, New York, 1955.

6. Knopp, K., *Theory and Application of Infinite Series*, Blackie & Son, Glasgow, 1928.

7. Landau, E., *Foundations of Analysis*, Chelsea, New York, 1951.

8. Perron, O., *Irrationalzahlen*, Chelsea, New York, 1948.

9. Russell, B., *Introduction to Mathematical Philosophy*, Macmillan Co., New York, 1924.

SELECTED ANSWERS and Hints

Chapter One

B1. $T = \{b, c, d, f, g\}$.

2. x is a vowel.

3. $\square$, $\{p\}$, $\{q\}$, $\{r\}$, $\{q, r\}$, $\{p, r\}$, $\{p, q\}$, S.

4. ± 4, 4, none, 0.

C3. If n were even then n^2 would be even, by B5; this contradicts the hypothesis that n^2 is odd.

E1. (a) $2 + 3 \neq 5$; (b) $1 = -1$; (c) There exists an integer which is not the square of an integer; (d) Each integer is even; (e) For every integer x and every integer y, $y^2 \neq x$; (f) For every integer z there exists an integer x such that $x + z \neq x$.

2. $Q'_R = \{5\}$, $Q'_S = \{6\}$, $R'_T = \{6\}$, $S'_T = \{5\}$.

3. (a) $S'_P = \{$Points in P exterior to the given circle$\}$.
(b) $S'_P = \{$Points distant at most two units from the given line$\}$.
(c) $S'_P = \{$Points at which the rectangle subtends at least 90°$\}$.

4. (a) $T' = \{s : s$ is a female$\}$.
(c) $T' = \{s : s$ has a brother$\}$.
(e) $T' = \{s :$ either s is male or s is not a senior$\}$.
(g) $T' = \{s :$ either s is not a junior or s is not taking a course in history$\}$.

G10. (1) If $x \in S \cup T$ then either $x \in S$ or $x \in T$. If also $x \in R$ then either $x \in R \cap S$ or $x \in R \cap T$; hence $x \in (R \cap S) \cup (R \cap T)$. Conversely, if $x \in (R \cap S) \cup (R \cap T)$ then either $x \in R \cap S$ or $x \in R \cap T$; in either case $x \in R$ and $x \in S \cup T$ and, therefore, $x \in R \cap (S \cup T)$.

13. (4) If it is false that either A or B is true then both A and B are false; hence $(\sim A) \wedge (\sim B)$. Conversely, if both A and B are false, then it is false that either A or B is true.

16. T consists of precisely those elements of U (because $S \cup T = U$) which do not belong to S (because $S \cap T = \square$); hence $T = S'_U$. Conversely, if $T = S'_U$ then T contains all elements of U (whence $S \cup T = U$) not in S (whence $T \cap S = \square$).

17. If $x \in R \cap T$ then $x \in R$ and $x \in T$. Then $x \in S$ and $x \in T$, whence $x \in S \cap T$. The other proof is similar.

18. For those x belonging to S and not to T. When $T \subset S$.

19. That $W \subset S$ and $W \subset T$ follows from 7. If $V \subset S$ and $V \subset T$ then $x \in V$ implies both $x \in S$ and $x \in T$, whence $x \in S \cap T$. Conversely, if $x \in S \cap T$ then both $x \in S$ and $x \in T$, whence $x \in W$ and $S \cap T \subset W$. Vice versa, if $x \in W$ then $x \in S$ and $x \in T$, whence $x \in S \cap T$ and $S \cap T \subset W$. That $W = S \cap T$ now follows from A4.

20. Similar to 19.

H3. $A \rightarrow B$; $A \rightarrow C$; $C \rightarrow A$. B, C, A are necessary, respectively, for A, A, and C. A is sufficient for B and for C, and C for A. The converse of $A \rightarrow B$ is "If $x^2 = 4$ then $x = 2$"; the converse of $C \rightarrow A$ is "If $x = 2$ then $x^3 = 8$". The contrapositive of $A \rightarrow B$ is "If $x^2 \neq 4$ then $x \neq 2$"; the contrapositive of $C \rightarrow A$ is "If $x \neq 2$ then $x^3 \neq 8$".

6. $\sim A \vee (A \vee B)$; $\sim(A \wedge B) \vee B$. The first is true because it is equivalent (intuitively) to $(\sim A \vee A) \vee B$. For, $\sim A \vee A$ is the law of excluded middle; since this law is assumed to hold, $\sim A \vee A$ is true and so, therefore, is the disjunction $(\sim A \vee A) \vee B$. To deal with $\sim(A \wedge B) \vee B$, use G3 and proceed similarly.

8. The disjunction $\sim A \vee B$ is true regardless of B if A is false, and true regardless of A if B is true.

10. $\sim B \rightarrow \sim A$ is the same as $\sim\sim B \vee \sim A$, or $B \vee \sim A$, or $\sim A \vee B$, or $A \rightarrow B$.

16.

Maine	N. H.	Vt.	Mass.	R. I.	Conn.
$\updownarrow$	$\updownarrow$	$\updownarrow$	$\updownarrow$	$\updownarrow$	$\updownarrow$
1	2	3	4	5	6

7. If each $y \in f(X)$ is the image of a unique $x \in X$ then $f(x) = f(x')$ implies $x = x'$, which is the contrapositive (see 1H2) of "$x \neq x'$ implies $f(x) \neq f(x')$". Vice versa, if "either $x = x'$ or $f(x) \neq f(x')$" then, for each x, $f(x)$ cannot be the image of any $x' \in X$ other than x.

8. Different subsets have different characteristic functions (cf. 2 and 7). A function on T has a domain with n elements; if the prescribed codomain (here $\{0, 1\}$) has two elements, then for each $x \in T$ the value $f(x)$ may be chosen in two ways, and if $x \neq x'$ the choice of $f(x')$ is independent of the choice of $f(x)$. There are therefore 2^n independent functions $f : T \rightarrow \{0, 1\}$ and, as a consequence, 2^n subsets of T. Observe that the function $f(x) \equiv 1$ corresponds to T and the functions $f(x) \equiv 0$ corresponds to $\square$.

9. Draw a diagram.

10. Yes; every point in p is the center of a circle of radius one. Yes; since the radius is prescribed, the point (center) and the circle determine each other uniquely.

11. Yes; every point in p is the center of a square of side one. The set $f^{-1}(P)$ is the set of squares of side one with center at P.

12. The equation $x^3 = c$ with $c \in I$ given and $x \in I$ sought is consistent (has a solution) if and only if c is the cube of an integer.

13. If the characteristic functions of R and S are f and g then the characteristic function

356

f' of R' is $f'(x) = 1 - f(x)$, that of $R \cap S$ is $h(x) = f(x) g(x)$, and that of $R \cup S$ is $h(x) = f(x) + g(x) - f(x) g(x)$.

14. In the foregoing remark on 13, note the behavior of f and f'.

15. The propositions whose equivalence is asserted are two ways of saying that no element of T is the image of any element of X.

16. The inclusion in (c) is obvious. To see that the inclusion may be proper, let $S = \{-1, 0\}$, $T = \{0, 1\}$, and on $X = \{-1, 0, 1\}$ let $f(-1) = f(1) = 1$ while $f(0) = 0$; then $f(S) = f(T) = \{0, 1\} = f(S) \cap f(T)$, but $f(S \cap T) = f(\{0\}) = \{0\}$. The same example shows that the inclusion in (d) may be proper, for $f(S)'_{f(X)} = \square$, while $f(S') = f(\{1\}) = \{1\}$.

17. (c) $x \in f^{-1}(S \cap T)$ if and only if $f(x) \in S \cap T$, whence both $f(x) \in S$ and $x \in f^{-1}(S)$, and $f(x) \in T$ and $x \in f^{-1}(T)$.

(d) $f(x) \in S'_Y$ if and only if $f(x) \in' S$, i.e., if and only if $x \in' f^{-1}(S)$.

33. $S \cup T = T \cup S$.

34. The correspondence $v \leftrightarrow \{v\}$ is clearly 1–1. A further element of W is $\square$.

35. g is the characteristic function of a subset U of S such that $U \neq T_k$ $(k = 1, \ldots, n)$. This is perhaps the simplest instance of "Cantor's diagonal process"; see 2D4.3.

36. A negative answer is established in 2D4.3.

Chapter Two

A1.2. $a^{k+1} = a^k \cdot a$.

.4. $a_n = 2^n b + 2^n - 1$; prove by induction (see A2.4).

.5.
$n = 2$				1		2		1
$n = 3$			1		3		3		1
$n = 4$		1		4		6		4		1
$n = 5$	1		5		10		10		5		1

2.3. (c) True if $n = 1$. Assume for n and add $(n + 1)^2$ to both sides; on right

$$(n + 1)\left[\frac{2n^2 + n}{6} + n + 1\right] = \frac{(n + 1)(2n^2 + n + 6)}{6} = \frac{(n + 1)(n + 2)(2n + 3)}{6}.$$

(h) True for $n = 1$. Assume true for n and multiply by 2, getting $4n \leq 2^{n+1}$. But $2(n + 1) = 2n + 2 \leq 4n$ if $n \geq 1$, whence $2(n + 1) \leq 2^{n+1}$.

.6. For $n = 1$, $\binom{1}{0} = 1 = \binom{1}{1} = \frac{1!}{1! \, 0!}$. Assume that $\binom{m}{k} = \frac{m!}{k! \, (m - k)!}$ for $k = 0,$ $\ldots, m$. Then, by the definitions in 2A1.5, for $k = 0, \ldots, m + 1$,

$$\binom{m + 1}{k} = \binom{m}{k} + \binom{m}{k - 1} = \frac{m!}{(k - 1)! \, (m - k)!}\left[\frac{1}{k} + \frac{1}{m - k + 1}\right]$$

$$= \frac{(m + 1)!}{k! \, (m - k + 1)!},$$

as desired.

If in A1.6 one found that $C_k^{n+1} = C_k^n + C_{k-1}^n$ then C_k^n and $\binom{n}{k}$ have precisely the same recursive definition and are therefore equal. Try to obtain the equality $C_k^n = \dfrac{n!}{k!\,(n-k)!}$ by an intuitive argument. To show that $\binom{n}{k}$ is always a natural number observe that $\binom{1}{0} = \binom{1}{1} = \binom{n}{0} = \binom{n}{n} = 1$ for $n = 1, 2, \ldots$. For $n \geq 2$ and $1 \leq k \leq n$, $\binom{n}{k}$ is the sum of the integers $\binom{n-1}{k}$ and $\binom{n-1}{k-1}$, and is therefore itself an integer.

B3. If $b = pa$ and $c = qa$ then $b + c = (p + q)a$.

4. (b) quotient -9, remainder 1.

6. If $a = qa'$ and $b = qb'$ with $(a', b') = 1$ then $q = (a, b)$; then $pa = pqa'$ and $pb = pqb'$ with $(a', b') = 1$, whence $(pa, pb) = pq$.

7. $84 = 7 \cdot 12 = 7 \cdot 3 \cdot 4 = 2^2 \cdot 3 \cdot 7$; $-36 = -4 \cdot 9 = -2^2 \cdot 3^2$.

9. With notation as in 6, $(a, b) = q$ and $[a, b] = qa'b'$, whence $(a, b)\,[a, b] = q^2a'b' = ab$.

11. For $n = 1, 2, \ldots$, $n(n + 1)(n + 2)$ is divisible by 6.

13. For example, $r = p + kb$, $s = q - ka$, with k any integer. Are these all?

15. (c) (α) $x = 4$, (β) inconsistent, (γ) $x = 4$, (δ) inconsistent, (ϵ) $x = 4$.

16. (a) (α) inconsistent, (β) $x = \pm 3$, (γ) $x = 3$, (δ) $x = -3$, (ϵ) $x = \pm 3$.

C1.2. Let $p = a/c$, $q = b/d$, with $c \neq 0$, $d \neq 0$. Then $pq = ab/cd = 0$ if and only if $ab = 0$, whence either $a = 0$ or $b = 0$ and, in the respective cases, $p = 0$ or $q = 0$.

.3. If $q/p = s/r$ then, on multiplying by pr and dividing out p on the left and r on the right (Is this legitimate?), we get $qr = ps$. With this, vice versa, we multiply by $1/pr$ and argue as before.

.6. The statement is obviously true if $n = 0$ or 1. To the statement for $n = k$ add r^{k+1} to both sides. After simplification on the right the numerator is $1 - r^{k+2}$, and the proof is complete.

.10. $a + (bc) = (a + b)(a + c)$. No; with any two of a, b, $c \in N$, I, R fixed the statement becomes an equation for the third, and this equation may be inconsistent or consistent in N, I, or R.

2.2. If $b \neq 0$ then $\sqrt{2} = -a/b \in R$, a contradiction. Hence $b = 0$ and, as a consequence, $a = 0$.

.4. If $t = r + s \in R$ then $s = t - r \in R$, a contradiction. If $t = rs \in R$ then, since $r \neq 0$, $s = t/r \in R$, a contradiction. Yes (how?). Yes (how?).

D1.2. $a \leq b$ excludes $a > b$, and $b \leq a$ excludes $b > a$; 1A gives $a = b$.

.4. Observe first that, if $c < 0$ then $c - c = 0 < -c$. Also, $b - a > 0$. By 3, $-c(b - a) > 0$, whence $ac > bc$.

.6. (i) $x > 9/5$. (iv) $x \geq 1/8$.

.8. For $n = 2$, $(1 + p)^2 = 1 + 2p + p^2 > 1 + 2p$ because $p^2 > 0$. For $k = 2, 3, \ldots$, if $(1 + p)^k > 1 + kp$ then, since $1 + p > 0$, it follows from 1D that

$$(1 + p)^{k+1} > (1 + kp)(1 + p) = 1 + (k + 1)p + kp^2 > 1 + (k + 1)p$$

because $kp^2 > 0$. When $p = 0$ the inequality becomes an equality.

.10. $a + 0(b - a) \leq a + t(b - a) \leq a + (b - a) = b$.

.13. (i) $(3 - 2x)(2 + 3x) < 0$ whenever one factor is positive and the other negative. This happens if either $x < -2/3$ or $x > 3/2$; it is illuminating to draw the graph of the parabola $y = 6 + 5x - 6x^2$.

(vi) Think of the curve $y = (x - a)(x - b)(x - c)$; it crosses the x-axis at $x = a$, b, and c. Clearly, $y > 0$ if $x > c$, $y < 0$ if $b < x < c$, $y > 0$ if $a < x < b$, and $y < 0$ if $x < a$.

.14. Let $m_1 = \min(a_1, a_2)$ and $M_1 = \max(a_1, a_2)$. By hypothesis $m_1 = a_1$ and $M_1 = a_2$. Suppose that $q \geq 1$ and that $m_q = \min(a_1, \ldots, a_q)$ and $M_q = \max(a_1, \ldots, a_q)$ have been defined, and are found among the numbers $a_1, \ldots, a_q$, and that $m_q \leq a_k \leq M_q$ for $k = 1, \ldots, q$. Given a_{q+1}, define $m_{q+1} = \min(m_q, a_{q+1})$ and $M_{q+1} = \max(M_q, a_{q+1})$, and $\min(a_1, \ldots, a_{q+1}) = m_{q+1}$ and $\max(a_1, \ldots, a_{q+1}) = M_{q+1}$. It is easy to verify the stated properties.

.16. E.g., $a = -2$, $b = -1$.

.18. The statement is true if $n = 0$. For $m = 0, 1, 2, \ldots$, suppose that $(a + b)^m = \sum_0^m \binom{m}{k} a^{m-k} b^k$. Multiply both sides by $(a + b)$. The result on the right is

$$\sum_0^m \binom{m}{k} a^{m+1-k} b^k + \sum_0^m \binom{m}{k} a^{m-k} b^{k+1}$$

$$= a^{m+1} + \sum_1^m \binom{m}{k} a^{m+1-k} b^k + \sum_0^{m-1} \binom{m}{k} a^{m-k} b^{k+1} + b^{m+1}$$

$$= a^{m+1} + \sum_1^m \binom{m}{k} a^{m+1-k} b^k + \sum_1^m \binom{m}{k-1} a^{m+1-k} b^k + b^{m+1}$$

$$= a^{m+1} + \sum_1^m \left[\binom{m}{k} + \binom{m}{k-1} \right] a^{m+1-k} b^k + b^{m+1}$$

By A1.5, this is equal to

$$a^{m+1} + \sum_1^m \binom{m+1}{k} a^{m+1-k} b^k + b^{m+1} = \sum_0^{m+1} \binom{m+1}{k} a^{m+1-k} b^k.$$

2.2. A. If $a \neq 0$ then $-a \neq 0$; either $|a| = a$ or $|a| = -a$, whence $|a| \neq 0$.

B. Trivial unless $a, b \neq 0$. If $ab > 0$ then a and b have the same sign; $|a| = \pm a$ and $|b| = \pm b$, where the signs are the same. Hence $|a| \, |b| = ab = |ab|$. Use a similar argument if $ab < 0$.

.5. (i) $-5 < x + 3 < 5$, whence $-8 < x < 2$.

(iv) The linear functions change signs at $x = -3/2$ and $x = -1$. For $x \leq -3/2$ we have $-(x + 1) + 2x + 3 = 1$, or $x = -1$, an inconsistency. For $-3/2 \leq x < -1$ we get $-(x + 1) - 2x - 3 = 1$ or $x = -5/3$, again an inconsistency. If $x > -1$ we must have $x + 1 - 2x - 3 = 1$, or $x = -3$. The proposed statement is therefore false for every x.

.8. It is obvious that both p_n and q_n increase with n. Show first that $e_{n+1}/e_n = -(\sqrt{2} - 1)q_n/q_{n+1}$; everything follows from this.

4.4. Let $x \in T$ or $x \in' T$ according as $x \in' S(x)$ or $x \in S(x)$.

Chapter Three

A1. If $||\overrightarrow{PX}|| = 5$ then X is on the surface of a sphere of radius 5 with center at P. If $||\overrightarrow{PX}|| = 0$ then $X = P$. If $||\overrightarrow{PX}|| > 6$ then X is outside a sphere of radius 6 with center at P.

C4. That $||\hat{V}|| = 1$ follows from (3b). The vectors rV and $r\hat{V}$ have the same direction; the direction of $|r|\hat{V}$ is the same if $r > 0$ and opposite if $r < 0$. $||rV|| = |r|\,||V|| = ||V||\,||r\hat{V}|| = ||V||\,||\,|r|\hat{V}||$.

6. (a) $t = (r + s)/2$. (b) $t = (qs + pr)/(p + q)$.

8. No. No. Yes. No. Reasons?

D8. These inequalities simply state the familiar geometric facts that the length of one side of a triangle cannot exceed the sum of the lengths of the other two, nor be exceeded by their difference. The left inequality will be an equality if $||U|| \geq ||V||$ and U and V have opposite directions. The right inequality will be an equality if U and V have the same direction. If both inequalities hold then either $U = 0$ or $V = 0$.

10. $P - Q$.

12. Upstream, $\cos^{-1} 2/5$ with bank.

E5. $R = P + tQ$

6. (a) $R = P + t(Q - P)$.　　　　　　　　(b) $R = 3Q + t(2P + 3Q)$

11. $R = U + x(V - U) + y(W - U)$; $0 \leq x, y, x + y \leq 1$.

13. $x(U - W) + y(V - W) = 0$ with $x, y \neq 0$ says that $U - W$ and $V - W$ are multiples of each other. The points U, V, and W are therefore collinear; which one is between the others depends on the signs of x and y.

15. Since U is a linear combination of V and W, every linear combination of U and V is a linear combination of V and W; thus, $aU + bV = -a(yV + zW)/x + bV = (b - ay/x)V - azW/x$. Proof of the converse is similar.

17. Let $w = \sum w_k$ and form P^*, where
$$wP^* = \sum w_k(P_k - Q) = \sum w_k P_k - wQ = w\overline{P} - wQ;$$
Thus, P^* is the position vector of $\overline{P}$ with respect to Q.

F2. Yes. Suppose that $\sum t_{k'} V_{k'} = 0$ with not all $t_{k'} = 0$ and k' running over a subset s of $1, \ldots, n$. Put $t_{k''} = 0$ if k'' is in the complement of s. Then $0 = \sum t_{k'} V_{k'} +$

$\sum t_{k''}V_{k''}$, and we have a nontrivial vanishing linear combination of V_k $(k = 1, 2, \ldots, n)$.

4. There exist constants u_{jk} such that, for $j = 1, \ldots, q$, $U_j = \sum_k u_{jk}V_k$. $X \in \langle U_j \rangle$ if and only if

$$X = \sum_j x_j U_j = \sum_j x_j \sum_k u_{jk}V_k = \sum_k (\sum_j x_j u_{jk})V_k,$$

whence $X \in \langle V_k \rangle$.

5. Sometimes. It is necessary that $\|V\|/\|U\|$ be rational. Is this sufficient?

7. $yY + zZ = (ay + cz)U + (by + dz)V = 0$ if and only if there exist y and z, not both 0, such that $ay + cz = 0$ and $by + dz = 0$. Multiply the first equation by d, the second by c, and subtract; the result is $(ad - bc)y = 0$. Similarly, $(ad - bc)z = 0$. Since not both $y = 0$ and $z = 0$, these equations will both hold if and only if $ad - bc = 0$.

8.
$$\sum u_k U_k = \sum u_k(V_k - U) = \sum u_k V_k - (\sum u_k)U$$
$$= \sum u_k V_k - (\sum u_j) \sum t_k V_k = \sum (u_k - t_k \sum u_j)V_k$$

In order that there exist nontrivial u_k it is necessary and sufficient, since the V_k are independent, that u_k be so chosen that $u_k - t_k \sum u_j \neq 0$ for some value of k.

G7. (a) $4Y + Z = 4(2, -1, -3) + (-1, 2, 1) = (7, -2, -11)$
(c) $R = \eta Y + \xi Z; (x, y, z) = (2\eta - \xi, -\eta + 2\xi, -3\eta + \xi)$
(e) $\eta Y + \xi Z + \theta W = (2\eta - \xi, -\eta + 2\xi, -3\eta + \xi + 2\theta) = 0$.
The vanishing of the first two components implies that $\eta = \xi = 0$; then the third yields $\theta = 0$.
(g) We must choose t, y, and z in such a way (if possible) that

$$Y + t(W - Z) = W + yY + zZ,$$

whence $y = 1, t = 1, z = -1$; the point of intersection is $W + Y$.

9. (b) $R = Z + t(R - Q)$, $R = (7, 4, 2) + t(9, -1, -3) = (x, y, z)$; $x = 7 + 9t$, $y = 4 - t, z = 2 - 3t; (x - 7)/9 = (y - 4)/-1 = (z - 2)/-3$.

10. (b) The line passes through (the terminal point of) Y and is parallel to Z.

$$(x, y, z) = (-1 + t, 2, -2 - 3t), (x + 1)/1 = (y - 2)/0 = (z + 2)/-3.$$

11. (b) The line through $U = (u_k)$ parallel to the line joining $V = (v_k)$ and $W = (w_k)$.

$$\frac{x_1 - u_1}{v_1 - w_1} = \frac{x_2 - u_2}{v_2 - w_2} = \frac{x_3 - u_3}{v_3 - w_3}; \quad \frac{x_1 - 5}{0} = \frac{y_1 - 2}{9} = \frac{z_1 + 3}{-3}.$$

$R = U + y(V - W); (x_1, x_2, x_3) = (5, 2 + 9y, -3 - 3y)$.

12. (b) Let $W = (w_k)$ and $Z = (z_k)$. $R = W + tZ$;
$(x_1, x_2, x_3) = (w_1 + tz_1, w_2 + tz_2, w_3 + tz_3); (x_1, x_2, x_3) = (-1 - 3t, 3, 2t)$.

13. (b) $R = U + v(V - U) + w(W - U)$;
$(x, y, z) = (1, -1, 2) + v(2, 2, -7) + w(-1, 1, 0)$;
$x = 1 + 2v - w, y = -1 + 2v + w, z = 2 - 7v$.

14. (b) Plane through (terminal point of) Y and parallel to $\langle Y, Z \rangle$.
$(x_1, x_2, x_3) = (3, -1, 2) + y(-1, 0, 2) + z(3, 0, -2)$;
$x_1 = 3 - y + 3z, x_2 = -1, x_3 = 2 + 2y - 2z$.

16. $(Y, \hat{Z}) = ||Y|| \cos \theta_{Y\hat{Z}}$ is the length of the (orthogonal) projection of Y onto $\hat{Z}$. $(Y, Z)\hat{Z}$ is a vector parallel to $\hat{Z}$, of length $|(Y, Z)|$, in the same direction as $\hat{Z}$ if $(Y, Z) > 0$, and in the opposite direction if $(Y, Z) < 0$. $(\hat{Y}, Z)\hat{Y}$ is the vectorial projection of Z on $\hat{Y}$.

9. Unless $X = 0$, $\theta_{X,X} = 0$ and $(X, X) = ||X||^2 > 0$.

10. (b) $||Y \pm Z||^2 = ||Y||^2 \pm 2(Y, Z) + ||Z||^2$; subtract.

12. $(X - Q, X - Q) = ||X - Q||^2$; cf. 1.1.

13. If $0 = \sum q_k Q_k$ then $0 = q_j ||Q_j||^2$, whence $q_j = 0 (j = 1, 2, 3)$.

3.14. Process and result important.

.19. (a) $\hat{N} \cdot X - q = 3, -2, -7, 5$.

.21. $(U - V) \cdot X = 0$.

.22. $N \cdot (U + tV) = p$; in nonexceptional cases, $t = (p - N \cdot U)/N \cdot V$.

.24. $\hat{N} \cdot X = \hat{N} \cdot Q$ is the plane with normal $\hat{N}$ passing through Q. The equations of the desired planes are $\hat{N} \cdot (X - Q) = 2, 5, -3, -7, 0$.

J8. $U \cdot V \times W = 0$ would imply U to be perpendicular to $V \times W$, and hence to lie in the plane of V and W, contradicting the independence of $\{U, V, W\}$. $U \cdot V \times W$ is positive or negative according as U makes an acute or obtuse angle with $V \times W$; in the respective cases the triad $\{U, V, W\}$ is positively or negatively oriented. Use 7 and geometric considerations to arrive at the evaluation of $|U \cdot V \times W|$.

9. Use the parallelepiped of 8 and follow changes in orientation with the order of U, V, and W.

10. If any one of t, U, or V is zero, the result is obvious. If none vanishes, then the respective vectors all have moduli $|t| \, ||U \times V||$ and their directions agree with $\pm U \times V$ according as $t > 0$ or $t < 0$.

13. The point Q is on the line, which has the direction of $N_1 \times N_2$, unless N_1 and N_2 are dependent. If $N_1 \times N_2 \neq 0$ then an equation for the line is therefore $R = Q + tN_1 \times N_2$.

14. The first equation in the form $X - R = yY + zZ$ shows that $X - R$ is in $\langle Y, Z \rangle$, and the second equation follows. The second equation says that the plane contains R and is perpendicular to Y and Z; hence $X - R$ is a linear combination of Y and Z.

15. The segment of shortest length with one endpoint on each line will be perpendicular to both lines and therefore parallel to $U \times V$. The length of the resolved part of $R - S$ along $U \times V$ is the required distance (cf. I6).

16. The equation will be true if, and only if, the vector from P to X is parallel to Q. This is the equation, therefore, of a line through P parallel to Q. An equivalent equation is $X = P + tQ$; check it.

17. $||(Q - U) \times V||$.

18. It follows from 8 that $U \cdot V \times W = 0$ if any two of the vectors U, V, W are equal. If $\sum \alpha_k Q_k = 0$ then scalar multiplication by P_j gives $\alpha_j = 0 \, (j = 1, 2, 3)$. To secure $(Q_j, P_k) = \delta_{jk}$, divide each Q_j by $P_1 \cdot P_2 \times P_3$.

K14. (a) $Q_1 \cdot Q_2 = (-1) \cdot 2 + 3(-1) = -5$, $Q_2 \cdot Q_3 = -8$, $Q_3 \cdot Q_1 = 11$.
    (b) $Q_1 \times Q_2 = (-5, 2, 4)$, $Q_1 \times Q_3 = (7, -1, -5)$.
    (c) $(X - Q_1) \cdot Q_2 = 0$, $2y - z + 5 = 0$.
    (e) $(X - Q_2) \cdot Q_1 \times Q_3 = 0$, $7x - y - 5z + 7 = 0$.
    (g) $(\alpha Q_2 + \beta Q_3) \cdot Q_1 = 0$, $-4\alpha + 11\beta = 0$; $\alpha = 11$, $\beta = 4$.
    (i) Angle between $Q_2 - Q_1$ and $Q_3 - Q_1$ is a right angle.
    (k) $(2, -3, 4)/\sqrt{29}$.
    (m) $P_1 = \hat{Q}_1 = (2, -1, 3)/\sqrt{14}$; $Q_2 - (Q_2, P_1)P_1 = (10, 23, 1)/14$,
        $P_2 = (10, 23, 1)/3\sqrt{70}$; $P_3 = (5, -2, -4)/3\sqrt{5}$.

15. (a) $N_1 = (3, -2, 2)/\sqrt{17}$.
    (c) $3(x - 2) - 2y + 2(z + 2) = 0$.
    (e) Normal to π_1; $(V \cdot N_1)N_1 = 18(3, -2, 2)/17$; parallel to π_1:

$$V - (V \cdot N_1)N_1 = (-20, 19, 49)/17.$$

    (g) Respective x, y, z intercepts are $2, -3, 3$.
    (i) Answer indeterminate. Choose *any* vector perpendicular to $(3, -2, 2)$, e.g., $(0, 1, 1)$. Then $X = (1, 1, -4) + t(0, 1, 1)$ is the equation of a line with the required property.

16. (b) If N_1 and N_2 are the respective normals and P is a point common to the planes then $X = P + tN_1 \times N_2$ is a vectorial equation of the line of intersection. Put $z = 0$ and find $P = (0, 16, 9)/5$. Hence $X = (0, 16, 9)/5 + t(4, 11, 5)$ is the required equation. The parametric equations are

$$x = 4t, \qquad y = \frac{16}{5} + 11t, \qquad z = \frac{9}{5} + 5t$$

    (d) $(3x - 2y + 2z - 6)/\sqrt{17} = \pm(x + y - 3z - 5)/\sqrt{11}$; these are the equations of planes bisecting opposite pairs of dihedral angles formed by π_1 and π_2.
    (f) As long as u and v are not both zero, the locus of the equation is clearly a plane π. If (x, y, z) satisfies both the equation of π_1 and the equation of π_2, then it must satisfy the equation of π.

17. (b) $(-4, 9, 6)/\sqrt{133}$
    (d) The squared distance to a point on λ_1 is

$$(4 - 3t)^2 + (1 + 2t)^2 + (2 + t)^2.$$

The minimum distance, obtained when $t = 4/7$, is $\sqrt{5 \cdot 23}/7$.
    (f) $\cos^{-1}(11/\sqrt{14 \cdot 13})$
    (h) The plane is $3(x + 10) - 2(y - 8) + (z - 1) = 0$. The point in this plane and on λ_2 is given by $u = -8$.

18. $\cos \alpha = (Y - R) \cdot V / \|Y - R\| \, \|V\|$. $(X - R) \cdot V = \|X - R\| \, \|V\| \cos \alpha$. Use $\pm \cos \alpha$; or, square both sides. The equation (unsimplified) is

$$16[2(x - 3) - 3(y - 2) + 2(z + 1)]^2 = 9 \cdot 13[(x - 3)^2 + (y - 2)^2 + (z + 1)]^2$$

20. $\|(Q - R) \times \hat{V}\| = r$; $\|(X - R) \times \hat{V}\| = r$; the equation (unsimplified) is

$$\left\| \frac{1}{\sqrt{17}} [2(y - 2) + 3(z + 1), 2(z + 1) - 2(x - 3), -3(x - 3) - 2(y - 2)] \right\| = 5$$

23. The line $X = (1, 2, -1) + t(3, -1, 2)$ meets the plane when $t = 5/14$.

26. There are expressions similar to those of (e) for q_{2k} and q_{3k} ($k = 1, 2, 3$).

Chapter Four

B2. Clearly $(x, f(x)) \in G$; if $(x, y) \in G$ then $y = f(x)$. (Cf. 5.) $y \in f(X)$ if and only if $y = f(x)$ for some $x \in X$; this is so if and only if $(x, f(x)) \in G$.

3. Binary operations: $S \cup T$, $S \cap T$, $S \cap T'$. Not: $S \times T$. $S \cup T$ is associative and commutative, and $\square$ is an identity, but no S except $\square$ has an inverse.

5. Given $f : X \rightarrow Y$, $E \cap (\{x\} \times Y) = \{(x, f(x))\}$. Given E with the stated property, define f by $x \rightarrow y = f(x)$ if $E \cap (\{x\} \times Y) = \{(x, y)\}$.

7. The situation is trivial if either $A = \theta$ or $B = 0$. It is necessary, moreover, that $A \cdot B = 0$ (cf. 3J9). On trying $X = yA \times B$ we obtain $y = -1/||A||^2$. $X = B \times A/||A||^2$ does satisfy the equation.

10. An important result.

C4. (c) If $a \circ x = b$ then $a^{-1} \circ (a \circ x) = a^{-1} \circ b$, whence $(a^{-1} \circ a) \circ x = e \circ x = x = a^{-1} \circ b$. In order that x satisfy the equation it is necessary, therefore, that $x = a^{-1} \circ b$. Vice-versa, $a \circ (a^{-1} \circ b) = (a \circ a^{-1}) \circ b = e \circ b = b$, and $a^{-1} \circ b$ does satisfy the equation. Uniqueness follows from (b).

5. By the property of f, $g \circ f = g$. By commutativity, $g \circ f = f \circ g$ which, by the property of g, is f. Hence $f = g$.

7. f is defined on $\pi \times \pi$ and its values lie in π; hence f is a binary operation on π. f is commutative. f is not associative (almost any triangle will supply a counter-example). Obviously, there is no identity.

10. Important; cf. 4E.

D1. Put $b = a$ to see that $e \in H$. Then take $a = e$ to see that $b \in H$ implies $b^{-1} \in H$. Then $a, b \in H$ imply that $a \circ (f^{-1})^{-1} = a \circ b \in H$; $\circ$ is a binary operation on H (i.e., H is closed under $\circ$). Being associative on G, $\circ$ is associative on H. Hence $\{H, \circ\}$ is a group. Note that if $\circ$ is commutative on G then it is commutative on H; the converse is not necessarily true.

3. Aside from the trivial group $\{e, \circ\}$, the only candidates are $\{e, a, \circ\}$ and $\{e, b, \circ\}$, but neither $\{e, a\}$ nor $\{e, b\}$ is closed under $\circ$.

5. The only points fixed under each motion of L are those of l.

6. Cones with axis l, or any figure of revolution with axis l; intersections of invariant configurations are invariant.

7. Yes. Yes.

E4. Let $e = 1, 2, 3$; $p = 2, 1, 3$; $q = 2, 3, 1$; $r = 1, 3, 2$; $s = 3, 1, 2$; $t = 3, 2, 1$. Sgn $e =$ sgn $q =$ sgn $s = 1$; sgn $p =$ sgn $r =$ sgn $t = -1$. In the body of the adjoining table, the entry is $l \circ a$, where a is in the margin at the top of the column and l is in the margin at the left of the row.

$l\backslash a$	e	p	q	r	s	t
e	e	p	q	r	s	t
p	p	e	r	q	t	s
q	q	t	s	p	e	r
r	r	s	t	e	p	q
s	s	r	e	t	q	p
t	t	q	p	s	r	e

It is obvious that $\{e\}$, $\{e, p\}$, $\{e, r\}$, and $\{e, t\}$ are subgroups of S_3, and that $\{e, k\}$ is not a subgroup if $k = q$ or s. As candidates for subgroups with three elements we must consider $\{e, j, k\}$ where j and k are chosen from p, q, r, s, t. By 2A2.6 there are $\binom{5}{2} = 10$ such possibilities. Observe, however, that $j \circ k$ must be e, or j, or k. This rules out $\{e, p, k\}$ with $k = q, r, s, t$, leaving 6 possibilities. $\{e, q, s\}$ is a subgroup, but $\{e, q, r\}$ and $\{e, q, t\}$ are not; neither is $\{e, r, s\}$, $\{e, r, t\}$, or $\{e, s, t\}$.

6. This is E3 with $T = 1$.

7. For 3, 2, 5, 1, 4, $J_f = 5$, $\operatorname{sgn} f = -1$, $f = (1, 4) \circ (1, 5) \circ (1, 3)$.

9. Let $m = n - \varphi_f$ and show by induction that each $g \in S_m$ having no fixed element can be expressed as the product of at most $(m - 1)$ transpositions.

G4. If $g \in G$ and $h \in H$ and $g \leftrightarrow h$ then $e_G = g \circ g^{-1} \leftrightarrow h * h^{-1} = e_H$. Yes.

5. Yes. Yes; $x + y \to b^{x+y} = b^x \cdot b^y$.

9. $f_a x \circ f_a y = (axa^{-1})(aya^{-1}) = axya^{-1} = f_a(xy)$.

H26. Since $\sum Re(z_k) = Re \sum z_k$ and, for any $z \in C$, $Re z \leq |z|$, the left inequality follows. Use induction to obtain the inequality on the right.

27. (b) $-(7 + 22i)/41 = -\sqrt{7^2 + 22^2}\, e^{i\alpha}/41$, where α is in the third quadrant and $\tan \alpha = 22/7$.
(d) $(-211 + 132i)/13\sqrt{13} = \sqrt{211^2 + 132^2}\, e^{i\alpha}/13\sqrt{13}$, where α is in the second quadrant and $\tan \alpha = -132/211$.

29. (a) All z. (c) z is inside the circle with center at the origin and radius 2. (e) z is outside or on the circle with center at i and radius 1. (g) $z = \pm 2e^{i\alpha}$ where $\alpha = \pi/4$. (i) With a, b and p fixed, the locus is a circle unless $p = 1$. What happens if $p = 1$? If $p \neq 1$, where is the circle? What family of circles does one get as p varies with a and b fixed? What happens as $p \to 0$? As $p \to +\infty$?

31. For $z^3 = 1$, $\rho = 1$, $\varphi = k\pi/3$ $(k = 0, 1, 2)$. For $z^m = p$, $\rho = p^{1/m}$, $\varphi = k\pi/m$ $(k = 0, 1, \ldots, m - 1)$. For $z^m = pe^{i\alpha}$, $\rho = p^{1/m}$, $\varphi = (\alpha + k\pi)/m$ $(k = 0, 1, \ldots, m - 1)$.

33. $f_k(z_j) = \delta_{kj}$; $g(z_j) = c_j$.

17. The equivalence-set containing (a, b) consists of all pairs (ka', kb') where (a', b') is (a, b) with all common factors of a and b divided out (i.e., "a/b" is in "lowest terms"), and $k = \pm 1, \pm 2, \ldots$. In one rigorous development of the rational numbers from the integers, a rational number is *defined* to be one of these equivalence-sets of ordered pairs. One must define addition and multiplication and verify that these operations have the usual properties (2C1.1).

9. Neither relation is reflexive.

11. (a) has R and T but not S; since $0 \in N$, (b) has S and T but not R; (c) has R and S but not T.

13. Let W denote the set of those pairs (a, b) with the property that $a \rho b$. Property R says that the diagonal of $A \times A$ is a subset of W, and property S says that W is symmetric with respect to the diagonal, i.e., if $(a, b) \in W$ then $(b, a) \in W$.

16. An equivalence set consists of all $f \in P$ such that $f(z) = a_f z + b_f + h(z)(z^2 + 1)$, where a_f and b_f are real numbers, determined uniquely by f, and $h \in P$. The result is of considerable theoretical interest.

J1. For A, $L = \{\alpha\}$, $U = \{\beta, \gamma, \delta\}$, inf $= \alpha = $ min, sup $= \beta = $ max. For B, $L = \{a\}$, $U = \{d, e\}$, inf $= a$, sup $= d = $ max, but there is no min.

2. Examples: α, β, γ; a, b, d, e; q, r, t.

5. (c) Yes. Proof?

7. Inf $\{\pi, \sigma\} = \{V : V \neq \square, V = U \cap W, U \in \pi, W \in \sigma\}$.

8. Observe that if $u, v \leq w$ then sup $\{u, v\} \leq w$.

Chapter Five

B16. (a) $(8, -5 + 5i, 7 + 20i)$. $z = [-5(2 + i)x + (4 - 3i)y]/25$.

17. (b) $-3 + 2(-1)^n + 2^{-n+1} - 3^{-n+1}$.

19. Sufficiency by 5. If $\alpha x = 0$ and $\alpha \neq 0$, multiply by α^{-1} to get $x = 0$. If $\alpha x = 0$ and $x \neq 0$ then, if α were $\neq 0$ the argument just given could be used to obtain the contradiction that $x = 0$.

20. Yes: (a), (c), (e). No: (b), (d), (f).

22. Lengthy but routine; an important result.

C3. $\beta x + \gamma y = 2\gamma + \beta \alpha + 3\gamma \alpha^2$; this vanishes (for all α) if and only if $\beta = \gamma = 0$. Hence x and y are independent. To arrive at $4 - \alpha - \alpha^2$ would require $2\gamma = 4$, $\beta = -1$, and $3\gamma = -1$, which impose two inconsistent requirements on γ. Take $\gamma = -1$ and $\beta = 3$ to obtain $-2 + 3\alpha - 3\alpha^2$.

5. (c) $a_3 = a_1 + 2a_2$; a_1 and a_2 are independent.

D4. We wish $\lambda(1, -2) + \mu(\alpha, -1) = (\lambda + \mu\alpha, -2\alpha - \mu) = 0$ to imply that $\lambda = \mu = 0$. Substitute $\mu = -2\lambda$ to obtain $\lambda(1 - 2\alpha) = 0$, whence $\lambda = 0$ unless $\alpha = \frac{1}{2}$.

6. $(\lambda\alpha + \mu\xi, \lambda\beta + \mu\eta) = 0$ must imply that $\lambda = \mu = 0$. This will be true if and only if $\alpha\eta - \beta\xi \neq 0$. Why?

8. $\lambda b_1 + b_2 + \mu b_3 = 0$ leads to the equation $\lambda = 0$, $2\lambda + \mu = 0$ and $3\lambda + 2\mu + \nu = 0$, whence $\lambda = \mu = \nu = 0$. $\alpha_1 = 2$, $\alpha_2 = -4$, $\alpha_3 = -1$.

10. Respective dimensions are 2, 3, 2, 2, 2, 1, 1, 3.

12. If no proper subset spans X_n then no element of S is a linear combination of the other elements of S and the set S is independent and, consequently, a basis. Conversely, if S is a basis, then S is an independent set; if a proper subset of S were to span X_n then some vector of S would be a linear combination of the others and S would not be independent.

13. The proof is straightforward; the result is important.

14. The map of $x = \sum \xi_k b_k$ is $f(x) = \sum \xi_k c_k$. Since c_k is a basis, $f(x) = 0$ only if $\xi_k = 0\,(k = 1, \ldots, n)$ and $x = 0$; hence $x \to f(x)$ is $1 - 1$. An arbitrary vector $y = \sum \xi_k c_k$ in y is the image of $x = \sum \xi_k b_k$, so that $f(X) = Y$. It is easily verified that $f(\alpha x + \alpha' x') = \alpha f(x) + \alpha' f(x')$, completing the proof.

15. That equality of dimension implies isomorphism is the content of 13. The converse follows from an adaptation of the argument in 12.

18. By the definition of $\langle A \rangle$, A spans $\langle A \rangle$. See now the first sentence of the second paragraph of 5.4.

E2. We need to augment the given sets to quadruples that are independent. (c) is easiest; for example, use $(1, 0, 0, 0)$, $(0, 1, 0, 0)$, and $(0, 0, 1, 0)$. (b) use $(0, 1, 0, 0)$ and $(1, 0, 0, 0)$. $(1, 0, 0, 0)$ works in (a).

4. The necessity of the stated conditions is obvious. If they are satisfied, conversely, then S is closed under multiplication by a scalar and, moreover, $x - x = 0 \in S$, $0 - y \in S$, and $x - (-y) = x + y \in S$, whence the result follows by the argument in the first paragraph of E.

6. Yes. No. Yes (how?). Yes.

7. Equivalence sets are flats $a + S$.

F3. For E2 (c) one complementary subspace is spanned by $(1, 0, 0, 0)$, $(0, 1, 0, 0)$, and $(0, 0, 1, 0)$; another is spanned by $(0, 1, 0, 0)$, $(0, 0, 1, 0)$, and $(0, 0, 0, 1)$. For E2 (b) one complementary subspace is spanned by $(0, 1, 0)$; another is spanned by $(1, 1, 0)$.

5. Use E4.

6. If $u \in X + Y$ then there exist $x \in X$ and $y \in Y$ such that $u = x + y$. Hence $X \leq W$ and $Y \leq W$ imply that $u \in W$, whence $X + Y \leq W$ and, further, $X + Y \leq \cap W$, where the intersection is taken over all $W \leq Z$ such that $X \leq W$ and $Y \leq W$. We wish now to show, vice versa, that if $v \in' X + Y$ then $v \in' \cap W$. If $v \in' X + Y$ then $X + Y$ is a subspace W such that $X \leq W$ and $Y \leq W$, whence $v \in' \cap W$.

9. $Z = X \oplus Y$ means that $Z = X + Y$ and $X \cap Y = \langle 0 \rangle$. For each $z \in Z$ there exist $x \in X$ and $y \in Y$ such that $z = x + y$. If also $z = x' + y'$ with $x' \in X$ and $y' \in Y$ then $x' - x = y - y'$; since the $x' - x \in X$ and $y - y' \in Y$, both $x = x'$ and $y = y'$.

10. That x and y exist means that $Z = X + Y$. That x and y are unique means that $X \cap Y = \langle 0 \rangle$; if, in fact, $W \neq 0 \in X \cap Y$, then $z = (x + w) + (y - w) \neq x + y$ and x and y would not be unique.

367

12. $16 \leq \dim (Y \cap Z) + 13,$ whence $\dim (Y \cap Z) \geq 3.$

16. To a basis for X adjoin successive vectors independent of those already in the set and such that u is not in the subspace generated by the resulting set; the process stops when the set contains $\dim Z - 1$ vectors.

18. Lengthy but routine. The result is important.

22. Let $w \in X + (Y \cap Z)$. Then $w = x + v$, with $v \in Y \cap Z$. Since $x \in Z$, $w \in Z$, while $v \in Y$ implies that $w \in X + Y$; hence $w \in (X + Y) \cap Z$. Now suppose, vice versa, that $w \in (X + Y) \cap Z$. Then $w = x + y$ with $x \in X$ and $y \in Y$, and also $w \in Z$. Since $x \in Z$, $y = w - x \in Z$; hence $w \in X + (Y \cap Z)$, completing the proof.

24. If $a \in S \cap T$ then there exist subspaces U and V such that $S = a + U$ and $T = a + V$. Then $W = U \cap V$ is a subspace and we show that $S \cap T = a + W$. If $b \in S \cap T$ then there exist vectors $u \in U$ and $v \in V$ such that $a + u = b = a + v$. Hence $u = v \in W$ and $b \in a + W$. Conversely, if $x = a + w$ with $w \in W$ then $x \in S$ and $x \in T$, whence $x \in S \cap T$. Hence $S \cap T = a + W$.

G13. (a) $(1, 6, -3)$,

    (b) $-10\xi_1 - 19\xi_2 + 12\xi_3,$

    (c) $\xi_1^2 + \xi_2^2,$

    (d) $x = (\lambda - \mu)q_1 + (2\lambda + 3\mu)q_2 - 2\lambda q_3,$

    (e) $3q_1 - q_2 - 3q_3 + (\lambda - 3\mu)q_1 + (-\lambda + 3\mu)q_3.$

16. Yes.

17. $\sum \gamma_k \eta_k = \sum_h (\sum_k \gamma_k \alpha_{kh})\xi_h,$ $\gamma_h' = \sum_k \gamma_k \alpha_{kh};$ similarly for δ and δ'.

Chapter Six

A8. $\beta(\lambda x + \mu y) = \lambda \beta x + \mu \beta y.$ Justify missing steps.

10. Use induction. Yes.

11. (c) is a counter-clockwise rotation of $45°$; the respective images of p_1 and p_2 are $(1, 1)/\sqrt{2}$ and $(-1, 1)/\sqrt{2}$.

(d) is a reflection in the x-axis. Every point on the line $-3\xi + 2\eta = 0$ is mapped by (e) onto $(0, 0)$; every point on the line $\eta = 2\xi$ is fixed; the point (ξ, η) is projected "parallel to $\eta = 3\xi/2$" onto the line $\eta = 2\xi$.

12. (b) $\eta_1 = \xi_1 - \xi_2,$ $\eta_2 = -\xi_1 + 2\xi_2.$

(d) $\eta_1 = 3\xi_1 + \xi_2,$ $\eta_2 = -4\xi_1 - \xi_2.$

14. With $w \neq 0$ let $\langle w \rangle$ be a straight line through 0. If $x = \alpha w$ then $Tx = \alpha Tw \in \langle Tw \rangle$; thus $T\langle w \rangle = \langle Tw \rangle$. The mapping T defined by $z = \rho e^{i\varphi} \to Tz = \rho^2 e^{i\varphi}$ even leaves every straight line through 0 *fixed*, but T is not linear because it is not homogeneous.

16. If the nontrivial linear combination $\sum \alpha_j x_j$ vanishes, then so does $L(\sum \alpha_j x_j) = \sum \alpha_j L x_j$, and this is a vanishing nontrivial combination of $L x_j$ $(j = 1, \ldots, h)$.

18. If $Kx = 0$ then $x(t + p) = x(t)(-\infty < t < \infty)$ and x is periodic with period p.

20. $M(\lambda x + \mu y)(\alpha) = \alpha(\lambda x + \mu y)(\alpha) = \lambda(\alpha x(\alpha)) + \mu(\alpha y(\alpha)) = (\lambda Mx + \mu My)(\alpha)$. The degree of Mx exceeds the degree of x by one.

B2. If $x \in X$ then $I_X x = x$ and $LI_X x = Lx$, whence $LI_X = L$ on X. The proof that $I_Y L = L$ on X is similar.

4. (a) $L(2, 3) = (13, 8)$; $M(2, 3) = 0$.
    (b) $b_1 = L(2, -1)$, but b_1 is not in the range of M; think about this.
    (c) $L^2 - 4L + I = 0$; $M(M - 1) = 0$.
    (d) L has no nontrivial fixed point. For M see A11 (e).
    (e) Cf. (c) above. For L, $\lambda = 2 \pm \sqrt{3}$; for M, $\lambda = 0, 1$.

6. $b \circ c(p_1) = p_1$, $b \circ c(p_2) = 5p_1 - 7p_2$.

7. For the associative law R_M and R_L must be subspaces, respectively, of the domain of L and of the domain of K. For the distributive laws, K and L have a common domain X and codomain Y; for the right distributive law, the range of M is a subspace of X while, for distributivity from the left, Y is a subspace of the domain of M.

8. $z \in R_{KL}$ if $z = KLx$ for some x in the domain of L; if $Lx = y$ then $z = Ky$ and $z \in R_K$; hence $R_{KL} \leq R_K$.

C5. Denote a mapping by L. Does $L^2 = L$, or $L^2 = I$, or neither?

7. $J^2 = 4H^2 - 4H + I = I$; $H^2 = \frac{1}{4}(I + 2J + J^2) = H$.

9. For each x, $J^2 x = Jx' = x$, whence $J^2 = I$.

10. If the projection is P then $Py_k = y_k$ $(k = 1, \ldots, q)$, while $Pz_k = 0$ $(k = q + 1, \ldots, r)$. In the first involution the y_h are fixed and $z_h \to -z_h$; vice-versa in the second.

D5. Solve the equations; when unique, the result displays the inverse.

6. $L^{-1} = \dfrac{1}{\Delta} \begin{bmatrix} \delta & -\beta \\ -\gamma & \alpha \end{bmatrix}$.

7. By argument on p. 153 (below), H^{-1} exists and equals J. Hence $H^{-1}HK = H^{-1} = K$.

9. Images of basis vectors must be dependent, violating 1(a). The condition is obviously not necessary; $L = 0$ is singular regardless of dim X or dim Y.

10. A noteworthy result.

11. K has left-inverse, hence inverse $K^{-1} = L$; K is nonsingular on Y, L is nonsingular on R_K, dim $Y = $ dim $R_K \leq$ dim X. For an example with dim $Y <$ dim X see 3.4.

E5. A projection H in a space X has rank $=$ dim HX and nullity dim $X -$ dim HX. A reflection has nullity zero and rank dim X.

7. If $y = (K + L)x$ then $y = Kx + Lx$, whence $y \in R_K + R_L$. If $U \leq V$ then, obviously, dim $U \leq$ dim V.

9. $\nu(K) = $ dim $X -$ dim R_k, $\nu(L) = $ dim $X -$ dim R_L, whence

$$\nu(K) + \nu(L) = 2 \dim X - \dim R_K - \dim R_L \leq 2 \dim X - \rho(K + L)$$
$$= \dim X + \nu(K + L).$$

11. $-\nu(K) - \nu(L) \leq -\nu(KL); \ \rho(k) + \rho(L) \leq \dim Y + \rho(KL).$

13. If $LM_{LX} = I_{LX}$ and $x \in X$, then $LM_{LX}Lx = Lx$, whence $LML = L$. If $LML = L$ and $y \in LX$, i.e., $y = Lx$ with $x \in X$, then $LMy = LMLx = Lx = y$, $LM = I_{LX}$, and M is a pseudo-inverse of L.

15. If $y = Lx$, then $MLMy = MLMLx = MLx = My$; hence $MLM = M$. If $MLM = M$ then $MLMLx = MLx$; if, further, M is nonsingular, then $LMLx = Lx$ ($x \in X$), and the result follows from 13.

G6. A12(d) $(Lp_1, Lp_2) = (3p_1 - 4p_2, p_1 - p_2),$

$$[\alpha_{jk}] = \begin{bmatrix} 3 & 1 \\ -4 & -1 \end{bmatrix}, \qquad (\eta_1, \eta_2) = (3\xi_1 + \xi_2, -4\xi_1 - \xi_2);$$

$$(L^{-1}p_1, L^{-1}p_2) = (-p_1 + 4p_2, -p_1 + 3p_2),$$

$$[\alpha_{jk}]^{-1} = \begin{bmatrix} -1 & -1 \\ 4 & 3 \end{bmatrix}, \qquad (\xi_1, \xi_2) = (-\eta_1 - \eta_2, 4\eta_1 + 3\eta_2).$$

7. (b) $Lp_1 = \begin{bmatrix} 3 \\ -1 \\ 1 \end{bmatrix}$, $Lp_2 = \begin{bmatrix} 1 \\ 2 \\ -3 \end{bmatrix}$; matrix of L is $\begin{bmatrix} 3 & 1 \\ -1 & 2 \\ 1 & -3 \end{bmatrix}$.

B_L is the plane $\eta_1 + 10\eta_2 + 7\eta_3 = 0$; L^{-1} is $\begin{bmatrix} 0 & -3 & -2 \\ 0 & -1 & -1 \end{bmatrix}$.

9. A $1 \times n$ matrix maps $\mathfrak{F}_n$ into $\mathfrak{F}_1$. A $\mu \times 1$ matrix maps F_1 into F_n. Each has rank 1.

Chapter Seven

A6. (a) $18, \ 6, \ 0, \ 0$; (b) $[3, 0, 0]^t$; $[\frac{1}{2}, 0, 0]^t$; (c) $[3, 0, 0]^t + \alpha[1, 2, 0]^t + \beta[0, 3, 1]^t$;
(e) By the first line when $\tau = -5$.

8. $[0, -\frac{5}{3}, \frac{2}{3}]^t + \tau[3, 7, 5]^t$.

10. No.

11. $xpy \leftrightarrow b(x - y) = 0$. The equivalence-sets are the flats $x + N_b$. (Cf. A2).

13. $cu = fu$ and $cv = fv$; hence $c(\alpha u + \beta v) = \alpha cu + \beta cv$.

15. By A2, $\dim N_f = 2$. Let W_0 be a unit normal to N_f. Let U and V lie in N_f and be chosen so that U, V, W_0 form an orthonormal basis for E_p. Then $W = f(W_0)W_0$. (Check?) Since $W = 0$ implies $f(W_0) = 0$, whence $f = 0$, the mapping is biunique.

B8. (a) $3f - 2g = [10 \ \ -11 \ \ -2 \ \ 11] \in X^d$.
(b) $(3f - 2g)(u + v) = -72$.
(d) $x = [0 \ \ 1 \ \ 0 \ \ 1]^t$; are there others?
(f) If $c = [\alpha \ \ \beta \ \ \gamma \ \ \delta]$ then $cu = \alpha + 3\beta + \delta$ and $cv = -\alpha + \beta + 3\gamma - 3\delta$. $c = [9\gamma - 10\delta, -3\gamma + 2\delta, 4\gamma, 4\delta]$, where γ and δ are parameters.

9. (a) and (c) only.

11. The sufficiency of the condition is obvious. If $fx = 0 \leftrightarrow gx = 0$ then $N_f = N_g (= N)$. If $fy \neq 0$ then $gy \neq 0$ and, by A2, $X = \langle y \rangle \oplus N$. If $x \in X$ then $x = \beta y + z$, with $z \in N$. Hence $fx = \beta fy$ and $gx = \beta gy$, whence $fx/gx = fy/gy$ and we must choose $\alpha = fy/gy$. Now verify that this α works.

12. Cf. A11.

14. If $m = 1$ the result follows from A2. For $k = 1, \ldots, m$ let N_μ denote the nullspace of a_μ and define $Y_k = {}_\mu\cap_1^k N_\mu$. Use 5F2 to prove, for $k = 1, \ldots, m - 1$, that if $\dim Y_k \geq n - k$ then $\dim Y_{k+1} \geq n - k - 1$. Hence $\dim Y_m \geq n - m > 0$ and Y_m is not trivial; i.e., there is an $x \in Y_m$ with $x \neq 0$. If $n > m$, therefore, then the system of equations has non-trivial solutions. One can think, speaking loosely, of $n - m$ of the variables as parameters, and solve for the others in terms of them; [cf. B8(f)]. This question will be treated more precisely in Chapter 9.

C3. (a) For example, $\alpha[3 \quad 2 \quad 0]^t + \beta[0 \quad 1 \quad 3]^t$.
(c) $8\xi + 5\eta - 7\zeta = 0$.

5. Suppose that $P, Q \leq X$. $a \in (P + Q)^\circ$ means that if $x \in P + Q$ then $ax = 0$. If $x \in P, Q$, then $x \in P + Q$, whence $ax = 0$. It follows that $a \in P^\circ$ and $a \in Q^\circ$, whence $a \in P^\circ \cap Q^\circ$, and $(P + Q)^\circ \subset P^\circ \cap Q^\circ$. Proof of the opposite inclusion is similar.

7. If $\{p_k\}$ is the basis for X dual to $\{b_k\}$ and $x = \sum \beta_k p_k$ then $b_k x = \beta_k$. If also $b_k \sum \gamma_i p_i = \beta_k$ then $\gamma_i = \beta_i$ $(j = 1, \ldots, n)$ and x is unique.

8. Since $X = Y \oplus Z$, each $x \in X$ is the sum, $y_x + z_x$, of a unique $y_x \in Y$ and $z_x \in Z$. If $f \in Z^\circ \cap Y^\circ$ and $x \in X$ then $fx = fy_x + fz_x = 0$, and $f = 0$; hence $Z^\circ \cap Y^\circ = \langle 0 \rangle$. By the definition of f_Y, if $z \in Z$ then $f_Y z = 0$; hence $f_Y \in Z^\circ$. The proof that $f_Z \in Y^\circ$ is similar. Vice versa, now, if $g \in Z^\circ$ then, for $x \in X$, $gx = gy_x$, whence g is f_y with $f = g$; hence $Z^\circ = \{f_Y\}$. Similarly, $Y^\circ = \{f_Z\}$. With $\dim Y = m$ and $\dim X = n$, let

$$\{p_k, p_{k'}\} \ (k = 1, \ldots, m; k' = m + 1, \ldots, n)$$

be a basis for X and let

$\{b_h, b_{h'}\} \ (h = 1, \ldots, m; h' = m + 1, \ldots, n)$ be a basis for X^d dual to $\{p_i\}$.

Then the isomorphism between Y^d and Z°, and between Z^d and Y° may be expressed symbolically by the following "equations"

$$\langle b_1, \ldots, b_m \rangle = Y^d = Z^\circ$$
$$\langle b_{m+1}, \ldots, b_n \rangle = Z^d = Y^\circ;$$

they suggest an explicit display of the isomorphisms.

10. Yes; use 1.

D16. (a) $N_K = \langle [-3, 1, 7]^t \rangle = R_{L^d}^0$; if $f = [\alpha, \beta] \in Y^d$ then $fK^d = [\alpha + 2\beta, 3\alpha - \beta, \beta] \in X^d$; $N_{K^d} = \langle 0 \rangle = R_K^0$. The point $[\lambda, \mu]^t \in Y$ is the image of the line $[\lambda, 0, \mu - 2\lambda]^t + \eta[-3, 1, 7]^t \in X$. A pseudo-inverse of K is M: $[\lambda, \mu]^t \rightarrow [\lambda, 0, -2\lambda + \mu]^t$, for $KMK = K$ (cf. 6E13); $M^d : [\theta, \varphi, \psi] \rightarrow [\varphi - 2\psi, \psi]$ is a right inverse of K^d.
(c) R_M is the plane $5\xi - \eta - 7\zeta = 0$; $N_M = \langle 0 \rangle$. An inverse of M on R_M is L:

$$[\xi, \eta, \zeta]^t \rightarrow \tfrac{1}{5}[\eta + 2\zeta, -2\eta + \zeta]^t$$

for, indeed, $LM = I_Y \cdot M^d$ on X^d into Y^d is $[\theta, \varphi, \psi] \to [3\theta + \varphi + 2\psi, \theta - 2\varphi + \psi]$; $N_{M^d} = \langle [5, -1, -7] \rangle$ and a pseudo-inverse of M^d, on Y^d into X^d, is $[\alpha, \beta] \to \frac{1}{5}[0, \alpha - 2\beta, 2\alpha + \beta]$ and, as expected, this is simply L^d. Note that the equation for R_M is a consistency condition for the equations defining M, with ξ, η, and ζ given and λ and μ sought.

18. See D7.2.

21. Use C8.

22. Yes. Range is $\langle b \rangle$ and rank is 1.

24. If dim $Y <$ dim X then L must be singular.

Chapter Eight

B12. $3L - 2M = \begin{bmatrix} 12 & 5 \\ 15 & -2 \end{bmatrix}$, $\quad LM = \begin{bmatrix} -24 & 16 \\ -15 & 10 \end{bmatrix}$, $\quad ML = \begin{bmatrix} -4 & -5 \\ -8 & -10 \end{bmatrix}$.

13. (a) $\begin{bmatrix} \delta & \epsilon & \zeta \\ \alpha & \beta & \gamma \end{bmatrix}$, $\quad$ (c) $\begin{matrix} \alpha\xi + 3\alpha\eta - 2\alpha\zeta \\ +3\beta\xi + 2\beta\eta - \beta\zeta, \\ -2\gamma\xi - \gamma\eta + \gamma\zeta \end{matrix}$ $\quad$ (e) $\begin{bmatrix} \alpha\delta & \alpha\epsilon & \alpha\zeta \\ \beta\delta & \beta\epsilon & \beta\zeta \\ \gamma\delta & \gamma\epsilon & \gamma\zeta \end{bmatrix}$.

14. $L = \begin{bmatrix} \alpha & \beta \\ \beta & \gamma \end{bmatrix}$.

15. If M denotes the given matrix, and I denotes the 2×2 identity matrix, then $LM = ML$ if and only if there are scalars α and β such that $L = \alpha I + \beta M$.

18. $KL = 0$ if and only if the third column of K has each element equal to zero.

C13. For $n = 1, 2, 3, \ldots, L^n = \begin{bmatrix} J^n & nJ^{n-1} \\ 0 & J^n \end{bmatrix}$.

14. For $n = 1, 2, 3, \ldots$, let $f(n, K) = I + K + \ldots + K^{n-1}$; then

$$L^n = \begin{bmatrix} I & 0 \\ f(n, K)J & K^n \end{bmatrix}.$$

16. Let $[x]^t = [y \quad z]^t$ and $[L] = \begin{bmatrix} M & Q \\ P & N \end{bmatrix}$, where y, z, M, N, P, and Q are block matrices of sizes determined in an obvious way by dim Y and dim Z. Now examine $[L][y \quad z]^t = [u \quad v]^t$. If Y is to be invariant, $z = 0$ must imply $v = 0$. This will hold if and only if $P = 0$. If Z is not invariant then it must be possible to have $y = 0$ and $u \neq 0$; for this it is necessary and sufficient that $Q \neq 0$. In order that Z be invariant under L but Y not, it is necessary and sufficient, by a similar argument, that $Q = 0$ and $P \neq 0$. Compare these results with 10.

17. $\alpha_{jk} = r_j L c_k$, where r_j is the j-th row vector of K and c_k is the k-th column vector of M.

18. LE_{jk} has every column zero except the k-th, which consists of the j-th column of L. If $E_{jk}L = LE_{jk}$ for all j and k then the k-th row of L is zero except possibly for its k-th element, and the j-th column of L is zero except possibly for its j-th element. Hence L must be a diagonal matrix; see E2.

D13. $\rho([L]') = \rho_R([L]) = \rho([L])$ by 3.

14. If $[L]$ has a right (left) inverse then $[L]$ is row-(column-) nonsingular. See 4H.

17. An important result.

18. The columns of $[L] [K]$ are linear combinations of the columns of $[L]$, and are therefore elements of $C[L]$; similarly for the rows of $[L] [K]$.

20. Yes. Yes.

22. We know that $\rho(T) = \rho([T])$. By 6E3,

$$\rho(LK) \leq \min(\rho(L), \rho(K)) \quad\text{and}\quad \nu(LK) \leq \nu(L) + \nu(K).$$

Since $\upsilon(L) = 0$, $\upsilon(LK) \leq \upsilon(K)$. Apply 6E1 to LK and its domain, and to K and its domain, to obtain $\rho(LK) \geq \rho(K)$. Since $\rho(L) < \rho(K)$ would yield a contradiction, we conclude that $\rho(LK) = \rho(K)$. (There must be an easier way!) Since 6E3 is unchanged if K and L are interchanged, so is the result here.

23. Use 6E3(a). Yes; L has only one independent row (or column), and the scalar factors yielding the other rows are (essentially) the ξ_k (or α_k). Cf. B13(e).

24. An important result; from our present viewpoint, rather obvious.

E5. In B18 we saw that if $E_{jk}L = LE_{jk}$ then L is necessarily diagonal; $L = [[\alpha_h]]$ $(h = 1, \ldots, n)$. Now $E_{jk}L$ has zeros except in the j-th row, where the element α_k appears in the k-th position, while LE_{jk} has zeros except in the k-th column, where the element α_j appears in the j-th position. If $j \neq k$, then $\alpha_j = \alpha_k$. Hence L must be a scalar matrix; $L = \alpha I_n$. It is easy to verify, conversely, that an $n \times n$ scalar matrix commutes with every $n \times n$ matrix.

7. Take transposes on both sides.

9. Proof easy. If J and K are upper-triangular, consider an element γ_{jk} of JK with $j > k$, i.e., an element below the diagonal in JK. It is the product of the j-th row b_j of J by the k-th column c_k of K. Now the first $j - 1$ elements of b_j are zero, thus annulling all the first k elements of c_k, and the remaining elements of c_k are zero. Hence $\gamma_{jk} = 0$ and JK is upper-triangular.

13. (Note that $L^t L$ is $n \times n$, LL^t is $\mu \times \mu$, and that both are symmetric.) Observe that if $x = [\xi_k]^t$ then $x^t x = \sum \xi_k^2 = 0$ if and only if $x = 0$. If $Lx \neq 0$ then $(Lx)^t Lx = x^t L^t L x > 0$, whence $L^t Lx \neq 0$. If $L^t Lx \neq 0$ then $x^t L^t Lx = (Lx)^t Lx > 0$ (for otherwise $Lx = 0$ and $L^t Lx = 0$) whence $Lx \neq 0$. Hence $Lx \neq 0$ if and only if $L^t Lx \neq 0$, and L and $L^t L$ both have rank ρ. The proof for LL^t is similar. (One may, for example, use row vectors y and their images yL.) Now let $L = \begin{bmatrix} 1 & 0 & 0 \\ 0 & 1 & 0 \end{bmatrix}$. Then $L^t L$ is a 3×3 matrix with rank 2, while $LL^t = I_2$. Show that if L is column-nonsingular (but row-singular) then $L^t L$ is regular, while LL^t is singular, and that if L is row-nonsingular, then LL^t is regular but $L^t L$ is singular; note that, in each case, L has maximal rank consistent with its size.

F8. $[[16 \quad 50]]$.

9. Calling the given matrix L, try to apply 6 with K of the form $\begin{bmatrix} 1 & 1 \\ \theta & \varphi \end{bmatrix}$, with $\theta \neq \varphi$.

You will find that, in order for the off-diagonal terms of the result to vanish, both θ and φ must satisfy the equation $\xi^2 - \xi - 4 = 0$, which has distinct real roots. Continuing, obtain

$$\left[\left[\frac{2\varphi - 3\theta}{\varphi - \theta} \quad \frac{3\varphi - 2\theta}{\varphi - \theta}\right]\right].$$

More systematic methods for handling problems of this kind will be developed later.

Chapter Nine

C18. (i) $(9, 2, 0, -1) + y(-2, 0, 1, 0)$.   (ii) Inconsistent.
(iii) $(1, -2, 2, -3)$.   (iv) $(1, 0, 0, 0) + x(-2, 1, 0, 0) + z(-5, 0, -2, 1)$.

19. If $S = \langle p_1, \ldots, p_m \rangle$, seek ξ_k's such that $\sum \xi_k p_k = b - a$. What difference does it make whether or not the p_k $(k = 1, \ldots, m)$ are independent?

21. Dimension is 3. Can find ten independent equations and solve them for certain ten of the variables with the other three variables as parameters. These solutions will satisfy the other seven equations.

D5. (i) $\begin{bmatrix} -5 & 3 & 0 & 0 \\ -2 & 1 & 0 & 0 \\ 4 & -3 & 1 & 0 \\ -9 & 3 & 0 & 1 \end{bmatrix} \begin{bmatrix} 1 & -3 & 2 & 1 & 2 \\ 2 & -5 & 4 & 2 & 6 \\ 2 & -3 & 4 & 0 & 12 \\ 3 & -12 & 6 & 13 & -10 \end{bmatrix} = \begin{bmatrix} 1 & 0 & 2 & 1 & 8 \\ 0 & 1 & 0 & 0 & 2 \\ 0 & 0 & 0 & -2 & 2 \\ 0 & 0 & 0 & 10 & -10 \end{bmatrix}$

The left multiplier here is

$$I_{3\cdot2+4} \quad I_{-3\cdot2+3} \quad I_{3\cdot2+1} \quad I_{-3\cdot1+4} \quad I_{-2\cdot1+3} \quad I_{-2\cdot1+2}.$$

By using the augmented matrix we are able to obtain the solution easily from the final result (the right member of the equation above); see E. For (ii) and (iii) see E10; for (iv) see G13.

E10. (ii) The inconsistency of this system is clear from the last two equations. The third and fourth rows of the matrix suggested in E are these:

$$\begin{bmatrix} 0 & 0 & 1 & 0 & \vdots & 2 & 1 & 2 & -2 & \vdots & 3 & \vdots & -7 \\ 0 & 0 & 0 & 1 & \vdots & 4 & 2 & 4 & -4 & \vdots & 9 & \vdots & -16 \end{bmatrix}$$

when double the third is subtracted from the fourth, the fourth becomes

$$[0 \quad 0 \quad -2 \quad 1 \cdot 0 \quad 0 \quad 0 \quad 0 \cdot 3 \cdot -2];$$

the inconsistency is now apparent from the underlined elements, when one reflects that they imply the "equation" $0 = 3$.
(iii) The first and last matrices are:

$$M = \begin{bmatrix} 1 & 0 & 0 & 0 & \vdots & 1 & -2 & 3 & 1 & \vdots & 8 & \vdots & -12 \\ 0 & 1 & 0 & 0 & \vdots & 3 & 0 & -1 & -1 & \vdots & 4 & \vdots & -6 \\ 0 & 0 & 1 & 0 & \vdots & 2 & 1 & 0 & 3 & \vdots & -9 & \vdots & 2 \\ 0 & 0 & 0 & 1 & \vdots & -2 & 1 & 2 & 0 & \vdots & 0 & \vdots & -2 \end{bmatrix} \quad \text{and}$$

$$M' = \begin{bmatrix} \dfrac{5}{6\cdot 13} & \dfrac{23}{6\cdot 13} & \dfrac{1}{13} & \dfrac{2}{3\cdot 13} & \vdots & 1 & 0 & 0 & 0 & \vdots & 1 & \vdots & \dfrac{-97}{3\cdot 13} \\[2mm] \dfrac{-8}{3\cdot 13} & \dfrac{10}{3\cdot 13} & \dfrac{2}{13} & \dfrac{17}{3\cdot 13} & \vdots & 0 & 1 & 0 & 0 & \vdots & -2 & \vdots & \dfrac{14}{3\cdot 13} \\[2mm] \dfrac{1}{3\cdot 13} & \dfrac{-11}{3\cdot 13} & \dfrac{3}{13} & \dfrac{-7}{3\cdot 13} & \vdots & 0 & 0 & 0 & 1 & \vdots & -3 & \vdots & \dfrac{86}{3\cdot 13} \\[2mm] \dfrac{1}{6} & \dfrac{1}{6} & 0 & \dfrac{1}{3} & \vdots & 0 & 0 & 1 & 0 & \vdots & 2 & \vdots & \dfrac{-11}{3} \end{bmatrix}$$

Now verify that the six rightmost columns of M, when multiplied by the four leftmost columns of M', yield the six rightmost columns of M'.

11. $(\xi, \eta, \zeta) = ((\alpha + 1)^2, 1, -(\alpha + 1))/(\alpha + 2)$ if $\alpha \neq 1, -2$. What happens if $\alpha = 1$ or $\alpha = -2$?

F3. $H^{-1}K = R = \begin{bmatrix} 1 & 0 & 2 & -1 \\ 0 & 1 & -1 & 3 \\ 0 & 0 & 0 & 0 \end{bmatrix}$, where $H^{-1} = \begin{bmatrix} 16 & 13 & 35 \\ 2 & 2 & 5 \\ 5 & 4 & 11 \end{bmatrix}$.

The first two rows of R are independent and therefore form a basis for the row-space of K. The columns $[-2\ \ 1\ \ 1\ \ 0]^t$ and $[1\ \ -3\ \ 0\ \ 1]^t$ are annulled by K; they form a basis for the column nullspace of K. The last row of H^{-1} is annulled by K and is therefore a basis for the row-nullspace of K.

G13. (iv) Using the process of E, we start with

$$T = \begin{bmatrix} 1 & 0 & 0 & 0 & \vdots & 1 & 2 & -1 & 3 & \vdots & 1 & \vdots & -7 \\ 0 & 1 & 0 & 0 & \vdots & 1 & 2 & 0 & 5 & \vdots & 1 & \vdots & -10 \\ 0 & 0 & 1 & 0 & \vdots & 4 & 8 & 1 & 22 & \vdots & 4 & \vdots & -40 \\ 0 & 0 & 0 & 1 & \vdots & 3 & 6 & 1 & 17 & \vdots & 3 & \vdots & -31 \end{bmatrix}$$

and arrive at

$$T' = \begin{bmatrix} 0 & 1 & 0 & 0 & \vdots & 1 & 2 & 0 & 5 & \vdots & 1 & \vdots & -10 \\ -1 & 1 & 0 & 0 & \vdots & 0 & 0 & 1 & 2 & \vdots & 0 & \vdots & -3 \\ 1 & -5 & 1 & 0 & \vdots & 0 & 0 & 0 & 0 & \vdots & 0 & \vdots & 3 \\ 1 & -4 & 0 & 1 & \vdots & 0 & 0 & 0 & 0 & \vdots & 0 & \vdots & 2 \end{bmatrix}$$

Since the matrix in columns 5 to 8 of T' is in row-reduced echelon form, the matrix M in columns 1 to 4 of T' is a pseudo-inverse of the matrix L in columns 5 to 8 of T. In order to use blocks, as in this section, we must first interchange, say, the second and third columns so as to get a regular 2×2 block in the upper left hand corner. Then

$$L = \begin{bmatrix} 1 & -1 & 2 & 3 \\ 1 & 0 & 2 & 5 \\ 4 & 1 & 8 & 22 \\ 3 & 1 & 6 & 17 \end{bmatrix}$$

and (cf. 11),

$$A = \begin{bmatrix} 1 & -1 \\ 1 & 0 \end{bmatrix}, \quad B = \begin{bmatrix} 2 & 3 \\ 2 & 5 \end{bmatrix}, \quad C = \begin{bmatrix} 4 & 1 \\ 3 & 1 \end{bmatrix}, \quad D = \begin{bmatrix} 8 & 22 \\ 6 & 17 \end{bmatrix}.$$

375

Now $A^{-1} = \begin{bmatrix} 0 & 1 \\ -1 & 1 \end{bmatrix}$. We verify incidentally that $D = CA^{-1}B$. With any 2×2 matrices P and T, we may form a pseudo-inverse M as in 10. The matrix M in T' (above) is obtained by taking $P = 0$ and $T = I$. Applying M to $[1 \quad 1 \quad 4 \quad 3]^t$ we obtain $[1 \quad 0 \quad 0 \quad 0]^t$, establishing the consistency of the system and supplying a particular solution. A basis for the column nullspace for L is $\{[-2 \quad 0 \quad 1 \quad 0]^t, [-5 \quad -2 \quad 0 \quad 1]^t\}$. Comparison with the answer given in C18(iv) reveals that the second and third rows have here been interchanged; why?

H7. Start with $M = \begin{bmatrix} 1 & 0 & 0 \\ 0 & 1 & 0 \\ 0 & 0 & 1 \\ 4 & 2 & -3 \\ 2 & -2 & 3 \\ 6 & 6 & -9 \\ 2 & -8 & 12 \\ -15 & 1 & -4 \end{bmatrix}$ and obtain $M' = \begin{bmatrix} \frac{1}{6} & \frac{1}{6} & 0 \\ \frac{-5}{6} & \frac{1}{6} & -3 \\ \frac{-2}{3} & \frac{1}{3} & -2 \\ 1 & 0 & 0 \\ 0 & 1 & 0 \\ 2 & -1 & 0 \\ -1 & 3 & 0 \\ \frac{-2}{3} & \frac{-11}{3} & 5 \end{bmatrix}$.

Rows 4 to 7 of M constitute L^t; let H consist of the first three rows of M'. Then L^tH is given by rows 4 to 7 of M'; it is in column-reduced echelon form. The first two columns of L^tH form a basis for the column-space of L^t. The last column of H is annulled by L^t and constitutes a basis for the column nullspace of L^t. The row-vectors $[-2 \quad 1 \quad 1 \quad 0]$ and $[1 \quad -3 \quad 0 \quad 1]$ form a basis for the row-nullspace of L^t. Compare with the result for L in F3 above.

9. Start with $M = \begin{bmatrix} 1 & 0 & 0 \\ 0 & 1 & 0 \\ 0 & 0 & 1 \\ \cdots & \cdots & \cdots \\ 2 & 3 & -2 \\ -3 & 1 & 1 \\ 7 & 5 & -5 \\ -11 & 0 & 5 \\ \cdots & \cdots & \cdots \\ 4 & -10 & 0 \end{bmatrix}$ and obtain $M' = \begin{bmatrix} 16 & 2 & 5 \\ 13 & 2 & 4 \\ 35 & 5 & 11 \\ \cdots & \cdots & \cdots \\ 1 & 0 & 0 \\ 0 & 1 & 0 \\ 2 & -1 & 0 \\ -1 & 3 & 0 \\ \cdots & \cdots & \cdots \\ -66 & -12 & -20 \end{bmatrix}$.

Rows 4 to 7 of M constitute J; let H consist of rows 1 to 3 of M'. Then JH is given by rows 4 to 7 of M'; it is in column-reduced echelon form. The first two columns of JH form a basis for the column-space of J. The last column of H is annulled by J and constitutes a basis for the column-nullspace of J. The row vectors $[-2 \quad 1 \quad 1 \quad 0]$ and $[1 \quad -3 \quad 0 \quad 1]$ form a basis for the row-nullspace of J. Compare all this with the results for K in F3 above.

13 and **14.** These are "leads" to I4.

$$K = \begin{bmatrix} 1 & 2 & -1 & 0 \\ -i & 1 - 2i & i & 0 \\ \dfrac{-1 - 2i}{5 \cdot 6} & \dfrac{i}{6} & \dfrac{1}{6} & 0 \\ \dfrac{-371 + 178i}{5 \cdot 6 \cdot 13} & \dfrac{22 - 123i}{6 \cdot 13} & \dfrac{-15 - 16i}{6 \cdot 13} & 1 \end{bmatrix}$$

and

$$M = \begin{bmatrix} 1 & \dfrac{-3 - 11i}{13} & \dfrac{29 + 11i}{13} \\ 0 & \dfrac{2 + 3i}{26} & \dfrac{12 - 8i}{13} \\ 0 & 0 & 1 \end{bmatrix}$$

then $KLM = J_{4,3,3}$. (This calculation is very tedious; it is most helpful to maintain a check column [row] when performing row [column] operations.)

7. Let the respective generators of U be designated by u_1, u_2, u_3, and those of V by v_1, v_2. Since the u's (v's) are independent, they form a basis for $U(V)$. Since $v_1 \in' U$ and $v_2 \in' U$, $U + V (= R_4)$ has a basis consisting of u_1, u_2, u_3, w, where either $w = v_1$ or $w = v_2$. As for $U \cap V$, one seeks α, β, γ, λ, μ such that $\alpha u_1 + \beta u_2 + \gamma u_3 = \lambda v_1 + \mu v_2$. It turns out that any multiple of $[-23 \quad -44 \quad -13 \quad 8 \quad -17]$ will work. Hence $U \cap V$ is $\langle 8v_1 - 17v_2 \rangle = \langle -23u_1 - 44u_2 - 13u_3 \rangle$.

10. (a)

$$U = \begin{bmatrix} I_2 & \begin{matrix} -1 & -2 \\ 2 & 3 \end{matrix} \\ 0 & 0 \end{bmatrix}$$

(b) Consistency conditions are $3\alpha - \beta + \gamma = 0$ and $4\alpha - \beta + 2\delta = 0$.

(c) $N_T = \langle [1 \quad -2 \quad 1 \quad 0]^t, [2 \quad -3 \quad 0 \quad 1]^t \rangle$.

(d) $x = N_T + \alpha[-12 \quad 10 \quad 0 \quad 0]^t + \beta[2 \quad -1 \quad 0 \quad 0]^t$.

(e) $Q = \begin{bmatrix} -\frac{3}{2} & \frac{1}{2} & 0 & 0 \\ \frac{5}{4} & -\frac{1}{4} & 0 & 0 \\ 3 & -2 & 1 & 0 \\ 2 & -1 & 0 & 1 \end{bmatrix}$.

(f) $[3 \quad -2 \quad 1 \quad 0]$ and $[2 \quad -1 \quad 0 \quad 1]$; these are the last two rows of Q.

(g) $R = \begin{bmatrix} I_2 & \begin{matrix} 1 & 2 \\ -2 & -3 \end{matrix} \\ 0 & I_2 \end{bmatrix}$.

Chapter Ten

A40. With $T = \begin{bmatrix} 0 & 1 \\ 1 & -1 \end{bmatrix}$, $T^t M T = \begin{bmatrix} 1 & 0 \\ 0 & -1 \end{bmatrix}$.

42. Yes; both have rank 2.

44. No; E of 27 yields a counter-example on X_2. See 50.

46. By the definition in 8F10, tr $(H + J) = $ tr $H + $ tr J, and tr $(\alpha H) = \alpha$ tr H. Hence b is linear in K and L. By 8F10, tr $KL = $ tr LK and $b(K, L) = b(L, K)$.

49. With S in the form $J_{n,\rho,s}$ of 36, the fact that $S(I - S) = 0$ implies that $p = \rho$; in this case the result is trivial. Compare 6C2; there dim $HX + $ dim $(I - H)X = $ dim X.

B20. $\theta = \bar{x}^t H x = \theta^t = x^t H^t \bar{x} = x^t \overline{H} \bar{x}$, while $\bar{\theta} = x^t \overline{H} \bar{x}$; hence $\theta = \bar{\theta}$ and θ is real. The converse is nontrivial. Let J be a square matrix, set $\theta = \bar{x}^t J x$, and suppose that $\theta = \bar{\theta}$ for all $x \in X$. By an argument similar to the one just given, $\bar{x}^t(\bar{J}^t - J)x = 0$ for all $x \in X$. Now $K = \bar{J}^t - J$ is anti-Hermitian. By a change of basis given by $x = Ty$ with T regular, we obtain $\varphi = \bar{y}^t \overline{T}^t K T y = 0$ for all $y \in X$, where $\overline{T}^t K T$ is the canonical form of K, namely, $i J_{n,\rho,s}$ with $J_{n,\rho,s}$ as in 19.1. If $\rho > 0$ then we can choose y so that $\varphi \neq 0$, a contradiction. Hence $\rho = 0$, $\overline{T}^t K T = 0$, and, since T is regular, $K = 0$ and $\bar{J}^t = J$; i.e., J is Hermitian.

26. If $T = \begin{bmatrix} 1 & 1 \\ 1 & -\dfrac{1}{2\alpha} & \dfrac{1}{2\alpha} \end{bmatrix}$ then $\overline{T}^t H T = [[1 \quad -1]]$.

27. If L is the matrix on the left and $T = \begin{bmatrix} \dfrac{1}{\sqrt{2}} & \dfrac{-i}{\sqrt{2}} & -1 \\ 0 & \sqrt{2} & -(2+i) \\ 0 & 0 & 1 \end{bmatrix}$

then $\overline{T}^t L T = [[1 \quad -1 \quad 0]]$.

29. $f_x y = b(x, y) = \sum_i (\sum_i \xi_i \beta_{ij})\eta_j = [f_x][y]$, where $[f_x] = [\sum_i \xi_i \beta_{ij}]$. The rank of f is equal to the number of linearly independent f_x's as x varies over X. Now each $[f_x]$ is a linear combination of rows of $[\beta_{ij}]$, and all such row-vectors occur as x varies over X. We are asking, therefore, for the dimension of the row-space of $[\beta_{ij}]$ and we know (8D3) that this is equal to the rank of $[\beta_{ij}]$ or, to the rank of b. A similar argument yields the same result for g.

C13. H of 26 and L of 27 are both indefinite.

14. If S is regular then $x^t M^t M x = \sum \xi_i^2$, where $[\xi_i] = [Mx]$, and this quantity is positive unless $x = 0$. If $K^t S K = I$, where K is regular, then $S = (K^t)^{-1} K^{-1} = M^t M$, with $M = K^{-1}$.

17. The canonical form of H is $[[1 \quad -1]]$. The locus of the equation $x^t H x = 1$ is a hyperbola.

18. Let $\eta_1 = \xi_1 + \xi_2 + \xi_3$, $\eta_2 = \xi_2$, $\eta_3 = \xi_3$. In the new coordinates the functional is $\bar{\eta}_1 \eta_1$; hence J is Hermitian and the canonical form of J is $D = [[1 \quad 0 \quad 0]]$. Of course, $J \geq 0$, but $J > 0$ is excluded by $e_2^t D e_2 = 0 = e_3^t D e_3$, where e_2 and e_3 are the second and third basis vectors in the new coordinate system.

Chapter Eleven

B8. $B = 14$; $D = 17$.

9. It has been stated in A (b), but not proved, that the terms in ξ, η, and ζ will constitute a linear form f, and the left member will be of the form $\alpha\xi + \beta\eta + \gamma\zeta - \delta$. Evaluating the determinant, we obtain $3\xi - 3\eta - \zeta = -4$. By inspection, the values $(-1, 2, -5)$ make the second column zero and therefore satisfy the equation.

C6. $|A| = |A^t| = |-A| = (-1)^n |A|$ by B3.

D14. (b) 748.

17. By C7, dW/dt is a sum of n determinants, in the k-th of which the k-th row of W has been differentiated once (more). Each determinant except the n-th has two equal rows. In the n-th we use the differential equation to replace $y_i^{(n)}$ by $-\sum_{k=0}^{n-1} \alpha_k y^{(k)}$. The rest is easy.

E9. $(I - A)x = 0$ if $x = [3 \quad -1]^t$.

15. If $|\alpha_{jk}| = 0$ then by E6 the system $\sum_j \eta_j \alpha_{jk} = 0 \ (k = 1, \ldots, n)$ has a nontrivial solution; but then $\sum_j \eta_j u_j = 0$ with some $\eta_j \neq 0$. Vice versa, if $\sum_j \eta_j u_j = 0$, with some $\eta_j \neq 0$, then $\sum_k (\sum_j \eta_j \alpha_{jk})v_k = 0$; since the v_k are independent, $\sum_j \eta_j \alpha_{jk} = 0$ $(k = 1, \ldots, n)$ and, since this system has a nontrivial solution, $|\alpha_{jk}| = 0$.

G8. (b) -19.

10. If $n = 2$ then $V_2 = \xi_2 - \xi_1$. In V_{n+1}, multiply column k by ξ_1 and subtract from column $k + 1$ $(k = 1, \ldots, n)$. The result is

$$
\begin{vmatrix}
1 & 0 & 0 & \cdots & 0 \\
1 & \xi_2 - \xi_1 & \xi_2^2 - \xi_2\xi_1 & \cdots & \xi_2^n - \xi_2^{n-1}\xi_1 \\
\cdot & \cdot & \cdot & & \cdot \\
1 & \xi_{n+1} - \xi_1 & \xi_{n+1}^2 - \xi_{n+1}\xi_1 & \cdots & \xi_{n+1}^n - \xi_{n+1}^{n-1}\xi_1
\end{vmatrix}
$$

$$
= (\xi_2 - \xi_1)(\xi_3 - \xi_1)(\xi_{n+1} - \xi_1)
\begin{vmatrix}
1 & \xi_2 & \cdots & \xi_2^{n-1} \\
1 & \xi_3 & \cdots & \xi_3^{n-1} \\
\cdot & \cdot & & \cdot \\
1 & \xi_{n+1} & \cdots & \xi_{n+1}^{n-1}
\end{vmatrix}
$$

Now use the inductive hypothesis.

H15. (b)
$$
A^{-1} = \frac{1}{58}
\begin{bmatrix}
\begin{vmatrix} -1 & 7 \\ 5 & -3 \end{vmatrix} & -\begin{vmatrix} 3 & 4 \\ 5 & -3 \end{vmatrix} & \begin{vmatrix} 3 & 4 \\ -1 & 7 \end{vmatrix} \\
-\begin{vmatrix} 2 & 7 \\ 0 & -3 \end{vmatrix} & \begin{vmatrix} 0 & 4 \\ 0 & -3 \end{vmatrix} & -\begin{vmatrix} 0 & 4 \\ 2 & 7 \end{vmatrix} \\
\begin{vmatrix} 2 & -1 \\ 0 & 5 \end{vmatrix} & \begin{vmatrix} 0 & 3 \\ 0 & 5 \end{vmatrix} & \begin{vmatrix} 0 & 3 \\ 2 & -1 \end{vmatrix}
\end{bmatrix}
$$

$$
= \frac{1}{58}
\begin{bmatrix}
-32 & 29 & 25 \\
6 & 0 & 8 \\
10 & 0 & -6
\end{bmatrix}
$$

K9. $\delta = m_{25,14}C_{25,14} + m_{25,15}C_{25,15} + m_{25,45}C_{25,45}$

$= m_{25,14}(-1)^{2+5+1+4}M_{25,14} + m_{25,15}(-1)^{2+5+1+5}M_{25,15} + M_{25,45}(-1)^{2+5+4+5}M_{25,45}$

$$= \begin{vmatrix} 4 & 3 \\ -2 & 1 \end{vmatrix} \begin{vmatrix} -1 & -4 & 5 \\ 0 & 2 & 4 \\ 2 & 3 & 2 \end{vmatrix} - \begin{vmatrix} 4 & -1 \\ -2 & -1 \end{vmatrix} \begin{vmatrix} -1 & -4 & 3 \\ 0 & 2 & 1 \\ 2 & 3 & -2 \end{vmatrix}$$

$$+ \begin{vmatrix} 3 & -1 \\ 1 & -1 \end{vmatrix} \begin{vmatrix} 2 & -1 & -4 \\ -3 & 0 & 2 \\ 5 & 2 & 3 \end{vmatrix} = 512$$

Chapter Twelve

A7. (c) Characteristic polynomial is $(\lambda - 1)^2(\lambda - 2)$. 1 is an eigenvalue with $a = 2$ and $g = 1$; the only corresponding eigenvector is $[1 \ \ 0 \ \ 0]^t$. 2 is an eigenvalue with $a = 1$ and $g = 1$; the corresponding eigenvector is $[0 \ \ 0 \ \ 1]^t$.

9. After p applications of L we have $\sum \alpha_j \lambda_j^p v_j = 0$. Let $p = 0, 1, \ldots, g - 1$. With $V = [\lambda_j^p]$ (cf. 11G10), these equations can be written as $[\alpha_1 v_1 \ \ \alpha_2 v_2 \ldots \alpha_g v_g]V = 0$. Since the λ_j are distinct, V^{-1} exists, whence $[\alpha_1 v_1 \ \ \alpha_2 v_2 \ldots \alpha_g v_g] = 0$ and, since $v_j \neq 0$, each $\alpha_j = 0$ and the vectors v_k are independent.

12. If $Lx = \lambda x$ with $x \neq 0$ then $(L + \mu I)x = (\lambda + \mu)x$.

15. If $P^2 = P$ and $Px = \lambda x$ then $(\lambda^2 - \lambda)x = 0$ and, if $x \neq 0$, $\lambda(\lambda - 1) = 0$. If $J^2 = I$ and $Jx = \lambda x$ then $(\lambda^2 - 1)x = 0$ and, if $x \neq 0$, then $\lambda^2 = 1$.

B5. (b) First solution. The characteristic polynomial is $\lambda(\lambda^2 - 15\lambda - 6)$, with real zeros $\lambda_0 = 0$ and $\lambda_{\pm}$. Corresponding eigenvectors are, respectively, $v_k = [5\lambda_k + 3 \ \ \ 7\lambda_k + 3 \ \ \ \lambda_k^2 - 6\lambda_k - 3]^t$, with $k = 0, +, -$. With the vectors v_k as basis, the matrix will be $[[0 \ \ \lambda_+ \ \ \lambda_-]]$, by A10.

Second solution. A similarity transformation by $\begin{bmatrix} 1 & 0 & 0 \\ 1 & 1 & 0 \\ -1 & 0 & 1 \end{bmatrix}$ yields $\begin{bmatrix} 0 & 4 & 5 \\ 0 & 1 & 2 \\ 0 & 10 & 14 \end{bmatrix}$;

note that $[1 \ \ 1 \ \ -1]^t = v_0$ of the first solution. Now the characteristic equation of $\begin{bmatrix} 1 & 2 \\ 10 & 14 \end{bmatrix}$ is $\lambda^2 - 15\lambda - 6$; its zeros are λ_+ and λ_- of the first solution. An eigenvector corresponding to λ_+ is $[2, \ \ \lambda_+ - 1]^t$. On using

$$\begin{bmatrix} 1 & 0 & 0 \\ 1 & 1 & 0 \\ -1 & 0 & 1 \end{bmatrix} \begin{bmatrix} 1 & 0 & 0 \\ 0 & 2 & 0 \\ 0 & \lambda_+ - 1 & 1 \end{bmatrix} = \begin{bmatrix} 1 & 0 & 0 \\ 1 & 2 & 0 \\ -1 & \lambda_+ - 1 & 1 \end{bmatrix}$$

to transform the given matrix by similarity we have

$$\tfrac{1}{2}\begin{bmatrix} 2 & 0 & 0 \\ -1 & 1 & 0 \\ \lambda_+ + 1 & -\lambda_+ + 1 & 2 \end{bmatrix} \begin{bmatrix} 1 & 4 & 5 \\ 2 & 5 & 7 \\ 3 & 6 & 9 \end{bmatrix} \begin{bmatrix} 1 & 0 & 0 \\ 1 & 2 & 0 \\ -1 & \lambda_+ - 1 & 1 \end{bmatrix}$$

$$= \begin{bmatrix} 0 & 5\lambda_+ + 3 & 5 \\ 0 & \lambda_+ & 1 \\ 0 & 0 & 15 - \lambda_+ \end{bmatrix},$$

which is super-diagonal. (Is it clear that $15 - \lambda_+ = \lambda_-$?) A similar stepwise process is effective in general.

7. Use B3 and experiment with powers of $[L]$.

D15. If $K = M^{-1}LM$ (with M regular) then, by induction, $K^q = M^{-1}L^qM$ for $q = 1$, $2, \ldots$. Consider the cases $q = p - 1$ and $q = p$.

E9. Use 7 (or 8).

10. $K^{-1} = \begin{bmatrix} \lambda^{-1} & -\lambda^{-2} & \lambda^{-3} \\ 0 & \lambda^{-1} & -\lambda^{-2} \\ 0 & 0 & \lambda^{-1} \end{bmatrix} \cdot L = K^{-1} - \lambda^{-1}$ is nilpotent of index 3. If the basis

in use is p_1, p_2, p_3 then, with the notation of D (especially D10), $N_1 = \langle p_1 \rangle$, $N_2 = \langle p_1, p_2 \rangle$, $w_{31} = p_3 = q_3Lp_3 = [\lambda^{-3} \quad -\lambda^{-2} \quad 0]^t = q_2$, $L^2p_3 = [\lambda^{-4} \quad 0 \quad 0] = q_1$. With the basis q_1, q_2, q_3, $[L] = J_3$ (as in D4).

11. Possible Segre characteristics are (3)(2), (21)(2), (111)(2), (3)(11), (21)(11), and (111)(11).

13. The order of L is 13.

$$L_\alpha = \begin{bmatrix} \alpha & 1 & 0 & 0 & 0 & 0 & 0 \\ 0 & \alpha & 1 & 0 & 0 & 0 & 0 \\ 0 & 0 & \alpha & 0 & 0 & 0 & 0 \\ 0 & 0 & 0 & \alpha & 1 & 0 & 0 \\ 0 & 0 & 0 & 0 & \alpha & 1 & 0 \\ 0 & 0 & 0 & 0 & 0 & \alpha & 0 \\ 0 & 0 & 0 & 0 & 0 & 0 & \alpha \end{bmatrix} \qquad L_\beta = \begin{bmatrix} \beta & 1 & 0 & 0 \\ 0 & \beta & 0 & 0 \\ 0 & 0 & \beta & 1 \\ 0 & 0 & 0 & \beta \end{bmatrix}$$

$$L_\gamma = \begin{bmatrix} \gamma & 0 \\ 0 & \gamma \end{bmatrix}$$

F13. The eigenvalues are ± 1 and $\pm i$. If λ is an eigenvalue then the corresponding eigenvector is $[1 \quad \lambda^3 \quad \lambda^2 \quad \lambda]^t$. By A10, the Jordan form is $[[1 \quad -1 \quad i \quad -i]]$.

Chapter Thirteen

A10. Use induction.

12. By 11, $|ax|/\|x\| \le \|a\|$ if $x \ne 0$.

13. X_0 is closed under addition (by 3) and under multiplication by a scalar (by 2). On Y, $\|y\| > 0$ if $y \ne 0$.

B17. Choose $y = x$.

19. These loci are related to spheres with center at z. "$= 1$" if x is on the surface of a sphere of radius 1, "≤ 16" if z is inside or on a sphere of radius 16, etc.

22. Lemma. If $(x, p_k) = 0$ $(k = 1, \ldots, n)$ then $x = 0$. Proof. If $x = \sum \xi_k p_k$ then $(x, x) = (x, \sum \xi_k p_k) = \sum \xi_k(x, p_k) = 0$. Corollary. The matrix $R = [(p_j, p_k)]$ is regular. Proof easy. Now try $q_j = \sum \alpha_{jk}p_k$. For each fixed j the equations $(q_j, p_k) = \sum_h \alpha_{jh}(p_h, p_k) = \delta_{jk}$ $(k = 1, \ldots, n)$ have matrix R, which is regular, and hence a unique solution α_{jh} $(h = 1, \ldots, n)$. Therefore, the q_j $(j = 1, \ldots, n)$ exist. If $\sum \beta_j q_j = 0$ then $\sum \bar\beta_j(q_j, p_k) = 0$, whence $\beta_k = 0$ $(k = 1, \ldots, n)$ and therefore the q_j are independent.

D7. Let p and q be as shown:

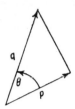

with $\|p\| = 1$, $\|q\| = \sqrt{2}$, and $\theta = \pi/4$. Then $\begin{bmatrix} p \cdot p & p \cdot q \\ q \cdot p & q \cdot q \end{bmatrix} = \begin{bmatrix} 1 & 1 \\ 1 & 2 \end{bmatrix}$; here $v \cdot$ denotes the scalar product of v and s in the sense of Chapter 3. p and q are not orthogonal. p is normalized but q is not. Take $p' = p$ and $q' = q - (q, p)p = [-1 \quad 1]^t$. With respect to the basis p', q' the matrix is I_2.

9. If the matrix is $[\alpha_{jk}]$, then $(p_j, p_k) = \alpha_{jk}$ and the vectors are orthogonal if and only if $\alpha_{jk} = \delta_{jk}\pi_k^2$, where $\pi_k^2 = (p_k, p_k)$, and normalized if and only if $\alpha_{kk} = \pi_k^2 = 1$ $(k = 1, \ldots, n)$.

11. The hyperplane H_0 divides X_n into two open half-spaces, and the vector u points into one of these, call it H_+, and away from the other, call it H_-. "≥ 0" yields $H_+ \cup H_0$; "> 0" yields H_+; "$= 1$" yields a flat in H_+, parallel to H_0, and unit distance from H_0; etc.

13. $(\|x\|^2 + \|y\|^2)^{1/2}$.

14. Expand. In the unitary case one can prove, for example, that $(x - iy, x + iy)$ is purely imaginary; so is $(x - y, x + y)$.

17. The scalar equations are simply $\xi_k = 0$ $(k = 1, \ldots, m)$. There are $n - m$ independent solutions and dim $Y = n - m$.

E9. $S'f = [\alpha \quad \beta \quad \gamma]^t$.

12. We are to choose α, β, γ, and δ in such a way that, for all λ, μ, ν, ρ

$$\int_0^1 (\alpha + \beta\xi + \gamma\zeta^2 + \delta\xi^3)(\lambda + \mu\xi + \nu\xi^2 + \rho\xi^3)\, d\xi = \lambda + \mu\eta + \nu\eta^2 + \rho\eta^3.$$

The equations for α, β, γ, and δ are:

$$\alpha + \frac{\beta}{2} + \frac{\gamma}{3} + \frac{\delta}{4} = 1$$

$$\frac{\alpha}{2} + \frac{\beta}{3} + \frac{\gamma}{4} + \frac{\delta}{5} = \eta$$

$$\frac{\alpha}{3} + \frac{\beta}{4} + \frac{\gamma}{5} + \frac{\delta}{6} = \eta^2$$

$$\frac{\alpha}{4} + \frac{\beta}{5} + \frac{\gamma}{6} + \frac{\delta}{7} = \eta^3.$$

F11. $[L] = \begin{bmatrix} i & -1 \\ 2 & 4i \end{bmatrix}$; with the same basis, $[L^a] = [L]^* = \begin{bmatrix} -i & 2 \\ -1 & -4i \end{bmatrix}$.

14. $\|Lx\|^2 = (Lx, Lx) = (L^aLx, x) = (L^2x, x) \leq \|L^2x\| \|x\| = \|L^2x\|$, where Schwarz's inequality has been used. The condition for equality of B9, when applied here, yields $(x, x)L^2x = (x, L^2x)x$ or $L^2x = (L^ax, Lx)x = (Lx, Lx)x = \|L^2x\|x$.

G8. (b) $\left|\begin{bmatrix} 31 & 3 + 6i \\ 3 - 6i & 15 \end{bmatrix}\right| = 420.$

10. If $y = Mx$ then $||y||^2 = \bar{y}^t y = \bar{x}^t \overline{M}^t M x = ||Mx||^2$, whence, if $\overline{M}^t M x = 0$ then $Mx = 0$. The converse is obvious. Hence $\overline{M}^t M$ and M have the same nullspace and nullity. Since they have the same domain, they must have the same rank.

H8. If $x = 0$ the result is trivial. If $x \neq 0$ then it follows from the definition $||L|| = v_2$ that $||L|| \geq ||Lx||/||x||$, or $||Lx|| \leq ||L|| \, ||x||$. It now follows that $||KLx|| \leq ||K|| \, ||Lx||$; on taking max for $||x|| = 1$ we obtain $||KL|| \leq ||K|| \, ||L||$.

9. $||L^a x||^2 = (L^a x, L^a x) = (LL^a x, x) \leq ||LL^a x|| \, ||x|| \leq ||L|| \, ||L^a x|| \, ||x||$. If $L^a x = 0$ the equality holds; if $L^a x \neq 0$ we divide it out; in either case, $||L^a x|| \leq ||L|| \, ||x||$. Now take max for $||x|| = 1$, obtaining $||L^a|| \leq ||L||$. A very similar argument yields $||L|| \leq ||L^a||$, and the equality follows. That $||L|| = 1$ if L is unitary follows from 2. Any projection which is not the identity, nor zero, is a non-unitary operator with norm 1.

12. See the first paragraph of H.

14. If $(I \pm S)x = 0$ then $x^t(I \pm S)x = 0$. Since $x^t S x = 0$ by 8E7, $x^t x = 0$, whence $x = 0$; hence $I \pm S$ is regular. Now $(I - S)L = I + S$, whence $L^t(I + S) = I - S$. It follows that

$$(I - S)LL^t(I + S) = (I + S)(I - S) = (I - S)(I + S).$$

Hence $LL^t = I$ and L is orthogonal. Further,

$$(I - S)(I + L) = I - S + I + S = 2I,$$

whence $(I + L)$ is regular and L does not have -1 as an eigenvalue. Conversely, from the equation $S(L + I) = L - I$ it follows that $(L^t + I)S^t = L^t - I$, whence $(I + L)S^t = I - L$, $S = (L - I)(L + I)^{-1}$, and $-S^t = (L + I)^{-1}(L - I)$. Since $(L + I)(L - I) = (L - I)(L + I)$, $S = -S^t$ and S is skew.

Chapter Fourteen

A17. First, $x = (\lambda - \mu)^{-1}(L - \mu)x$ and $y = -(\lambda - \mu)^{-1}(L - \lambda)y$. Hence
$$(x, y) = -|\lambda - \mu|^{-2}((L - \mu)x, (L - \lambda)y)$$
$$= -|\lambda - \mu|^{-2}((L^a - \bar{\lambda})(L - \mu)x, y)$$
$$= -|\lambda - \mu|^{-2}((L - \mu)(L^a - \bar{\lambda})x, y) = 0 \text{ by 6.}$$

19. No.

21. Eigenvalues and their multiplicities.

23. Its spectral representation would be simply zero.

B7. $L = L^a$. Why?

8. $J = \begin{bmatrix} 3 & 1 - 2i & 0 \\ 1 + 2i & 2 & 0 \\ 0 & 0 & 3 \end{bmatrix} = J^* = K.$

10. If $H > 0$ and $y = Hx$ then $(x, y) = (x, Hx) > 0$. For the converse, work in $\langle x, y \rangle$, arrange coordinates so that $x = [1 \ \ 0]^t$ and $y = [\lambda \ \ \mu]^t$. Then L_2 with

$[L_2] = \begin{bmatrix} \lambda & 0 \\ \mu & v \end{bmatrix}$ with $v > 0$ is positive because also $\lambda > 0$. Now let L coincide with L_2 on $\langle x, y \rangle$ and be the identity on $\langle x, y \rangle$; then $L > 0$.

11. $\mu \geq$ max $\{|\alpha|^3, |\beta|^3\}$.

12. Yes.

15. If $H = J^2$ then $T^{-1}HT = T^{-1}JTT^{-1}JT = (T^{-1}JT)^2$.

C13. $r(x) = r(\hat{x})$.

15. $||H||^2 = [\text{max } ||H(\hat{x})||]^2 = \text{max } ||H(\hat{x})||^2 = \text{max } (H\hat{x}, H\hat{x})$
$= \text{max } (\hat{x}, H^2\hat{x}) = \lambda_1$, where λ_1 is the largest eigenvalue of H^2.

18. Since $(\hat{x}, (H + P)\hat{x}) = (\hat{x}, H\hat{x}) + (\hat{x}, P\hat{x}) > (\hat{x}, H\hat{x})$, the respective eigenvalues of $H + P$ are *greater* than those of H.

D11. $Q = \begin{bmatrix} 1 & 1 & 7 \\ 0 & 1 & 2 \\ 0 & 0 & 1 \end{bmatrix}$.

13. (b) The characteristic polynomial is $(\lambda - 2)(\lambda + 1)^2$, and

$$\begin{bmatrix} 1 & 1 & 1 \\ 1 & -1 & 0 \\ 1 & 1 & -2 \end{bmatrix} \begin{bmatrix} 0 & 1 & 1 \\ 1 & 0 & 1 \\ 1 & 1 & 0 \end{bmatrix} \begin{bmatrix} 1 & 1 & 1 \\ 1 & -1 & 1 \\ 1 & 0 & -2 \end{bmatrix} = [[6 \quad -2 \quad -6]].$$

Why are the numbers on the diagonal *not* the eigenvalues? What adjustment will produce the eigenvalues on the diagonal?

13. (c) $(\xi - 2\eta - 2\zeta)^2 - 2(\eta + 2\zeta)^2 + 7\zeta^2$.

E21. $\begin{cases} 3\sqrt{5}\xi = \quad\quad 5\beta - \sqrt{5}\gamma \\ 3\sqrt{5}\eta = 3\alpha \;\; + \beta + \sqrt{5}\gamma. \\ 3\sqrt{5}\zeta = -3\alpha - \beta + 2\sqrt{5}\gamma \end{cases}$ Substitute into the differential equation and then multiply on the left by $\begin{bmatrix} 0 & 3 & -3 \\ 5 & 1 & -1 \\ \sqrt{5} & \sqrt{5} & 2\sqrt{5} \end{bmatrix}$.

24. $\begin{cases} 9\xi = \quad 2\alpha + 4\beta - 3\gamma \\ 9\eta = \quad 2\alpha - 2\beta + 6\gamma \\ 9\zeta = \quad -\alpha + 4\beta + 6\gamma \end{cases}$ yields $[[10 \quad 16 \quad 45]]$.

F9. $U = \dfrac{1}{\sqrt{2}} \begin{bmatrix} 1 & i \\ 1 & -i \end{bmatrix}$.

10. The eigenvalues are 0 and $\pm 7i$. Take

$$Q = \begin{bmatrix} -\dfrac{15}{7\sqrt{5}} & 0 & \dfrac{2}{7} \\[2mm] \dfrac{4}{7\sqrt{5}} & \dfrac{1}{\sqrt{5}} & \dfrac{6}{7} \\[2mm] \dfrac{2}{7\sqrt{5}} & -\dfrac{2}{\sqrt{5}} & \dfrac{3}{7} \end{bmatrix}.$$

G15. Imitate the argument which yielded G3.

18. With $R = \begin{bmatrix} \sqrt{\dfrac{2}{3}} & 0 & \dfrac{1}{\sqrt{3}} \\ -\dfrac{1}{2}\sqrt{\dfrac{2}{3}} & \dfrac{1}{\sqrt{2}} & \dfrac{1}{\sqrt{3}} \\ -\dfrac{1}{2}\sqrt{\dfrac{2}{3}} & -\dfrac{1}{\sqrt{2}} & \dfrac{1}{\sqrt{3}} \end{bmatrix}$,

$$R^t Q R = \begin{bmatrix} -\dfrac{1}{2} & \dfrac{\sqrt{3}}{2} & 0 \\ -\dfrac{\sqrt{3}}{2} & -\dfrac{1}{2} & 0 \\ 0 & 0 & 1 \end{bmatrix}.$$

H3. (a) $L = \begin{bmatrix} \sqrt{2} & 0 & 0 \\ 0 & \sqrt{5} & 0 \\ 0 & 0 & 3 \end{bmatrix}\begin{bmatrix} 0 & 0 & \dfrac{1+2}{\sqrt{2}} \\ 0 & \dfrac{2-i}{\sqrt{5}} & 0 \\ 1 & 0 & 0 \end{bmatrix} = HU.$

INDEX
of Special Symbols

* Other meanings may be assigned temporarily in limited contexts.

Symbol	Meaning	First Occurrence
$\sum, \pi$	Addition, multiplication	2C1
R	Set of real numbers	2D
$\Re$ or R	Ordered field $\{R, +, \cdot\}$ of real numbers	2D1, 4F
$\mathcal{E}_3$	Three-dimensional Euclidean space	Intro. to 3
$\overrightarrow{PQ}$	Vector from P to Q in $\mathcal{E}_3$	3A
$\\|\overrightarrow{PQ}\\|$	Length of $\overrightarrow{PQ}$	3A
E_P	Set of vectors issuing from P in $\mathcal{E}_3$	3B
$\hat{V}$	Vector of length in one direction of V	3C
$\langle V_k \rangle$	Set of all linear combinations of vectors V_k	3F4, 5C3
δ_{jk}	1 if $j = k$, 0 if $j = k$ (Kronecker delta)	3G3.1
(X, Y) or $X \cdot Y$	Scalar product of vectors X and Y in E_P	3I
$U \times V$	Vector product of vector U and V in E_P	3J
$\circ$	Binary operation	4B
$\{S, \circ\}$	System consisting of a set S and a binary operation $\circ$ on S	4B
$\mathcal{F} = \{F, \circ, *\}$	A field, often denoted briefly by F	4F
C	The set of complex numbers	4H
$\mathcal{C}$ or C	The field $\{C, +, \cdot\}$ of complex numbers	4H
$\leq$	Partial order	4J
$X \leq Y$	With X and Y linear spaces, X is a sub*space* of Y	5E
$\{X, +; \mathcal{F}, \cdot\}$	Linear space, denoted by $\mathcal{X}$ or (when context is obvious) by X, consisting of an Abelian group $\{X, +\}$ and an external operation $\cdot$ on $\{X, +\}$ by a field $\mathcal{F}$	5B
$\langle 0 \rangle$	Trivial linear space	5B14
$\mathcal{X} \oplus \mathcal{Y}$	Direct sum of linear spaces $\mathcal{X}$ and $\mathcal{Y}$	5B22, 5F
$X + Y$	Sum of subspaces X and Y; $\oplus$ if $X \cap Y = \langle 0 \rangle$	5F
$F_n(F_\infty)$	If $\mathcal{F} = \{F, +, \cdot\}$ then F_n is linear space of ordered n-tuples (infinite sequences) of elements of F, with $+$ and $\cdot$ defined component-wise	5B9, 12
F^s	If $\mathcal{F} = \{F, +, \cdot\}$ and S is any non-void set then F^s is the linear space $\{F^s, +; \mathcal{F}, \cdot\}$ of functions on S into F	5B12
$\dim X$	Dimension of linear space X	5D
$u + Y$	With u a vector and Y a subspace, the flat $\{u + y : y \in Y\}$	5E
$[\alpha_{jk}]$	Matrix with entry α_{jk} in jth row and kth column	5G8
R_L	Range of (linear mapping) L	6A
$\rho(L)$	Rank of L $(= \dim R_L)$	6D
N_L	Nullspace of L $(= \{x : Lx = 0\})$	6D

Symbol	Meaning	First Occurrence
$\nu(L)$	Nullity of L ($= \dim N_L$)	6D
L^{-1}	Inverse of nonsingular L	6D
$\mathscr{L}(X, Y)$	Space of linear maps $L : X \to Y$	6B1
$[M]^t$	Transpose of a matrix $[M]$	7A, 7D
X^d	Space dual to space X ($= \mathscr{L}(X, \mathscr{F}_1)$)	7B
B° (W°)	Subspace of X (of X^d) orthogonal to $B \leq X^d (W \leq X)$	7C
L^d	Mapping on Y^d into X^d dual to $L : X \to Y$	7D1
$\mathfrak{M}_{\mu n}$	Set of all matrices with μ rows and n columns	8A
$[L]$	Matrix of linear transformation L (with respect to assigned bases in domain and codomain)	8A
ρ_C	Column rank ($= \dim$ of col. space C)	8D
ρ_R	Row rank ($= \dim$ of row space R)	8D
ν_C (ν_R)	Column (row) nullity	8D
$[[\beta_j]]$	Diagonal square matrix, with β_j ($j = 1, \ldots, n$) on the diagonal and zeros elsewhere	8E2
$\operatorname{tr} L$	Trace of a square matrix; $\operatorname{tr} [\alpha_{jk}] = \sum \alpha_{kk}$	8F10
$I_{\kappa,\lambda}, I_{\gamma\cdot\kappa}, I_{\gamma\cdot\kappa+\lambda}$	Elementary row matrices	9D1
$\det A, |A|$	Determinant of a square matrix A	11B1
$f(L; \lambda)$	Characteristic polynomial $|\lambda - L|$ of L	12A2
$\|x\|$	Norm of a vector x in a normed space	13A
(x, y)	Inner (scalar) product of vectors x and y in a unitary space	13B (3I)
$S^\perp$	Subspace of vectors orthogonal to a set S	13B21
L^a	Adjoint of an operator L on a unitary space	13F
$[L]^*$	$\overline{[L]}^t$	13F

INDEX

References are of the form S(P), where S is the designation of a section and P is the number of a page. For example, 4E(99) refers to section 4E on page 99.